Elementary Differential Equations

By Earl D. Rainville

EARL D. RAINVILLE

Professor of Mathematics, The University of Michigan

Elementary Differential Equations

THIRD EDITION

The Macmillan Company, New York
Collier-Macmillan Limited, London

Sixth Printing, 1967

Library of Congress catalog card number: 64-10582

THE MACMILLAN COMPANY, NEW YORK
COLLIER-MACMILLAN CANADA, LTD., TORONTO, ONTARIO

Printed in the United States of America

Chapters 1–19 appear under the title *A Short Course in Differential Equations*, Third edition,
© Copyright 1964 by The Macmillan Company.

Some material in this book is from *The Laplace Transform: An Introduction*, © Copyright
1963 by Earl D. Rainville.

Preface to
the Third Edition

This edition includes four new chapters devoted to the Laplace transform. Three other chapters have been rewritten with emphasis on the
use of the transform in certain applications. Other topics to which new
sections are devoted include the transverse displacements of a beam,
diffusion in a quarter-infinite solid, an asymptotic series, and an introduction to the idea of canonical variables in certain boundary value
problems. There is a slight increase in the space devoted to some of the
material included in earlier editions.

Altogether about one third of the text and exercises is new. The number of exercises has been increased to more than 1,800. Almost all of my
recently published book on the Laplace transform is included here.

I am disturbed at the recent increase in the number of students
whose large vocabulary of advanced mathematical terms, ideas, and
theorems is matched only by their complete inability to solve any but
the simplest of specific problems. At a recent mathematics meeting I
heard one speaker express alarm at the manipulative skill being developed by the students. Such fears have not yet caused me any loss of
sleep. As in all my texts, I have here made a serious attempt to aid the
reader in developing a considerable skill in solving problems using the
mathematical concepts and tools presented.

As in the earlier editions, I have tried to exhibit both the techniques
for obtaining solutions and the basic ideas and theories behind these
techniques. The numerous exercises have been constructed carefully
with the double aim of developing the student's skill and adding to his
understanding. Definitions and statements of fact are made with care.

The material is arranged to permit great flexibility in the choice of topics for a semester course. Except for Chapters 1, 2, 7, 18 through 21, and either 8 and 9 or 11 and 12, any chapter on ordinary differential equations can be omitted as a whole without interfering with the study of later chapters. Parts of chapters can be omitted in many instances.

For a course aiming at reaching power series as rapidly as is consistent with some treatment of more elementary methods, a reasonable set of omissions would be Chapters 4 and 6; Chapters 8 and 9 or 11 and 12; Chapter 10; Sections 81 through 84 of Chapter 16; Chapter 17; the latter parts of Chapters 18 and 19; and whatever applications the instructor cares to omit.

This book has sufficient material for a full-year course, if the individual topics are taken up with the attention to detail that a full-year course suggests.

Chapters 1 through 19 of this book appear separately as *A Short Course in Differential Equations*, Third edition. The shorter version is intended for courses that do not include discussion of infinite-series methods.

I am grateful for the comments and suggestions received from many of my colleagues here at Michigan and from instructors and students in other colleges and universities. I am pleased to acknowledge in particular the aid and encouragement I received from Professors Jack R. Britton and L. C. Snively and Dean C. A. Hutchinson of the University of Colorado; Professor William N. Huff of the University of Oklahoma; Professor Phillip E. Bedient of Franklin and Marshall College; Professor Ralph L. Shively of Swarthmore College; and Professors D. G. Dickson. R. V. Churchill, R. C. F. Bartels, and G. E. Hay, and Ernest W. Reynolds, Jr., M.D., all of the University of Michigan. I remain indebted also to E. F. Ziegler, M.D., of Pasadena, California.

I wish also to express my gratitude to Professor Bedient for his independent reading of the proof sheets for this book.

EARL D. RAINVILLE

Ann Arbor, Michigan

Contents

Contents

Contents

Contents

Contents

Elementary Differential Equations

CHAPTER 1

Definitions, Elimination of

Arbitrary Constants

1. Examples of differential equations

A differential equation is one that involves at least one derivative of an unknown function. As in equation (3) below, a derivative may be involved implicitly through the presence of differentials. Our aim is to solve differential equations; that is, to find the unknown function, or functions, which occur.

Differential equations arise frequently in physics, engineering, and chemistry, and on occasion in such subjects as biology, physiology, and economics. The solution of differential equations plays an important role in the study of the motions of heavenly bodies such as planets, moons and artificial satellites.

The following are examples of differential equations:

(1) $$\frac{dy}{dx} = \cos x,$$

(2) $$\frac{d^2y}{dx^2} + k^2y = 0,$$

1

(3)
$$(x^2 + y^2)\, dx - 2xy\, dy = 0,$$

(4)
$$\frac{\partial u}{\partial t} = h^2 \left(\frac{\partial^2 u}{\partial x^2} + \frac{\partial^2 u}{\partial y^2} \right),$$

(5)
$$L \frac{d^2 i}{dt^2} + R \frac{di}{dt} + \frac{1}{C} i = E\omega \cos \omega t,$$

(6)
$$\frac{\partial^2 V}{\partial x^2} + \frac{\partial^2 V}{\partial y^2} = 0,$$

(7)
$$\left(\frac{d^2 w}{dx^2} \right)^3 - xy \frac{dw}{dx} + w = 0,$$

(8)
$$\frac{d^3 x}{dy^3} + x \frac{dx}{dy} - 4xy = 0,$$

(9)
$$\frac{d^2 y}{dx^2} + 7 \left(\frac{dy}{dx} \right)^3 - 8y = 0,$$

(10)
$$\frac{d^2 y}{dt^2} + \frac{d^2 x}{dt^2} = x,$$

(11)
$$x \frac{\partial f}{\partial x} + y \frac{\partial f}{\partial y} = nf.$$

When an equation involves one or more derivatives with respect to a particular variable, that variable is called an *independent* variable. A variable is called *dependent* if a derivative of that variable occurs.

In the equation

(5)
$$L \frac{d^2 i}{dt^2} + R \frac{di}{dt} + \frac{1}{C} i = E\omega \cos \omega t$$

i is the dependent variable, t the independent variable, and L, R, C, E, and ω are called parameters. The equation

(6)
$$\frac{\partial^2 V}{\partial x^2} + \frac{\partial^2 V}{\partial y^2} = 0$$

has one dependent variable V and two independent variables.

Since the equation

(3)
$$(x^2 + y^2)\, dx - 2xy\, dy = 0$$

may be written

$$x^2 + y^2 - 2xy \frac{dy}{dx} = 0$$

or

$$(x^2 + y^2) \frac{dx}{dy} - 2xy = 0,$$

we may consider either variable to be dependent, the other being the independent one.

Oral Exercise

Identify the independent variables, the dependent variables, and the parameters in the equations given as examples in this section.

2. Definitions

A relation defining an explicit function is called a solution of a differential equation if it satisfies that equation in the ordinary sense of checking upon direct substitution. For example, let us verify that

$$y = e^{2x}$$

is a solution of the equation

(1) $$\frac{d^2y}{dx^2} + \frac{dy}{dx} - 6y = 0.$$

We substitute our tentative solution into the left member of equation (1) and find that

$$\frac{d^2y}{dx^2} + \frac{dy}{dx} - 6y = 4e^{2x} + 2e^{2x} - 6e^{2x} \equiv 0,$$

which completes the desired verification.

Consider, however, the differential equation

(2) $$(4x^3 - y^3)\,dx + (2y - 3xy^2)\,dy = 0$$

and the relation

(3) $$x^4 - xy^3 + y^2 = c,$$

in which c is a constant. It is surely not convenient to solve equation (3) for either x or y. But differentiation of both members of (3) produces

$$4x^3\,dx - y^3\,dx - 3xy^2\,dy + 2y\,dy = 0,$$

which is merely a rearrangement of (2). If x and y are related by equation (3), then x, y, dx, and dy are related by (2). Therefore we wish to call the relation (3) a solution of equation (2). This suggests a broader definition of the term solution, which we now state.

Any relation, free from derivatives, that involves one or more of the variables and that is consistent with the differential equation will be called a solution of the equation.

An equation involving partial derivatives is called a *partial differential equation;* one involving ordinary derivatives is called an *ordinary differential equation.*

The *order* of a differential equation is the order of the highest-ordered derivative appearing in the equation. For instance,

$$(4) \qquad \frac{d^2y}{dx^2} + 2b\left(\frac{dy}{dx}\right)^3 + y = 0$$

is an equation of "order two." It is also referred to as a "second-order equation."

The *degree* of an ordinary differential equation is the algebraic degree in the highest-ordered derivative in the equation.

The equation

$$\left(\frac{d^2y}{dx^2}\right)^3 + \frac{d^2y}{dx^2}\left(\frac{dy}{dx}\right)^4 - x^7y = \sin x$$

is of degree three, because in so far as the second derivative alone is concerned, the equation is a cubic. Equation (4) is of degree one.

Any equation of the form

$$(5) \qquad M(x, y)\, dx + N(x, y)\, dy = 0$$

is of order one and degree one. All the equations which we shall solve in Chapter 2 may be written in the form (5).

A very important concept is that of the linearity or nonlinearity of a differential equation. An equation is said to be *linear* if each term of the equation is either linear in all the dependent variables and their various derivatives or does not contain any of them. Otherwise the equation is said to be *nonlinear.* The term $y\dfrac{dy}{dx}$ is of degree two in y and its derivative together and is therefore nonlinear. Every linear equation is of degree one, but not every equation of degree one is linear. Note that equation (4) above is nonlinear.

The equation

$$x^2y'' + xy' + (x^2 - n^2)y = 4x^3$$

is linear in y. The manner in which the independent variable enters the equation has nothing to do with the property of linearity.

Oral Exercises

For each of the following, state whether the equation is ordinary or partial, linear or nonlinear, and give its order and degree.

1. $\dfrac{d^2x}{dt^2} + k^2x = 0.$

2. $\dfrac{\partial^2 w}{\partial t^2} = a^2 \dfrac{\partial^2 w}{\partial x^2}.$

3. $(x^2 + y^2)\, dx + 2xy\, dy = 0.$

4. $y' + P(x)y = Q(x).$

5. $y''' - 3y' + 2y = 0.$

6. $yy'' = x.$

7. $\dfrac{\partial^2 u}{\partial x^2} + \dfrac{\partial^2 u}{\partial y^2} + \dfrac{\partial^2 u}{\partial z^2} = 0.$

8. $\dfrac{d^4y}{dx^4} = w(x).$

9. $x\dfrac{d^2y}{dt^2} - y\dfrac{d^2x}{dt^2} = c_1.$

10. $L\dfrac{di}{dt} + Ri = E.$

11. $(x + y)\, dx + (3x^2 - 1)\, dy = 0.$

12. $x(y'')^3 + (y')^4 - y = 0.$

13. $\left(\dfrac{d^3w}{dx^3}\right)^2 - 2\left(\dfrac{dw}{dx}\right)^4 + yw = 0.$

14. $\dfrac{dy}{dx} = 1 - xy + y^2.$

15. $y'' + 2y' - 8y = x^2 + \cos x.$

16. $a\, da + b\, db = 0.$

3. The elimination of arbitrary constants

In practice, differential equations arise in many ways, some of which we shall encounter later. There is one way of arriving at a differential equation which is useful in that it gives us a feeling for the kinds of solutions to be expected. In this section we shall start with a relation (the solution) involving arbitrary constants, and, by elimination of those arbitrary constants, come to a differential equation satisfied by the original relation. In a sense we start with the answer and find the problem.

Methods for the elimination of arbitrary constants vary with the way in which the constants enter the given relation. A method which is efficient for one problem may be poor for another. One fact persists throughout. Since each differentiation yields a new relation, the number of derivatives that need be used is the same as the number of arbitrary constants to be eliminated. We shall in each case determine the differential equation that is:

(a) Of order equal to the number of arbitrary constants in the given relation;

(b) Consistent with that relation;

(c) Free from arbitrary constants.

EXAMPLE (a): Eliminate* the arbitrary constants c_1 and c_2 from the relation

(1) $$y = c_1 e^{-2x} + c_2 e^{3x}.$$

Since two constants are to be eliminated, obtain the two derivatives,

(2) $$y' = -2c_1 e^{-2x} + 3c_2 e^{3x},$$
(3) $$y'' = 4c_1 e^{-2x} + 9c_2 e^{3x}.$$

The elimination of c_1 from equations (2) and (3) yields

$$y'' + 2y' = 15c_2 e^{3x};$$

the elimination of c_1 from equations (1) and (2) yields

$$y' + 2y = 5c_2 e^{3x}.$$

Hence

$$y'' + 2y' = 3(y' + 2y),$$

or

$$y'' - y' - 6y = 0.$$

Another method for obtaining the differential equation in this example proceeds as follows. We know from a theorem in elementary algebra that the three equations (1), (2), and (3) considered as equations in the two unknowns c_1 and c_2 can have solutions only if

(4) $$\begin{vmatrix} -y & e^{-2x} & e^{3x} \\ -y' & -2e^{-2x} & 3e^{3x} \\ -y'' & 4e^{-2x} & 9e^{3x} \end{vmatrix} = 0.$$

Since e^{-2x} and e^{3x} cannot be zero, equation (4) may be rewritten, with the factors e^{-2x} and e^{3x} removed, as

$$\begin{vmatrix} y & 1 & 1 \\ y' & -2 & 3 \\ y'' & 4 & 9 \end{vmatrix} = 0$$

---

* By differentiations and pertinent legitimate mathematical procedures. Elimination by erasure, for instance, is not permitted.

from which the differential equation

$$y'' - y' - 6y = 0$$

follows immediately.

This latter method has the advantage of making it easy to see that the elimination of the constants $c_1, c_2, \cdots, c_n$ from a relation of the form

$$y = c_1 e^{m_1 x} + c_2 e^{m_2 x} + \cdots + c_n e^{m_n x}$$

will always lead to a linear differential equation

$$a_0 \frac{d^n y}{dx^n} + a_1 \frac{d^{n-1} y}{dx^{n-1}} + \cdots + a_{n-1} \frac{dy}{dx} + a_n y = 0,$$

in which the coefficients $a_0, a_1, \cdots, a_n$ are constants. The study of such differential equations will receive much of our attention.

EXAMPLE (b): Eliminate the constant a from the equation

$$(x - a)^2 + y^2 = a^2.$$

Direct differentiation of the relation yields

$$2(x - a) + 2yy' = 0,$$

from which

$$a = x + yy'.$$

Therefore, using the original equation, we find that

$$(yy')^2 + y^2 = (x + yy')^2,$$

or

$$y^2 = x^2 + 2xyy',$$

which may be written in the form

$$(x^2 - y^2) \, dx + 2xy \, dy = 0.$$

Another method will be used in this example as an illustration of a device which is frequently helpful. The method is based upon the isolation of an arbitrary constant.

The equation

$$(x - a)^2 + y^2 = a^2$$

may be put in the form

$$x^2 + y^2 - 2ax = 0,$$

or

$$\frac{x^2 + y^2}{x} = 2a.$$

Then differentiation of both members leads to

$$\frac{x(2x\,dx + 2y\,dy) - (x^2 + y^2)\,dx}{x^2} = 0,$$

or

$$(x^2 - y^2)\,dx + 2xy\,dy = 0,$$

as desired.

EXAMPLE (c): Eliminate B and α from the relation

(5) $x = B \cos(\omega t + \alpha),$

in which ω is a parameter (not to be eliminated).

First we obtain two derivatives of x with respect to t:

(6) $\dfrac{dx}{dt} = -\omega B \sin(\omega t + \alpha),$

(7) $\dfrac{d^2x}{dt^2} = -\omega^2 B \cos(\omega t + \alpha).$

Comparison of equations (5) and (7) shows at once that

$$\frac{d^2x}{dt^2} + \omega^2 x = 0.$$

EXAMPLE (d): Eliminate c from the equation

$$cxy + c^2x + 4 = 0.$$

At once we get

$$c(y + xy') + c^2 = 0.$$

Since $c \neq 0$,

$$c = -(y + xy')$$

and substitution into the original equation leads us to the result

$$x^3(y')^2 + x^2yy' + 4 = 0.$$

Exercises

In each of the following, eliminate the arbitrary constants.

1. $x^3 - 3x^2y = c.$ ANS. $(x - 2y)\,dx - x\,dy = 0.$

2. $y \sin x - xy^2 = c.$ ANS. $y(\cos x - y)\,dx + (\sin x - 2xy)\,dy = 0.$

3. $PV = C.$

4. $x^2 y = 1 + cx.$ ANS. $(x^2 y + 1)\, dx + x^3\, dy = 0.$

5. $cy^2 = x^2 + y.$ ANS. $2xy\, dx - (y + 2x^2)\, dy = 0.$

6. $x = A \sin(\omega t + \beta)$: ω a parameter, not to be eliminated.

ANS. $\dfrac{d^2 x}{dt^2} + \omega^2 x = 0.$

7. $x = c_1 \cos \omega t + c_2 \sin \omega t$; ω a parameter. ANS. $\dfrac{d^2 x}{dt^2} + \omega^2 x = 0.$

8. $y = cx + c^2 + 1.$ ANS. $y = xy' + (y')^2 + 1.$

9. $y = mx + \dfrac{h}{m}$; h a parameter, m to be eliminated.

ANS. $y = xy' + \dfrac{h}{y'}.$

10. $y^2 = 4ax.$ ANS. $2x\, dy - y\, dx = 0.$

11. $y = ax^2 + bx + c.$ ANS. $y''' = 0.$

12. $y = c_1 + c_2 e^{2x}.$ ANS. $y'' - 2y' = 0.$

13. $y = 4 + c_1 e^{2x}.$ ANS. $y' - 2y = -8.$

14. $y = c_1 + c_2 e^{-3x}.$ ANS. $y'' + 3y' = 0.$

15. $y = c_1 e^{-x} + c_2 e^{-3x}.$ ANS. $y'' + 4y' + 3y = 0.$

16. $y = x + c_1 e^{-x} + c_2 e^{-3x}.$ ANS. $y'' + 4y' + 3y = 4 + 3x.$

17. $y = c_1 e^x + c_2 e^{-2x}.$ ANS. $y'' + y' - 2y = 0.$

18. $y = x^2 + c_1 e^x + c_2 e^{-2x}.$ ANS. $y'' + y' - 2y = 2(1 + x - x^2).$

19. $y = c_1 e^{-x} + c_2 x e^{-x}.$ ANS. $y'' + 2y' + y = 0.$

20. $y = A e^{2x} + B x e^{2x}.$ ANS. $y'' - 4y' + 4y = 0.$

21. $y = c_1 e^{2x} \cos 3x + c_2 e^{2x} \sin 3x.$ ANS. $y'' - 4y' + 13y = 0.$

22. $y = c_1 e^{ax} \cos bx + c_2 e^{ax} \sin bx$; a and b are parameters.

ANS. $y'' - 2ay' + (a^2 + b^2)y = 0.$

23. $y = c_1 x + c_2 e^{-x}.$ ANS. $(x + 1)y'' + xy' - y = 0.$

24. $y = x^2 + c_1 x + c_2 e^{-x}.$ ANS. $(x + 1)y'' + xy' - y = x^2 + 2x + 2.$

25. $y = c_1 x^2 + c_2 e^{2x}.$

ANS. $x(1 - x)y'' + (2x^2 - 1)y' - 2(2x - 1)y = 0.$

4. Families of curves

A relation involving a parameter, as well as one or both of the coordinates of a point in a plane, represents a family of curves, one curve corresponding to each value of the parameter. For instance, the equation

(1) $$(x - c)^2 + (y - c)^2 = 2c^2,$$

or

(2) $$x^2 + y^2 - 2c(x + y) = 0,$$

may be interpreted as the equation of a family of circles, each having its center on the line $y = x$ and each passing through the origin. Figure 1 shows several elements, or members, of this family.

If the constant c in equation (1) or in equation (2) is treated as an arbitrary constant and eliminated as in the preceding section, the result is called the *differential equation of the family represented by equation* (1). In this example, the elimination of c is easily performed by isolating c,

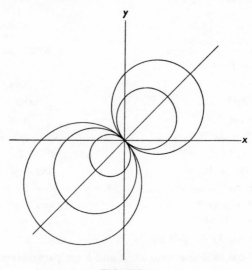

FIGURE 1

then differentiating throughout the equation with respect to x. Thus, from

$$\frac{x^2 + y^2}{x + y} = 2c$$

we find that

$$\frac{(x + y)(2x\,dx + 2y\,dy) - (x^2 + y^2)(dx + dy)}{(x + y)^2} = 0.$$

Therefore

(3) $$(x^2 + 2xy - y^2)\,dx - (x^2 - 2xy - y^2)\,dy = 0$$

is the differential equation of the family of circles represented by equation (1).

Note that equation (3) associates with each point (x, y) in the plane a definite slope

(4)
$$\frac{dy}{dx} = \frac{x^2 + 2xy - y^2}{x^2 - 2xy - y^2},$$

except where the denominator on the right in (4) vanishes. An examination of the method that was used to get (4) from (1) shows that at any point (x, y), equation (4) gives the slope of that curve of the family (1) which passes through the point in question.

A simple and convenient check is now revealed. When the denominator on the right of equation (4) vanishes, the curve passing through that point must have a vertical tangent. From

$$x^2 - 2xy - y^2 = 0$$

we see that

(5)
$$y = (\sqrt{2} - 1)x$$

or

(6)
$$y = -(\sqrt{2} + 1)x.$$

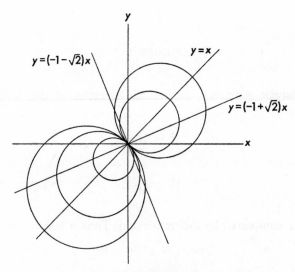

FIGURE 2

In Figure 2, the straight lines (5) and (6) appear along with the family (1). It is seen that the lines (5) and (6) cut the members of the family of circles in precisely those points of vertical tangency.

For a two-parameter family of curves, the differential equation will be of order two, and such a simple geometric interpretation is not available.

EXAMPLE (a): Find the differential equation of the family of parabolas (Figure 3), having their vertices at the origin and their foci on the y-axis.

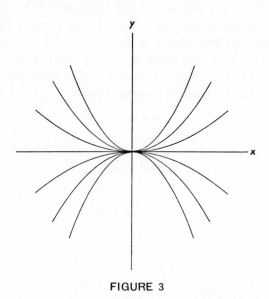

FIGURE 3

From analytic geometry, we find the equation of this family of parabolas to be

(7) $x^2 = 4ay.$

Then from

$$\frac{x^2}{y} = 4a$$

the a may be eliminated by differentiation. Thus it follows that

(8) $2xy\,dx - x^2\,dy = 0.$

We may write the differential equation of the family (7) as

(9) $2y\,dx - x\,dy = 0,$

because $x = 0$ is still a solution of (9), and nothing is lost in removing the factor x from the left member of (8).

EXAMPLE (b): Find the differential equation of the family of circles (Figure 4) having their centers on the y-axis.

Since a member of the family of circles of this example may have its center anywhere on the y-axis and its radius of any magnitude, we are dealing with the two-parameter family

(10) $x^2 + (y - b)^2 = r^2.$

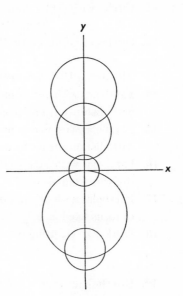

We shall eliminate both b and r and arrive, of course, at a second-order differential equation for the family (10).

At once

$$x + (y - b)y' = 0,$$

from which

$$\frac{x + yy'}{y'} = b.$$

Then

$$\frac{y'[1 + yy'' + (y')^2] - y''(x + yy')}{(y')^2} = 0,$$

so the desired differential equation is

$$xy'' - (y')^3 - y' = 0.$$

FIGURE 4

Exercises

In each exercise, obtain the differential equation of the family of plane curves described and sketch several representative members of the family.

1. Straight lines through the origin.   ANS. $y\,dx - x\,dy = 0.$
2. Straight lines through the fixed point (h, k). The h and k are not to be eliminated.   ANS. $(y - k)\,dx - (x - h)\,dy = 0.$
3. Straight lines with slope and y-intercept equal.
                              ANS. $y\,dx - (x + 1)\,dy = 0.$
4. Straight lines with slope and x-intercept equal.
                              ANS. $(y')^2 = xy' - y.$
5. Straight lines with algebraic sum of the intercepts fixed as k.
                              ANS. $(xy' - y)(y' - 1) + ky' = 0.$
6. Straight lines at a fixed distance p from the origin.
                              ANS. $(xy' - y)^2 = p^2[1 + (y')^2].$
7. Circles with center at the origin.   ANS. $x\,dx + y\,dy = 0.$

8. Circles with center on the x-axis.   ANS. $yy'' + (y')^2 + 1 = 0$.

9. Circles with fixed radius r and tangent to the x-axis.

ANS. $(y \pm r)^2(y')^2 + y^2 \pm 2ry = 0$.

10. Circles tangent to the x-axis.

ANS. $[1 + (y')^2]^3 = [yy'' + 1 + (y')^2]^2$.

11. Circles with center on the line $y = -x$, and passing through the origin.

ANS. $(x^2 - 2xy - y^2)\,dx + (x^2 + 2xy - y^2)\,dy = 0$.

12. Circles of radius unity. Use the fact that the radius of curvature is one.

ANS. $(y'')^2 = [1 + (y')^2]^3$.

13. All circles. Use the curvature.   ANS. $y'''[1 + (y')^2] = 3y'(y'')^2$.

14. Parabolas with vertex on the x-axis, with axis parallel to the y-axis, and with distance from focus to vertex fixed as a.   ANS. $a(y')^2 = y$.

15. Parabolas with vertex on the y-axis, with axis parallel to the x-axis, and with distance from focus to vertex fixed as a.   ANS. $x(y')^2 = a$.

16. Parabolas with axis parallel to the y-axis and with distance from vertex to focus fixed as a.   ANS. $2ay'' = 1$.

17. Parabolas with axis parallel to the x-axis and with distance from vertex to focus fixed as a.   ANS. $2ay'' + (y')^3 = 0$.

18. Work Ex. 17, using differentiation with respect to y.

ANS. $2a\dfrac{d^2x}{dy^2} = 1$.

19. Use the fact that

$$\frac{d^2x}{dy^2} = \frac{d}{dy}\left(\frac{dx}{dy}\right) = \frac{dx}{dy}\frac{d}{dx}\left(\frac{dx}{dy}\right) = \frac{dx}{dy}\frac{d}{dx}\left(\frac{dy}{dx}\right)^{-1} = \frac{-y''}{(y')^3}$$

to prove that the answers to Exs. 17 and 18 are equivalent.

20. Parabolas with vertex and focus on the x-axis.   ANS. $yy'' + (y')^2 = 0$.

21. Parabolas with axis parallel to the x-axis.   ANS. $y'y''' - 3(y'')^2 = 0$.

22. Central conics with center at the origin and vertices on the coordinate axes.   ANS. $xyy'' + x(y')^2 - yy' = 0$.

23. The confocal central conics

$$\frac{x^2}{a^2 + \lambda} + \frac{y^2}{b^2 + \lambda} = 1$$

with a and b held fixed.   ANS. $(xy' - y)(yy' + x) = (a^2 - b^2)y'$.

24. The cubics $cy^2 = x^2(x - a)$ with a held fixed.

ANS. $2x(x - a)y' = y(3x - 2a)$.

25. The cubics of Ex. 24 with c held fixed and a to be eliminated.

ANS. $2cy(xy' - y) = x^3$.

26. The quartics $c^2y^2 = x(x - a)^3$ with a held fixed.

ANS. $2x(x - a)y' = y(4x - a)$.

27. The quartics of Ex. 26 with c held fixed and a to be eliminated.

ANS. $c^2(2xy' - y)^3 = 27x^4y$.

28. The strophoids $y^2 = \dfrac{x^2(a + x)}{a - x}$.

ANS. $(x^4 - 4x^2y^2 - y^4)\,dx + 4x^3y\,dy = 0$.

29. The cissoids $y^2 = \dfrac{x^3}{a - x}$.   ANS. $2x^3y' = y(y^2 + 3x^2)$.

30. The trisectrices of Maclaurin $y^2(a + x) = x^2(3a - x)$.

ANS. $(3x^4 - 6x^2y^2 - y^4)\,dx + 8x^3y\,dy = 0$.

31. Circles through the intersections of the circle $x^2 + y^2 = 1$ and the line $y = x$. Use the "$u + kv$" form; that is, the equation

$$x^2 + y^2 - 1 + k(y - x) = 0.$$

ANS. $(x^2 - 2xy - y^2 + 1)\,dx + (x^2 + 2xy - y^2 - 1)\,dy = 0$.

32. Circles through the fixed points $(a, 0)$ and $(-a, 0)$. Use the method of Ex. 31.   ANS. $2xy\,dx + (y^2 + a^2 - x^2)\,dy = 0$.

33. The circles $r = 2a(\sin \theta - \cos \theta)$.

ANS. $(\cos \theta - \sin \theta)\,dr + r(\cos \theta + \sin \theta)\,d\theta = 0$.

34. The cardioids $r = a(1 - \sin \theta)$.

ANS. $(1 - \sin \theta)\,dr + r \cos \theta\,d\theta = 0$.

35. The cissoids $r = a \sin \theta \tan \theta$. (See Ex. 29.)

ANS. $\sin \theta \cos \theta\,dr - r(1 + \cos^2 \theta)\,d\theta = 0$.

36. The strophoids $r = a(\sec \theta + \tan \theta)$.   ANS. $\dfrac{dr}{d\theta} = r \sec \theta$.

37. The trisectrices of Maclaurin $r = a(4 \cos \theta - \sec \theta)$. (See Ex. 30.)

ANS. $\cos \theta(4 \cos^2 \theta - 1)\,dr + r \sin \theta(4 \cos^2 \theta + 1)\,d\theta = 0$.

CHAPTER 2

Equations of Order One
and Degree One

5. General solutions of ordinary differential equations

An ordinary differential equation of the nth order has, in general, a solution containing n arbitrary constants.* We shall call such a solution the general solution. Other terms frequently used are complete solution, complete primitive, and complete integral.

6. Separation of variables

The general equation of the first order and first degree is

(1) $$M \, dx + N \, dy = 0,$$

where M and N may be functions of both x and y. Some equations of the type (1) are so simple that they can be put in the form

---

* A proof and a precise statement appear, for example, in E. L. Ince, *Ordinary Differential Equations* (London: Longmans, Green and Co., 1927).

16

(2) $$A(x) \, dx + B(y) \, dy = 0;$$

that is, the variables can be separated. Then the solution can be written at once. For it is only a matter of finding a function F whose total differential is the left member of (2). Then $F = c$, where c is an arbitrary constant, is the desired result.

EXAMPLE (a): Solve the equation

(3) $$2(y + 3) \, dx - xy \, dy = 0.$$

Separation of the variables leads to

$$\frac{2 \, dx}{x} - \frac{y \, dy}{y + 3} = 0,$$

or

(4) $$\frac{2 \, dx}{x} - \left[1 - \frac{3}{y + 3}\right] dy = 0.$$

Hence we could write the solution as

(5) $$2 \ln x - y + 3 \ln (y + 3) = c.$$

Although (5) is a correct solution, the presence of two logarithmic terms suggests that we put the arbitrary constant in logarithmic form also. Thus, directly from (4) we may write the solution as

(6) $$2 \ln x - y + 3 \ln (y + 3) + \ln c_1 = 0,$$

where c_1 is an arbitrary constant different from the c of (5).

From (6) we get

$$y = 2 \ln x + 3 \ln (y + 3) + \ln c_1,$$

from which it follows that

(7) $$e^y = c_1 x^2 (y + 3)^3,$$

which is more compact than (5).

Of course, (5) can be transformed into (7) quite easily. From (5)

$$y + c = 2 \ln x + 3 \ln (y + 3),$$

or

$$e^{y+c} = x^2 (y + 3)^3.$$

Now we put

$$e^c = \frac{1}{c_1}$$

and arrive at (7).

The problem of changing one form of solution into another form is one which arises frequently when two or more persons solve the same differential equation and a check on the results is desired. Unless the use to which the solution will be put is known, there is little reason for preference for one form over another, except for considerations of compactness, symmetry, and other esthetic qualities. It is essentially a matter of individual inclination. Section 7 contains further remarks on the form of solutions.

EXAMPLE (b): Solve the equation

$$(8) \qquad (1 + y^2)\, dx + (1 + x^2)\, dy = 0,$$

with the "boundary condition" that when $x = 0$, $y = -1$.

From the differential equation we get

$$\frac{dx}{1 + x^2} + \frac{dy}{1 + y^2} = 0$$

from which it follows at once that

$$(9) \qquad \text{Arctan } x + \text{Arctan } y = c.$$

In the solution (9), each "Arctan" stands for the principal value of the inverse tangent and is subject to the restriction

$$-\tfrac{1}{2}\pi < \text{Arctan } x < \tfrac{1}{2}\pi.$$

The boundary condition that $y = -1$ when $x = 0$ permits us to determine the value of c that must be used to obtain the particular solution desired here. Since Arctan $0 = 0$ and Arctan $(-1) = -\tfrac{1}{4}\pi$, the solution of the boundary value problem is

$$(10) \qquad \text{Arctan } x + \text{Arctan } y = -\tfrac{1}{4}\pi.$$

Suppose next that we wish to sketch the curve (10). Resorting to a device of trigonometry, we take the tangent of each side of (10). Since

$$\tan (\text{Arctan } x) = x$$

and

$$\tan (A + B) = \frac{\tan A + \tan B}{1 - \tan A \tan B},$$

we are led to the equation

$$\frac{x + y}{1 - xy} = -1,$$

or

(11) $$xy - x - y - 1 = 0.$$

Now (11) is the equation of an equilateral hyperbola with asymptotes $x = 1$ and $y = 1$. But if we turn to (10), we see from

$$\text{Arctan } x = -\tfrac{1}{4}\pi - \text{Arctan } y$$

that, since $(- \text{Arctan } y) < \tfrac{1}{2}\pi$,

$$\text{Arctan } x < \tfrac{1}{4}\pi.$$

Hence $x < 1$, and equation (10) represents only one branch of the hyperbola (11). In Figure 5, the solid curve is the graph of equation (10); the solid curve and the dotted curve together are the graph of equation (11).

Each branch of the hyperbola (11) is a solution of the differential equation, one branch for $x < 1$, the other for $x > 1$. In this problem we were forced onto the left branch, equation (10), by the boundary condition that $y = -1$ when $x = 0$.

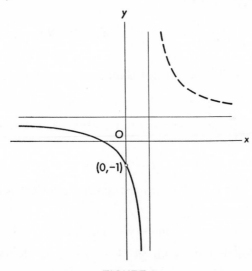

FIGURE 5

One distinction between the solutions (10) and (11) can be seen by noting that a computing machine, given the differential equation (8) and seeking a solution that passes through the point $(0, -1)$, would draw only the left branch of the curve in Figure 5. The barrier (asymptote) at $x = 1$ would prevent the machine from learning of the existence of the other branch of the hyperbola (11).

7. On the form of solutions

Consider the equation

(1) $$2x(y + 1)\, dx - y\, dy = 0.$$

Separating the variables in equation (1), we obtain

(2) $$2x\, dx = \left(1 - \frac{1}{y + 1}\right) dy.$$

Therefore, the general solution of equation (1) is

(3) $$x^2 = y - \ln(y + 1) + c.$$

Suppose, however, that we wish to solve a boundary value problem consisting of the differential equation (1) and the condition that when $x = 0$, $y = -2$. Putting $y = -2$ into the right member of equation (3) would lead to the use of $\ln(-1)$. Since (-1) has no real logarithm, we prefer to avoid this complication. Hence we seek other forms for the general solution of equation (1).

Since

$$d \ln(-y - 1) = \frac{-dy}{-y - 1} = \frac{dy}{y + 1},$$

it is possible to write the general solution of equation (2) in the form

(4) $$x^2 = y - \ln(-y - 1) + c_1.$$

Substituting $x = 0$ and $y = -2$ into equation (4) causes no trouble. It leads us to the equation

$$0 = -2 - \ln(1) + c_1,$$

from which we find $c_1 = 2$. Thus the desired solution of the boundary value problem is

$$x^2 = y + 2 - \ln(-y - 1), \quad \text{for } y < -1.$$

It can be seen that the solution (3) is useful for the range $y > -1$, while the solution (4) is useful for $y < -1$. In at least two ways it is possible to write a solution combining the advantages of (3) with those of (4).

Since

$$d \ln[c_2(y + 1)] = \frac{c_2\, dy}{c_2(y + 1)} = \frac{dy}{y + 1},$$

the general solution of equation (1) may be written in the form

(5) $x^2 = y - \ln [c_2(y + 1)].$

In adjusting the solution (5) to our immediate purpose, we place $x = 0$, $y = -2$ and find that

$$0 = -2 - \ln (-c_2),$$

so that $\ln (-c_2) = -2$, or $c_2 = -e^{-2}$. Hence the desired solution is

$$x^2 = y - \ln [-e^{-2}(y + 1)],$$

or

$$x^2 = y + 2 - \ln [-(y + 1)].$$

In equation (5), c_2 will turn out to be negative when a boundary condition requires that $y < -1$ and positive when it is required that $y > -1$.

From equation (5) it is not difficult to obtain the relation

(6) $(y + 1)e^{x^2} = c_3 e^y$

as another form of the solution of the differential equation (1).

In this book we shall usually leave solutions in forms similar to (5) or (6) above. Whenever an answer such as equation (3) is given, it is implied that the user will adjust its form to his particular purpose. The result should be verified by direct appeal to the differential equation so the validity of the transition from one solution to another does not enter the argument.

8. The exp *u* notation

The function e^u enters our work frequently, and sometimes the exponent u is complicated. Even a simple example such as $e^{x^{\frac{1}{2}}}y^2$ may be undesirable in print, because exponents are usually set in small type. It is customary in advanced mathematics to use the notation

(1) $\exp u = e^u.$

That is, exp is used to denote the exponential function in much the same way that sin is used to denote the sine function.

EXAMPLE (a): For $e^{x^{\frac{1}{2}}}y^2$ we write $\exp (x^{\frac{1}{2}}y^2)$.

EXAMPLE (b): Equation (6) of the preceding section may be written as

(2) $(y + 1) \exp (x^2) = c_3 \exp (y).$

Most people retain the notation e^u when u is simple, even though in the same equation the exp notation may have been used elsewhere. Equation (2) is sometimes written in the form

$$(3) \qquad\qquad (y + 1) \exp (x^2) = c_3 e^y.$$

A few minutes of practice should make the reader feel at home with the symbol exp u. Some familiarity with this notation will result from verification of simple identities such as the following:

$$(4) \qquad\qquad \exp (x) \cdot \exp (y) = \exp (x + y),$$
$$(5) \qquad\qquad [\exp (x)]^k = \exp (kx),$$
$$(6) \qquad\qquad \exp (\ln y) = y,$$
$$(7) \qquad\qquad \exp \left(\frac{x}{y}\right) \exp \left(\frac{y}{x}\right) = \exp \left(\frac{x^2 + y^2}{xy}\right),$$
$$(8) \qquad\qquad \exp (3 \ln x) = [\exp (\ln x)]^3 = x^3,$$
$$(9) \qquad\qquad \exp (x - 2 \ln x) = x^{-2} e^x.$$

We shall use the exp notation whenever it seems to add to the clarity of the printed result.

Exercises

In Exs. 1–26, obtain the general solution.

1. $(4 + x)y' = y^3$.   ANS. $2y^2 \ln [c(4 + x)] = -1$.
2. $\exp (y^2) \, dx + x^2 y \, dy = 0$.   ANS. $x \exp (-y^2) + 2 = cx$.
3. $\cos x \cos y \, dx + \sin x \sin y \, dy = 0$.   ANS. $\sin x = c \cos y$.
4. $3y \, dx = 2x \, dy$.   ANS. $x^3 = cy^2$.
5. $my \, dx = nx \, dy$.   ANS. $x^m = cy^n$.
6. $y' = xy^2$.   ANS. $y(x^2 + c) + 2 = 0$.
7. $\dfrac{dV}{dP} = \dfrac{-V}{P}$.   ANS. $PV = C$.
8. $e^x(y - 1) \, dx + 2(e^x + 4) \, dy = 0$.   ANS. $(y - 1)^2(e^x + 4) = c^2$.
9. $dr = e(r \sin \theta \, d\theta - \cos \theta \, dr)$.   ANS. $r(1 + e \cos \theta) = c$.
10. $(xy - x) \, dx + (xy + y) \, dy = 0$.   ANS. $(y - 1) \exp (x + y) = c(x + 1)$.
11. $(y + 1) \, dx = 2xy \, dy$.   ANS. $e^{2y} = cx(y + 1)^2$.
12. $x^2 \, dx + y(x - 1) \, dy = 0$.
13. $(xy + x) \, dx = (x^2 y^2 + x^2 + y^2 + 1) \, dy$.   ANS. $\ln (x^2 + 1) = y^2 - 2y + 4 \ln [c(y + 1)]$.
14. $x \cos^2 y \, dx + \tan y \, dy = 0$.   ANS. $x^2 + \tan^2 y = c^2$.
15. $x^2 yy' = e^y$.   ANS. $x(y + 1) = (1 + cx)e^y$.

16. $\tan^2 y \, dy = \sin^3 x \, dx$.   ANS. $\cos^3 x - 3 \cos x = 3(\tan y - y + c)$.

17. $y' = \cos^2 x \cos y$.   ANS. $4 \ln (\sec y + \tan y) = 2x + \sin 2x + c$.

18. $y' = y \sec x$.   ANS. $y = c(\sec x + \tan x)$.

19. $dx = t(1 + t^2) \sec^2 x \, dt$.   ANS. $2x + \sin 2x = c + (1 + t^2)^2$.

20. $(e^{2x} + 4)y' = y$.   ANS. $y^8(1 + 4e^{-2x}) = c^2$.

21. $\alpha \, d\beta + \beta \, d\alpha + \alpha\beta(3 \, d\alpha + d\beta) = 0$.   ANS. $c\alpha\beta = \exp(-3\alpha - \beta)$.

22. $(1 + \ln x) \, dx + (1 + \ln y) \, dy = 0$.   ANS. $x \ln x + y \ln y = c$.

23. $x \, dx - \sqrt{a^2 - x^2} \, dy = 0$.

                        ANS. $y - c = - \sqrt{a^2 - x^2}$, the lower half of
                                the circle $x^2 + (y - c)^2 = a^2$.

24. $x \, dx + \sqrt{a^2 - x^2} \, dy = 0$.

                        ANS. $y - c = \sqrt{a^2 - x^2}$, the upper half of
                                the circle $x^2 + (y - c)^2 = a^2$.

25. $a^2 \, dx = x \sqrt{x^2 - a^2} \, dy$.   ANS. $x = a \sec \dfrac{y + c}{a}$.

26. $y \ln x \ln y \, dx + dy = 0$.   ANS. $x \ln x + \ln \ln y = x + c$.

In Exs. 27–33, obtain the particular solution satisfying the boundary condition indicated.

27. $\dfrac{dr}{dt} = -4rt$; when $t = 0$, $r = r_0$.   ANS. $r = r_0 \exp(-2t^2)$.

28. $2xyy' = 1 + y^2$; when $x = 2$, $y = 3$.   ANS. $y^2 = 5x - 1$.

29. $xyy' = 1 + y^2$; when $x = 2$, $y = 3$.   ANS. $5x^2 - 2y^2 = 2$.

30. $y' = x \exp(y - x^2)$; when $x = 0$, $y = 0$.

                        ANS. $2e^{-y} = 1 + \exp(-x^2)$.

31. $xy^2 \, dx + e^x \, dy = 0$; when $x \to \infty$, $y \to \tfrac{1}{2}$.

                        ANS. $y = e^x/(2e^x - x - 1)$.

32. $(2a^2 - r^2) \, dr = r^3 \sin \theta \, d\theta$; when $\theta = 0$, $r = a$.

33. $v \dfrac{dv}{dx} = g$; when $x = x_0$, $v = v_0$.   ANS. $v^2 - v_0^2 = 2g(x - x_0)$.

9. Homogeneous functions

Polynomials in which all terms are of the same degree, such as

$$
\begin{aligned}
& x^2 - 3xy + 4y^2, \\
& x^3 + y^3, \\
& x^4 y + 7y^5,
\end{aligned}
$$

(1)

are called *homogeneous* polynomials. We wish now to extend that concept of homogeneity so it will apply to functions other than polynomials.

If we assign a physical dimension, say length, to each variable x and y in the polynomials in (1), then each polynomial itself also has a physical dimension, length to some power. This suggests the desired generalization. If, when certain variables are thought of as lengths, a function has physical dimension length to the kth power, then we shall call that function homogeneous of degree k in those variables. For example, the function

(2) $$f(x, y) = 2y^3 \exp\left(\frac{y}{x}\right) - \frac{x^4}{x + 3y}$$

is of dimension (length)^3 when x and y are lengths. Therefore that function is said to be homogeneous of degree 3 in x and y.

We permit the degree k to be any number. The function $\sqrt{x + 4y}$ is called homogeneous of degree $\frac{1}{2}$ in x and y. The function

$$\frac{x}{\sqrt{x^2 + y^2}}$$

is homogeneous of degree zero in x and y.

A formal definition of homogeneity is: *The function $f(x, y)$ is said to be homogeneous of degree k in x and y if, and only if,*

(3) $$f(\lambda x, \lambda y) = \lambda^k f(x, y).$$

The definition is easily extended to functions of more than two variables.

For the function $f(x, y)$ of equation (2), the formal definition of homogeneity leads us to consider

$$f(\lambda x, \lambda y) = 2\lambda^3 y^3 \exp\left(\frac{\lambda y}{\lambda x}\right) - \frac{\lambda^4 x^4}{\lambda x + 3\lambda y}.$$

But we see at once that

$$f(\lambda x, \lambda y) = \lambda^3 f(x, y);$$

hence $f(x, y)$ is homogeneous of degree 3 in x and y, as stated previously.

The following theorems prove useful in the next section.

THEOREM 1: *If $M(x, y)$ and $N(x, y)$ are both homogeneous and of the same degree, the function $\dfrac{M(x, y)}{N(x, y)}$ is homogeneous of degree zero.*

THEOREM 2: *If $f(x, y)$ is homogeneous of degree zero in x and y, $f(x, y)$ is a function of $\dfrac{y}{x}$ alone.*

Proof of Theorem 1 is left to the student.

Proof of Theorem 2: Let us put $y = vx$. Then Theorem 2 states that if $f(x, y)$ is homogeneous of degree zero, $f(x, y)$ is a function of v alone. Now

(4) $f(x, y) = f(x, vx) = x^0 f(1, v) = f(1, v),$

in which the x is now playing the role taken by λ in the definition (3) above. By (4), $f(x, y)$ depends on v alone as stated in Theorem 2.

Oral Exercises

Determine in each exercise whether the function is homogeneous or not. If it is homogeneous, state the degree of the function.

1. $4x^2 - 3xy + y^2$.

2. $x^3 - xy + y^3$.

3. $2y + \sqrt{x^2 + y^2}$.

4. $\sqrt{x - y}$.

5. e^x.

6. $\tan x$.

7. $\exp\left(\dfrac{x}{y}\right)$.

8. $\tan \dfrac{3y}{x}$.

9. $(x^2 + y^2) \exp\left(\dfrac{2x}{y}\right) + 4xy$.

10. $x \sin \dfrac{y}{x} - y \sin \dfrac{x}{y}$.

11. $\dfrac{x^2 + 3xy}{x - 2y}$.

12. $\dfrac{x^5}{x^2 + 2y^2}$.

13. $(u^2 + v^2)^{\frac{3}{2}}$.

14. $(u^2 - 4v^2)^{-\frac{1}{2}}$.

15. $y^2 \tan \dfrac{x}{y}$.

16. $\dfrac{(x^2 + y^2)^{\frac{1}{2}}}{(x^2 - y^2)^{\frac{1}{2}}}$.

17. $\dfrac{a + 4b}{a - 4b}$.

18. $\ln \dfrac{x}{y}$.

19. $x \ln x - y \ln y$.

20. $x \ln x - x \ln y$.

10. Equations with homogeneous coefficients

Suppose the coefficients M and N in an equation of order one and degree one,

(1) $M(x, y)\, dx + N(x, y)\, dy = 0,$

are both homogeneous functions and are of the *same degree* in x and y. By Theorems 1 and 2 of Section 9, the ratio M/N is a function of y/x alone. Hence equation (1) may be put in the form

(2) $\dfrac{dy}{dx} + g\left(\dfrac{y}{x}\right) = 0.$

This suggests the introduction of a new variable v by putting $y = vx$. Then (2) becomes

(3) $$x\frac{dv}{dx} + v + g(v) = 0,$$

in which the variables are separable. We can obtain the solution of (3) by the method of Section 6, insert y/x for v, and thus arrive at the solution of (1). We have shown that the substitution $y = vx$ will transform equation (1) into an equation in v and x in which the variables are separable.

The above method would have been equally successful had we used $x = vy$ to obtain from (1) an equation in y and v. See Example (b) below.

EXAMPLE (a): Solve the equation

(4) $$(x^2 - xy + y^2)\,dx - xy\,dy = 0.$$

Since the coefficients in (4) are both homogeneous and of degree two in x and y, let us put $y = vx$. Then (4) becomes

$$(x^2 - x^2v + x^2v^2)\,dx - x^2v(v\,dx + x\,dv) = 0,$$

from which the factor x^2 should be removed at once. That done, we have to solve

$$(1 - v + v^2)\,dx - v(v\,dx + x\,dv) = 0,$$

or

$$(1 - v)\,dx - xv\,dv = 0.$$

Hence we separate variables to get

$$\frac{dx}{x} + \frac{v\,dv}{v - 1} = 0.$$

Then from

$$\frac{dx}{x} + \left[1 + \frac{1}{v - 1}\right]dv = 0$$

the solution is seen to be

$$\ln x + v + \ln(v - 1) = \ln c,$$

or

$$x(v - 1)e^v = c.$$

In terms of the original variables, the solution is

$$x\left(\frac{y}{x} - 1\right)\exp\left(\frac{y}{x}\right) = c,$$

or

$$(y - x) \exp\left(\frac{y}{x}\right) = c.$$

EXAMPLE (b): Solve the equation

(5) $$xy \, dx + (x^2 + y^2) \, dy = 0.$$

Again the coefficients in the equation are homogeneous and of degree two. We could use $y = vx$, but the relative simplicity of the dx term in (5) suggests that we put

$$x = vy.$$

Then $dx = v \, dy + y \, dv$, and equation (5) is replaced by

$$vy^2(v \, dy + y \, dv) + (v^2y^2 + y^2) \, dy = 0,$$

or

$$v(v \, dy + y \, dv) + (v^2 + 1) \, dy = 0.$$

Hence we need to solve

(6) $$vy \, dv + (2v^2 + 1) \, dy = 0,$$

which leads at once to

$$\ln (2v^2 + 1) + 4 \ln y = \ln c,$$

or

$$y^4(2v^2 + 1) = c.$$

Thus the desired solution is

$$y^4 \left(\frac{2x^2}{y^2} + 1\right) = c;$$

that is,

(7) $$y^2(2x^2 + y^2) = c.$$

Since the left member of the solution (7) cannot be negative, we may, for symmetry's sake, change the arbitrary constant to c_1^4, writing

$$y^2(2x^2 + y^2) = c_1^4.$$

It is worth-while for the student to attack equation (5) using $y = vx$. That method leads directly to the equation

$$(v^3 + 2v) \, dx + x(v^2 + 1) \, dv = 0.$$

Frequently in equations with homogeneous coefficients, it is quite immaterial whether one uses $y = vx$ or $x = vy$.

Exercises

In Exs. 1–19 obtain the general solution.

1. $(x - 2y) dx + (2x + y) dy = 0.$
ANS. $\ln (x^2 + y^2) + 4 \text{ Arctan } (y/x) = c.$

2. $2(2x^2 + y^2) dx - xy dy = 0.$ ANS. $x^4 = c^2(4x^2 + y^2).$

3. $xy dx - (x^2 + 3y^2) dy = 0.$ ANS. $x^2 = 6y^2 \ln (y/c).$

4. $x^2 y' = 4x^2 + 7xy + 2y^2.$ ANS. $x^2(y + 2x) = c(y + x).$

5. $3xy dx + (x^2 + y^2) dy = 0.$

6. $(x - y)(4x + y) dx + x(5x - y) dy = 0.$
ANS. $x(y + x)^2 = c(y - 2x).$

7. $(5v - u) du + (3v - 7u) dv = 0.$ ANS. $(3v + u)^2 = c(v - u).$

8. $(x^2 + 2xy - 4y^2) dx - (x^2 - 8xy - 4y^2) dy = 0.$
ANS. $x^2 + 4y^2 = c(x + y).$

9. $(x^2 + y^2) dx - xy dy = 0.$ ANS. $y^2 = 2x^2 \ln (x/c).$

10. $v^2 dx + x(v - 4x) dv = 0.$ ANS. $xv^2 = c(v - 2x).$

11. $(2x + y)^2 dx = xy dy.$ ANS. $x^3(x + y) = c \exp (y/x).$

12. $y dx = (x + \sqrt{y^2 - x^2}) dy.$ ANS. $\text{Arcsin } (x/y) = \ln (y/c).$

13. $(3x^2 - 2xy + 3y^2) dx = 4xy dy.$ ANS. $(y - x)(y + 3x)^3 = cx^3.$

14. $[x \csc (y/x) - y] dx + x dy = 0.$ ANS. $\ln (x/c) = \cos (y/x).$

15. $x dx + \sin^2 (y/x)[y dx - x dy] = 0.$
ANS. $4x \ln (x/c) - 2y + x \sin (2y/x) = 0.$

16. $(x - y \ln y + y \ln x) dx + x(\ln y - \ln x) dy = 0.$
ANS. $(x - y) \ln x + y \ln y = cx + y.$

17. $[x - y \text{ Arctan } (y/x)] dx + x \text{ Arctan } (y/x) dy = 0.$
ANS. $2y \text{ Arctan } (y/x) = x \ln [c^2(x^2 + y^2)/x^4].$

18. $v(v^2 + u^2) du + u(v^2 - u^2) dv = 0.$

19. $(y^3 - 4xy^2 - 2x^3) dx + x^2(2y + x) dy = 0.$
ANS. $x^2(y - 2x)^2 = c^2(x^2 + y^2).$

20. Prove that with the aid of the substitution $y = vx$, you can solve any equation of the form

$$y^n f(x) dx + H(x, y)(y dx - x dy) = 0,$$

where $H(x, y)$ is homogeneous in x and y.

In Exs. 21–33 find the solution indicated.

21. $(x - y) dx + (3x + y) dy = 0;$ when $x = 2, y = -1.$
ANS. $2(x + 2y) + (x + y) \ln (x + y) = 0.$

22. $(y - \sqrt{x^2 + y^2}) dx - x dy = 0;$ when $x = \sqrt{3}, y = 1.$
ANS. $x^2 = 9 - 6y.$

23. $(y + \sqrt{x^2 + y^2})\, dx - x\, dy = 0$; when $x = \sqrt{3}$, $y = 1$.

ANS. $x^2 = 2y + 1$.

24. $[x \cos^2 (y/x) - y]\, dx + x\, dy = 0$; when $x = 1$, $y = \pi/4$.

ANS. $\tan (y/x) = \ln (e/x)$.

25. $(y^2 + 7xy + 16x^2)\, dx + x^2\, dy = 0$; when $x = 1$, $y = 1$.

ANS. $x - y = 5(y + 4x) \ln x$.

26. $y^2\, dx + (x^2 + 3xy + 4y^2)\, dy = 0$; when $x = 2$, $y = 1$.

ANS. $4(2y + x) \ln y = 2y - x$.

27. $xy\, dx + 2(x^2 + 2y^2)\, dy = 0$; when $x = 0$, $y = 1$.

ANS. $y^4(3x^2 + 4y^2) = 4$.

28. $y(2x^2 - xy + y^2)\, dx - x^2(2x - y)\, dy = 0$; when $x = 1$, $y = \frac{1}{2}$.

ANS. $y^2 \ln x = 2y^2 + xy - x^2$.

29. $y(9x - 2y)\, dx - x(6x - y)\, dy = 0$; when $x = 1$, $y = 1$.

ANS. $3x^3 - x^2y - 2y^2 = 0$.

30. $y(x^2 + y^2)\, dx + x(3x^2 - 5y^2)\, dy = 0$; when $x = 2$, $y = 1$.

ANS. $2y^5 - 2x^2y^3 + 3x = 0$.

31. $(16x + 5y)\, dx + (3x + y)\, dy = 0$; the curve to pass through the point $(1, -3)$.   ANS. $y + 3x = (y + 4x) \ln (y + 4x)$.

32. $v(3x + 2v)\, dx - x^2\, dv = 0$; when $x = 1$, $v = 2$.

ANS. $2x^3 + 2x^2v - 3v = 0$.

33. $(3x^2 - 2y^2)y' = 2xy$; when $x = 0$, $y = -1$.   ANS. $x^2 = 2y^2(y + 1)$.

34. From Theorems 1 and 2, page 24, it follows that if F is homogeneous of degree k in x and y, F can be written in the form

(A) $$F = x^k\, \varphi \left(\frac{y}{x}\right).$$

Use (A) to prove Euler's theorem that if F is a homogeneous function of degree k in x and y,

$$x \frac{\partial F}{\partial x} + y \frac{\partial F}{\partial y} = kF.$$

11. Exact equations

In Section 6 it was noted that when an equation can be put in the form

$$A(x)\, dx + B(y)\, dy = 0,$$

the general solution can be determined by integration; that is, by finding a function whose differential is $A(x)\, dx + B(y)\, dy$.

That idea can be extended to some equations of the form

(1) $$M(x, y)\, dx + N(x, y)\, dy = 0$$

in which separation of variables may not be possible. Suppose that a function $F(x, y)$ can be found that has for its total differential the expression $M\, dx + N\, dy$; that is,

(2) $$dF = M\, dx + N\, dy.$$

Then certainly

(3) $$F(x, y) = c$$

is the general solution of (1). For, from (3) it follows that

$$dF = 0,$$

or, in view of (2),

$$M\, dx + N\, dy = 0,$$

as desired.

Two things, then, are needed: first, to find out under what conditions on M and N a function F exists such that its total differential is exactly $M\, dx + N\, dy$; second, if those conditions are satisfied, actually to determine the function F. If there exists a function F such that

$$M\, dx + N\, dy$$

is exactly the total differential of F, we call equation (1) an *exact equation*.

If the equation

(1) $$M\, dx + N\, dy = 0$$

is exact, then by definition F exists such that

$$dF = M\, dx + N\, dy.$$

But, from calculus,

$$dF = \frac{\partial F}{\partial x}\, dx + \frac{\partial F}{\partial y}\, dy,$$

so

$$M = \frac{\partial F}{\partial x}, \quad N = \frac{\partial F}{\partial y}.$$

These two equations lead to

$$\frac{\partial M}{\partial y} = \frac{\partial^2 F}{\partial y\, \partial x}$$

and

$$\frac{\partial N}{\partial x} = \frac{\partial^2 F}{\partial x\, \partial y}.$$

Again from calculus

$$\frac{\partial^2 F}{\partial y\, \partial x} = \frac{\partial^2 F}{\partial x\, \partial y},$$

provided these partial derivatives are continuous. Therefore, if (1) is an exact equation, then

(4)
$$\frac{\partial M}{\partial y} = \frac{\partial N}{\partial x}.$$

Thus, for (1) to be exact it is necessary that (4) be satisfied.

Let us now show that if condition (4) is satisfied, then (1) is an exact equation. Let $\varphi(x, y)$ be a function for which

$$\frac{\partial \varphi}{\partial x} = M.$$

The function φ is the result of integrating $M\, dx$ with respect to x while holding y constant.   Now

$$\frac{\partial^2 \varphi}{\partial y\, \partial x} = \frac{\partial M}{\partial y};$$

hence, if (4) is satisfied, then also

(5)
$$\frac{\partial^2 \varphi}{\partial x\, \partial y} = \frac{\partial N}{\partial x}.$$

Let us integrate both sides of this last equation with respect to x, holding y fixed. In the integration with respect to the x, the "arbitrary constant" may be any function of y. Let us call it $B'(y)$, for ease in indicating its integral. Then integration of (5) with respect to x yields

(6)
$$\frac{\partial \varphi}{\partial y} = N + B'(y).$$

Now a function F can be exhibited, namely,

$$F = \varphi(x, y) - B(y),$$

for which

$$
\begin{aligned}
dF &= \frac{\partial \varphi}{\partial x}\, dx + \frac{\partial \varphi}{\partial y}\, dy - B'(y)\, dy \\
&= M\, dx + [N + B'(y)]\, dy - B'(y)\, dy \\
&= M\, dx + N\, dy.
\end{aligned}
$$

Hence, equation (1) is exact. We have completed a proof of the theorem stated below.

THEOREM 3: *If* M, N, $\dfrac{\partial M}{\partial y}$, *and* $\dfrac{\partial N}{\partial x}$ *are continuous functions of* x *and* y,

then a necessary and sufficient condition that

(1) $$M\,dx + N\,dy = 0$$

be an exact equation is that

(4) $$\frac{\partial M}{\partial y} = \frac{\partial N}{\partial x}.$$

Furthermore, the proof contains the germ of a method for obtaining the solution, a method used in Examples (a) and (b) below. It will be found, however, that with a little practice, we can write the solutions of very many exact equations after inspection. See Examples (c) and (d). No matter what method is used, the result should be checked by differentiation.

EXAMPLE (a): Solve the equation

(7) $$3x(xy - 2)\,dx + (x^3 + 2y)\,dy = 0.$$

First, from the fact that

$$\frac{\partial M}{\partial y} = 3x^2 \qquad \text{and} \qquad \frac{\partial N}{\partial x} = 3x^2,$$

we conclude that equation (7) is exact. Therefore, its solution is $F = c$, where

(8) $$\frac{\partial F}{\partial x} = M = 3x^2 y - 6x,$$

and

(9) $$\frac{\partial F}{\partial y} = N = x^3 + 2y.$$

Let us attempt to determine F from equation (8). Integration of both sides of (8) with respect to x, holding y constant, yields

(10) $$F = x^3 y - 3x^2 + T(y),$$

where the usual arbitrary constant in indefinite integration is now necessarily a function $T(y)$, as yet unknown. To determine $T(y)$, we use the fact that the function F of equation (10) must also satisfy equation (9).

Exact Equations

Hence

$$x^3 + T'(y) = x^3 + 2y,$$
$$T'(y) = 2y.$$

No arbitrary constant is needed in obtaining $T(y)$, since one is being introduced on the right in the solution $F = c$. Then

$$T(y) = y^2,$$

and from (10)

$$F = x^3y - 3x^2 + y^2.$$

Finally, the solution of equation (7) is seen to be

$$x^3y - 3x^2 + y^2 = c.$$

EXAMPLE (b): Solve the equation

(11) $\qquad (2x^3 - xy^2 - 2y + 3)\, dx - (x^2y + 2x)\, dy = 0.$

Here

$$\frac{\partial M}{\partial y} = -2xy - 2 = \frac{\partial N}{\partial x},$$

so equation (11) is exact.

The solution of (11) is $F = c$, where

(12) $\qquad \dfrac{\partial F}{\partial x} = 2x^3 - xy^2 - 2y + 3$

and

(13) $\qquad \dfrac{\partial F}{\partial y} = -x^2y - 2x.$

Because (13) is simpler than (12), and for variety's sake, let us start the determination of F from equation (13).

At once, from (13)

$$F = -\tfrac{1}{2}x^2y^2 - 2xy + Q(x),$$

where $Q(x)$ will be determined from (12). The latter yields

$$-xy^2 - 2y + Q'(x) = 2x^3 - xy^2 - 2y + 3,$$
$$Q'(x) = 2x^3 + 3.$$

Therefore

$$Q(x) = \tfrac{1}{2}x^4 + 3x,$$

and the desired solution of (11) is

$$-\tfrac{1}{2}x^2y^2 - 2xy + \tfrac{1}{2}x^4 + 3x = \tfrac{1}{2}c,$$

or

$$x^4 - x^2y^2 - 4xy + 6x = c.$$

EXAMPLE (c): Solve the equation of Example (a) by inspection.
Suppose that we have tested

(7) $$3x(xy - 2)\, dx + (x^3 + 2y)\, dy = 0$$

and found that it is exact. Then we may write the general solution by inspection; that is, by careful observation of the left member of (7), we shall find a function of which it is the total differential.

First, the term $3x^2y\, dx$ suggests the differential of x^3y. Hence we search (7) for the necessary companion term $x^3\, dy$ and group the two terms. Any term such as $-6x\, dx$, which contains only one variable, is an exact differential as it stands. Thus we are led to rewrite equation (7) as

$$(3x^2y\, dx + x^3\, dy) - 6x\, dx + 2y\, dy = 0,$$

from which it follows that

$$x^3y - 3x^2 + y^2 = c.$$

EXAMPLE (d): Solve the equation

(11) $$(2x^3 - xy^2 - 2y + 3)\, dx - (x^2y + 2x)\, dy = 0$$

of Example (b) by inspection.
The grouping

$$2x^3\, dx - (xy^2\, dx + x^2y\, dy) - (2y\, dx + 2x\, dy) + 3\, dx = 0$$

leads at once to the result

$$\tfrac{1}{2}x^4 - \tfrac{1}{2}x^2y^2 - 2xy + 3x = \tfrac{1}{2}c,$$
$$x^4 - x^2y^2 - 4xy + 6x = c.$$

Exercises

Test each of the following equations for exactness and solve the equation. The equations which are not exact may, of course, be solved by methods discussed in the preceding sections.

1. $(x + y)\, dx + (x - y)\, dy = 0$.   ANS. $x^2 + 2xy - y^2 = c$.
2. $(6x + y^2)\, dx + y(2x - 3y)\, dy = 0$.   ANS. $3x^2 + xy^2 - y^3 = c$.
3. $(2xy - 3x^2)\, dx + (x^2 + y)\, dy = 0$.   ANS. $x^2y - x^3 + \tfrac{1}{2}y^2 = c$.

4. $(y^2 - 2xy + 6x)\,dx - (x^2 - 2xy + 2)\,dy = 0.$
ANS. $xy^2 - x^2y + 3x^2 - 2y = c.$

5. $(2xy + y)\,dx + (x^2 - x)\,dy = 0.$ ANS. $y = cx(x - 1)^{-3}.$

6. $(x - 2y)\,dx + 2(y - x)\,dy = 0.$ ANS. $x^2 + 2y^2 = 4xy + c.$

7. Do Ex. 6 by another method.

8. $(2x - 3y)\,dx + (2y - 3x)\,dy = 0.$ ANS. $x^2 + y^2 = 3xy + c.$

9. Do Ex. 8 by another method.

10. $v(2uv^2 - 3)\,du + (3u^2v^2 - 3u + 4v)\,dv = 0.$
ANS. $v(u^2v^2 - 3u + 2v) = c.$

11. $(\cos 2y - 3x^2y^2)\,dx + (\cos 2y - 2x \sin 2y - 2x^3y)\,dy = 0.$
ANS. $\tfrac{1}{2} \sin 2y + x \cos 2y - x^3y^2 = c.$

12. $(1 + y^2)\,dx + (x^2y + y)\,dy = 0.$
ANS. $2 \operatorname{Arctan} x + \ln (1 + y^2) = c.$

13. $(1 + y^2 + xy^2)\,dx + (x^2y + y + 2xy)\,dy = 0.$
ANS. $2x + y^2(1 + x)^2 = c.$

14. $(w^3 + wz^2 - z)\,dw + (z^3 + w^2z - w)\,dz = 0.$
ANS. $(w^2 + z^2)^2 = 4wz + c.$

15. $(2xy - \tan y)\,dx + (x^2 - x \sec^2 y)\,dy = 0.$ ANS. $x^2y - x \tan y = c.$

16. $(\cos x \cos y - \cot x)\,dx - \sin x \sin y\,dy = 0.$
ANS. $\sin x \cos y = \ln (c \sin x).$

17. $(r + \sin \theta - \cos \theta)\,dr + r(\sin \theta + \cos \theta)\,d\theta = 0.$
ANS. $r^2 + 2r(\sin \theta - \cos \theta) = c.$

18. $x(3xy - 4y^3 + 6)\,dx + (x^3 - 6x^2y^2 - 1)\,dy = 0.$
ANS. $x^3y - 2x^2y^3 + 3x^2 - y = c.$

19. $(\sin \theta - 2r \cos^2 \theta)\,dr + r \cos \theta(2r \sin \theta + 1)\,d\theta = 0.$
ANS. $r \sin \theta - r^2 \cos^2 \theta = c.$

20. $[2x + y \cos (xy)]\,dx + x \cos (xy)\,dy = 0.$ ANS. $x^2 + \sin (xy) = c.$

21. $2xy\,dx + (y^2 + x^2)\,dy = 0.$ ANS. $y(3x^2 + y^2) = c.$

22. $2xy\,dx + (y^2 - x^2)\,dy = 0.$ ANS. $x^2 + y^2 = cy.$

23. $(xy^2 + y - x)\,dx + x(xy + 1)\,dy = 0.$ ANS. $x^2y^2 + 2xy - x^2 = c.$

24. $3y(x^2 - 1)\,dx + (x^3 + 8y - 3x)\,dy = 0;$ when $x = 0,\ y = 1.$
ANS. $xy(x^2 - 3) = 4(1 - y^2).$

25. $(1 - xy)^{-2}\,dx + [y^2 + x^2(1 - xy)^{-2}]\,dy = 0;$ when $x = 2,\ y = 1.$
ANS. $xy^4 - y^3 + 5xy - 3x = 5.$

26. $(3 + y + 2y^2 \sin^2 x)\,dx + (x + 2xy - y \sin 2x)\,dy = 0.$
ANS. $y^2 \sin 2x = c + 2x(3 + y + y^2).$

27. $2x[3x + y - y \exp (-x^2)]\,dx + [x^2 + 3y^2 + \exp (-x^2)]\,dy = 0.$
ANS. $x^2y + y^3 + 2x^3 + y \exp (-x^2) = c.$

28. $(xy^2 + x - 2y + 3)\,dx + x^2y\,dy = 2(x + y)\,dy;$ when $x = 1,\ y = 1.$
ANS. $(xy - 2)^2 + (x + 3)^2 = 2y^2 + 15.$

12. Methods of solution

Many texts present the material covered in Chapters 2 and 4 of this book as a collection of methods for solving equations of order one and degree one. A reader sometimes gets the impression that such techniques are isolated devices, a "bag of tricks." Actually, the only techniques presented here are the method of integrating an exact equation and two procedures for trying to make an equation exact if it is not exact in its original form. We already (Section 11) know how to handle an exact equation.

If an equation is not exact, it is natural to attempt to make it exact by the introduction of an appropriate factor, which is then called an *integrating factor*. Separation of variables (Section 6) is a simple example of the integrating factor technique. In Section 13 we shall solve the general linear equation of order one by first obtaining an integrating factor. Sections 17 and 18 contain additional developments of the same basic idea.

A second method for converting some equations into exact ones is to introduce a new variable, or variables, chosen by intelligent reaction to the form of the equation. Section 10 contains a simple instance in which the homogeneity of the coefficients suggests the ratio of the original variables as a new one because of Theorem 2, page 24. Chapter 4 contains other examples of appropriately chosen changes of variable.

13. The linear equation of order one

An equation that is linear and of order one in the dependent variable y must by definition (page 4) be of the form

(1) $$A(x)\, dy + B(x)y\, dx = C(x)\, dx.$$

By dividing each member of equation (1) by $A(x)$, we obtain

(2) $$\boldsymbol{dy + P(x)y\, dx = Q(x)\, dx,}$$

which we choose as the standard form for the linear equation of order one.

For the moment, suppose that there exists for equation (2) an integrating factor $v(x)$, a function of x alone. Then

(3) $$v\, dy + vP(x)y\, dx = vQ(x)\, dx$$

must be an exact equation. But (3) is easily put into the form

$$M\,dx + N\,dy = 0$$

with

$$M = vPy - vQ,$$

and

$$N = v,$$

in which v, P, and Q are functions of x alone.

Therefore, if equation (3) is to be exact, it follows from the requirement

$$\frac{\partial M}{\partial y} = \frac{\partial N}{\partial x}$$

that v must satisfy the equation

(4) $$vP = \frac{dv}{dx}.$$

From (4), v may be obtained readily, for

$$P\,dx = \frac{dv}{v},$$

so

$$\ln v = \int P\,dx,$$

or

(5) $$v = \exp\left(\int P\,dx\right).$$

That is, if equation (2) has an integrating factor independent of y, then that factor must be as given by equation (5).

It remains to be shown that the v given by equation (5) is actually an integrating factor of

(2) $$dy + P(x)y\,dx = Q(x)\,dx.$$

Let us apply the factor throughout (2), obtaining

(6) $$\exp\left(\int P\,dx\right)dy + P\exp\left(\int P\,dx\right)y\,dx = Q\exp\left(\int P\,dx\right)dx.$$

The left member of (6) is the differential of the product

$$y\exp\left(\int P\,dx\right);$$

the right member of (6) is an exact differential since it is independent of y. Hence equation (6) is exact, which is what we wished to show.

Of course one integrating factor is sufficient. Hence we may use in the exponent $\left(\int P\,dx\right)$ any function whose differential is $P\,dx$.

With an integrating factor at hand, we can lay down the following rule for integrating any linear equation of order one:

(a) Put the equation into standard form:

$$dy + Py\ dx = Q\ dx;$$

(b) Obtain the integrating factor exp $(\int P\ dx)$;
(c) Apply the integrating factor to the equation in its standard form;
(d) Solve the resultant exact equation.

Note, in integrating the exact equation, that *the integral of the left member is always the product of the dependent variable and the integrating factor used.*

EXAMPLE (a): Solve the equation

$$2(y - 4x^2)\ dx + x\ dy = 0.$$

The equation is linear in y. When put in standard form it becomes

(7) $$dy + \frac{2}{x} y\ dx = 8x\ dx.$$

Then an integrating factor is

$$\exp\left(\int \frac{2\ dx}{x}\right) = \exp(2 \ln x) = [\exp(\ln x)]^2 = x^2.$$

Next we apply the integrating factor to (7), thus obtaining the exact equation

(8) $$x^2\ dy + 2xy\ dx = 8x^3\ dx.$$

The solution of (8) is

(9) $$x^2y = 2x^4 + c$$

and should be checked, particularly since verification of the result is so easy.

From (9) we get (8) by differentiation. Then the original differential equation follows from (8) by a simple adjustment. Hence (9) is a solution of the original equation.

EXAMPLE (b): Solve the equation

$$y\ dx + (3x - xy + 2)\ dy = 0.$$

Since the product $y \, dy$ occurs here, the equation is not linear in y. It is, however, linear in x. Therefore we arrange the terms as in

$$y \, dx + (3 - y)x \, dy = -2 \, dy$$

and pass to the standard form,

(10) $$dx + \left(\frac{3}{y} - 1\right) x \, dy = -\frac{2}{y} \, dy.$$

Now

$$\int \left(\frac{3}{y} - 1\right) dy = 3 \ln y - y + c_1,$$

so that an integrating factor for equation (10) is

$$\exp(3 \ln y - y) = \exp(3 \ln y) \cdot e^{-y} = [\exp(\ln y)]^3 \cdot e^{-y} = y^3 e^{-y}.$$

Application of this integrating factor to equation (10) leads to the exact equation

$$y^3 e^{-y} \, dx + y^2(3 - y)e^{-y}x \, dy = -2y^2 e^{-y} \, dy,$$

from which we get

$$xy^3 e^{-y} = -2 \int y^2 e^{-y} \, dy$$

$$= 2y^2 e^{-y} + 4ye^{-y} + 4e^{-y} + c.$$

Thus we may write the solution as

$$xy^3 = 2y^2 + 4y + 4 + ce^y.$$

Exercises

In Exs. 1–25, find the general solution.

1. $(x^5 + 3y) \, dx - x \, dy = 0$.   ANS. $2y = x^5 + cx^3$.

2. $2(2xy + 4y - 3) \, dx + (x + 2)^2 \, dy = 0$.

ANS. $y = 2(x + 2)^{-1} + c(x + 2)^{-4}$.

3. $y' = x - 2y$.   ANS. $4y = 2x - 1 + ce^{-2x}$.

4. $(y + 1) \, dx + (4x - y) \, dy = 0$.

ANS. $20x = 4y - 1 + c(y + 1)^{-4}$.

5. $u \, dx + (1 - 3u)x \, du = 3u^2 e^{3u} \, du$.   ANS. $xu = (u^3 + c)e^{3u}$.

6. $u \, dx + (1 - 3u)x \, du = 3u \, du$.   ANS. $xu = ce^{3u} - u - \frac{1}{3}$.

7. $y' = x - 4xy$. Solve by two methods.

ANS. $4y = 1 + c \exp(-2x^2)$.

8. $y' = \csc x + y \cot x$.   ANS. $y = c \sin x - \cos x$.

9. $y' = \csc x - y \cot x$.   ANS. $y \sin x = x + c$.

10. $(2xy + x^2 + x^4)\, dx - (1 + x^2)\, dy = 0.$

ANS. $y = (1 + x^2)(c + x - \text{Arctan } x).$

11. $(y - \cos^2 x)\, dx + \cos x\, dy = 0.$

ANS. $y(\sec x + \tan x) = c + x - \cos x.$

12. $y' = x - 2y \cot 2x.$ ANS. $4y \sin 2x = c + \sin 2x - 2x \cos 2x.$

13. $(y - x + xy \cot x)\, dx + x\, dy = 0.$

ANS. $xy \sin x = c + \sin x - x \cos x.$

14. $\dfrac{dy}{dx} - my = c_1 e^{mx},$ where c_1 and m are constants.

ANS. $y = (c_1 x + c_2)e^{mx}.$

15. $\dfrac{dy}{dx} - m_2 y = c_1 e^{m_1 x},$ where $c_1,\ m_1,\ m_2$ are constants and $m_1 \neq m_2.$

ANS. $y = c_3 e^{m_1 x} + c_2 e^{m_2 x},$ where $c_3 = \dfrac{c_1}{m_1 - m_2}.$

16. $v\, dx + (2x + 1 - vx)\, dv = 0.$ ANS. $xv^2 = v + 1 + ce^v.$

17. $x(x^2 + 1)y' + 2y = (x^2 + 1)^3.$

ANS. $x^2 y = \tfrac{1}{4}(x^2 + 1)^3 + c(x^2 + 1).$

18. $2y(y^2 - x)dy = dx.$ ANS. $x = y^2 - 1 + c \exp(-y^2).$

19. $(1 + xy)\, dx - (1 + x^2)\, dy = 0.$ ANS. $y = x + c(1 + x^2)^{\frac{1}{2}}.$

20. $2y\, dx = (x^2 - 1)(dx - dy).$

ANS. $(x - 1)y = (x + 1)[c + x - 2 \ln (x + 1)].$

21. $dx - (1 + 2x \tan y)\, dy = 0.$

ANS. $2x \cos^2 y = y + c + \sin y \cos y.$

22. $(1 + \cos x)y' = \sin x(\sin x + \sin x \cos x - y).$

ANS. $y = (1 + \cos x)(c + x - \sin x).$

23. $y' = 1 + 3y \tan x.$ ANS. $3y \cos^3 x = c + 3 \sin x - \sin^3 x.$

24. $(x + a)y' = bx - ny;$ a, b, n are constants with $n \neq 0,\ n \neq -1.$

ANS. $n(n + 1)y = b(nx - a) + c(x + a)^{-n}.$

25. Solve the equation of Ex. 24 for the exceptional cases $n = 0$ and $n = -1.$

ANS. If $n = 0,\ y = bx + c - ab \ln (x + a).$

If $n = -1,\ y = ab + c(x + a) + b(x + a) \ln (x + a).$

26. In the standard form $dy + Py\, dx = Q\, dx$ put $y = vw,$ thus obtaining

$$w(dv + Pv\, dx) + v\, dw = Q\, dx.$$

Then, by first choosing v so that

$$dv + Pv\, dx = 0$$

and later determining $w,$ show how to complete the solution of

$$dy + Py\, dx = Q\, dx.$$

In Exs. 27–33 find the particular solution indicated.

27. $(2x + 3)y' = y + (2x + 3)^{\frac{1}{2}}$; when $x = -1$, $y = 0$.

ANS. $2y = (2x + 3)^{\frac{1}{2}} \ln (2x + 3)$.

28. $y' = x^3 - 2xy$; when $x = 1$, $y = 1$.

ANS. $2y = x^2 - 1 + 2 \exp (1 - x^2)$.

29. $L\dfrac{di}{dt} + Ri = E$, where L, R, and E are constants; when $t = 0$, $i = 0$.

ANS. $i = \dfrac{E}{R}\left[1 - \exp\left(-\dfrac{Rt}{L}\right)\right]$.

30. $\dfrac{di}{dt} + Ri = E \sin \omega t$; when $t = 0$, $i = 0$.

ANS.   Let $Z^2 = R^2 + \omega^2 L^2$. Then
$$i = EZ^{-2}\left[R \sin \omega t - \omega L \cos \omega t + \omega L \exp\left(-\dfrac{Rt}{L}\right)\right].$$

31. Find that solution of $y' = 2(2x - y)$ which passes through the point $(0, -1)$. ANS. $y = 2x - 1$.

32. Find that solution of $y' = 2(2x - y)$ which passes through the point $(0, 1)$. ANS. $y = 2x - 1 + 2e^{-2x}$.

33. $(1 + t^2)\, ds + 2t[st^2 - 3(1 + t^2)^2]\, dt = 0$; when $t = 0$, $s = 2$.

ANS. $s = (1 + t^2)[3 - \exp (-t^2)]$.

Miscellaneous Exercises

In each exercise, find the general solution, unless the statement of the exercise stipulates otherwise.

1. $y' = \exp (2x - y)$. ANS. $2e^y = e^{2x} + c$.

2. $(x + y)\, dx + x\, dy = 0$. ANS. $x(x + 2y) = c$.

3. $y^2\, dx - x(2x + 3y)\, dy = 0$. ANS. $y^2(x + y) = cx$.

4. $(x^2 + 1)\, dx + x^2 y^2\, dy = 0$. ANS. $xy^3 = 3(1 + cx - x^2)$.

5. $(x^3 + y^3)\, dx + y^2(3x + ky)\, dy = 0$; k is constant.

ANS. $ky^4 + 4xy^3 + x^4 = c$.

6. $y' = x^3 - 2xy$; when $x = 1$, $y = 2$.

ANS. $2y = x^2 - 1 + 4 \exp (1 - x^2)$.

7. $\dfrac{dy}{dx} - \cos x = \cos x \tan^2 y$. ANS. $2 \sin x = y + \sin y \cos y + c$.

8. $\cos x \dfrac{dy}{dx} = 1 - y - \sin x$. ANS. $y(1 + \sin x) = (x + c) \cos x$.

9. $\sin \theta \dfrac{dr}{d\theta} = -1 - 2r \cos \theta$. ANS. $r \sin^2 \theta = c + \cos \theta$.

10. $y(x + 3y) \, dx + x^2 \, dy = 0.$ ANS. $x^2 y = c(2x + 3y).$

11. $\dfrac{dy}{dx} = \sec^2 x \sec^3 y.$ ANS. $3 \tan x + c = 3 \sin y - \sin^3 y.$

12. $y(2x^3 - x^2 y + y^3) \, dx - x(2x^3 + y^3) \, dy = 0.$
ANS. $2x^2 y \ln (cx) = 4x^3 - y^3.$

13. $(1 + x^2)y' = x^4 y^4.$ ANS. $x^3 y^3 + 1 = y^3(c + 3x - 3 \operatorname{Arctan} x).$

14. $y(3 + 2xy^2) \, dx + 3(x^2 y^2 + x - 1) \, dy = 0.$
ANS. $x^2 y^3 = 3(c + y - xy).$

15. $(2x^2 - 2xy - y^2) \, dx + xy \, dy = 0.$ ANS. $x^3 = c(y - x) \exp (y/x).$

16. $y(x^2 + y^2) \, dx + x(3x^2 - 5y^2) \, dy = 0;$ when $x = 2, y = 1.$
ANS. $2y^5 - 2x^2 y^3 + 3x = 0.$

17. $y' + ay = b;$ a and b are constants. Solve by two methods.
ANS. $y = b/a + ce^{-ax}.$

18. $(x - y) \, dx - (x + y) \, dy = 0.$ Solve by two methods.
ANS. $x^2 - 2xy - y^2 = c.$

19. $\dfrac{dx}{dt} = \cos x \cos^2 t.$ ANS. $4 \ln (\sec x + \tan x) = 2t + \sin 2t + c.$

20. $(\sin y - y \sin x) \, dx + (\cos x + x \cos y) \, dy = 0.$
ANS. $x \sin y + y \cos x = c.$

21. $(1 + 4xy - 4x^2 y) \, dx + (x^2 - x^3) \, dy = 0;$ when $x = 2, y = \frac{1}{4}.$
ANS. $2x^4 y = x^2 + 2x + 2 \ln (x - 1).$

22. $3x^3 y' = 2y(y - 3).$ ANS. $y = c(y - 3) \exp (x^{-2}).$

23. $(2y \cos x + \sin^4 x) \, dx = \sin x \, dy;$ when $x = \frac{1}{2}\pi, y = 1.$
ANS. $y = 2 \sin^2 x \sin^2 \frac{1}{2}x.$

24. $xy(dx - dy) = x^2 \, dy + y^2 \, dx.$ ANS. $x = y \ln (cxy).$

25. $a^2(dy - dx) = x^2 \, dy + y^2 \, dx;$ a is constant.
ANS. $2 \operatorname{Arctan} (y/a) = \ln [c(x + a)/(x - a)].$

26. $(y - \sin^2 x) \, dx + \sin x \, dy = 0.$
ANS. $y(\csc x - \cot x) = x + c - \sin x.$

27. $(x - y) \, dx + (3x + y) \, dy = 0;$ when $x = 2, y = -1.$
ANS. $2(x + 2y) + (x + y) \ln (x + y) = 0.$

28. $y \, dx = (2x + 1)(dx - dy).$ ANS. $3y = (2x + 1) + c(2x + 1)^{-\frac{1}{2}}.$

In solving Exs. 29–33, recall that the principal value Arcsin x of the inverse sine function is restricted as follows:

$$-\tfrac{1}{2}\pi \leq \operatorname{Arcsin} x \leq \tfrac{1}{2}\pi.$$

29. $\sqrt{1 - y^2} \, dx + \sqrt{1 - x^2} \, dy = 0.$
ANS. $\operatorname{Arcsin} x + \operatorname{Arcsin} y = c,$ or a part of the ellipse $x^2 + 2c_1 xy + y^2 + c_1^2 - 1 = 0,$ where $c_1 = \cos c.$

30. Solve the equation of Ex. 29 with the added condition that when $x = 0$, $y = \frac{1}{2}\sqrt{3}$.

ANS. Arcsin x + Arcsin $y = \frac{1}{3}\pi$, or that arc of the ellipse $x^2 + xy + y^2 = \frac{3}{4}$ that is indicated by a heavy solid line in Figure 6.

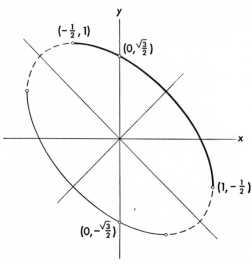

FIGURE 6

31. Solve the equation of Ex. 29 with the added condition that when $x = 0$, $y = -\frac{1}{2}\sqrt{3}$.

ANS. Arcsin x + Arcsin $y = -\frac{1}{3}\pi$, or that arc of the ellipse $x^2 + xy + y^2 = \frac{3}{4}$, that is indicated by a light solid line in Figure 6.

32. Show that after the answers to Exs. 30 and 31 have been deleted, the remaining arcs of the ellipse

$$x^2 + xy + y^2 = \frac{3}{4}$$

are not solutions of the differential equation

$$\sqrt{1 - y^2}\, dx + \sqrt{1 - x^2}\, dy = 0.$$

For this purpose consider the sign of the slope of the curve.

33. For the equation

$$\sqrt{1 - y^2}\, dx - \sqrt{1 - x^2}\, dy = 0$$

state and solve four problems analogous to Exs. 29–32 above.

34. $v\, du = (e^v + 2uv - 2u)\, dv.$ ANS. $v^2 u = ce^{2v} - (v + 1)e^v.$

35. $y\, dx = (3x + y^3 - y^2)\, dy$; when $x = 1$, $y = -1$.

ANS. $x = y^2\,[1 + y \ln\,(-y)].$

36. $y^2\,dx - (xy + 2)\,dy = 0.$ 　　　　　　　ANS.　$xy = cy^2 - 1.$

37. $(x^2 - 2xy - y^2)\,dx - (x^2 + 2xy - y^2)\,dy = 0.$

　　　　　　　　　ANS.　$(x + y)(x^2 - 4xy + y^2) = c^3.$

38. $y^2\,dx + (xy + y^2 - 1)\,dy = 0;$ when $x = -1,\ y = 1.$

　　　　　　　ANS.　$y^2 + 2xy + 1 = 2 \ln y.$

39. $y(y^2 - 3x^2)\,dx + x^3\,dy = 0.$ 　　　　ANS.　$2x^6 = y^2(x^4 + c).$

40. $y' = \cos x - y \sec x;$ when $x = 0,\ y = 1.$

　　　　　　ANS.　$y(1 + \sin x) = \cos x(x + 2 - \cos x).$

41. Find that solution of $y' = 3x + y$ which passes through the point $(-1, 0).$ 　　　　　　ANS.　$y = -3(x + 1).$

42. Find that solution of $y' = 3x + y$ which passes through the point $(-1, 1).$ 　　　ANS.　$y = \exp{(x + 1)} - 3(x + 1).$

43. $y' = y \tan x + \cos x.$ 　　　ANS.　$2y = \sin x + (x + c) \sec x.$

44. $(x^2 - 1 + 2y)\,dx + (1 - x^2)\,dy = 0;$ when $x = 2,\ y = 1.$

　　　　　ANS.　$(x + 1)y = (x - 1)[x + 1 + 2 \ln{(x - 1)}].$

45. $(x^3 - 3xy^2)\,dx + (y^3 - 3x^2y)\,dy = 0.$ 　　ANS.　$x^4 - 6x^2y^2 + y^4 = c.$

46. $(1 - x^2)y' = 1 - xy - 3x^2 + 2x^4.$ 　　ANS.　$y = x - x^3 + c(1 - x^2)^{\frac{1}{2}}.$

47. $(y^2 + y)\,dx - (y^2 + 2xy + x)\,dy = 0;$ when $x = 3,\ y = 1.$

　　　　　　　ANS.　$2y^2 + y = x.$

48. $(y^3 - x^3)\,dx = xy(x\,dx + y\,dy).$

　　　　　　ANS.　$2x^2 \ln{(x + y)} = cx^2 + 2xy - y^2.$

49. $y' = \sec x - y \tan x.$ 　　　　　ANS.　$y = \sin x + c \cos x.$

50. $x^2y' = y(1 - x).$ 　　　　　　ANS.　$x \ln{(cxy)} = -1.$

51. $xy' = x - y + xy \tan x.$ 　　ANS.　$xy \cos x = c + \cos x + x \sin x.$

52. $(3x^4y - 1)\,dx + x^5\,dy = 0;$ when $x = 1,\ y = 1.$

　　　　　　　ANS.　$x^4y = 2x - 1.$

53. $y^2\,dx + x^2\,dy = 2xy\,dy.$ 　　　ANS.　$y^2 = x(y + c).$

54. $(\sin x \sin y + \tan x)\,dx - \cos x \cos y\,dy = 0.$

　　　　　　ANS.　$\cos x \sin y = \ln{(c \sec x)}.$

55. $(3xy - 4y - 1)\,dx + x(x - 2)\,dy = 0;$ when $x = 1,\ y = 2.$

　　　　　　ANS.　$2x^2(x - 2)y = x^2 - 5.$

CHAPTER **3**

Elementary Applications

14. Velocity of escape from the earth

Many physical problems involve differential equations of order one and degree one.

Consider the problem of determining the velocity of a particle projected in a radial direction outward from the earth and acted upon by only one force, the gravitational attraction of the earth.

We shall assume an initial velocity in a radial direction so that the motion of the particle takes place entirely on a line through the center of the earth.

According to the Newtonian law of gravitation, the acceleration of the particle will be inversely proportional to the square of the distance from the particle to the center of the earth. Let r be that variable distance, and let R be the radius of the earth. If t represents time, v the velocity of the particle, a its acceleration, and k the constant of proportionality in the Newtonian law, then

$$a = \frac{dv}{dt} = \frac{k}{r^2}.$$

The acceleration is negative because the velocity is decreasing. Hence the constant k is negative. When $r = R$, then $a = -g$, the acceleration of gravity at the surface of the earth. Thus

45

$$-g = \frac{k}{R^2},$$

from which

$$a = -\frac{gR^2}{r^2}.$$

We wish to express the acceleration in terms of the velocity and the distance. We have $a = \dfrac{dv}{dt}$ and $v = \dfrac{dr}{dt}$. Hence

$$a = \frac{dv}{dt} = \frac{dr}{dt}\frac{dv}{dr} = v\frac{dv}{dr},$$

so the differential equation for the velocity is now seen to be

(1) $$v\frac{dv}{dr} = -\frac{gR^2}{r^2}.$$

The method of separation of variables applies to equation (1) and leads at once to the solution

$$v^2 = \frac{2gR^2}{r} + C.$$

Suppose the particle leaves the earth's surface with the velocity v_0. Then $v = v_0$ when $r = R$, from which the constant C is easily determined to be

$$C = v_0^2 - 2gR.$$

Thus a particle projected in a radial direction outward from the earth's surface with an initial velocity v_0 will travel with a velocity v given by the equation

(2) $$v^2 = \frac{2gR^2}{r} + v_0^2 - 2gR.$$

It is of considerable interest to determine whether the particle will escape from the earth. Now at the surface of the earth, at $r = R$, the velocity is positive, $v = v_0$. An examination of the right member of equation (2) shows that the velocity of the particle will remain positive if, and only if,

(3) $$v_0^2 - 2gR \geqq 0.$$

For, if the inequality (3) is satisfied, the velocity given by equation (2) will remain positive, since it cannot vanish, is continuous, and is positive at $r = R$. On the other hand, if the inequality (3) is not satisfied, then

$v_0{}^2 - 2gR < 0$, and there will be a critical value of r for which the right member of equation (2) is zero. That is, the particle would stop, the velocity would change from positive to negative, and the particle would return to the earth.

A particle projected from the earth with a velocity v_0 such that $v_0 \geqq \sqrt{2gR}$ will escape from the earth. Hence, the minimum such velocity of projection,

$$(4) \qquad\qquad v_e = \sqrt{2gR},$$

is called the *velocity of escape*.

The radius of the earth is approximately $R = 3960$ miles. The acceleration of gravity at the surface of the earth is approximately $g = 32.16$ feet per second per second, or $g = 6.09(10)^{-3}$ miles per second per second. For the earth, the velocity of escape is easily found to be $v_e = 6.95$ miles per second.

Of course, the gravitational pull of other celestial bodies, the moon, the sun, Mars, Venus, etc. has been neglected in the idealized problem treated here. It is not difficult to see that such approximations are justified, since we are interested in only the critical initial velocity v_e. Whether the particle actually recedes from the earth forever or becomes, for instance, a satellite of some heavenly body, is of no consequence in the present problem.

If in this study we happen to be thinking of the particle as an idealization of a ballistic-type rocket, then other elements must be considered. Air resistance in the first few miles may not be negligible. Methods for overcoming such difficulties are not suitable topics for discussion here.

It must be realized that the formula $v_e = \sqrt{2gR}$ applies equally well for the velocity of escape from the other members of the solar system, as long as R and g are given their appropriate values.

15. Newton's law of cooling

Experiment has shown that under certain conditions, a good approximation to the temperature of an object can be obtained by using Newton's law of cooling: The temperature of a body changes at a rate which is proportional to the difference in temperature between the outside medium and the body itself. We shall assume here that the constant of proportionality is the same whether the temperature is increasing or decreasing.

Suppose, for instance, that a thermometer, which has been at the reading 70 °F inside a house, is placed outside where the air temperature is 10 °F. Three minutes later it is found that the thermometer reading is 25 °F. We wish to predict the thermometer reading at various later times.

Let u (°F) represent the temperature of the thermometer at time t (min.), the time being measured from the instant the thermometer is placed outside. We are given that when $t = 0$, $u = 70$ and when $t = 3$, $u = 25$.

According to Newton's law, the time rate of change of temperature, du/dt, is proportional to the temperature difference $(u - 10)$. Since the thermometer temperature is decreasing, it is convenient to choose $(-k)$ as the constant of proportionality. Thus the u is to be determined from the differential equation

(1) $$\frac{du}{dt} = -k(u - 10),$$

and the conditions that

(2) $$\text{when } t = 0, u = 70$$

and

(3) $$\text{when } t = 3, u = 25.$$

We need to know the thermometer reading at two different times because there are two constants to be determined, the k in equation (1) and the "arbitrary" constant which occurs in the solution of the differential equation (1).

From equation (1) it follows at once that

$$u = 10 + Ce^{-kt}.$$

Then condition (2) yields $70 = 10 + C$ from which $C = 60$, so we have

(4) $$u = 10 + 60e^{-kt}.$$

The value of k will be determined now by using the condition (3). Putting $t = 3$ and $u = 25$ into equation (4) we get

$$25 = 10 + 60e^{-3k},$$

from which $e^{-3k} = \frac{1}{4}$, so $k = \frac{1}{3} \ln 4$.

Thus, the temperature is given by the equation

(5) $$u = 10 + 60 \exp\left(-\tfrac{1}{3}t \ln 4\right).$$

Since ln 4 = 1.39, equation (5) may be replaced by

(6) $u = 10 + 60 \exp(-0.46t)$,

which is convenient when a table of values of e^{-x} is available.

16. Simple chemical conversion

It is known from the results of chemical experimentation that, in certain reactions in which a substance A is being converted into another substance, the time rate of change of the amount x of unconverted substance is proportional to x.

Let the amount of unconverted substance be known at some specified time; that is, let $x = x_0$ at $t = 0$. Then the amount x at any time $t > 0$ is determined by the differential equation

(1) $$\frac{dx}{dt} = -kx$$

and the condition that $x = x_0$ when $t = 0$. Since the amount x is decreasing as time increases, the constant of proportionality in equation (1) is taken to be $(-k)$.

From equation (1) it follows that

$$x = Ce^{-kt}.$$

But $x = x_0$ when $t = 0$. Hence $C = x_0$. Thus we have the result

(2) $$x = x_0 e^{-kt}.$$

Let us now add another condition, which will enable us to determine k. Suppose it is known that at the end of half a minute, at $t = 30$ (sec.), two-thirds of the original amount x_0 has already been converted. Let us determine how much unconverted substance remains at $t = 60$ (sec.).

When two-thirds of the substance has been converted, one-third remains unconverted. Hence $x = \frac{1}{3}x_0$ when $t = 30$. Equation (2) now yields the relation

$$\tfrac{1}{3}x_0 = x_0 e^{-30k}$$

from which k is easily found to be $\frac{1}{30}$ ln 3. Then with t measured in seconds, the amount of unconverted substance is given by the equation

(3) $$x = x_0 \exp(-\tfrac{1}{30}t \ln 3).$$

At $t = 60$,

$$x = x_0 \exp(-2 \ln 3) = x_0(3)^{-2} = \tfrac{1}{9}x_0.$$

Exercises

1. The radius of the moon is roughly 1080 miles. The acceleration of gravity at the surface of the moon is about $0.165g$, where g is the acceleration of gravity at the surface of the earth. Determine the velocity of escape for the moon. ANS. 1.5 mi./sec.

2. Determine to two significant figures the velocity of escape for each of the celestial bodies listed below. The data given are rough and g may be taken to be $6.1(10)^{-3}$ mi./sec².

	Accel. of gravity at surface	*Radius in miles*	*Ans. in mi./sec.*
Venus	$0.85g$	3,800	6.3
Mars	$0.38g$	2,100	3.1
Jupiter	$2.6g$	43,000	37
Sun	$28g$	432,000	380
Ganymede	$0.12g$	1,780	1.6

3. A thermometer reading 18 °F is brought into a room the temperature of which is 70 °F. One minute later the thermometer reading is 31 °F. Determine the temperature reading as a function of time and in particular, find the temperature reading five minutes after the thermometer is first brought into the room.
ANS. $u = 70 - 52 \exp(-0.29t)$; when $t = 5$, $u = 58$.

4. A thermometer reading 75 °F is taken out where the temperature is 20 °F. The reading is 30 °F four minutes later. Find (a) the thermometer reading seven minutes after the thermometer was brought outside, and (b) the time taken for the reading to drop from 75 °F to within a half degree of the air temperature. ANS. (a) 23 °F; (b) 11.5 min.

5. At 1:00 P.M., a thermometer reading 70 °F is taken outside where the air temperature is -10 °F, ten below zero. At 1:02 P.M., the reading is 26 °F. At 1:05 P.M., the thermometer is taken back indoors where the air is at 70 °F. What is the thermometer reading at 1:09 P.M.?

6. At 9 A.M., a thermometer reading 70 °F is taken outdoors where the temperature is 15 °F. At 9:05 A.M., the thermometer reading is 45 °F. At 9:10 A.M., the thermometer is taken back indoors where the temperature is fixed at 70 °F. Find (a) the reading at 9:20 A.M. and (b) when the reading, to the nearest degree, will show the correct (70 °F) indoor temperature. ANS. (a) 58 °F; (b) 9:46 A.M.

7. At 2:00 P.M., a thermometer reading 80 °F is taken outside where the air temperature is 20 °F. At 2:03 P.M., the temperature reading yielded by the thermometer is 42 °F. Later, the thermometer is brought inside

where the air is at 80 °F. At 2:10 P.M., the reading is 71 °F. When was
the thermometer brought indoors?   ANS.   At 2:05 P.M.

 8. Suppose that a chemical reaction proceeds according to the law given
    in Section 16 above. If half the substance A has been converted at the
    end of ten seconds, find when nine-tenths of the substance will have
    been converted.   ANS.   33 sec.

 9. The conversion of a substance B follows the law used in Section 16
    above. If only a fourth of the substance has been converted at the end
    of ten seconds, find when nine-tenths of the substance will have been
    converted.   ANS.   80 sec.

10. For a substance C, the time rate of conversion is proportional to the
    square of the amount x of unconverted substance. Let k be the numer-
    ical value of the constant of proportionality and let the amount of
    unconverted substance be x_0 at time $t = 0$. Determine x for all $t \geqq 0$.
                                        ANS. $x = x_0/(1 + x_0 kt)$.

11. Two substances, A and B, are being converted into a single compound
    C. In the laboratory it has been shown that, for these substances, the
    following law of conversion holds: the time rate of change of the
    amount x of compound C is proportional to the product of the amounts
    of unconverted substances A and B. Assume the units of measure so
    chosen that one unit of the compound C is formed from the combina-
    tion of one unit of A with one unit of B. If at time $t = 0$ there are
    a units of substance A, b units of substance B, and none of the com-
    pound C, present, show that the law of conversion may be expressed
    by the equation

    $$\frac{dx}{dt} = k(a - x)(b - x).$$

Solve this equation with the given initial condition.

ANS.   If $b \neq a, x = \dfrac{ab[\exp{(b - a)kt} - 1]}{b \exp{(b - a)kt} - a}$; if $b = a, x = a^2 kt/(akt + 1)$.

12. In the solution of Ex. 11, above assume that $k > 0$ and investigate the
    behavior of x as $t \to \infty$.   ANS.   If $b \geqq a, x \to a$; if $b \leqq a, x \to b$.

13. Radium decomposes at a rate proportional to the quantity of radium
    present. Suppose that it is found that in 25 years approximately 1.1
    per cent of a certain quantity of radium has decomposed. Determine
    approximately how long it will take for one-half the original amount of
    radium to decompose.   ANS.   1600 years.

14. A certain radioactive substance has a half-life of 38 hours. Find how
    long it takes for 90% of the radioactivity to be dissipated.
                                                          ANS.   126 hrs.

15. A bacterial population B is known to have a rate of growth proportional to B itself. If between noon and 2 P.M. the population triples, at what time, no controls being exerted, should B become 100 times what it was at noon?   ANS.   About 8:22 P.M.

16. In the motion of an object through a certain medium (air at certain pressures is an example), the medium furnishes a resisting force proportional to the square of the velocity of the moving object. Suppose a body falls, due to the action of gravity, through such a medium. Let t represent time, and v represent velocity, positive downward. Let g be the usual constant acceleration of gravity and let w be the weight of the body. Use Newton's law, force equals mass times acceleration, to conclude that the differential equation of the motion is

$$\frac{w}{g}\frac{dv}{dt} = w - kv^2,$$

where kv^2 is the magnitude of the resisting force furnished by the medium.

17. Solve the differential equation of Ex. 16 with the initial condition that $v = v_0$ when $t = 0$. Introduce the constant $a^2 = w/k$ to simplify the formulas.   ANS. $\dfrac{a+v}{a-v} = \dfrac{a+v_0}{a-v_0}\exp\left(\dfrac{2gt}{a}\right).$

18. List a consistent set of units for the dimensions of the variables and parameters of Exs. 16–17 above.

ANS. t in sec. g in ft./sec.^{2}
v in ft./sec. k in (lb.)(sec.^{2})/(ft.^{2})
w in lb. a in ft./sec.

19. There are mediums that resist motion through them with a force proportional to the first power of the velocity. For such a medium, state and solve problems analogous to Exs. 16–18 above, except that for convenience a constant $b = w/k$ may be introduced to replace the a^2 of Ex. 17. Show that b has the dimensions of a velocity.
ANS. $v = b +$

$$(v_0 - b)\exp\left(-\frac{gt}{b}\right).$$

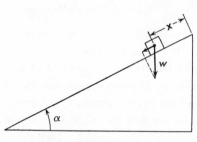

FIGURE 7

20. Figure 7 shows a weight, w pounds, sliding down an inclined plane which makes an angle α with the horizontal. Assume that no force other than gravity is acting on the weight; that is, there is no friction, no air resistance, etc. At

time $t = 0$, let $x = x_0$ and let the initial velocity be v_0. Determine x for $t > 0$.   ANS. $x = \frac{1}{2}gt^2 \sin \alpha + v_0 t + x_0$.

21. A long, very smooth board is inclined at an angle of 10° with the horizontal. A weight starts from rest ten feet from the bottom of the board and slides downward under the action of gravity alone. Find how long it will take the weight to reach the bottom of the board and determine the terminal speed.   ANS.   1.9 sec. and 10.5 ft./sec.

22. Add to the conditions of Ex. 20 above a retarding force of magnitude kv, where v is the velocity. Determine v and x under the assumption that the weight starts from rest with $x = x_0$. Use the notation $a = kg/w$.   ANS. $v = a^{-1}g \sin \alpha \, (1 - e^{-at})$;

$$x = x_0 + a^{-2}g \sin \alpha \, (-1 + e^{-at} + at).$$

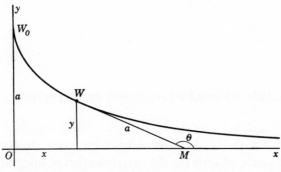

FIGURE 8

23. A man, standing at O in Figure 8, holds a rope of length a to which a weight is attached, initially at W_0. The man walks to the right dragging the weight after him. When the man is at M, the weight is at W. Find the differential equation of the path (called the tractrix) of the weight and solve the equation.   ANS. $x = a \ln \dfrac{a + \sqrt{a^2 - y^2}}{y} - \sqrt{a^2 - y^2}$.

CHAPTER 4

Additional Topics on Equations of
Order One and Degree One

17. Integrating factors found by inspection

In Section 13 we found that any linear equation of order one can be solved with the aid of an integrating factor. In Section 18 there is some discussion of tests for the determination of integrating factors.

At present we are concerned with equations that are simple enough to enable us to find integrating factors by inspection. The ability to do this depends largely upon recognition of certain common exact differentials and upon experience.

Below are four exact differentials which occur frequently:

$$(1) \qquad d(xy) = x\,dy + y\,dx,$$

$$(2) \qquad d\left(\frac{x}{y}\right) = \frac{y\,dx - x\,dy}{y^2},$$

$$(3) \qquad d\left(\frac{y}{x}\right) = \frac{x\,dy - y\,dx}{x^2},$$

$$(4) \qquad d\left(\operatorname{Arctan}\frac{y}{x}\right) = \frac{x\,dy - y\,dx}{x^2 + y^2}.$$

Note the homogeneity of the coefficients of dx and dy in each of these differentials.

A differential involving only one variable, one such as $x^{-2}\,dx$, is an exact differential.

EXAMPLE (a): Solve the equation

(5) $y \, dx + (x + x^3 y^2) \, dy = 0.$

Let us group the terms of like degree, writing the equation in the form

$$(y \, dx + x \, dy) + x^3 y^2 \, dy = 0.$$

Now the combination $(y \, dx + x \, dy)$ attracts attention, so we rewrite the equation, obtaining

(6) $d(xy) + x^3 y^2 \, dy = 0.$

Since the differential of xy is present in equation (6), any factor that is a function of the product xy will not disturb the integrability of that term. But the other term contains the differential dy, hence should contain a function of y alone. Therefore, let us divide by $(xy)^3$ and write

$$\frac{d(xy)}{(xy)^3} + \frac{dy}{y} = 0.$$

The equation above is integrable as it stands. Its solution is

$$-\frac{1}{2x^2 y^2} + \ln y = -\ln c,$$

or

$$2x^2 y^2 \ln (cy) = 1.$$

EXAMPLE (b): Solve the equation

(7) $y(x^3 - y) \, dx - x(x^3 + y) \, dy = 0.$

Let us regroup the terms of (7) to obtain

(8) $x^3(y \, dx - x \, dy) - y(y \, dx + x \, dy) = 0.$

Recalling that

$$d\left(\frac{x}{y}\right) = \frac{y \, dx - x \, dy}{y^2},$$

we divide the terms of equation (8) throughout by y^2 to get

(9) $x^3 \, d\left(\frac{x}{y}\right) - \frac{d(xy)}{y} = 0.$

Equation (9) will be made exact by introducing a factor, if it can be found, to make the coefficient of $d(x/y)$ a function of (x/y) and the coefficient of $d(xy)$ a function of (xy). Some skill in obtaining such factors can be developed with a little practice. When a factor can be found by inspection, that method is frequently the most rapid one.

There is a straightforward attack on equation (9) which has its good points. Assume that the integrating factor desired is $x^k y^n$, where k and n are to be determined. Applying that factor, we obtain

$$(10) \qquad x^{k+3} y^n \, d\left(\frac{x}{y}\right) - x^k y^{n-1} \, d(xy) = 0.$$

Since the coefficient of $d(x/y)$ is to be a function of the ratio (x/y), the exponents of x and y in that coefficient must be numerically equal, but of opposite sign. That is,

$$(11) \qquad k + 3 = -n.$$

In a similar manner, from the coefficient of $d(xy)$ it follows that we must put

$$(12) \qquad k = n - 1.$$

From equations (11) and (12) we conclude that $k = -2$, $n = -1$. The desired integrating factor is $x^{-2} y^{-1}$ and (10) becomes

$$\frac{x}{y} d\left(\frac{x}{y}\right) - \frac{d(xy)}{x^2 y^2} = 0$$

of which the solution is

$$\tfrac{1}{2}\left(\frac{x}{y}\right)^2 + \frac{1}{xy} = \frac{c}{2}.$$

Finally, we may write the desired solution of equation (7) as

$$x^3 + 2y = cxy^2.$$

EXAMPLE (c): Solve the equation

$$3x^2 y \, dx + (y^4 - x^3) \, dy = 0.$$

Since two terms in the coefficients of dx and dy are of degree three and the other coefficient is not of degree three, let us regroup the terms to get

$$(3x^2 y \, dx - x^3 \, dy) + y^4 \, dy = 0,$$

or

$$y \, d(x^3) - x^3 \, dy + y^4 \, dy = 0.$$

The form of the first two terms now suggests the numerator in the differential of a quotient, as in

$$d\left(\frac{u}{v}\right) = \frac{v\,du - u\,dv}{v^2}.$$

Therefore, we divide each term of our equation by y^2 and obtain

$$\frac{y\,d(x^3) - x^3\,dy}{y^2} + y^2\,dy = 0,$$

or

$$d\left(\frac{x^3}{y}\right) + y^2\,dy = 0.$$

Hence the solution of the original equation is

$$\frac{x^3}{y} + \frac{y^3}{3} = \frac{c}{3}$$

or

$$3x^3 + y^4 = cy.$$

Exercises

Except when the exercise indicates otherwise, find the general solution.

1. $y(2xy + 1)\,dx - x\,dy = 0.$ ANS. $x(xy + 1) = cy.$

2. $y(y^3 - x)\,dx + x(y^3 + x)\,dy = 0.$ ANS. $2xy^3 - x^2 = cy^2.$

3. $(x^3y^3 + 1)\,dx + x^4y^2\,dy = 0.$ ANS. $x^3y^3 = -3\ln(cx).$

4. $2t\,ds + s(2 + s^2t)\,dt = 0.$ ANS. $1 + s^2t = cs^2t^2.$

5. $y(x^4 - y^2)\,dx + x(x^4 + y^2)\,dy = 0.$ ANS. $y(3x^4 + y^2) = cx^3.$

6. $y(y^2 + 1)\,dx + x(y^2 - 1)\,dy = 0.$ ANS. $x(y^2 + 1) = cy.$

7. Do Ex. 6 by a second method.

8. $y(x^3 - y^5)\,dx - x(x^3 + y^5)\,dy = 0.$ ANS. $x^4 = y^4(c + 4xy).$

9. $y(x^2 - y^2 + 1)\,dx - x(x^2 - y^2 - 1)\,dy = 0.$

ANS. $x^2 + cxy + y^2 = 1.$

10. $(x^3 + xy^2 + y)\,dx + (y^3 + x^2y + x)\,dy = 0.$

ANS. $(x^2 + y^2)^2 = c - 4xy.$

11. $y(x^2 + y^2 - 1)\,dx + x(x^2 + y^2 + 1)\,dy = 0.$

ANS. $xy + \text{Arctan}\,(y/x) = c.$

12. $(x^3 + xy^2 - y)\,dx + (y^3 + x^2y + x)\,dy = 0.$

ANS. $2\,\text{Arctan}\,(y/x) = c - x^2 - y^2.$

13. $y(x^3e^{xy} - y)\,dx + x(y + x^3e^{xy})\,dy = 0.$ ANS. $2x^2e^{xy} + y^2 = cx^2.$

14. $xy(y^2 + 1)\,dx + (x^2y^2 - 2)\,dy = 0$; when $x = 1$, $y = 1$.

ANS. $x^2(y^2 + 1) = 2 + 4\ln y.$

15. $y^2(1 - x^2)\,dx + x(x^2y + 2x + y)\,dy = 0.$

ANS. $x^2y + x + y = cxy^2.$

16. $y(x^2y^2 - 1) \, dx + x(x^2y^2 + 1) \, dy = 0.$ ANS. $x^2y^2 = 2 \ln (cx/y).$

17. $x^4y' = -x^3y - \csc (xy).$ ANS. $2x^2 \cos (xy) = cx^2 - 1.$

18. $[1 + y \tan (xy)] \, dx + x \tan (xy) \, dy = 0.$ ANS. $\cos (xy) = ce^x.$

19. $y(x^2y^2 - m) \, dx + x(x^2y^2 + n) \, dy = 0.$ ANS. $x^2y^2 = 2 \ln (cx^m/y^n).$

20. $x(x^2 - y^2 - x) \, dx - y(x^2 - y^2) \, dy = 0$; when $x = 2$, $y = 0$.

ANS. $3(x^2 - y^2)^2 = 4(x^3 + 4).$

21. $y(x^2 + y) \, dx + x(x^2 - 2y) \, dy = 0$; when $x = 1$, $y = 2$.

ANS. $x^2y - y^2 + 2x = 0.$

22. $y(x^3y^3 + 2x^2 - y) \, dx + x^3(xy^3 - 2) \, dy = 0$; when $x = 1$, $y = 1$.

ANS. $x^3y^3 + 4x^2 - 7xy + 2y = 0.$

23. $y(2 - 3xy) \, dx - x \, dy = 0.$ ANS. $x^2(1 - xy) = cy.$

24. $y(2x + y^2) \, dx + x(y^2 - x) \, dy = 0.$ ANS. $x(x + y^2) = cy.$

25. $y \, dx + 2(y^4 - x) \, dy = 0.$ ANS. $y^4 + x = cy^2.$

26. $y(3x^3 - x + y) \, dx + x^2(1 - x^2) \, dy = 0.$

ANS. $y \ln (cx) = x(1 - x^2).$

27. $2x^5y' = y(3x^4 + y^2).$ ANS. $x^4 = y^2(1 + cx).$

28. $(x^ny^{n+1} + ay) \, dx + (x^{n+1}y^n + bx) \, dy = 0.$

ANS.   If $n \neq 0$, $x^ny^n = n \ln (cx^{-a}y^{-b})$.

If $n = 0$, $xy = c_1x^{-a}y^{-b}.$

29. $(x^{n+1}y^n + ay) \, dx + (x^ny^{n+1} + ax) \, dy = 0.$

ANS.   If $n \neq 1$, $(n - 1)(xy)^{n-1}(x^2 + y^2 - c) = 2a$.

If $n = 1$, $x^2 + y^2 - c = -2a \ln (xy).$

18. The determination of integrating factors

Let us see what progress can be made on the problem of the determination of an integrating factor for the equation

(1) $M \, dx + N \, dy = 0.$

Suppose u, possibly a function of both x and y, is to be an integrating factor of (1). Then the equation

(2) $uM \, dx + uN \, dy = 0$

must be exact. Therefore, by the result of Section 11,

$$\frac{\partial}{\partial y} (uM) = \frac{\partial}{\partial x} (uN).$$

Hence u must satisfy the partial differential equation

$$u \frac{\partial M}{\partial y} + M \frac{\partial u}{\partial y} = u \frac{\partial N}{\partial x} + N \frac{\partial u}{\partial x},$$

or

(3) $$u\left(\frac{\partial M}{\partial y} - \frac{\partial N}{\partial x}\right) = N\frac{\partial u}{\partial x} - M\frac{\partial u}{\partial y}.$$

Furthermore, by reversing the argument above, it can be seen that if u satisfies equation (3), then u is an integrating factor for equation (1). We have "reduced" the problem of solving the ordinary differential equation (1) to the problem of obtaining a particular solution of the partial differential equation (3).

Not much has been gained, since we have developed no methods for attacking an equation such as (3). Therefore, we turn the problem back into the realm of ordinary differential equations by restricting u to be a function of only one variable.

First let u be a function of x alone. Then $\frac{\partial u}{\partial y} = 0$ and $\frac{\partial u}{\partial x}$ becomes $\frac{du}{dx}$. Then (3) reduces to

$$u\left(\frac{\partial M}{\partial y} - \frac{\partial N}{\partial x}\right) = N\frac{du}{dx},$$

or

(4) $$\frac{1}{N}\left(\frac{\partial M}{\partial y} - \frac{\partial N}{\partial x}\right)dx = \frac{du}{u}.$$

If the left member of the above equation is a function of x alone, then we can determine u at once. Indeed, if

(5) $$\frac{1}{N}\left(\frac{\partial M}{\partial y} - \frac{\partial N}{\partial x}\right) = f(x),$$

then the desired integrating factor is $u = \exp\left(\int f(x)\, dx\right)$.

By a similar argument, assuming that u is a function of y alone, we are led to the conclusion that if

(6) $$\frac{1}{M}\left(\frac{\partial M}{\partial y} - \frac{\partial N}{\partial x}\right) = g(y),$$

then an integrating factor for equation (1) is $u = \exp\left(-\int g(y)\, dy\right)$.

Our two results are expressed in the following rules.

If $\frac{1}{N}\left(\frac{\partial M}{\partial y} - \frac{\partial N}{\partial x}\right) = f(x)$, a function of x alone, then $\exp\left(\int f(x)\, dx\right)$ is an integrating factor for the equation

(1) $$M\, dx + N\, dy = 0.$$

If $\dfrac{1}{M}\left(\dfrac{\partial M}{\partial y} - \dfrac{\partial N}{\partial x}\right) = g(y)$, a function of y alone, then $\exp\left(-\int g(y)\,dy\right)$ is an integrating factor for equation (1).

EXAMPLE (a): Solve the equation

(7) $(4xy + 3y^2 - x)\,dx + x(x + 2y)\,dy = 0.$

Here $M = 4xy + 3y^2 - x$, $N = x^2 + 2xy$, so

$$\frac{\partial M}{\partial y} - \frac{\partial N}{\partial x} = 4x + 6y - (2x + 2y) = 2x + 4y.$$

Hence

$$\frac{1}{N}\left(\frac{\partial M}{\partial y} - \frac{\partial N}{\partial x}\right) = \frac{2x + 4y}{x(x + 2y)} = \frac{2}{x}.$$

Therefore an integrating factor for equation (7) is

$$\exp\left(2\int \frac{dx}{x}\right) = \exp\left(2\ln x\right) = x^2.$$

Returning to the original equation (7), we insert the integrating factor and obtain

(8) $(4x^3y + 3x^2y^2 - x^3)\,dx + (x^4 + 2x^3y)\,dy = 0,$

which we know must be an exact equation. The methods of Section 11 apply. We are then led to put equation (8) in the form

$$(4x^3y\,dx + x^4\,dy) + (3x^2y^2\,dx + 2x^3y\,dy) - x^3\,dx = 0,$$

from which the solution

$$x^4y + x^3y^2 - \tfrac{1}{4}x^4 = \tfrac{1}{4}c,$$

or

$$x^3(4xy + 4y^2 - x) = c$$

follows at once.

EXAMPLE (b): Solve the equation

(9) $y(x + y + 1)\,dx + x(x + 3y + 2)\,dy = 0.$

First we form

$$\frac{\partial M}{\partial y} = x + 2y + 1, \qquad \frac{\partial N}{\partial x} = 2x + 3y + 2.$$

Then we see that

$$\frac{\partial M}{\partial y} - \frac{\partial N}{\partial x} = -x - y - 1,$$

so

$$\frac{1}{N}\left(\frac{\partial M}{\partial y} - \frac{\partial N}{\partial x}\right) = -\frac{x + y + 1}{x(x + 3y + 2)}$$

is not a function of x alone. But

$$\frac{1}{M}\left(\frac{\partial M}{\partial y} - \frac{\partial N}{\partial x}\right) = -\frac{x + y + 1}{y(x + y + 1)} = -\frac{1}{y}.$$

Therefore $\exp(\ln y) = y$ is the desired integrating factor for (9).

Using the integrating factor, we write

$$(xy^2 + y^3 + y^2)\,dx + (x^2y + 3xy^2 + 2xy)\,dy = 0,$$

or

$$(xy^2\,dx + x^2y\,dy) + (y^3\,dx + 3xy^2\,dy) + (y^2\,dx + 2xy\,dy) = 0.$$

Then the solution of (9) is found to be

$$\tfrac{1}{2}x^2y^2 + xy^3 + xy^2 = \tfrac{1}{2}c,$$

or

$$xy^2(x + 2y + 2) = c.$$

EXAMPLE (c): Solve the equation

(10) $$y(x + y)\,dx + (x + 2y - 1)\,dy = 0.$$

From $\dfrac{\partial M}{\partial y} = x + 2y$, $\dfrac{\partial N}{\partial x} = 1$, we conclude at once that

$$\frac{1}{N}\left(\frac{\partial M}{\partial y} - \frac{\partial N}{\partial x}\right) = \frac{x + 2y - 1}{x + 2y - 1} = 1.$$

Hence e^x is an integrating factor for (10). Then

$$(xye^x + y^2e^x)\,dx + (xe^x + 2ye^x - e^x)\,dy = 0$$

is an exact equation. Grouping the terms in the following manner,

$$[xye^x\,dx + (xe^x - e^x)\,dy] + (y^2e^x\,dx + 2ye^x\,dy) = 0,$$

leads us at once to the solution

$$e^x(x - 1)y + y^2e^x = c,$$

or

$$y(x + y - 1) = ce^{-x}.$$

Exercises

Solve each of the following equations.

1. $(x^2 + y^2 + 1) \, dx + x(x - 2y) \, dy = 0.$

ANS. $x^2 - y^2 + xy - 1 = cx.$

2. $2y(x^2 - y + x) \, dx + (x^2 - 2y) \, dy = 0.$ ANS. $y(x^2 - y) = ce^{-2x}.$

3. $y(2x - y + 1) \, dx + x(3x - 4y + 3) \, dy = 0.$

ANS. $xy^3(x - y + 1) = c.$

4. $y(4x + y) \, dx - 2(x^2 - y) \, dy = 0.$ ANS. $2x^2 + xy + 2y \ln y = cy.$

5. $(xy + 1) \, dx + x(x + 4y - 2) \, dy = 0.$

ANS. $xy + \ln x + 2y^2 - 2y = c.$

6. $(2y^2 + 3xy - 2y + 6x) \, dx + x(x + 2y - 1) \, dy = 0.$

ANS. $x^2(y^2 + xy - y + 2x) = c.$

7. $y(y + 2x - 2) \, dx - 2(x + y) \, dy = 0.$ ANS. $y(2x + y) = ce^x.$

8. $y^2 dx + (3xy + y^2 - 1) \, dy = 0.$ ANS. $y^2(y^2 + 4xy - 2) = c.$

9. $2y(x + y + 2) \, dx + (y^2 - x^2 - 4x - 1) \, dy = 0.$

ANS. $x^2 + 2xy + y^2 + 4x + 1 = cy.$

10. $2(2y^2 + 5xy - 2y + 4)dx + x(2x + 2y - 1) \, dy = 0.$

ANS. $x^4(y^2 + 2xy - y + 2) = c.$

11. $3(x^2 + y^2) \, dx + x(x^2 + 3y^2 + 6y) \, dy = 0.$

ANS. $x(x^2 + 3y^2) = ce^{-y}.$

12. $y(8x - 9y) \, dx + 2x(x - 3y) \, dy = 0.$ ANS. $x^3y(2x - 3y) = c.$

13. Do Ex. 12 by another method.

14. $y(2x^2 - xy + 1) \, dx + (x - y) \, dy = 0.$

ANS. $y(2x - y) = c \exp(-x^2).$

15. Euler's theorem (Ex. 34, page 29) on homogeneous functions states that if F is a homogeneous function of degree k in x and y, then

$$x \frac{\partial F}{\partial x} + y \frac{\partial F}{\partial y} = kF.$$

Use Euler's theorem to prove the result that if M and N are homogeneous functions of the same degree, and if $Mx + Ny \neq 0$, then

$$\frac{1}{Mx + Ny}$$

is an integrating factor for the equation

(1) $M \, dx + N \, dy = 0.$

16. In the result to be proved in Ex. 15 above there is an exceptional case, namely, when $Mx + Ny = 0$. Solve equation (1) when $Mx + Ny = 0$.

ANS. $y = cx.$

Use the integrating factor in the result of Ex. 15 above to solve each of the equations in Exs. 17–20. The student should realize, from its position in the exercises instead of in the text, that the method of Ex. 15 is not being strongly recommended.

17. $xy\, dx - (x^2 + 2y^2)\, dy = 0.$ ANS. $x^2 = 4y^2 \ln (y/c).$

18. $v^2\, dx + x(x + v)\, dv = 0.$ ANS. $xv^2 = c(x + 2v).$

19. $v(u^2 + v^2)\, du - u(u^2 + 2v^2)\, dv = 0.$ ANS. $u^2 = 2v^2 \ln (cv^2/u).$

20. $(x^2 + y^2)\, dx - xy\, dy = 0.$ (Ex. 9, page 28.)

19. Substitution suggested by the equation

An equation of the form

$$M\, dx + N\, dy = 0$$

may not yield at once (or at all) to the methods of Chapter 2. Even then the usefulness of those methods is not exhausted. It may be possible by some change of variables to transform the equation into one of a type which we know how to solve.

A natural source of suggestions for useful transformations is the differential equation itself. If a particular function of one or both variables stands out in the equation, then it is worth while to examine the equation after that function has been introduced as a new variable. For instance, in the equation

(1) $$(x + 2y - 1)\, dx + 3(x + 2y)\, dy = 0$$

the combination $(x + 2y)$ occurs twice and so attracts attention. Hence we put

$$x + 2y = v,$$

and since no other function of x and y stands out, we retain either x or y for the other variable. The solution is completed in Example (a) below.

In the equation

(2) $$(1 + 3x \sin y)\, dx - x^2 \cos y\, dy = 0,$$

the presence of both $\sin y$ and its differential $\cos y\, dy$, and the fact that y appears in the equation in no other manner, leads us to put $\sin y = w$ and to obtain the differential equation in w and x. See Example (b) below.

EXAMPLE (a): Solve the equation

(1) $$(x + 2y - 1)\, dx + 3(x + 2y)\, dy = 0.$$

As suggested above, put

$$x + 2y = v.$$

Then

$$dx = dv - 2\, dy$$

and equation (1) becomes

$$(v - 1)(dv - 2\, dy) + 3v\, dy = 0,$$

or

$$(v - 1)\, dv + (v + 2)\, dy = 0.$$

Now the variables can be separated. From the equation in the form

$$\frac{v - 1}{v + 2}\, dv + dy = 0,$$

we get

$$\left[1 - \frac{3}{v + 2} \right] dv + dy = 0$$

and then

$$v - 3 \ln (v + 2) + y + c = 0.$$

But $v = x + 2y$, so our final result is

$$x + 3y + c = 3 \ln (x + 2y + 2).$$

EXAMPLE (b): Solve the equation

(2) $$(1 + 3x \sin y)\, dx - x^2 \cos y\, dy = 0.$$

Put $\sin y = w$. Then $\cos y\, dy = dw$ and (2) becomes

$$(1 + 3xw)\, dx - x^2\, dw = 0,$$

an equation linear in w. From the standard form

$$dw - \frac{3}{x} w\, dx = \frac{dx}{x^2}$$

an integrating factor is seen to be

$$\exp (-3 \ln x) = x^{-3}.$$

Application of the integrating factor yields the exact equation

$$x^{-3}\, dw - 3x^{-4}w\, dx = x^{-5}\, dx,$$

from which we get

$$x^{-3}w = -\tfrac{1}{4}x^{-4} + \tfrac{1}{4}c,$$

or

$$4xw = cx^4 - 1.$$

Hence (2) has the solution

$$4x \sin y = cx^4 - 1.$$

20. Bernoulli's equation

A well-known equation which fits into the category of Section 19 is Bernoulli's equation,

$$(1) \qquad\qquad y' + P(x)y = Q(x)y^n.$$

If $n = 1$ in (1), the variables are separable, so we concentrate on the case $n \neq 1$. Equation (1) may be put in the form

$$(2) \qquad\qquad y^{-n}\,dy + Py^{-n+1}\,dx = Q\,dx.$$

But the differential of y^{-n+1} is $(1-n)y^{-n}\,dy$, so equation (2) may be simplified by putting

$$y^{-n+1} = z,$$

from which

$$(1-n)y^{-n}\,dy = dz.$$

Thus the equation in z and x is

$$dz + (1-n)Pz\,dx = (1-n)Q\,dx,$$

a linear equation in standard form. Hence any Bernoulli equation can be solved with the aid of the above change of dependent variable (unless $n = 1$, when no substitution is needed).

EXAMPLE (a): Solve the equation

$$(3) \qquad\qquad y(6y^2 - x - 1)\,dx + 2x\,dy = 0.$$

First let us group the terms according to powers of y, writing

$$2x\,dy - y(x+1)\,dx + 6y^3\,dx = 0.$$

Now it can be seen that the equation is a Bernoulli equation, since it involves only terms containing respectively dy, y, and y^n ($n = 3$ here). Therefore, we divide throughout by y^3, obtaining

$$2xy^{-3}\,dy - y^{-2}(x+1)\,dx = -6\,dx.$$

This equation is linear in y^{-2}, so we put $y^{-2} = v$, obtain $dv = -2y^{-3}\,dy$, and need to solve the equation

$$x\,dv + v(x + 1)\,dx = 6\,dx,$$

or

(4) $$dv + v(1 + x^{-1})\,dx = 6x^{-1}\,dx.$$

Since

$$\exp(x + \ln x) = xe^x$$

is an integrating factor for (4), the equation

$$xe^x\,dv + ve^x(x + 1)\,dx = 6e^x\,dx$$

is exact. Its solution

$$xve^x = 6e^x + c,$$

together with $v = y^{-2}$, leads us to the final result

$$y^2(6 + ce^{-x}) = x.$$

EXAMPLE (b): Solve the equation

(5) $$6y^2\,dx - x(2x^3 + y)\,dy = 0.$$

This is a Bernoulli equation with x as the dependent variable, so it can be treated in the manner used in Example (a). That method of attack is left for the exercises.

Equation (5) can equally well be treated as follows. Note that if each member of (5) be multiplied by x^2, the equation becomes

(6) $$6y^2x^2\,dx - x^3(2x^3 + y)\,dy = 0.$$

In (6), the variable x appears only in the combinations x^3 and its differential $3x^2\,dx$. Hence a reasonable choice for a new variable is $w = x^3$. The equation in w and y is

$$2y^2\,dw - w(2w + y)\,dy = 0,$$

an equation with coefficients homogeneous of degree two in y and w. The further change of variable $w = zy$ leads to the equation

$$2y\,dz - z(2z - 1)\,dy = 0,$$
$$\frac{4\,dz}{2z - 1} - \frac{2\,dz}{z} - \frac{dy}{y} = 0.$$

Therefore, we have

$$2\ln(2z - 1) - 2\ln z - \ln y = \ln c,$$

or

$$(2z - 1)^2 = cyz^2.$$

But $z = w/y = x^3/y$, so the solution we seek is

$$(2x^3 - y)^2 = cyx^6.$$

Exercises

In Exs. 1–21 obtain the general solution.

1. $(3x - 2y + 1) \, dx + (3x - 2y + 3) \, dy = 0.$
ANS. $5(x + y + c) = 2 \ln (15x - 10y + 11).$

2. $\sin y(x + \sin y) \, dx + 2x^2 \cos y \, dy = 0.$
ANS. $x^3 \sin^2 y = c(3x + \sin y)^2.$

3. $\dfrac{dy}{dx} = (9x + 4y + 1)^2.$ ANS. $3 \tan (6x + c) = 2(9x + 4y + 1).$

4. $y' = y - xy^3 e^{-2x}.$
ANS. $e^{2x} = y^2(x^2 + c).$

5. $\dfrac{dy}{dx} = \sin (x + y).$ ANS. $x + c = \tan (x + y) - \sec (x + y).$

6. $xy \, dx + (x^2 - 3y) \, dy = 0.$ ANS. $x^2 y^2 = 2y^3 + c.$

7. $(3 \tan x - 2 \cos y) \sec^2 x \, dx + \tan x \sin y \, dy = 0.$
ANS. $\cos y \tan^2 x = \tan^3 x + c.$

8. $(x + 2y - 1) \, dx + (2x + 4y - 3) \, dy = 0.$ Solve by two methods.
ANS. $(x + 2y - 1)^2 = 2y + c.$

9. Solve the equation

$$6y^2 \, dx - x(2x^3 + y) \, dy = 0$$

of Example (b) above by treating it as a Bernoulli equation in the dependent variable x.

10. $2x^3 y' = y(y^2 + 3x^2).$ Solve by two methods. ANS. $y^2(c - x) = x^3.$

11. $(3 \sin y - 5x) \, dx + 2x^2 \cot y \, dy = 0.$
ANS. $x^3(\sin y - x)^2 = c \sin^2 y.$

12. $y' = 1 + 6x \exp (x - y).$ ANS. $\exp (y - x) = 3x^2 + c.$

13. $\dfrac{dv}{du} = (u - v)^2 - 2(u - v) - 2.$

ANS. $(u - v - 3) \exp (4u) = c(u - v + 1).$

14. $2y \, dx + x(x^2 \ln y - 1) \, dy = 0.$ ANS. $y(1 + x^2 - x^2 \ln y) = cx^2.$

15. $\cos y \sin 2x \, dx + (\cos^2 y - \cos^2 x) \, dy = 0.$
ANS. $\cos^2 x(1 + \sin y) = \cos y(y + c - \cos y).$

16. $(ke^{2v} - u) \, du = 2e^{2v}(e^{2v} + ku) \, dv.$
ANS. $2k \operatorname{Arctan} (ue^{-2v}) = \ln [c(u^2 + e^{4v})].$

17. $y' \tan x \sin 2y = \sin^2 x + \cos^2 y$.

ANS. $(\sin^2 x + 3 \cos^2 y) \sin x = c$.

18. $(x + 2y - 1) \, dx - (x + 2y - 5) \, dy = 0$.

19. $y(x \tan x + \ln y) \, dx + \tan x \, dy = 0$.

ANS. $\sin x \ln y = x \cos x - \sin x + c$.

20. $xy' - y = x^k y^n$, where $n \neq 1$ and $k + n \neq 1$.

ANS. $(k + n - 1)y^{1-n} = (1 - n)x^k + cx^{1-n}$.

21. The equation of Ex. 20 for the values of k and n not included there.

ANS.   If $n = 1$ and $k \neq 0$, $x^k = k \ln (cy/x)$.

If $n = 1$ and $k = 0$, $y = cx^2$.

If $n \neq 1$ but $k + n = 1$, $y^{1-n} = (1 - n)x^{1-n} \ln (cx)$.

In Exs. 22–27, find the particular solution required.

22. $4(3x + y - 2) \, dx - (3x + y) \, dy = 0$; when $x = 1$, $y = 0$.

ANS. $7(4x - y - 4) = 8 \ln \dfrac{21x + 7y - 8}{13}$.

23. $y' = 2(3x + y)^2 - 1$; when $x = 0$, $y = 1$.

ANS. $4 \operatorname{Arctan} (3x + y) = 8x + \pi$.

24. $2xyy' = y^2 - 2x^3$. Find the solution that passes through the point $(1, 2)$.   ANS. $y^2 = x(5 - x^2)$.

25. $(y^4 - 2xy) \, dx + 3x^2 \, dy = 0$; when $x = 2$, $y = 1$.

ANS. $x^2 = y^3(x + 2)$.

26. $(2y^3 - x^3) \, dx + 3xy^2 \, dy = 0$; when $x = 1$, $y = 1$. Solve by two methods.   ANS. $5x^2y^3 = x^5 + 4$.

27. $(x^2 + 6y^2) \, dx - 4xy \, dy = 0$; when $x = 1$, $y = 1$. Solve by three methods.   ANS. $2y^2 = x^2(3x - 1)$.

21. Coefficients linear in the two variables

Consider the equation

(1) $(a_1x + b_1y + c_1) \, dx + (a_2x + b_2y + c_2) \, dy = 0$,

in which the a's, b's, and c's are constants. We know already how to solve the special case in which $c_1 = 0$ and $c_2 = 0$, for then the coefficients in (1) are each homogeneous and of degree one in x and y. It is reasonable to attempt to reduce equation (1) to that situation.

In connection with (1) consider the lines

(2) $a_1x + b_1y + c_1 = 0$,

$a_2x + b_2y + c_2 = 0$.

They may be parallel or they may intersect. There will not be two lines if a_1 and b_1 are zero, or if a_2 and b_2 are zero, but equaticn (1) will then be linear in one of its variables.

If the lines (2) intersect, let the point of intersection be (h, k). Then the translation

$$(3) \qquad\qquad\qquad \begin{aligned} x &= u + h, \\ y &= v + k \end{aligned}$$

will change the equations (2) into equations of lines through the origin of the uv coordinate system, namely,

$$(4) \qquad\qquad\qquad \begin{aligned} a_1u + b_1v &= 0, \\ a_2u + b_2v &= 0. \end{aligned}$$

Therefore, since $dx = du$ and $dy = dv$, the change of variables

$$\begin{aligned} x &= u + h, \\ y &= v + k, \end{aligned}$$

where (h, k) is the point of intersection of the lines (2), will transform the differential equation (1) into

$$(5) \qquad\qquad (a_1u + b_1v)\, du + (a_2u + b_2v)\, dv = 0,$$

an equation which we know how to solve.

If the lines (2) do not intersect, there exists a constant k such that

$$a_2x + b_2y = k(a_1x + b_1y),$$

so that equation (1) appears in the form

$$(6) \qquad (a_1x + b_1y + c_1)\, dx + [k(a_1x + b_1y) + c_2]\, dy = 0.$$

The recurrence of the expression $(a_1x + b_1y)$ in (6) suggests the introduction of a new variable $w = a_1x + b_1y$. Then the new equation, in w and x or in w and y, is one with variables separable, since its coefficients contain only w and constants.

EXAMPLE (a): Solve the equation

$$(7) \qquad\qquad (x + 2y - 4)\, dx - (2x + y - 5)\, dy = 0.$$

The lines

$$\begin{aligned} x + 2y - 4 &= 0, \\ 2x + y - 5 &= 0 \end{aligned}$$

intersect at the point $(2, 1)$. Hence put

$$x = u + 2,$$
$$y = v + 1.$$

Then equation (7) becomes

(8) $$(u + 2v)\, du - (2u + v)\, dv = 0,$$

which has coefficients homogeneous and of degree one in u and v. There-fore let $u = vz$, which transforms (8) into

$$(z + 2)(z\, dv + v\, dz) - (2z + 1)\, dv = 0,$$

or

$$(z^2 - 1)\, dv + v(z + 2)\, dz = 0.$$

Separation of the variables v and z leads us to the equation

$$\frac{dv}{v} + \frac{(z + 2)\, dz}{z^2 - 1} = 0.$$

With the aid of partial fractions. we can write the above equation in the form

$$\frac{2\, dv}{v} + \frac{3\, dz}{z - 1} - \frac{dz}{z + 1} = 0.$$

Hence we get

$$2 \ln v + 3 \ln (z - 1) - \ln (z + 1) = \ln c$$

from which it follows that

$$v^2(z - 1)^3 = c(z + 1),$$

or

$$(vz - v)^3 = c(vz + v).$$

Now $vz = u$, so our solution appears as

$$(u - v)^3 = c(u + v).$$

But $u = x - 2$ and $v = y - 1$. Therefore the desired result in terms of x and y is

$$(x - y - 1)^3 = c(x + y - 3).$$

For other methods of solution of equation (7), see Exs. 23 and 30 below.

EXAMPLE (b): Solve the equation

(9) $$(2x + 3y - 1)\, dx + (2x + 3y + 2)\, dy = 0,$$

with the condition that $y = 3$ when $x = 1$.

The lines

$$2x + 3y - 1 = 0$$

and

$$2x + 3y + 2 = 0$$

are parallel. Therefore we proceed, as we should have upon first glancing at the equation, to put

$$2x + 3y = v.$$

Then $2\,dx = dv - 3\,dy$, and equation (9) is transformed into

$$(v - 1)(dv - 3\,dy) + 2(v + 2)\,dy = 0,$$

or

(10) $$(v - 1)\,dv - (v - 7)\,dy = 0.$$

Equation (10) is easily solved, thus leading us to the relation

$$v - y + c + 6\ln(v - 7) = 0.$$

Therefore the general solution of (9) is

$$2x + 2y + c = -6\ln(2x + 3y - 7).$$

But $y = 3$ when $x = 1$, so $c = -8 - 6\ln 4$. Hence the particular solution required is

$$x + y - 4 = -3\ln\left[\tfrac{1}{4}(2x + 3y - 7)\right].$$

Exercises

In Exs. 1–18 find the general solution.

1. $(y - 2)\,dx - (x - y - 1)\,dy = 0.$

ANS. $x - 3 = (2 - y)\ln[c(y - 2)].$

2. $(x - 4y - 9)\,dx + (4x + y - 2)\,dy = 0.$

ANS. $\ln[(x - 1)^2 + (y + 2)^2] - 8\operatorname{Arctan}\dfrac{x - 1}{y + 2} = c.$

3. $(2x - y)\,dx + (4x + y - 6)\,dy = 0.$

ANS. $(x + y - 3)^3 = c(2x + y - 4)^2.$

4. $(x - 4y - 3)\,dx - (x - 6y - 5)\,dy = 0.$

ANS. $(x - 2y - 1)^2 = c(x - 3y - 2).$

5. $(2x + 3y - 5)\,dx + (3x - y - 2)\,dy = 0.$ Solve by two methods.

6. $2\,dx + (2x - y + 3)\,dy = 0.$ Use a change of variable.

ANS. $y + c = -\ln(2x - y + 4).$

7. Solve the equation of Ex. 6 by using the fact that the equation is linear in x.

8. $(x - y + 2) dx + 3 dy = 0.$ ANS. $x + c = 3 \ln (x - y + 5).$

9. Solve Ex. 8 by another method.

10. $(x + y - 1) dx + (2x + 2y + 1) dy = 0.$

ANS. $x + 2y + c = 3 \ln (x + y + 2).$

11. $(3x + 2y + 7) dx + (2x - y) dy = 0.$ Solve by two methods.

12. $(x - 2) dx + 4(x + y - 1) dy = 0.$

ANS. $2(y + 1) = -(x + 2y) \ln [c(x + 2y)].$

13. $(x - 3y + 2) dx + 3(x + 3y - 4) dy = 0.$

ANS. $\ln [(x - 1)^2 + 9(y - 1)^2] - 2 \operatorname{Arctan} \dfrac{x - 1}{3(y - 1)} = c.$

14. $(6x - 3y + 2) dx - (2x - y - 1) dy = 0.$

ANS. $3x - y + c = 5 \ln (2x - y + 4).$

15. $(9x - 4y + 4) dx - (2x - y + 1) dy = 0.$

ANS. $y - 1 = 3(y - 3x - 1) \ln [c(3x - y + 1)].$

16. $(x + 3y - 4) dx + (x + 4y - 5) dy = 0.$

ANS. $y - 1 = (x + 2y - 3) \ln [c(x + 2y - 3)].$

17. $(x + 2y - 1) dx - (2x + y - 5) dy = 0.$

ANS. $(x - y - 4)^3 = c(x + y - 2).$

18. $(x - 1) dx - (3x - 2y - 5) dy = 0.$

ANS. $(2y - x + 3)^2 = c(y - x + 2).$

In Exs. 19–22 obtain the particular solution indicated.

19. $(2x - 3y + 4) dx + 3(x - 1) dy = 0;$ when $x = 3, y = 2.$

ANS. $3(y - 2) = -2(x - 1) \ln \dfrac{x - 1}{2}.$

20. The equation of Ex. 19 but with the condition: when $x = -1, y = 2.$

ANS. $3(y - 2) = -2(x - 1) \ln \dfrac{1 - x}{2}.$

21. $(x + y - 4) dx - (3x - y - 4) dy = 0;$ when $x = 4, y = 1.$

ANS. $2(x + 2y - 6) = 3(x - y) \ln \dfrac{x - y}{3}.$

22. The equation of Ex. 21 but with the condition: when $x = 3, y = 7.$

ANS. $y - 5x + 8 = 2(y - x) \ln \dfrac{y - x}{4}.$

23. Prove that the change of variables

$$x = \alpha_1 u + \alpha_2 v, \qquad y = u + v$$

will transform the equation

(A) $(a_1 x + b_1 y + c_1) dx + (a_2 x + b_2 y + c_2) dy = 0$

into an equation in which the variables u and v are separable, if α_1 and

α_2 are roots of the equation

(B) $a_1\alpha^2 + (a_2 + b_1)\alpha + b_2 = 0,$

and if $\alpha_2 \neq \alpha_1$.

Note that this method of solution of (A) is not practical for us unless the roots of equation (B) are real and distinct.

Solve Exs. 24–29 by the method indicated in Ex. 23.

24. Ex. 4 above. As a check, the equation (B) for this case is

$$\alpha^2 - 5\alpha + 6 = 0,$$

so we may choose $\alpha_1 = 2$ and $\alpha_2 = 3$.

The equation in u and v turns out to be

$$(v - 1)\, du - 2(u + 2)\, dv = 0.$$

25. Ex. 3 above.   **26.** Ex. 10 above.
27. Ex. 17 above.   **28.** Ex. 18 above.
29. Example (a) in the text of this section.
30. Prove that the change of variables

$$x = \alpha_1 u + \beta v, \qquad y = u + v$$

will transform the equation

(A) $(a_1 x + b_1 y + c_1)\, dx + (a_2 x + b_2 y + c_2)\, dy = 0$

into an equation that is linear in the variable u, if α_1 is a root of the equation

(B) $a_1\alpha^2 + (a_2 + b_1)\alpha + b_2 = 0,$

and if β is any number such that $\beta \neq \alpha_1$.

Note that this method is not practical for us unless the roots of equation (B) are real. But they need not be distinct as they had to be in the theorem of Ex. 23. The method of this exercise is particularly useful when the roots of (B) are equal.

Solve Exs. 31–35 by the method indicated in Ex. 30.

31. Ex. 16 above. The only possible α_1 is (-2). Then β may be chosen to be anything else.
32. Ex. 12 above.   **33.** Ex. 15 above.   **34.** Ex. 18 above.
35. Ex. 4 above. As seen in Ex. 24, the roots of the "α-equation" are 2 and 3. If you choose $\alpha_1 = 2$, for example, then you may make β anything except 2. Of course, if you choose $\alpha_1 = 2$ and $\beta = 3$, then you are reverting to the method of Ex. 23.

22. Solutions involving nonelementary integrals

In solving differential equations we frequently are confronted with the need for integrating an expression that is not the differential of any elementary* function. Following is a short list of nonelementary integrals:

$$\int \exp{(-x^2)}\, dx \qquad \int \frac{e^{-x}}{x}\, dx \qquad \int x\tan x\, dx$$

$$\int \sin x^2\, dx \qquad \int \frac{\sin x}{x}\, dx \qquad \int \frac{dx}{\ln x}$$

$$\int \cos x^2\, dx \qquad \int \frac{\cos x}{x}\, dx \qquad \int \frac{dx}{\sqrt{1-x^3}}.$$

Integrals involving the square root of a polynomial of degree greater than two are, in general, nonelementary. In special instances they may degenerate into elementary integrals.

The following example presents two ways of dealing with problems in which nonelementary integrals arise.

EXAMPLE: Solve the equation

$$y' - 2xy = 1$$

with the boundary condition that when $x = 0$, $y = 1$.

The equation being linear in y, we write

$$dy - 2xy\, dx = dx,$$

obtain the integrating factor $\exp{(-x^2)}$, and prepare to solve

(1) $$\exp{(-x^2)}\, dy - 2xy \exp{(-x^2)}\, dx = \exp{(-x^2)}\, dx.$$

The left member is, of course, the differential of $y \exp{(-x^2)}$. But the right member is not the differential of any elementary function; that is, $\int \exp{(-x^2)}\, dx$ is a nonelementary integral.

---

* By an elementary function we mean a function studied in the ordinary beginning calculus course. For example, polynomials, exponentials, logarithms, trigonometric, and inverse trigonometric functions are elementary. All functions obtained from them by a finite number of applications of the elementary operations of addition, subtraction, multiplication, division, extraction of roots, and raising to powers are elementary. Finally, we include such functions as sin (sin x), in which the argument in a function previously classed as elementary is replaced by an elementary function.

There are various ways to proceed. We could write a "solution" in the form

$$y \exp(-x^2) = \int \exp(-x^2)\, dx,$$

but that is evidently incomplete. We cannot satisfy the boundary condition with the above form of solution because putting $x = 0$ in the indefinite integral is meaningless.

Let us turn to power series for help. From the series

$$\exp(-x^2) = \sum_{n=0}^{\infty} \frac{(-1)^n x^{2n}}{n!},$$

obtained in calculus, it follows that

$$\int \exp(-x^2)\, dx = c + \sum_{n=0}^{\infty} \frac{(-1)^n x^{2n+1}}{n!(2n+1)}.$$

Thus the differential equation (1) has the solution

$$y \exp(-x^2) = c + \sum_{n=0}^{\infty} \frac{(-1)^n x^{2n+1}}{n!(2n+1)}.$$

Since $y = 1$ when $x = 0$, c may be found from

$$1 = c + 0.$$

Therefore, the particular solution desired is

$$(2) \qquad y \exp(-x^2) = 1 + \sum_{n=0}^{\infty} \frac{(-1)^n x^{2n+1}}{n!(2n+1)}.$$

An alternative procedure is the introduction of a definite integral. In calculus, the error function defined by

$$(3) \qquad \operatorname{erf} x = \frac{2}{\sqrt{\pi}} \int_0^x \exp(-\beta^2)\, d\beta$$

is sometimes* studied. Since, from (3),

$$\frac{d}{dx} \operatorname{erf} x = \frac{2}{\sqrt{\pi}} \exp(-x^2),$$

we may integrate the exact equation (1) as follows:

---

* See E. D. Rainville, *Unified Calculus and Analytic Geometry* (New York: The Macmillan Co., 1961), pp. 605–607.

(4) $y \exp(-x^2) = \frac{1}{2} \sqrt{\pi} \operatorname{erf} x + c.$

Since erf $0 = 0$, the condition that $y = 1$ when $x = 0$ yields $c = 1$. Hence, as an alternative to (2) we obtain

(5) $y \exp(-x^2) = 1 + \frac{1}{2} \sqrt{\pi} \operatorname{erf} x.$

Equation (5) means the same as

(6) $y \exp(-x^2) = 1 + \int_0^x \exp(-\beta^2)\, d\beta.$

Writing a solution in the form of (6) implies that the definite integral is to be evaluated by power series, approximate integration such as Simpson's rule, mechanical quadrature, or any other available tool. If it happens, as in this case, that the definite integral is itself a tabulated function, that is a great convenience, but it is not vital. The essential thing is to reduce the solution to a computable form.

Exercises

In each exercise, express the solution with the aid of power series or definite integrals.

1. $y' = y[1 - \exp(-x^2)].$ ANS. $\ln(cy) = x - \frac{1}{2}\sqrt{\pi}\operatorname{erf} x.$

2. $(xy - \sin x)\, dx + x^2\, dy = 0.$ ANS. $xy = c + \int_0^x \dfrac{\sin w}{w}\, dw,$

$$\text{or } y = cx^{-1} + \sum_{n=0}^{\infty} (-1)^n \frac{x^{2n}}{(2n+1)(2n+1)!}.$$

3. $y' = 1 - 4x^3 y.$ ANS. $y = \exp(-x^4)\left[c + \displaystyle\int_0^x \exp(\beta^4)\, d\beta\right].$

4. $(y\cos^2 x - x\sin x)\, dx + \sin x \cos x\, dy = 0.$

ANS. $y \sin x = c + \displaystyle\int_0^x \beta \tan \beta\, d\beta.$

5. $(1 + xy)\, dx - x\, dy = 0$; when $x = 1$, $y = 0$.

ANS. $y = e^x \displaystyle\int_1^x \frac{e^{-\beta}}{\beta}\, d\beta.$

6. $\left[x \exp\left(\dfrac{y^2}{x^2}\right) - y\right] dx + x\, dy = 0$; when $x = 1$, $y = 2$.

ANS. $\ln x = \displaystyle\int_{y/x}^2 \exp(-\beta^2)\, d\beta.$

7. $x(2y + x)\, dx - dy = 0$; when $x = 0$, $y = 1$.

ANS. $2y = 2\exp(x^2) - x + \frac{1}{2}\sqrt{\pi}\exp(x^2)\operatorname{erf} x.$

Miscellaneous Exercises

In each exercise, find the general solution unless the statement of the exercise stipulates otherwise.

1. $(y^2 - 3y - x) dx + (2y - 3) dy = 0.$
$$\text{ANS.} \quad y^2 - 3y - x + 1 = ce^{-x}.$$

2. $(y^3 + y + 1) dx + x(x - 3y^2 - 1) dy = 0.$
$$\text{ANS.} \quad y^3 - xy + y + 1 = cx.$$

3. $(x + 3y - 5) dx - (x - y - 1) dy = 0.$
$$\text{ANS.} \quad 2(y - 1) = (x + y - 3) \ln [c(x + y - 3)].$$

4. $(x^5 - y^2) dx + 2xy \, dy = 0.$ \qquad ANS. $x^5 + 4y^2 = cx.$

5. $(2x + y - 4) dx + (x - 3y + 12) dy = 0.$
$$\text{ANS.} \quad 2x^2 + 2xy - 3y^2 - 8x + 24y = c.$$

6. Solve in two ways the equation $y' = ax + by + c$ with $b \neq 0.$
$$\text{ANS.} \quad b^2 y = c_1 e^{bx} - abx - a - cb.$$

7. $y^3 \sec^2 x \, dx - (1 - 2y^2 \tan x) dy = 0.$ \qquad ANS. $y^2 \tan x = \ln (cy).$

8. $x^3 y \, dx + (3x^4 - y^3) dy = 0.$ \qquad ANS. $15x^4 y^{12} = 4y^{15} + c.$

9. $(a_1 x + ky + c_1) dx + (kx + b_2 y + c_2) dy = 0.$
$$\text{ANS.} \quad a_1 x^2 + 2kxy + b_2 y^2 + 2c_1 x + 2c_2 y = c.$$

10. $(x - 4y + 7) dx + (x + 2y + 1) dy = 0.$
$$\text{ANS.} \quad (x - y + 4)^3 = c(x - 2y + 5)^2.$$

11. $xy \, dx + (y^4 - 3x^2) dy = 0.$ \qquad ANS. $x^2 = y^4(1 + cy^2).$

12. $(x + 2y - 1) dx - (2x + y - 5) dy = 0.$

13. $(5x + 3e^y) dx + 2xe^y \, dy = 0.$ \qquad ANS. $x^3(x + e^y)^2 = c.$

14. $(3x + y - 2) dx + (3x + y + 4) dy = 0.$
$$\text{ANS.} \quad x + y + c = 3 \ln (3x + y + 7).$$

15. $(x - 3y + 4) dx + 2(x - y - 2) dy = 0.$
$$\text{ANS.} \quad (x + y - 8)^4 = c(x - 2y + 1).$$

16. $(x - 2) dx + 4(x + y - 1) dy = 0.$
$$\text{ANS.} \quad 2(y + 1) = -(x + 2y) \ln [c(x + 2y)].$$

17. $y \, dx = x(1 + xy^4) dy.$ \qquad ANS. $y(5 + xy^4) = cx.$

18. $2x \, dv + v(2 + v^2 x) dx = 0;$ when $x = 1, v = \frac{1}{2}.$
$$\text{ANS.} \quad xv^2(5x - 1) = 1.$$

19. $2(x - y) dx + (3x - y - 1) dy = 0.$
$$\text{ANS.} \quad (x + y - 1)^4 = c(4x - 2y - 1).$$

20. $(2x - 5y + 12) dx + (7x - 4y + 15) dy = 0.$
$$\text{ANS.} \quad (x + 2y - 3)^3 = c(x - y + 3).$$

21. $y \, dx + x(x^2 y - 1) dy = 0.$ \qquad ANS. $y^2(2x^2 y - 3) = cx^2.$

22. $\dfrac{dy}{dx} = \tan y \cot x - \sec y \cos x.$ \quad ANS. $\sin y + \sin x \ln (c \sin x) = 0.$

23. $[1 + (x + y)^2] dx + [1 + x(x + y)] dy = 0.$

ANS. $y^2 = (x + y)^2 + 2 \ln (x + y) + c.$

24. $(x - 2y - 1) dx - (x - 3) dy = 0.$ Solve by two methods.

ANS. $(x - 3)^2(x - 3y) = c.$

25. $(2x - 3y + 1) dx - (3x + 2y - 4) dy = 0.$ Solve by two methods.

ANS. $x^2 + x - 3xy - y^2 + 4y = c.$

26. $(4x + 3y - 7) dx + (4x + 3y + 1) dy = 0.$

ANS. $x + y + c = 8 \ln (4x + 3y + 25).$

27. Find a change of variables that will reduce any equation of the form

$$xy' = yf(xy)$$

to an equation in which the variables are separable.

28. $(x + 4y + 3) dx - (2x - y - 3) dy = 0.$

ANS. $3(y + 1) = (x + y) \ln [c(x + y)].$

29. $(3x - 3y - 2) dx - (x - y + 1) dy = 0.$

ANS. $2(y - 3x + c) = 5 \ln (2x - 2y - 3).$

30. $(x - 6y + 2) dx + 2(x + 2y + 2) dy = 0.$

ANS. $4y = -(x - 2y + 2) \ln [c(x - 2y + 2)].$

31. $(x^4 - 4x^2y^2 - y^4) dx + 4x^3y \, dy = 0;$ when $x = 1, y = 2.$

ANS. $y^2(5 - 3x) = x^2(5 + 3x).$

32. $(x - y - 1) dx - 2(y - 2) dy = 0.$

ANS. $(x + y - 5)^2(x - 2y + 1) = c.$

33. $(x - 3y + 3) dx + (3x + y + 9) dy = 0.$

ANS. $\ln [(x + 3)^2 + y^2] = c + 6 \operatorname{Arctan} [(x + 3)/y].$

34. $(2x + 4y - 1) dx - (x + 2y - 3) dy = 0.$

ANS. $\ln (x + 2y - 1) = y - 2x + c.$

35. $4y \, dx + 3(2x - 1)(dy + y^4 \, dx) = 0;$ when $x = 1, y = 1.$

ANS. $y^3(2x - 1)(5x - 4) = 1.$

36. $y(x - 1) dx - (x^2 - 2x - 2y) dy = 0.$ ANS. $x^2 - 2x - 4y = cy^2.$

37. $(6xy - 3y^2 + 2y) dx + 2(x - y) dy = 0.$ ANS. $y(2x - y) = ce^{-3x}.$

38. $y' = x - y + 2.$ Solve by two methods.

ANS. $\ln (x - y + 1) = c - x.$

39. $(x + y - 2) dx - (x - 4y - 2) dy = 0.$

ANS. $\ln [(x - 2)^2 + 4y^2] + \operatorname{Arctan} \dfrac{x - 2}{2y} = c.$

40. $4 \, dx + (x - y + 2)^2 \, dy = 0.$ ANS. $y + 2 \operatorname{Arctan} \dfrac{x - y + 2}{2} = c.$

CHAPTER 5

Orthogonal Trajectories

23. Orthogonal trajectories; rectangular coordinates

Suppose that we have a family of curves

(1) $$f(x, y, c) = 0,$$

one curve corresponding to each c in some range of values of the parameter c. In certain applications, as illustrated in Section 25 below, it is
found desirable to know what curves have the property that wherever
any one of them intersects a curve of the family (1) it does so at right
angles.

That is, we wish to determine a family of curves

(2) $$g(x, y, k) = 0$$

such that at any intersection of a curve of the family (2) with a curve
of the family (1) the tangents to the two curves are perpendicular.
The families (1) and (2) are then said to be *orthogonal trajectories** of
each other.

---

* The word orthogonal comes from the Greek $o\rho\theta\eta$ (right) and $\gamma\omega\nu\iota\alpha$ (angle);
the word trajectory comes from the Latin *trajectus* (cut across). Hence a curve
that cuts across certain others at right angles is called an orthogonal trajectory
of those others.

79

If two curves are to be orthogonal, then at each point of inter-section the slopes of the curves must be negative reciprocals of each other. That fact leads us to a method for finding orthogonal trajec-tories of a given family of curves. First we find the differential equation of the given family. Then replacing $\dfrac{dy}{dx}$ by $-\dfrac{dx}{dy}$ in that equation yields the differential equation of the orthogonal trajectories to the given curves. It remains only to solve the latter differential equation.

So far we have solved differential equations of only one form,

$$M\,dx + N\,dy = 0.$$

For such an equation

$$\frac{dy}{dx} = -\frac{M}{N},$$

so the differential equation of the orthogonal trajectories is

$$\frac{dy}{dx} = \frac{N}{M}$$

or

$$N\,dx - M\,dy = 0.$$

EXAMPLE: Find the orthogonal trajectories of all parabolas with

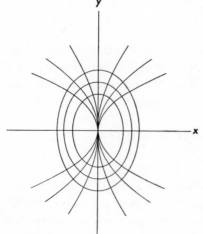

FIGURE 9

vertices at the origin and foci on the x-axis.

The algebraic equation of such parabolas is

$$(3) \qquad y^2 = 4ax.$$

Hence, from

$$\frac{y^2}{x} = 4a,$$

we find the differential equation of the family (3) to be

$$(4) \qquad 2x\,dy - y\,dx = 0.$$

Therefore the orthogonal trajec-tories of the family (3) must satisfy the equation

$$(5) \qquad 2x\,dx + y\,dy = 0.$$

From (5) it follows that

(6) $2x^2 + y^2 = b^2,$

where b is the arbitrary constant. Thus the orthogonal trajectories of (3) are certain ellipses (6) with centers at the origin. See Figure 9.

Exercises

In each exercise, find the orthogonal trajectories of the given family of curves. Draw a few representative curves of each family whenever a figure is requested.

1. $x - 4y = c$. Draw the figure.   ANS. $4x + y = k$.

2. $x^2 + y^2 = c^2$. Draw the figure.   ANS. $y = kx$.

3. $x^2 - y^2 = c_1$. Draw the figure.   ANS. $xy = c_2$.

4. Circles through the origin with centers on the x-axis. Draw the figure.
            ANS.   Circles through the origin with centers on the y-axis.

5. Straight lines with slope and y-intercept equal. Draw the figure.
                            ANS. $(x + 1)^2 + y^2 = a^2$.

6. $y^2 = cx^3$. Draw the figure.   ANS. $2x^2 + 3y^2 = k^2$.

7. $e^x + e^{-y} = c_1$.   ANS. $e^y - e^{-x} = c_2$.

8. $y = c_1(\sec x + \tan x)$.   ANS. $y^2 = 2(c_2 - \sin x)$.

9. $x^3 = 3(y - c)$. Draw the figure.   ANS. $x(y - k) = 1$.

10. $x = c \exp (y^2)$.   ANS. $y = c_1 \exp (-x^2)$.

11. $y = ce^{-mx}$, with m held fixed. Draw the figure.
                            ANS. $my^2 = 2(x - c_1)$.

12. Ellipses with centers at $(0, 0)$ and two vertices at $(1, 0)$ and $(-1, 0)$.
                            ANS. $x^2 + y^2 = 2 \ln (cx)$.

13. $x^2 - y^2 = cx$.   ANS. $y(y^2 + 3x^2) = c_1$.

14. The cissoids, $y^2 = x^3/(a - x)$. See also Ex. 14 of Section 24 below.
                            ANS. $(x^2 + y^2)^2 = b(2x^2 + y^2)$.

15. The trisectrices of Maclaurin, $(a + x)y^2 = x^2(3a - x)$. See also Ex. 15 of Section 24 below.   ANS. $(x^2 + y^2)^5 = cy^3(5x^2 + y^2)$.

16. $ax^2 + by^2 = c$, with a and b held fixed.   ANS. $y^a = kx^b$.

17. $ax^2 + y^2 = 2acx$, with a held fixed.
                    ANS.   If $a \neq 2$, $(2 - a)x^2 + y^2 = c_1 y^a$.
                    If $a = 2$, $x^2 = -y^2 \ln (c_2 y)$.

18. $y(x^2 + c) + 2 = 0$.   ANS. $y^3 = -3 \ln (kx)$.

19. $x^n + y^n = a^n$, with n held fixed and $n \neq 2$.   ANS. $x^{2-n} - y^{2-n} = c$.

20. $y^2 = x^2(1 - cx)$.   ANS. $x^2 + 3y^2 = c_1 y$.

21. $y^2 = 4x^2(1 - cx)$.   ANS. $2x^2 = 3y^2(1 - c_1 y^2)$.

22. $y^2 = ax^2(1 - cx)$, with a held fixed.

            ANS.   If $a \neq 2$, $(a - 2)x^2 = 3y^2(1 - c_1y^{a-2})$.

                   If $a = 2$, $x^2 = -3y^2 \ln (c_2y)$.

23. $y(x^2 + 1) = cx$.   ANS. $y^2 = x^2 + 2 \ln [k(x^2 - 1)]$.

24. $y = 3x - 1 + ce^{-3x}$.   ANS. $27x = 9y - 1 + ke^{-9y}$.

25. $y^2(2x^2 + y^2) = c^2$.   ANS. $y^2 = 2x^2 \ln (kx)$.

26. $y^4 = c^2(x^2 + 4y^2)$.   ANS. $x^8(2x^2 + 5y^2) = k^2$.

27. $x^4(4x^2 + 3y^2) = c^2$.   ANS. $y^8 = k^2(3x^2 + 2y^2)$.

28. For the family $x^2 + 3y^2 = cy$, find that member of the orthogonal trajectories which passes through $(1, 2)$.   ANS. $y^2 = x^2(3x + 1)$.

24. Orthogonal trajectories; polar coordinates

     Consider a curve whose equation is expressed in polar coordinates. In calculus it is shown that the angle ψ (Figure 10), measured positive in the counterclockwise direction from the radius vector to the tangent line at a point, is given by

$$\tan \psi = r \frac{d\theta}{dr}.$$

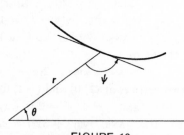   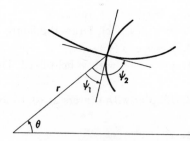

FIGURE 10   FIGURE 11

     If two curves are orthogonal, as they are shown in Figure 11, then $\psi_2 = \psi_1 + \pi/2$ and thus $\tan \psi_2 = - \cot \psi_1 = -1/\tan \psi_1$. Therefore, if two curves are to cut one another at right angles, then at the point of intersection the value of the product

$$r \frac{d\theta}{dr}$$

for one curve must be the negative reciprocal of the value of that product for the other curve.

     When polar coordinates are used, suppose a family of curves has the differential equation

(1) $$P\,dr + Q\,d\theta = 0.$$

Then

$$\frac{d\theta}{dr} = -\frac{P}{Q}$$

so

(2) $$r\frac{d\theta}{dr} = -\frac{Pr}{Q}.$$

Hence the family of the orthogonal trajectories of the solutions of (1) must be solutions of the equation

$$r\frac{d\theta}{dr} = +\frac{Q}{Pr},$$

or

(3) $$Q\,dr - r^2 P\,d\theta = 0.$$

E XA M PL E : Find the orthogonal trajectories of the family of cardioids $r = a(1 + \cos\theta)$. A few curves of each family are shown in Figure 12.

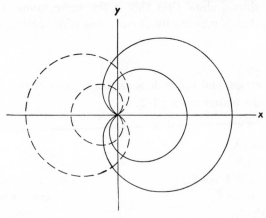

FIGURE 12

From

$$\frac{r}{1 + \cos\theta} = a$$

the differential equation

$$(1 + \cos\theta)\,dr + r\sin\theta\,d\theta = 0$$

follows at once. Then the differential equation of the orthogonal trajectories is

$$r \sin \theta \, dr - r^2(1 + \cos \theta) \, d\theta = 0$$

or

$$\sin \theta \, dr - r(1 + \cos \theta) \, d\theta = 0.$$

Separating the variables, we use the form

$$\frac{dr}{r} - \frac{(1 + \cos \theta) \, d\theta}{\sin \theta} = 0,$$

or

$$\frac{dr}{r} - \csc \theta \, d\theta - \frac{\cos \theta}{\sin \theta} \, d\theta = 0.$$

Hence

$$\ln r - \ln (\csc \theta - \cot \theta) - \ln \sin \theta = \ln b,$$

so the orthogonal trajectories of the original family of cardioids are seen to be

$$r = b \sin \theta(\csc \theta - \cot \theta),$$

or

$$r = b(1 - \cos \theta).$$

The student should show that this is the same family as the one we started with; that is, the family of cardioids is self-orthogonal.

Exercises

In each exercise, find the orthogonal trajectories of the given family of curves. Draw the figures in Exs. 1–8.

1. $r = a \cos^2 \theta$.   ANS. $r^2 = b \sin \theta$.

2. $r = a \cos 2\theta$.   ANS. $r^4 = b \sin 2\theta$.

3. $r = 2a \sin \theta$.   ANS. $r = 2b \cos \theta$.

4. $r = 2a(\sin \theta + \cos \theta)$.   ANS. $r = 2b(\sin \theta - \cos \theta)$.

5. $r = a(1 + \sin \theta)$.   ANS. $r = b(1 - \sin \theta)$.

6. $r^2 = a \sin 2\theta$.   ANS. $r^2 = b \cos 2\theta$.

7. $r = 4a \sec \theta \tan \theta$.   ANS. $r^2(1 + \sin^2 \theta) = b^2$.

8. $r^2 \cos 2\theta = c_1$.   ANS. $r^2 \sin 2\theta = c_2$.

9. $r = k/(1 + 2 \cos \theta)$.   ANS. $r^2 \sin^3 \theta = b(1 + \cos \theta)$.

10. $r = k/(2 + \cos \theta)$.   ANS. $r \sin^3 \theta = b(1 + \cos \theta)^2$.

11. $r = k/(1 + \epsilon \cos \theta)$ with ϵ fixed. What are k and ϵ geometrically?   ANS. $r^\epsilon \sin^{\epsilon+1} \theta = b(1 + \cos \theta)$.

12. $r = a(1 - 2 \sin \theta)$.   ANS. $r^2 = b \cos \theta(1 + \sin \theta)$.

13. The strophoids, $r = a(\sec \theta + \tan \theta)$.   ANS. $r = be^{-\sin \theta}$.

14. The cissoids, $r = a \sin \theta \tan \theta$.   ANS. $r^2 = b(1 + \cos^2 \theta)$.

15. The trisectrices of Maclaurin, $r = a(4 \cos \theta - \sec \theta)$.

ANS. $r^5 = b \sin^3 \theta (4 \cos^2 \theta + 1)$.

16. $r = a(1 + \sin^2 \theta)$.   ANS. $r^2 = b \cos \theta \cot \theta$.

25. Electric potential

The electric force between two particles charged with electricity is proportional to the magnitude of the two charges and inversely proportional to the square of the distance between them. An electric field is a portion of space the electrical properties of which we wish to consider. Those properties are determined by the distribution of electric* charges in the field. Very often interest is centered not upon the whole field but upon some portion which may itself not contain any electric charges.

The resultant electric force at a point P in an electric field is the force that would be exerted on a unit positive charge of electricity placed at P without disturbing the previous distribution of electric charges in the field. That resultant force has direction as well as magnitude at each point; it is a vector.

A curve whose tangent at each point on the curve is in the direction of the resultant electric force at that point is called a line of force or a flux line.

The difference in electric potential between two points in an electric field is the amount of work necessary for the electric force to perform to move a unit positive charge from one point to the other. Thus, electric potential is defined except for algebraic sign and an additive constant. If some fixed position in the electric field is used as a place of zero potential and if a convention of signs is introduced, then the electric potential is completely defined. Since our interest will be concentrated upon the family of curves on which the potential is constant, the concept of difference in potential† suffices.

Laplace showed that in any region in space not occupied by an electric charge, the potential function V satisfies the partial differential equation

---

* Electrostatic charges are the only ones being considered in this discussion.

† For the student who has had advanced calculus it may help to know that electric potential is a function of the coordinates such that at each point the directional derivative of the potential is the negative of the component of electric force in that direction.

$$(1) \qquad\qquad \frac{\partial^2 V}{\partial x^2} + \frac{\partial^2 V}{\partial y^2} + \frac{\partial^2 V}{\partial z^2} = 0$$

where x, y, z are the rectangular space coordinates in the electric field. If the distribution of charges in the field is such that the potential function is independent of the z coordinate, then the problem is two-dimensional and the potential function must satisfy the equation

$$(2) \qquad\qquad \frac{\partial^2 V}{\partial x^2} + \frac{\partial^2 V}{\partial y^2} = 0.$$

We shall restrict our study to two-dimensional situations, but we are not yet prepared to attack the relatively difficult problem of determining appropriate solutions of (2).

Curves along which the potential is constant,

$$(3) \qquad\qquad V = c,$$

are called equipotential curves. An important theorem in electricity states that:

The flux lines are the orthogonal trajectories of the equipotential curves.

Given the potential function, or the family of equipotential curves, for an electric field, we shall determine the corresponding flux lines. This is simply a problem of finding the orthogonal trajectories of a given family of curves. The material of this and the next two sections is in the nature of physical interpretations of problems in orthogonal trajectories rather than actual applications. For example, in practice, it is not necessary to resort to the methods we are studying here to determine the flux lines when the equipotential curves are known.

EXAMPLE: Suppose two wires perpendicular to the xy-plane and piercing it at the points $(1, 0)$ and $(-1, 0)$ carry static electric charges of equal intensity but opposite sign. Then it can be shown that the equipotential lines are the circles

$$(4) \qquad\qquad x^2 + y^2 - 2cx + 1 = 0.$$

Obtain the flux lines and draw the figure.

From (4) it follows by elimination of c that the family of equipotential curves has the differential equation

$$(5) \qquad\qquad (x^2 - y^2 - 1)\, dx + 2xy\, dy = 0.$$

Since the flux lines must be orthogonal to the solutions of (5), the differential equation of the family of flux lines is

(6) $2xy\,dx - (x^2 - y^2 - 1)\,dy = 0.$

Equation (6) is linear in x^2. It can also be solved by finding the integrating factor y^{-2} by inspection. By one or the other of these methods, the general solution of equation (6) is found to be

(7) $x^2 + y^2 - 1 = 2ky.$

Equation (7) is the desired equation of the family of flux lines. From (7) we get

(8) $x^2 + (y - k)^2 = 1 + k^2,$

so the flux lines are seen to be circles with centers on the y-axis and passing through both the points $(1, 0)$ and $(-1, 0)$. See Figure 13.

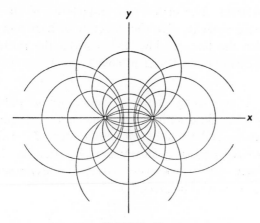

FIGURE 13

26. Steady-state temperatures

Consider the situation in which some physical object has been subjected to unvarying temperature conditions for a time sufficiently long that the temperatures within the object have stopped changing. In such an instance the temperatures in the object are said to have reached the steady-state condition.

If x, y, z are rectangular space coordinates and T denotes steady-state temperature, then it can be shown that in the interior of the object the function T must satisfy Laplace's equation

(1)
$$\frac{\partial^2 T}{\partial x^2} + \frac{\partial^2 T}{\partial y^2} + \frac{\partial^2 T}{\partial z^2} = 0.$$

If the temperature conditions are such that there is no variation of temperature (no flow of heat) in some one direction, taken as the direction of the z-axis, then the problem is two-dimensional and equation (1) may be replaced by

(2)
$$\frac{\partial^2 T}{\partial x^2} + \frac{\partial^2 T}{\partial y^2} = 0.$$

Again we make no attempt to solve the partial differential equation (2) with its associated boundary conditions.

The curves along which the temperature is constant,

$$T = c,$$

are called isotherms. The orthogonal trajectories of the isotherms are the curves whose tangents give the direction of heat flow at any point. They are called the lines of flow. Being given the isotherms we shall determine the corresponding lines of flow.

EXAMPLE: A very long concrete wedge whose right section is a circular sector of angle α and radius R has one of its plane faces kept at temperature T_1 and the other at temperature T_2, while the curved surface is insulated against heat transfer. Except near the ends of the wedge the steady-state temperature variation is essentially two-dimensional and T is known to be given by

$$T = T_1 + \frac{T_2 - T_1}{\alpha} \text{Arctan} \frac{y}{x}.$$

where the coordinates x and y are defined in Figure 14. Draw the isotherms and the lines of flow.

In this problem when T is constant, y/x is also constant, so the isotherms have the form

$$y = cx.$$

Hence the differential equation of the isotherms is

$$y \, dx - x \, dy = 0$$

and that of the lines of flow is

$$x \, dx + y \, dy = 0.$$

Therefore the lines of flow are

$$x^2 + y^2 = k^2.$$

Both families of curves are shown in Figure 14.

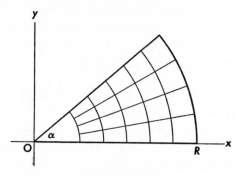

FIGURE 14

27. Two-dimensional steady-state fluid flow

If certain problems in the flow of a fluid are sufficiently idealized, they become two-dimensional steady-state problems in which orthogonal trajectories play an important part. In such problems the members of one family of curves

(1) $\psi(x, y) = c$

are called streamlines and the members of the family orthogonal to the family (1),

(2) $\varphi(x, y) = k,$

are called equipotential curves. Also, the function ψ is known as the stream function and φ is the velocity potential. Both the functions ψ and φ are solutions of the same partial differential equation that is satisfied by steady-state temperature and by electrostatic potential. The directional derivative of the velocity potential represents the component of the fluid velocity in that direction.

We are considering a two-dimensional fluid flow in which conditions are identical in all planes parallel to the xy-plane, and there is no flow in the direction perpendicular to the xy-plane. As an example we may visualize such a problem as that in which a large body of the fluid is flowing with uniform velocity parallel to the x-axis. An object is immersed in the fluid and allowed to remain for a long time. We are interested in the streamline pattern near the immersed object after the temporary disturbances due to the immersion of the object have disappeared so far as measurable effects are concerned.

Since streamlines are perhaps easy for us to visualize, and therefore make interesting answers, we shall assume that we are given either the equipotential curves or, what amounts to the same thing, the velocity potential function. Then we are to determine and draw the streamlines. Natural boundaries of the flow are streamlines.

EXAMPLE: Consider the effect of a long cylindrical object immersed in a fluid which is flowing with uniform velocity in a direction perpendicular to the axis of the cylinder. Away from the ends of the cylinder the pattern of streamlines will be identical in planes perpendicular to the axis of the cylinder. Let us choose as our unit of length the radius of the cylinder.

Given the equipotential curves

(3) $$(r^2 + 1) \cos \theta = cr$$

in polar coordinates with the origin $r = 0$ at the center of the circular cross section, determine and sketch the streamlines.

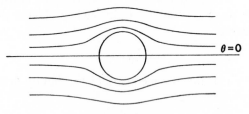

FIGURE 15

We are to find the orthogonal trajectories of the family (3). First we obtain the differential equation of the equipotentials (3) in the usual manner, by isolating c and differentiating both members of the equation to get

$$\left(1 - \frac{1}{r^2}\right) \cos \theta \, dr - \left(r + \frac{1}{r}\right) \sin \theta \, d\theta = 0,$$

or

(4) $$(r^2 - 1) \cos \theta \, dr - r(r^2 + 1) \sin \theta \, d\theta = 0.$$

Then the differential equation of the streamlines is

(5) $$(r^2 + 1) \sin \theta \, dr + r(r^2 - 1) \cos \theta \, d\theta = 0.$$

From (5) it follows that

$$\frac{r^2 + 1}{r(r^2 - 1)} \, dr + \frac{\cos \theta}{\sin \theta} \, d\theta = 0,$$

or

$$\frac{2r^2 - (r^2 - 1)}{r(r^2 - 1)} \, dr + \frac{\cos \theta}{\sin \theta} \, d\theta = 0,$$

so we need merely to solve the equation

(6) $$\frac{2r \, dr}{r^2 - 1} - \frac{dr}{r} + \frac{\cos \theta}{\sin \theta} \, d\theta = 0.$$

The solution of (6) is

$$\ln (r^2 - 1) - \ln r + \ln \sin \theta = \ln k,$$

which may be written as

(7) $$(r^2 - 1) \sin \theta = kr.$$

Equation (7) is the desired family of streamlines, of which several are shown in Figure 15.

CHAPTER 6

Hyperbolic Functions

28. Definition of the hyperbolic functions

Two particular combinations of exponential functions appear with such frequency in both pure and applied mathematics that it has been worth-while to use special symbols for those combinations. The hyperbolic sine of x, written sinh x, is defined by

$$(1) \qquad \qquad \textbf{sinh } x = \frac{e^x - e^{-x}}{2};$$

the hyperbolic cosine of x, written* cosh x, is defined by

$$(2) \qquad \qquad \textbf{cosh } x = \frac{e^x + e^{-x}}{2}.$$

The use of symbols and names so similar to those of trigonometry may seem unwise. Some justification will appear in the next section, where the basic formulas for these new functions are shown to bear a striking resemblance to those of ordinary trigonometry. It will be shown also that the hyperbolic sine and cosine are related to the equilateral hyperbola in much the same way that the ordinary (circular) sine and cosine are related to the circle.

---

* Another common notation is Sh x to replace our sinh x, and with it Ch x to replace our cosh x.

Four more hyperbolic functions are defined in a manner to be expected, namely,

$$\tanh x = \frac{\sinh x}{\cosh x}, \qquad \operatorname{sech} x = \frac{1}{\cosh x},$$

$$\operatorname{csch} x = \frac{1}{\sinh x}, \qquad \coth x = \frac{1}{\tanh x}.$$

In solving differential equations we use the functions $\sinh x$ and $\cosh x$ more often than the other four functions.

29. Basic formulas of hyperbolic trigonometry

From the definitions of $\sinh x$ and $\cosh x$ it follows that

$$\sinh^2 x = \tfrac{1}{4}(e^{2x} - 2 + e^{-2x})$$

and

$$\cosh^2 x = \tfrac{1}{4}(e^{2x} + 2 + e^{-2x}),$$

so

$$(1) \qquad\qquad \cosh^2 x - \sinh^2 x = 1,$$

an identity similar to the well-known identity $\cos^2 x + \sin^2 x = 1$ in circular trigonometry. See also Exs. 2 and 3 below.

Directly from the definition we find that

$$y = \sinh u$$

is equivalent to

$$y = \tfrac{1}{2}(e^u - e^{-u}).$$

Hence, if u is a function of x, then

$$\frac{dy}{dx} = \tfrac{1}{2}(e^u + e^{-u})\frac{du}{dx},$$

that is,

$$(2) \qquad \frac{d}{dx}\sinh u = \cosh u\,\frac{du}{dx}.$$

The same method yields the result

$$(3) \qquad \frac{d}{dx}\cosh u = \sinh u\,\frac{du}{dx}.$$

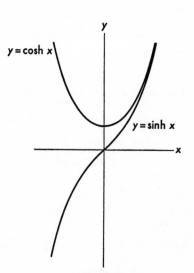

FIGURE 16

The derivations of the corresponding formulas for the derivatives of the other hyperbolic functions are left as exercises.

The curves $y = \cosh x$ and $y = \sinh x$ are exhibited in Figure 16, page 93. Note the important properties:

(a) $\cosh x \geqq 1$ for all real x;
(b) the only real value of x for which $\sinh x = 0$ is $x = 0$;
(c) $\cosh (-x) = \cosh x$; that is, $\cosh x$ is an even function of x;
(d) $\sinh (-x) = -\sinh x$; $\sinh x$ is an odd function of x.

The hyperbolic functions have no real period. Corresponding to the period 2π possessed by the circular functions, there is a period $2\pi i$ for the six hyperbolic functions.

The hyperbolic cosine curve is that in which a transmission line, cable, piece of string, watch chain, etc., hangs between two points at which it is suspended. This result is obtained in Chapter 19.

With regard to the word hyperbolic in the names of the functions being treated here, consider the equations

$$(4) \qquad x = a \cosh t, \quad y = a \sinh t.$$

In the equations (4), let t be a parameter and a a fixed constant. Then those equations are parametric equations of an equilateral hyperbola because from

$$\cosh^2 t - \sinh^2 t = 1$$

it follows that

$$\frac{x^2}{a^2} - \frac{y^2}{a^2} = 1$$

or

$$x^2 - y^2 = a^2.$$

This is analogous to the result that the two equations

$$x = a \cos t, \quad y = a \sin t,$$

are parametric equations of the circle $x^2 + y^2 = a^2$.

In elementary trigonometry texts there is usually given a line representation of the six trigonometric functions in a figure based upon a circle of radius unity. A similar line representation* of the six hyperbolic functions can be obtained.

The formulas used to define the hyperbolic sine and cosine also have analogs in the study of the trigonometric functions. The definition

---

* See C. A. Hutchinson, "Line Representation of the Hyperbolic Functions," *Amer. Math. Monthly*, **40** (1933), 413–414.

given on page 121 for the exponential function with pure imaginary exponent may be used to derive the pertinent formulas. The results are shown in Ex. 24, page 96.

Exercises

In Exs. 1–16, prove the stated property of the hyperbolic functions. Use the definitions, the results in the text, or the properties obtained in any previous exercises.

1. $\sinh(-x) = -\sinh x; \cosh(-x) = \cosh x; \tanh(-x) = -\tanh x.$

2. $\operatorname{sech}^2 x = 1 - \tanh^2 x.$

3. $\operatorname{csch}^2 x = \coth^2 x - 1.$

4. $e^x = \cosh x + \sinh x; e^{-x} = \cosh x - \sinh x.$

5. $\sinh^2 y = \frac{1}{2}(\cosh 2y - 1).$

6. $\cosh^2 y = \frac{1}{2}(\cosh 2y + 1).$

7. $\cosh 2y = \cosh^2 y + \sinh^2 y$
$= 2\cosh^2 y - 1$
$= 2\sinh^2 y + 1.$

8. $\sinh 2y = 2\sinh y \cosh y.$

9. $\sinh(x+y) = \sinh x \cosh y + \cosh x \sinh y;$
$\sinh(x-y) = \sinh x \cosh y - \cosh x \sinh y.$

10. $\cosh(x+y) = \cosh x \cosh y + \sinh x \sinh y;$
$\cosh(x-y) = \cosh x \cosh y - \sinh x \sinh y.$

11. $\tanh(x+y) = \dfrac{\tanh x + \tanh y}{1 + \tanh x \tanh y};$
$\tanh(x-y) = \dfrac{\tanh x - \tanh y}{1 - \tanh x \tanh y}.$

12. $\dfrac{d}{dx}\cosh u = \sinh u \dfrac{du}{dx}.$

13. $\dfrac{d}{dx}\tanh u = \operatorname{sech}^2 u \dfrac{du}{dx}.$

14. $\dfrac{d}{dx}\operatorname{csch} u = -\operatorname{csch} u \coth u \dfrac{du}{dx}.$

15. $\dfrac{d}{dx}\operatorname{sech} u = -\operatorname{sech} u \tanh u \dfrac{du}{dx}.$

16. $\dfrac{d}{dx}\coth u = -\operatorname{csch}^2 u \dfrac{du}{dx}.$

17. Obtain the differential equation formed by eliminating the constants c_1 and c_2 from $y = c_1 \sinh(kx) + c_2 \cosh(kx)$.

ANS. $\dfrac{d^2y}{dx^2} - k^2 y = 0.$

18. Solve the equation

$$(y \sinh x - y + 2x)\, dx + (\cosh x - x)\, dy = 0.$$

ANS. $y \cosh x - xy + x^2 = c.$

19. Solve the equation $xy\, dx + (x^2 + 1)(1 - y \tanh y)\, dy = 0.$

ANS. $y^2(x^2 + 1) = c \cosh^2 y.$

20. Solve the equation $y' \sinh x = 1 - 2y \cosh x.$

ANS. $y \sinh^2 x = c + \cosh x.$

21. Find the orthogonal trajectories of the curves $\sin x \cosh y = c.$

ANS. $\cos x \sinh y = k.$

22. Define the inverse hyperbolic sine of x, written $y = \sinh^{-1} x$, by the equation

$$x = \sinh y$$

or

(A) $$x = \tfrac{1}{2}(e^y - e^{-y}).$$

Put (A) in the form

$$e^{2y} - 2xe^y - 1 = 0$$

and thus conclude that

$$y = \sinh^{-1} x = \ln (x + \sqrt{x^2 + 1}),$$

pointing out why $y = \ln (x - \sqrt{x^2 + 1})$ is thrown out.

23. With the notation of Ex. 22, show that

$$d \sinh^{-1} x = \frac{dx}{\sqrt{1 + x^2}}.$$

24. For real x, define e^{ix} by

$$e^{ix} = \cos x + i \sin x.$$

Then prove that

$$\sin x = \frac{e^{ix} - e^{-ix}}{2i}, \quad \cos x = \frac{e^{ix} + e^{-ix}}{2}.$$

CHAPTER **7**

Linear Differential Equations

30. The general linear equation

The general linear differential equation of order n may be written

$$(1) \quad b_0(x) \frac{d^n y}{dx^n} + b_1(x) \frac{d^{n-1} y}{dx^{n-1}} + \cdots + b_{n-1}(x) \frac{dy}{dx} + b_n(x)y = R(x).$$

The functions $R(x)$ and $b_i(x)$; $i = 0, 1, \cdots, n$, are to be independent of the variable y. If $R(x)$ is identically zero, equation (1) is said to be *homogeneous;* if $R(x)$ is not identically zero, equation (1) is called *non-homogeneous.* Here the word homogeneous is being used with reference to the quantities $y, y', y'', \cdots, y^{(n)}$; it has nothing to do with the way in which x enters the equation. In this chapter we shall obtain some fundamental and important properties of linear equations.

To simplify the wording of statements relating to solutions of linear differential equations, we shall adopt a common convention. When a relation $y = f(x)$ is a solution of a linear differential equation, we shall also call $f(x)$ itself a solution of the differential equation.

First we prove that if y_1 and y_2 are solutions of the homogeneous equation

97

(2) $\qquad b_0(x)y^{(n)} + b_1(x)y^{(n-1)} + \cdots + b_{n-1}(x)y' + b_n(x)y = 0,$

and if c_1 and c_2 are constants, then

$$y = c_1y_1 + c_2y_2$$

is a solution of equation (2).

The statement that y_1 and y_2 are solutions of (2) means that

(3) $\qquad b_0y_1^{(n)} + b_1y_1^{(n-1)} + \cdots + b_{n-1}y_1' + b_ny_1 = 0$

and

(4) $\qquad b_0y_2^{(n)} + b_1y_2^{(n-1)} + \cdots + b_{n-1}y_2' + b_ny_2 = 0.$

Now let us multiply each member of (3) by c_1, each member of (4) by c_2, and add the results. We get

(5) $\quad b_0[c_1y_1^{(n)} + c_2y_2^{(n)}] + b_1[c_1y_1^{(n-1)} + c_2y_2^{(n-1)}] + \cdots$
$$+ b_{n-1}[c_1y_1' + c_2y_2'] + b_n[c_1y_1 + c_2y_2] = 0.$$

Since $c_1y_1' + c_2y_2' = (c_1y_1 + c_2y_2)'$, etc., equation (5) is neither more nor less than the statement that $c_1y_1 + c_2y_2$ is a solution of equation (2). The proof is completed. The special case $c_2 = 0$ is worth noting; that is, for a homogeneous linear equation any constant times a solution is also a solution.

In a similar manner, or by iteration of the above result, it can be seen that if y_i; $i = 1, 2, \cdots, k$, are solutions of equation (2), and if c_i; $i = 1, 2, \cdots, k$, are constants, then

$$y = c_1y_1 + c_2y_2 + \cdots + c_ky_k$$

is a solution of equation (2).

31. Linear independence

Given the functions $f_1(x), \cdots, f_n(x)$, if constants $c_1, c_2, \cdots, c_n$, not all zero, exist such that

(1) $\qquad c_1f_1(x) + c_2f_2(x) + \cdots + c_nf_n(x) = 0$

identically in some interval $a \leqq x \leqq b$, then the functions $f_1(x), f_2(x), \cdots, f_n(x)$ are said to be *linearly dependent*. If no such relation exists, the functions are said to be *linearly independent*. That is, the functions $f_1, f_2, \cdots, f_n$ are linearly independent when equation (1) implies that $c_1 = c_2 = \cdots = c_n = 0$.

If the functions of a set are linearly dependent, then at least one of them is a linear combination of the others; if they are linearly independent, then none of them is a linear combination of the others.

32. The Wronskian

With the definitions of Section 31 in mind, we shall now obtain a sufficient condition that n functions be linearly independent over an interval $a \leqq x \leqq b$.

Let us assume that each of the functions $f_1(x), f_2(x), \cdots, f_n(x)$ is differentiable at least $(n - 1)$ times in the interval $a \leqq x \leqq b$. Then from the equation

$$(1) \qquad c_1f_1 + c_2f_2 + \cdots + c_nf_n = 0,$$

it follows by successive differentiation that

$$c_1f_1' + c_2f_2' + \cdots + c_nf_n' = 0,$$
$$c_1f_1'' + c_2f_2'' + \cdots + c_nf_n'' = 0,$$
$$\cdots$$
$$c_1f_1^{(n-1)} + c_2f_2^{(n-1)} + \cdots + c_nf_n^{(n-1)} = 0.$$

Considered as a system of equations in $c_1, c_2, \cdots, c_n$, the n linear equations directly above will have no solution except the one with each of the c's equal to zero, if the determinant of the system does not vanish. That is, if

$$(2) \qquad \begin{vmatrix} f_1 & f_2 & \cdots & f_n \\ f_1' & f_2' & \cdots & f_n' \\ f_1'' & f_2'' & \cdots & f_n'' \\ \cdots \\ f_1^{(n-1)} & f_2^{(n-1)} & \cdots & f_n^{(n-1)} \end{vmatrix} \neq 0,$$

then the functions $f_1, f_2, \cdots, f_n$ are linearly independent. The determinant in (2) is called the *Wronskian* of the n functions involved. We have shown that the nonvanishing of the Wronskian is a sufficient condition that the functions be linearly independent.

The nonvanishing of the Wronskian on an interval is not a necessary condition for linear independence. The Wronskian may vanish even when the functions are linearly independent, as exhibited in Ex. 9 below.

If the n functions involved are solutions of a homogeneous linear differential equation, the situation is simplified as is shown by the theorem below. Proof is omitted.

THEOREM 4: *If, on the interval $a \leqq x \leqq b$, $b_0(x) \neq 0$, b_0, b_1, $\cdots$, b_n are continuous, and y_1, y_2, $\cdots$, y_n are solutions of the equation*

$$(3) \qquad b_0 y^{(n)} + b_1 y^{(n-1)} + \cdots + b_{n-1} y' + b_n y = 0,$$

then a necessary and sufficient condition that y_1, $\cdots$, y_n be linearly independent is the nonvanishing of the Wronskian of y_1, $\cdots$, y_n on the interval $a \leqq x \leqq b$.

The functions $\cos \omega t$, $\sin \omega t$, $\sin (\omega t + \alpha)$, in which t is the variable and ω and α are constants, are linearly dependent because there exist constants c_1, c_2, c_3 such that

$$c_1 \cos \omega t + c_2 \sin \omega t + c_3 \sin (\omega t + \alpha) = 0$$

for all t. Indeed, one set of such constants is $c_1 = \sin \alpha$, $c_2 = \cos \alpha$, $c_3 = -1$.

One of the best-known sets of n linearly independent functions of x is the set 1, x, x^2, $\cdots$, x^{n-1}. The linear independence of the powers of x follows at once from the fact that if c_1, c_2, $\cdots$, c_n are not all zero, the equation

$$c_1 + c_2 x + \cdots + c_n x^{n-1} = 0$$

can have, at most, $(n - 1)$ distinct roots and so cannot vanish identically in any interval. See also Ex. 1 below.

Exercises

1. Obtain the Wronskian of the functions

$$1, x, x^2, \cdots, x^{n-1} \text{ for } n > 1.$$

ANS. $W = 0!\,1!\,2! \cdots (n-1)!.$

2. Show that the functions e^x, e^{2x}, e^{3x} are linearly independent.

ANS. $W = 2e^{6x} \neq 0.$

3. Show that the functions e^x, $\cos x$, $\sin x$ are linearly independent.

ANS. $W = 2e^x \neq 0.$

4. By determining constants c_1, c_2, c_3, c_4, not all zero and which are such that $c_1 f_1 + c_2 f_2 + c_3 f_3 + c_4 f_4 = 0$ identically, show that the functions

$$f_1 = x, f_2 = e^x, f_3 = xe^x, f_4 = (2 - 3x)e^x$$

are linearly dependent.

ANS.   One such set of c's is: $c_1 = 0$, $c_2 = -2$, $c_3 = 3$, $c_4 = 1.$

5. Show that $\cos (\omega t - \beta)$, $\cos \omega t$, $\sin \omega t$ are linearly dependent functions of t.

6. Show that 1, sin x, cos x are linearly independent.

7. Show that 1, sin^2 x, cos^2 x are linearly dependent.

8. Show that two nonvanishing differentiable functions of x are linearly dependent if, and only if, their Wronskian vanishes identically. This statement is not true for more than two functions.

9. Let $f_1(x) = 1 + x^3$ for $x \leqq 0$, $f_1(x) = 1$ for $x \geqq 0$;

$f_2(x) = 1$ for $x \leqq 0$, $f_2(x) = 1 + x^3$ for $x \geqq 0$;

$f_3(x) = 3 + x^3$ for all x.

Show that: (a) f, f', f'' are continuous for all x for each of f_1, f_2, f_3;

(b) the Wronskian of f_1, f_2, f_3 is zero for all x;

(c) f_1, f_2, f_3 are linearly independent over the interval $-1 \leqq x \leqq 1$.

In part (c) you must show that if $c_1f_1(x) + c_2f_2(x) + c_3f_3(x) = 0$ for all x in $-1 \leqq x \leqq 1$, $c_1 = c_2 = c_3 = 0$. Use $x = -1, 0, 1$ successively to obtain three equations to solve for $c_1, c_2,$ and c_3.

33. General solution of a homogeneous equation

Let $y_1, y_2, \cdots, y_n$ be linearly independent solutions of the homogeneous equation

$$(1) \qquad b_0(x)y^{(n)} + b_1(x)y^{(n-1)} + \cdots + b_{n-1}(x)y' + b_n(x)y = 0.$$

Then the general solution of equation (1) is

$$(2) \qquad y = c_1y_1 + c_2y_2 + \cdots + c_ny_n,$$

where $c_1, c_2, \cdots, c_n$ are arbitrary constants.

In a sense each particular solution of the linear differential equation (1) is a special case (some choice of the c's) of the general solution (2). The basic ideas needed for a proof of this important result are exhibited here for the equation of order two. No additional complications enter for equations of higher order.

Consider the equation

$$(3) \qquad b_0(x)y'' + b_1(x)y' + b_2(x)y = 0.$$

Let the relation

$$(4) \qquad y = f(x)$$

be any particular solution of equation (3), the solution being valid in some interval $a < x < b$ in which $b_0(x)$ does not vanish and in which the functions b_1/b_0 and b_2/b_0 possess derivatives of all orders.

We assume (it can be proved) that at $x = \alpha$, within the stipulated interval, $f(x)$ is sufficiently well behaved to insure that the Taylor series for $f(x)$,

$$(5) \qquad f(x) = \sum_{k=0}^{\infty} \frac{f^{(k)}(\alpha)(x - \alpha)^k}{k!},$$

converges to $f(x)$ in some interval about $x = \alpha$.

Then the solution $f(x)$ is completely determined by knowledge of $f(\alpha)$ and $f'(\alpha)$, the values of f and f' taken at some point α within the interval. For, since we can divide by $b_0(x)$, equation (3) yields y'' in terms of y, y', and the known coefficients in the equation. Then $y''(\alpha) = f''(\alpha)$ can be determined. Successive differentiation of the equation for y'' will yield the higher derivatives. Thus $f^{(k)}(\alpha)$ can be computed for $k = 2, 3, \cdots$, from the values of $f(\alpha)$ and $f'(\alpha)$. Then, using Taylor's series (5), we see that $f(x)$ is determined by the differential equation and the two values $f(\alpha)$ and $f'(\alpha)$.

Now let $y_1(x)$, $y_2(x)$ be any two linearly independent solutions of equation (3). Further, let α be chosen as some point in the interval, $a < \alpha < b$, where the Wronskian of y_1 and y_2 does not vanish,

$$(6) \qquad \begin{vmatrix} y_1(\alpha) & y_2(\alpha) \\ y_1'(\alpha) & y_2'(\alpha) \end{vmatrix} \neq 0.$$

Consider the solution

$$(7) \qquad y = c_1 y_1(x) + c_2 y_2(x),$$

from which

$$y' = c_1 y_1'(x) + c_2 y_2'(x).$$

We wish to choose c_1 and c_2 so that the y of equation (7) will become the solution $f(x)$. But we can surely force that y to be such that $y(\alpha) = f(\alpha)$ and $y'(\alpha) = f'(\alpha)$. That is, the equations

$$(8) \qquad c_1 y_1(\alpha) + c_2 y_2(\alpha) = f(\alpha),$$
$$c_1 y_1'(\alpha) + c_2 y_2'(\alpha) = f'(\alpha),$$

can be solved for c_1 and c_2 because of the inequality (6), the nonvanishing of the Wronskian. Then $f(x)$ and $y(x)$ have the same Taylor series (5), so they are identical.

It is necessary to keep in mind that the above discussion used the fact that $b_0(x) \neq 0$ in the interval $a < x < b$. It is easy to see that the linear equation

$$xy' - 2y = 0$$

has the general solution $y = cx^2$ and also such particular solutions as

$$y_1 = x^2, \qquad 0 \leqq x,$$
$$= -4x^2, \qquad x < 0.$$

The solution y_1 is not a special case of the general solution. But in any interval throughout which $b_0(x) = x \neq 0$, this particular solution is a special case of the general solution. It was, of course, made up by piecing together at $x = 0$ two parts, each drawn from the general solution.

34. General solution of a nonhomogeneous equation

Let y_p be any particular solution (not necessarily involving any arbitrary constants) of the equation

(1) $$b_0 y^{(n)} + b_1 y^{(n-1)} + \cdots + b_{n-1} y' + b_n y = R(x)$$

and let y_c be a solution of the corresponding homogeneous equation

(2) $$b_0 y^{(n)} + b_1 y^{(n-1)} + \cdots + b_{n-1} y' + b_n y = 0.$$

Then

(3) $$y = y_c + y_p$$

is a solution of equation (1). For, using the y of equation (3) we see that

$$b_0 y^{(n)} + \cdots + b_n y = (b_0 y_c^{(n)} + \cdots + b_n y_c)$$
$$+ (b_0 y_p^{(n)} + \cdots + b_n y_p)$$
$$= 0 + R(x) = R(x).$$

If $y_1, y_2, \cdots, y_n$ are linearly independent solutions of equation (2), then

(4) $$y_c = c_1 y_1 + c_2 y_2 + \cdots + c_n y_n,$$

in which the c's are arbitrary constants, is the general solution of equation (2). The right member of equation (4) is called the *complementary function* for equation (1).

The general solution of the nonhomogeneous equation (1) is the sum of the complementary function and any particular solution.

For instance, consider the equation

(5) $$y'' - y = 4.$$

It is easily seen that $y = -4$ is a solution of equation (5). Therefore the y_p in equation (3) may be taken to be (-4). As we shall see later, the homogeneous equation

$$y'' - y = 0$$

has as its general solution

$$y_c = c_1 e^x + c_2 e^{-x}.$$

Thus the complementary function for equation (5) is $(c_1 e^x + c_2 e^{-x})$ and a particular solution of (5) is $y_p = -4$. Hence the general solution of equation (5) is

$$y = c_1 e^x + c_2 e^{-x} - 4,$$

in which c_1 and c_2 are arbitrary constants.

35. Differential operators

Let D denote differentiation with respect to x, D^2 differentiation twice with respect to x, and so on; that is, for integral k,

$$D^k y = \frac{d^k y}{dx^k}.$$

The expression

$$(1) \qquad A = a_0 D^n + a_1 D^{n-1} + \cdots + a_{n-1} D + a_n$$

is called a differential operator of order n. It may be defined as that operator which, when applied to any function* y, yields the result

$$(2) \qquad Ay = a_0 \frac{d^n y}{dx^n} + a_1 \frac{d^{n-1} y}{dx^{n-1}} + \cdots + a_{n-1} \frac{dy}{dx} + a_n y.$$

The coefficients $a_0, a_1, \cdots, a_n$ in the operator A may be functions of x, but in this book the only operators used will be those with constant coefficients.

Two operators A and B are said to be equal if, and only if, the same result is produced when each acts upon the function y. That is, $A = B$ if, and only if, $Ay = By$ for all functions y possessing the derivatives necessary for the operations involved.

The product AB of two operators A and B is defined as that operator which produces the same result as is obtained by using the operator B followed by the operator A. Thus $ABy = A(By)$. The product of two

---

* The function y is assumed to possess as many derivatives as may be encountered in whatever operations take place.

differential operators always exists and is a differential operator. For operators with *constant coefficients*, but not usually for those with variable coefficients, it is true that $AB = BA$.

EXAMPLE (a): Let $A = D + 2$ and $B = 3D - 1$.
Then

$$By = (3D - 1)y = 3\frac{dy}{dx} - y$$

and

$$A(By) = (D + 2)\left(3\frac{dy}{dx} - y\right)$$

$$= 3\frac{d^2y}{dx^2} - \frac{dy}{dx} + 6\frac{dy}{dx} - 2y$$

$$= 3\frac{d^2y}{dx^2} + 5\frac{dy}{dx} - 2y$$

$$= (3D^2 + 5D - 2)y.$$

Hence $AB = (D + 2)(3D - 1) = 3D^2 + 5D - 2$.

Now consider BA. Acting upon y, the operator BA yields

$$B(Ay) = (3D - 1)\left(\frac{dy}{dx} + 2y\right)$$

$$= 3\frac{d^2y}{dx^2} + 6\frac{dy}{dx} - \frac{dy}{dx} - 2y$$

$$= 3\frac{d^2y}{dx^2} + 5\frac{dy}{dx} - 2y.$$

Hence

$$BA = 3D^2 + 5D - 2 = AB.$$

EXAMPLE (b): Let $G = xD + 2$, and $H = D - 1$. Then

$$G(Hy) = (xD + 2)\left(\frac{dy}{dx} - y\right)$$

$$= x\frac{d^2y}{dx^2} - x\frac{dy}{dx} + 2\frac{dy}{dx} - 2y$$

$$= x\frac{d^2y}{dx^2} + (2 - x)\frac{dy}{dx} - 2y,$$

so

$$GH = xD^2 + (2 - x)D - 2.$$

On the other hand

$$H(Gy) = (D - 1)\left(x\frac{dy}{dx} + 2y\right)$$

$$= \frac{d}{dx}\left(x\frac{dy}{dx} + 2y\right) - \left(x\frac{dy}{dx} + 2y\right)$$

$$= x\frac{d^2y}{dx^2} + \frac{dy}{dx} + 2\frac{dy}{dx} - x\frac{dy}{dx} - 2y$$

$$= x\frac{d^2y}{dx^2} + (3 - x)\frac{dy}{dx} - 2y;$$

that is,

$$HG = xD^2 + (3 - x)D - 2.$$

It is worthy of notice that here we have two operators G and H (one of them with variable coefficients), the product of which is dependent on the order of the factors. On this topic see also Exs. 17–22 in the next section.

The sum of two differential operators is obtained by expressing each in the form

$$a_0D^n + a_1D^{n-1} + \cdots + a_{n-1}D + a_n$$

and adding corresponding coefficients. For instance, if

$$A = 3D^2 - D + x - 2$$

and

$$B = x^2D^2 + 4D + 7,$$

then

$$A + B = (3 + x^2)D^2 + 3D + x + 5.$$

Differential operators are linear operators; that is, if A is any differential operator, if c_1 and c_2 are constants, and if f_1 and f_2 are any functions of x each possessing the required number of derivatives, then

$$A(c_1f_1 + c_2f_2) = c_1Af_1 + c_2Af_2.$$

36. The fundamental laws of operation

Let A, B, and C be any differential operators as defined in Section 35. With the above definitions of addition and multiplication, it follows that differential operators satisfy the following:

(1) The commutative law of addition:

$$A + B = B + A.$$

(2) The associative law of addition:

$$(A + B) + C = A + (B + C).$$

(3) The associative law of multiplication:

$$(AB)C = A(BC).$$

(4) The distributive law of multiplication with respect to addition:

$$A(B + C) = AB + AC.$$

If A, B, and C are operators with *constant coefficients*, then they also satisfy

(5) The commutative law of multiplication:

$$AB = BA.$$

Therefore, differential operators with constant coefficients satisfy all the laws of ordinary algebra* with regard to addition and multiplication. In Chapter 10 we shall touch upon the question of division of operators.

If m and n are any two positive integers, then

$$D^m D^n = D^{m+n},$$

a useful result which follows immediately from the definitions.

Since for purposes of addition and multiplication the operators with constant coefficients behave just as algebraic polynomials behave, it is legitimate to use the tools of elementary algebra. In particular, synthetic division may be used to factor operators with constant coefficients.

Exercises

Perform the indicated multiplications in Exs. 1–4.

1. $(4D + 1)(D - 2)$.   ANS. $4D^2 - 7D - 2$.
2. $(2D - 3)(2D + 3)$.   ANS. $4D^2 - 9$.
3. $(D + 2)(D^2 - 2D + 5)$.   ANS. $D^3 + D + 10$.
4. $(D - 2)(D + 1)^2$.   ANS. $D^3 - 3D - 2$.

In Exs. 5–16, factor each of the operators.

5. $2D^2 + 3D - 2$.   ANS. $(D + 2)(2D - 1)$.
6. $2D^2 - 5D - 12$.
7. $D^3 - 2D^2 - 5D + 6$.   ANS. $(D - 1)(D + 2)(D - 3)$.

* See any college algebra—for example, J. R. Britton and L. C. Snively, *Algebra for College Students* (New York: Rinehart and Co., 1954), pp. 31–32.

8. $4D^3 - 4D^2 - 11D + 6$.

9. $D^4 - 4D^2$.   ANS. $D^2(D-2)(D+2)$.

10. $D^3 - 3D^2 + 4$.

11. $D^3 - 21D + 20$.   ANS. $(D-1)(D-4)(D+5)$.

12. $2D^3 - D^2 - 13D - 6$.

13. $2D^4 + 11D^3 + 18D^2 + 4D - 8$.   ANS. $(D+2)^3(2D-1)$.

14. $8D^4 + 36D^3 - 66D^2 + 35D - 6$.

15. $D^4 + D^3 - 2D^2 + 4D - 24$.   ANS. $(D-2)(D+3)(D^2+4)$.

16. $D^3 - 11D - 20$.   ANS. $(D-4)(D^2+4D+5)$.

Perform the indicated multiplications in Exs. 17–22.

17. $(D-x)(D+x)$.   ANS. $D^2 + 1 - x^2$.

18. $(D+x)(D-x)$.   ANS. $D^2 - 1 - x^2$.

19. $D(xD-1)$.   ANS. xD^2.

20. $(xD-1)D$.   ANS. $xD^2 - D$.

21. $(xD+2)(xD-1)$.   ANS. $x^2D^2 + 2xD - 2$.

22. $(xD-1)(xD+2)$.   ANS. $x^2D^2 + 2xD - 2$.

37. Some properties of differential operators

Since for constant m and positive integral k,

(1) $$D^k e^{mx} = m^k e^{mx},$$

it is easy to find the effect an operator has upon e^{mx}. Let $f(D)$ be a polynomial in D,

(2) $$f(D) = a_0 D^n + a_1 D^{n-1} + \cdots + a_{n-1} D + a_n.$$

Then

$$f(D)e^{mx} = a_0 m^n e^{mx} + a_1 m^{n-1} e^{mx} + \cdots + a_{n-1} m e^{mx} + a_n e^{mx},$$

so

(3) $$f(D)e^{mx} = e^{mx} f(m).$$

If m is a root of the equation $f(m) = 0$, then in view of equation (3),

$$f(D)e^{mx} = 0.$$

EXAMPLE: Let $f(D) = 2D^2 + 5D - 12$. Then the equation $f(m) = 0$ is

$$2m^2 + 5m - 12 = 0,$$

or

$$(m + 4)(2m - 3) = 0,$$

of which the roots are $m_1 = -4$ and $m_2 = \frac{3}{2}$.

With the aid of equation (3) above it can be seen that

$$(2D^2 + 5D - 12)e^{-4x} = 0$$

and that

$$(2D^2 + 5D - 12) \exp\left(\tfrac{3}{2}x\right) = 0.$$

In other words, $y_1 = e^{-4x}$ and $y_2 = \exp\left(\tfrac{3}{2}x\right)$ are solutions of

$$(2D^2 + 5D - 12)y = 0.$$

Next consider the effect of the operator $(D - m)$ on the product of e^{mx} and a power of x. Since

$$(D - m)(x^k e^{mx}) = kx^{k-1}e^{mx} + mx^k e^{mx} - mx^k e^{mx},$$

we get

$$(D - m)(x^k e^{mx}) = kx^{k-1}e^{mx}.$$

Then

$$(D - m)^2(x^k e^{mx}) = k(D - m)(x^{k-1}e^{mx})$$
$$= k(k - 1)x^{k-2}e^{mx}.$$

Repeating the operation, we are led to

$$(D - m)^k(x^k e^{mx}) = k(k - 1) \cdots 2 \cdot 1 x^0 e^{mx}$$
$$= k!e^{mx}.$$

But $(D - m)e^{mx} = 0$. Therefore, for all $n > k$,

(4) $$(D - m)^n(x^k e^{mx}) = 0.$$

It will be convenient to think of the exponent of x in (4) as varying rather than the exponent of the operator $(D - m)$. Hence we rewrite (4) as

(5) $$\boldsymbol{(D - m)^n(x^k e^{mx}) = 0 \text{ for } k = 0, 1, 2, \cdots, (n - 1).}$$

Equation (5) forms the basis for all the solutions obtained in the next chapter.

38. The *n*th derivative of a product

It is often convenient to be able to write down for a product of functions a derivative of fairly high order without first obtaining the derivatives of lower order. For instance, we may wish to form the fourth derivative of the function

$$y = x^2 e^{3x},$$

but may have no need for the first, second, or third derivatives.

A formula for the nth derivative of the product of two functions was discovered by Leibnitz. Since that formula is not always included in a first course in calculus, it will be stated here.

Consider the product

(1) $$y = uv$$

in which u and v are functions of the independent variable x. Let us use the notation

$$u^{(n)} = \frac{d^n u}{dx^n},$$

including $u^{(0)} = u$ and $u^{(1)} = u'$, together with similar notations for derivatives of v and y. From equation (1) we obtain, by the usual rule for the derivative of a product, the result

$$y' = u'v + uv',$$

or

(2) $$y^{(1)} = u^{(1)}v^{(0)} + u^{(0)}v^{(1)}.$$

Let us now differentiate both members of equation (2) with respect to x, keeping in mind that each term on the right side of equation (2) is itself a product of functions. We thus get

$$y^{(2)} = u^{(2)}v^{(0)} + u^{(1)}v^{(1)} + u^{(1)}v^{(1)} + u^{(0)}v^{(2)},$$

or

(3) $$y^{(2)} = u^{(2)}v^{(0)} + 2u^{(1)}v^{(1)} + u^{(0)}v^{(2)}.$$

Another such step brings us to the result

(4) $$y^{(3)} = u^{(3)}v^{(0)} + 3u^{(2)}v^{(1)} + 3u^{(1)}v^{(2)} + u^{(0)}v^{(3)},$$

for the third derivative of a product. The resemblance of equations (3) and (4) to the binomial expansions

$$(a + b)^2 = a^2 + 2ab + b^2$$

and

$$(a + b)^3 = a^3 + 3a^2b + 3ab^2 + b^3$$

is striking. It encourages one to go on to the general formula.

Leibnitz' rule for the nth derivative of a product is: If $y = uv$, then

$$(5) \qquad y^{(n)} = \sum_{k=0}^{n} C_{n,k} u^{(n-k)} v^{(k)},$$

in which $C_{n,k}$ is the binomial coefficient,

$$C_{n,k} = \frac{n!}{k!(n-k)!} = \frac{n(n-1)\cdots(n-k+1)}{k!}.$$

Equation (5) may be validated quite easily by induction with the aid of the relation

$$(6) \qquad\qquad C_{n,k} + C_{n,k+1} = C_{n+1,k+1},$$

the latter being a fundamental property of the Pascal triangle.*

Leibnitz' rule is particularly simple to use when the factors involved are simple exponentials, powers of x, or sines or cosines.

EXAMPLE (a): Find the fourth derivative of the product

$$y = x^2 e^{3x}.$$

First we have in mind the coefficients in the binomial expansion $(a + b)^4$—or we build the Pascal triangle far enough to obtain them. The required coefficients are 1, 4, 6, 4, 1. As we write down the product we form the successive derivatives from each end, first writing

$$y^{(4)} = 1 \cdot (x^2)(\quad) + 4(\quad)(\quad) + 6(\quad)(\quad) + 4(\quad)(\quad) + 1(\quad)(e^{3x})$$

and then filling in the empty spaces with the proper derivatives in succession. Thus we arrive, in one step after a bit of practice, at the result

$$y^{(4)} = (x^2)(81e^{3x}) + 4(2x)(27e^{3x}) + 6(2)(9e^{3x}) + 4(0)(3e^{3x}) + (0)(e^{3x}),$$

or

$$y^{(4)} = 9e^{3x}(9x^2 + 24x + 12).$$

EXAMPLE (b): Find the third derivative of $w = e^{2x} \cos 3x$. We form

$$w^{(3)} = (e^{2x})(\quad) + 3(\quad)(\quad) \\ + 3(\quad)(\quad) + (\quad)(\cos 3x),$$

and fill in the spaces to obtain

---

* See J. R. Britton and L. C. Snively, *Algebra for College Students* (New York: Rinehart and Co., 1954), pp. 277–279.

$$w^{(3)} = (e^{2x})(27 \sin 3x) + 3(2e^{2x})(-9 \cos 3x)$$
$$+ 3(4e^{2x})(-3 \sin 3x) + (8e^{2x})(\cos 3x),$$

or

$$w^{(3)} = e^{2x}[(27 - 36) \sin 3x + (8 - 54) \cos 3x].$$

Finally, we have

$$w^{(3)} = -e^{2x}(9 \sin 3x + 46 \cos 3x).$$

The method is particularly pleasant, of course, when some of the terms drop out as happened in Example (a).

EXAMPLE (c): Find the fourth derivative of $v = x \sin 3x$.
At once, since $3^4 = 81$ and $3^3 \cdot 4 = 108$, we write

$$v^{(4)} = 81x \sin 3x - 108 \cos 3x.$$

Exercises

Answers to these exercises can be verified, and the efficacy of the method investigated, by also obtaining the desired derivative by successive differentiation.

1. Find $y^{(2)}$ from $y = x^3 e^x$.   ANS. $y^{(2)} = e^x(x^3 + 6x^2 + 6x)$.

2. Find $y^{(2)}$ from $y = x^4 e^{-x}$.

3. Find $y^{(2)}$ from $y = x \sin 2x$.   ANS. $y^{(2)} = -4x \sin 2x + 4 \cos 2x$.

4. Find $y^{(2)}$ from $y = x \cos 2x$.

5. Find $y^{(3)}$ from $y = x^2 \cos 4x$.

      ANS. $y^{(3)} = 64x^2 \sin 4x - 96x \cos 4x - 24 \sin 4x$.

6. Find $y^{(3)}$ from $y = x^2 \sin 3x$.

7. Find $v^{(3)}$ from $v = x e^{3x}$.   ANS. $v^{(3)} = 27e^{3x}(x + 1)$.

8. Find $v^{(3)}$ from $v = x \sin 4x$.   ANS. $v^{(3)} = -64x \cos 4x - 48 \sin 4x$.

9. Find $y^{(4)}$ from $y = x e^{-2x}$.   ANS. $y^{(4)} = 16e^{-2x}(x - 2)$.

10. Find $y^{(4)}$ from $y = x e^{-3x}$.

11. Find $y^{(4)}$ from $y = x \sin 2x$.   ANS. $y^{(4)} = 16x \sin 2x - 32 \cos 2x$.

12. Find $y^{(4)}$ from $y = x \cos 2x$.

13. Find $y^{(4)}$ from $y = x^2 e^x$.

14. Find $y^{(4)}$ from $y = x^2 e^{-x}$.

15. Find $y^{(4)}$ from $y = x^2 \sin x$.

      ANS. $y^{(4)} = x^2 \sin x - 8x \cos x - 12 \sin x$.

16. Find $y^{(4)}$ from $y = x^2 \cos x$.

CHAPTER 8

Linear Equations with Constant Coefficients

39. Introduction

Two methods for solving linear differential equations with constant coefficients are presented in this book. A classical technique is treated in this and the next chapter. Chapters 11 and 12 contain a development of the Laplace transform and its use in solving differential equations. Each method has its advantages and its disadvantages. Each is theoretically sufficient; both are necessary for maximum efficiency.

40. The auxiliary equation; distinct roots

Any linear homogeneous differential equation with constant coefficients,

$$(1) \qquad a_0 \frac{d^n y}{dx^n} + a_1 \frac{d^{n-1}y}{dx^{n-1}} + \cdots + a_{n-1} \frac{dy}{dx} + a_n y = 0,$$

may be written in the form

$$(2) \qquad\qquad f(D)y = 0,$$

where $f(D)$ is a linear differential operator. As we saw in the preceding chapter, if m is any root of the algebraic equation $f(m) = 0$, then

113

$$f(D)e^{mx} = 0,$$

which means simply that $y = e^{mx}$ is a solution of equation (2). The equation

(3) $$f(m) = 0$$

is called the *auxiliary equation* associated with (1) or (2).

The auxiliary equation for (1) is of degree n. Let its roots be m_1, $m_2, \cdots, m_n$. If these roots are all real and distinct, then the n solutions

$$y_1 = \exp(m_1 x), \; y_2 = \exp(m_2 x), \; \cdots, \; y_n = \exp(m_n x)$$

are linearly independent and the general solution of (1) can be written at once. It is

$$y = c_1 \exp(m_1 x) + c_2 \exp(m_2 x) + \cdots + c_n \exp(m_n x),$$

in which $c_1, c_2, \cdots, c_n$ are arbitrary constants.

Repeated roots of the auxiliary equation will be treated in the next section. Imaginary roots will be avoided until Section 43, where the corresponding solutions will be put into a desirable form.

EXAMPLE (a): Solve the equation

$$\frac{d^3y}{dx^3} - 4\frac{d^2y}{dx^2} + \frac{dy}{dx} + 6y = 0.$$

First write the auxiliary equation

$$m^3 - 4m^2 + m + 6 = 0,$$

whose roots $m = -1, 2, 3$ may be obtained by synthetic division. Then the general solution is seen to be

$$y = c_1 e^{-x} + c_2 e^{2x} + c_3 e^{3x}.$$

EXAMPLE (b): Solve the equation

$$(3D^3 + 5D^2 - 2D)y = 0.$$

The auxiliary equation is

$$3m^3 + 5m^2 - 2m = 0$$

and its roots are $m = 0, -2, \frac{1}{3}$. Using the fact that $e^{0x} = 1$, the desired solution may be written

$$y = c_1 + c_2 e^{-2x} + c_3 \exp\left(\tfrac{1}{3}x\right).$$

EXAMPLE (c): Solve the equation

$$\frac{d^2x}{dt^2} - 4x = 0$$

with the conditions that when $t = 0$, $x = 0$ and $\frac{dx}{dt} = 3$.

The auxiliary equation is

$$m^2 - 4 = 0,$$

with roots $m = 2, -2$. Hence the general solution of the differential equation is

$$x = c_1e^{2t} + c_2e^{-2t}.$$

It remains to enforce the conditions at $t = 0$. Now

$$\frac{dx}{dt} = 2c_1e^{2t} - 2c_2e^{-2t}.$$

Thus the condition that $x = 0$ when $t = 0$ requires that

$$0 = c_1 + c_2,$$

and the condition that $\frac{dx}{dt} = 3$ when $t = 0$ requires that

$$3 = 2c_1 - 2c_2.$$

From the simultaneous equations for c_1 and c_2 we conclude that $c_1 = \frac{3}{4}$ and $c_2 = -\frac{3}{4}$. Therefore

$$x = \tfrac{3}{4}(e^{2t} - e^{-2t}),$$

which can also be put in the form

$$x = \tfrac{3}{2} \sinh (2t).$$

Exercises

In Exs. 1–22, find the general solution. When the operator D is used, it is implied that the independent variable is x.

1. $(D^2 + 2D - 3)y = 0$.   ANS. $y = c_1e^x + c_2e^{-3x}$.
2. $(D^2 + 2D)y = 0$.
3. $(D^2 + D - 6)y = 0$.   ANS. $y = c_1e^{2x} + c_2e^{-3x}$.
4. $(D^2 - 5D + 6)y = 0$.
5. $(D^3 + 3D^2 - 4D)y = 0$.   ANS. $y = c_1 + c_2e^x + c_3e^{-4x}$.
6. $(D^3 - 3D^2 - 10D)y = 0$.

7. $(D^3 + 6D^2 + 11D + 6)y = 0.$ ANS. $y = c_1e^{-x} + c_2e^{-2x} + c_3e^{-3x}.$

8. $(D^3 + 3D^2 - 4D - 12)y = 0.$

9. $(4D^3 - 7D + 3)y = 0.$

ANS. $y = c_1e^x + c_2 \exp\left(\frac{1}{2}x\right) + c_3 \exp\left(-\frac{3}{2}x\right).$

10. $(4D^3 - 13D - 6)y = 0.$

11. $\dfrac{d^3x}{dt^3} + \dfrac{d^2x}{dt^2} - 2\dfrac{dx}{dt} = 0.$ ANS. $x = c_1 + c_2e^t + c_3e^{-2t}.$

12. $\dfrac{d^3x}{dt^3} - 19\dfrac{dx}{dt} + 30x = 0.$

13. $(9D^3 - 7D + 2)y = 0.$

ANS. $y = c_1e^{-x} + c_2 \exp\left(\frac{1}{3}x\right) + c_3 \exp\left(\frac{2}{3}x\right).$

14. $(4D^3 - 21D - 10)y = 0.$

15. $(D^3 - 14D + 8)y = 0.$

ANS. $y = c_1e^{-4x} + c_2 \exp\left[(2 + \sqrt{2})x\right] + c_3 \exp\left[(2 - \sqrt{2})x\right].$

16. $(D^3 - D^2 - 4D - 2)y = 0.$

17. $(4D^4 - 8D^3 - 7D^2 + 11D + 6)y = 0.$

ANS. $y = c_1e^{-x} + c_2e^{2x} + c_3 \exp\left(-\frac{1}{2}x\right) + c_4 \exp\left(\frac{3}{2}x\right).$

18. $(4D^4 - 16D^3 + 7D^2 + 4D - 2)y = 0.$

19. $(4D^4 + 4D^3 - 13D^2 - 7D + 6)y = 0.$

20. $(4D^5 - 8D^4 - 17D^3 + 12D^2 + 9D)y = 0.$

21. $(D^2 - 4aD + 3a^2)y = 0,\ a$ real $\neq 0.$

22. $[D^2 - (a + b)D + ab]y = 0,\ a$ and b real and unequal.

In Exs. 23–24, find the particular solution indicated.

23. $(D^2 - 2D - 3)y = 0;$ when $x = 0,\ y = 0,$ and $y' = -4.$
ANS. $y = e^{-x} - e^{3x}.$

24. $(D^2 - D - 6)y = 0;$ when $x = 0,\ y = 0,$ and when $x = 1,\ y = e^3.$
ANS. $y = (e^{3x} - e^{-2x})/(1 - e^{-5}).$

In Exs. 25–29, find for $x = 1$ the y value for the particular solution required.

25. $(D^2 - 2D - 3)y = 0;$ when $x = 0,\ y = 4$ and $y' = 0.$
ANS. When $x = 1,\ y = e^3 + 3e^{-1} = 21.2.$

26. $(D^3 - 4D)y = 0;$ when $x = 0,\ y = 0,\ y' = 0,$ and $y'' = 2.$
ANS. When $x = 1,\ y = \sinh^2 1.$

27. $(D^2 - D - 6)y = 0;$ when $x = 0,\ y = 3$ and $y' = -1.$
ANS. When $x = 1,\ y = 20.4.$

28. $(D^2 + 3D - 10)y = 0;$ when $x = 0,\ y = 0,$ and when $x = 2,\ y = 1.$
ANS. When $x = 1,\ y = 0.135.$

29. $(D^3 - 2D^2 - 5D + 6)y = 0;$ when $x = 0,\ y = 1,\ y' = -7,$ and $y'' = -1.$ ANS. When $x = 1,\ y = -19.8.$

41. The auxiliary equation; repeated roots

Suppose that in the equation

(1) $$f(D)y = 0$$

the operator $f(D)$ has repeated factors; that is, the auxiliary equation $f(m) = 0$ has repeated roots. Then the method of the previous section does not yield the general solution. Let the auxiliary equation have three equal roots $m_1 = b$, $m_2 = b$, $m_3 = b$. The corresponding part of the solution yielded by the method of Section 40 is

(2) $$\begin{aligned} y &= c_1 e^{bx} + c_2 e^{bx} + c_3 e^{bx}, \\ y &= (c_1 + c_2 + c_3)e^{bx}. \end{aligned}$$

Now (2) can be replaced by

(3) $$y = c_4 e^{bx}$$

with $c_4 = c_1 + c_2 + c_3$. Thus, corresponding to the three roots under consideration, this method has yielded only the solution (3). The difficulty is present, of course, because the three solutions corresponding to the roots $m_1 = m_2 = m_3 = b$ are not linearly independent.

What is needed is a method for obtaining n linearly independent solutions corresponding to n equal roots of the auxiliary equation. Suppose the auxiliary equation $f(m) = 0$ has the n equal roots

$$m_1 = m_2 = \cdots = m_n = b.$$

Then the operator $f(D)$ must have a factor $(D - b)^n$. We wish to find n linearly independent y's for which

(4) $$(D - b)^n y = 0.$$

Turning to the result (5) near the end of Section 37 and writing $m = b$, we find that

(5) $$(D - b)^n (x^k e^{bx}) = 0 \text{ for } k = 0, 1, 2, \cdots, (n - 1).$$

The functions $y_k = x^k e^{bx}$; $k = 0, 1, 2, \cdots, (n - 1)$ are linearly independent because aside from the common factor e^{bx} they contain only the respective powers $x^0, x^1, x^2, \cdots, x^{n-1}$.

The general solution of equation (4) is

(6) $$y = c_1 e^{bx} + c_2 x e^{bx} + \cdots + c_n x^{n-1} e^{bx}.$$

Furthermore, if $f(D)$ contains the factor $(D - b)^n$, then the equation

(1) $$f(D)y = 0$$

can be written

(7) $$g(D)(D - b)^n y = 0$$

where $g(D)$ contains all the factors of $f(D)$ except $(D - b)^n$. Then any solution of

(4) $$(D - b)^n y = 0$$

is also a solution of (7) and therefore of (1).

Now we are in a position to write the solution of equation (1) whenever the auxiliary equation has only real roots. Each root of the auxiliary equation is either distinct from all the other roots or it is one of a set of equal roots. Corresponding to a root m_i distinct from all others, there is the solution

(8) $$y_i = c_i \exp{(m_i x)},$$

and corresponding to n equal roots $m_1, m_2, \cdots , m_n$, each equal to b, there is the solution

(9) $$y = c_1 e^{bx} + c_2 x e^{bx} + \cdots + c_n x^{n-1} e^{bx}.$$

The sum of such solutions (8) and (9) yields the proper number of solutions, a number equal to the order of the differential equation, because there is one solution corresponding to each root of the auxiliary equation. The solutions thus obtained can be proved to be linearly independent.

EXAMPLE (a): Solve the equation

(10) $$(D^4 - 7D^3 + 18D^2 - 20D + 8)y = 0.$$

With the aid of synthetic division, it is easily seen that the auxiliary equation

$$m^4 - 7m^3 + 18m^2 - 20m + 8 = 0$$

has the roots $m = 1, 2, 2, 2$. Then the general solution of equation (10) is

$$y = c_1 e^x + c_2 e^{2x} + c_3 x e^{2x} + c_4 x^2 e^{2x},$$

or

$$y = c_1 e^x + (c_2 + c_3 x + c_4 x^2)e^{2x}.$$

EXAMPLE (b): Solve the equation

$$\frac{d^4 y}{dx^4} + 2\frac{d^3 y}{dx^3} + \frac{d^2 y}{dx^2} = 0.$$

The auxiliary equation is

$$m^4 + 2m^3 + m^2 = 0,$$

with roots $m = 0, 0, -1, -1$. Hence the desired solution is

$$y = c_1 + c_2 x + c_3 e^{-x} + c_4 x e^{-x}.$$

Exercises

In Exs. 1–20 find the general solution.

1. $(D^2 - 6D + 9)y = 0.$ ANS. $y = (c_1 + c_2 x)e^{3x}.$
2. $(D^2 + 4D + 4)y = 0.$
3. $(4D^3 + 4D^2 + D)y = 0.$ ANS. $y = c_1 + (c_2 + c_3 x) \exp(-\tfrac{1}{2}x).$
4. $(D^3 - 8D^2 + 16D)y = 0.$
5. $(D^4 + 6D^3 + 9D^2)y = 0.$

ANS. $y = c_1 + c_2 x + (c_3 + c_4 x)e^{-3x}.$

6. $(D^3 - 3D^2 + 4)y = 0.$
7. $(4D^3 - 3D + 1)y = 0.$ ANS. $y = c_1 e^{-x} + (c_2 + c_3 x) \exp(\tfrac{1}{2}x).$
8. $(D^4 - 3D^3 - 6D^2 + 28D - 24)y = 0.$
9. $(4D^4 - 4D^3 - 23D^2 + 12D + 36)y = 0.$

ANS. $y = (c_1 + c_2 x)e^{2x} + (c_3 + c_4 x) \exp(-\tfrac{3}{2}x).$

10. $(D^3 + 6D^2 + 12D + 8)y = 0.$
11. $(D^5 - D^3)y = 0.$ ANS. $y = c_1 + c_2 x + c_3 x^2 + c_4 e^x + c_5 e^{-x};$
    or $y = c_1 + c_2 x + c_3 x^2 + c_6 \cosh x + c_7 \sinh x.$
12. $(D^5 - 16D^3)y = 0.$
13. $(4D^4 + 4D^3 - 3D^2 - 2D + 1)y = 0.$
14. $(54D^4 - 27D^3 - 9D^2 + 7D - 1)y = 0.$
15. $(D^4 - 2D^3 - 3D^2 + 4D + 4)y = 0.$

ANS. $y = (c_1 + c_2 x)e^{-x} + (c_3 + c_4 x)e^{2x}.$

16. $(4D^4 + 4D^3 - 3D^2 - 2D + 1)y = 0.$
17. $(4D^5 + 4D^4 - 9D^3 - 11D^2 + D + 3)y = 0.$
18. $(D^5 - 15D^3 + 10D^2 + 60D - 72)y = 0.$
19. $(D^4 + 2D^3 - 6D^2 - 16D - 8)y = 0.$
    ANS. $y = (c_1 + c_2 x)e^{-2x} + c_3 \exp[(1 + \sqrt{3})x] + c_4 \exp[(1 - \sqrt{3})x].$
20. $(D^4 - 2D^3 - 5D^2 + 2)y = 0.$

In Exs. 21–26, find the particular solution indicated.

21. $(D^2 + 4D + 4)y = 0;$ when $x = 0$, $y = 1$ and $y' = -1.$

ANS. $y = (1 + x)e^{-2x}.$

22. The equation of Ex. 21 with the condition that the graph of the solution pass through the points $(0, 2)$ and $(2, 0)$.

ANS. $y = (2 - x)e^{-2x}.$

23. $(D^3 - 3D - 2)y = 0$; when $x = 0$, $y = 0$, $y' = 9$, $y'' = 0$.

ANS. $y = 2e^{2x} + (3x - 2)e^{-x}$.

24. $(D^4 + 3D^3 + 2D^2)y = 0$; when $x = 0$, $y = 0$, $y' = 4$, $y'' = -6$, $y''' = 14$.   ANS. $y = 2(x + e^{-x} - e^{-2x})$.

25. The equation of Ex. 24 with the conditions: when $x = 0$, $y = 0$, $y' = 3$, $y'' = -5$, $y''' = 9$.   ANS. $y = 2 - e^{-x} - e^{-2x}$.

26. $(D^3 + D^2 - D - 1)y = 0$; when $x = 0$, $y = 1$, when $x = 2$, $y = 0$, and also as $x \to \infty$, $y \to 0$.   ANS. $y = \frac{1}{2}(2 - x)e^{-x}$.

In Exs. 27–29, find for $x = 2$ the y value for the particular solution required.

27. $(4D^2 - 4D + 1)y = 0$; when $x = 0$, $y = -2$, $y' = 2$.

ANS.   When $x = 2$, $y = 4e$.

28. $(D^3 + 2D^2)y = 0$; when $x = 0$, $y = -3$, $y' = 0$, $y'' = 12$.

ANS.   When $x = 2$, $y = 3e^{-4} + 6$.

29. $(D^3 + 5D^2 + 3D - 9)y = 0$; when $x = 0$, $y = -1$, when $x = 1$, $y = 0$, and also as $x \to \infty$, $y \to 0$.   ANS.   When $x = 2$, $y = e^{-6}$.

42. A definition of exp z for imaginary z

Since the auxiliary equation may have imaginary roots, we need now to lay down a definition of exp z for imaginary z.

Let $z = \alpha + i\beta$ with α and β real. Since it is desirable to have the ordinary laws of exponents remain valid, it is wise to require that

$$(1) \qquad \exp(\alpha + i\beta) = e^\alpha \cdot e^{i\beta}.$$

To e^α with α real, we attach the usual meaning.

Now consider $e^{i\beta}$, β real. In calculus it is shown that for all real x

$$(2) \qquad e^x = 1 + \frac{x}{1!} + \frac{x^2}{2!} + \frac{x^3}{3!} + \cdots + \frac{x^n}{n!} + \cdots,$$

or

$$(2) \qquad e^x = \sum_{n=0}^{\infty} \frac{x^n}{n!}.$$

If we now tentatively put $x = i\beta$ in (2) as a definition of $e^{i\beta}$, we get

$$(3) \qquad e^{i\beta} = 1 + \frac{i\beta}{1!} + \frac{i^2\beta^2}{2!} + \frac{i^3\beta^3}{3!} + \frac{i^4\beta^4}{4!} + \cdots + \frac{i^n\beta^n}{n!} + \cdots.$$

Separating the even powers of β from the odd powers of β in (3) yields

(4)
$$e^{i\beta} = 1 + \frac{i^2\beta^2}{2!} + \frac{i^4\beta^4}{4!} + \cdots + \frac{i^{2k}\beta^{2k}}{(2k)!} + \cdots$$

$$+ \frac{i\beta}{1!} + \frac{i^3\beta^3}{3!} + \cdots + \frac{i^{2k+1}\beta^{2k+1}}{(2k+1)!} + \cdots,$$

or

(4)
$$e^{i\beta} = \sum_{k=0}^{\infty} \frac{i^{2k}\beta^{2k}}{(2k)!} + \sum_{k=0}^{\infty} \frac{i^{2k+1}\beta^{2k+1}}{(2k+1)!}.$$

Now $i^{2k} = (-1)^k$, so we may write

(5)
$$e^{i\beta} = 1 - \frac{\beta^2}{2!} + \frac{\beta^4}{4!} + \cdots + \frac{(-1)^k\beta^{2k}}{(2k)!} + \cdots$$

$$+ i\left[\frac{\beta}{1!} - \frac{\beta^3}{3!} + \cdots + \frac{(-1)^k\beta^{2k+1}}{(2k+1)!} + \cdots\right],$$

or

(5)
$$e^{i\beta} = \sum_{k=0}^{\infty} \frac{(-1)^k\beta^{2k}}{(2k)!} + i\sum_{k=0}^{\infty} \frac{(-1)^k\beta^{2k+1}}{(2k+1)!}.$$

But the series on the right in (5) are precisely those for $\cos\beta$ and $\sin\beta$ as developed in calculus. Hence we are led to the tentative result

(6)
$$e^{i\beta} = \cos\beta + i\sin\beta.$$

The student should realize that the manipulations above have no meaning in themselves at this stage (assuming that infinite series with complex terms are not a part of the content of elementary mathematics). What has been accomplished is this: the formal manipulations above have suggested the meaningful definition (6). Combining (6) with (1) we now put forward a reasonable *definition* of exp $(\alpha + i\beta)$, namely,

(7)
$$\exp(\alpha + i\beta) = e^{\alpha}(\cos\beta + i\sin\beta), \quad \alpha \text{ and } \beta \text{ real.}$$

Replacing β by $(-\beta)$ in (7) yields a result which is of value to us in the next section,

$$\exp(\alpha - i\beta) = e^{\alpha}(\cos\beta - i\sin\beta).$$

It is interesting and important that with the definition (7), the function e^z for complex z retains many of the properties possessed by the function e^x for real x. Such matters are often studied in detail in books on complex variables.* Here we need in particular to know that if

---

* For example, R. V. Churchill, *Complex Variables and Applications* (2nd edition; New York: McGraw-Hill Book Co., 1960), pp. 46–50.

$$y = \exp{(a + ib)x},$$

with a, b, and x real, then

$$(D - a - ib)y = 0.$$

The result desired follows at once by differentiation, with respect to x, of the function

$$y = e^{ax}(\cos bx + i \sin bx).$$

43. The auxiliary equation; imaginary roots

Consider a differential equation $f(D)y = 0$ for which the auxiliary equation $f(m) = 0$ has real coefficients. From elementary algebra we know that if the auxiliary equation has any imaginary roots, those roots must occur in conjugate pairs. Thus if

$$m_1 = a + ib$$

is a root of the equation $f(m) = 0$, with a and b real and $b \neq 0$, then

$$m_2 = a - ib$$

is also a root of $f(m) = 0$. It must be kept in mind that this result is a consequence of the reality of the coefficients in the equation $f(m) = 0$. Imaginary roots do not necessarily appear in pairs in an algebraic equation whose coefficients involve imaginaries.

We can now construct in usable form solutions of

$$(1) \qquad\qquad\qquad f(D)y = 0$$

corresponding to imaginary roots of $f(m) = 0$. For, since $f(m)$ is assumed to have real coefficients, any imaginary roots appear in conjugate pairs $m_1 = a + ib$ and $m_2 = a - ib$. Then, according to the preceding section, equation (1) is satisfied by

$$(2) \qquad y = c_1 \exp{[(a + ib)x]} + c_2 \exp{[(a - ib)x]}.$$

Taking x to be real along with a and b, we get from (2) the result

$$(3) \qquad y = c_1 e^{ax}(\cos bx + i \sin bx) + c_2 e^{ax}(\cos bx - i \sin bx).$$

Now (3) may be written

$$y = (c_1 + c_2)e^{ax} \cos bx + i(c_1 - c_2)e^{ax} \sin bx.$$

Finally, let $c_1 + c_2 = c_3$, and $i(c_1 - c_2) = c_4$, where c_3 and c_4 are new arbitrary constants. Then equation (1) is seen to have the solutions

(4) $$y = c_3 e^{ax} \cos bx + c_4 e^{ax} \sin bx,$$

corresponding to the two roots $m_1 = a + ib$ and $m_2 = a - ib, (b \neq 0)$ of the auxiliary equation.

Taking a, b, x, and y to be real, it follows readily from equation (4) that c_3 and c_4 are real. But $c_1 + c_2 = c_3$, and $i(c_1 - c_2) = c_4$, so

$$c_1 = \tfrac{1}{2}(c_3 - ic_4)$$

and

$$c_2 = \tfrac{1}{2}(c_3 + ic_4).$$

Hence, if $c_4 \neq 0$, c_1 and c_2 are conjugate complex numbers.

The reduction of the solution (2) above to the desirable form (4) has been done once and that is enough. Whenever a pair of conjugate imaginary roots of the auxiliary equation appears, we write down at once in the form given on the right in equation (4) the particular solution corresponding to those two roots.

EXAMPLE (a): Solve the equation

$$(D^3 - 3D^2 + 9D + 13)y = 0.$$

For the auxiliary equation

$$m^3 - 3m^2 + 9m + 13 = 0,$$

one root, $m_1 = -1$, is easily found. When the factor $(m + 1)$ is removed by synthetic division, it is seen that the other two roots are solutions of the quadratic

$$m^2 - 4m + 13 = 0.$$

Those roots are found to be $m_2 = 2 + 3i$ and $m_3 = 2 - 3i$. The auxiliary equation has the roots $m = -1$, $2 \pm 3i$. Hence the general solution of the differential equation is

$$y = c_1 e^{-x} + c_2 e^{2x} \cos 3x + c_3 e^{2x} \sin 3x.$$

Repeated imaginary roots lead to solutions analogous to those brought in by repeated real roots. For instance, if the roots $m = a \pm ib$ occur three times, then the corresponding six linearly independent solutions of the differential equation are those appearing in the expression

$$(c_1 + c_2 x + c_3 x^2)e^{ax} \cos bx + (c_4 + c_5 x + c_6 x^2)e^{ax} \sin bx.$$

EXAMPLE (b): Solve the equation

$$(D^4 + 8D^2 + 16)y = 0.$$

The auxiliary equation $m^4 + 8m^2 + 16 = 0$ may be written

$$(m^2 + 4)^2 = 0,$$

so its roots are seen to be $m = \pm 2i, \pm 2i$. The roots $m_1 = 2i$ and $m_2 = -2i$ occur twice each. Thinking of $2i$ as $0 + 2i$ and recalling that $e^{0x} = 1$, we write the solution of the differential equation as

$$y = (c_1 + c_2 x) \cos 2x + (c_3 + c_4 x) \sin 2x.$$

In such exercises as those below a fine check can be obtained by direct substitution of the result and its appropriate derivatives into the differential equation. The verification is particularly effective because the operations performed in the check are so different from those performed in obtaining the solution.

Exercises

Find the general solution except when the exercise stipulates otherwise.

1. Verify directly that the relation

$$(4) \qquad\qquad y = c_3 e^{ax} \cos bx + c_4 e^{ax} \sin bx$$

satisfies the equation

$$[(D - a)^2 + b^2]y = 0.$$

2. $(D^2 - 2D + 5)y = 0$. Verify your answer.

ANS. $y = c_1 e^x \cos 2x + c_2 e^x \sin 2x.$

3. $(D^2 - 2D + 2)y = 0.$

4. $(D^2 + 9)y = 0$. Verify your answer.   ANS. $y = c_1 \cos 3x + c_2 \sin 3x.$

5. $(D^2 - 9)y = 0.$ ANS. $y = c_1 \cosh 3x + c_2 \sinh 3x.$

6. $(D^2 + 4D + 5)y = 0$. Verify your answer.

7. $(D^2 - 6D + 25)y = 0.$ ANS. $y = e^{3x}(c_1 \cos 4x + c_2 \sin 4x).$

8. $(D^3 + D^2 + 4D + 4)y = 0$. Verify your answer.

9. $(D^2 - 1)y = 0$; when $x = 0$, $y = y_0$ and $y' = 0$.

ANS. $y = y_0 \cosh x.$

10. $(D^2 + 1)y = 0$; when $x = 0$, $y = y_0$ and $y' = 0$.   ANS. $y = y_0 \cos x.$

11. $(D^4 + 2D^3 - 11D^2 - 52D)y = 0.$

12. $(D^3 + 5D^2 + 17D + 13)y = 0$;   when $x = 0$, $y = 0$, $y' = 1$,   and $y'' = 6$.   ANS. $y = e^{-x} - e^{-2x} \cos 3x.$

13. $(D^5 - 2D^3 - 2D^2 - 3D - 2)y = 0.$
14. $(D^4 - 2D^3 + 2D^2 - 2D + 1)y = 0.$ Verify your answer.
15. $(D^4 + 18D^2 + 81)y = 0.$

ANS. $y = (c_1 + c_2 x) \cos 3x + (c_3 + c_4 x) \sin 3x.$

16. $(2D^4 + 11D^3 - 4D^2 - 69D + 34)y = 0.$ Verify your answer.
17. $(D^6 + 6D^4 + 9D^2 + 4)y = 0.$
18. $(16D^3 - 11D - 5)y = 0.$
19. $\dfrac{d^2x}{dt^2} + k^2x = 0,$ k real; when $t = 0,$ $x = 0$ and $\dfrac{dx}{dt} = v_0.$ Verify your

result completely. ANS. $x = (v_0/k) \sin kt.$

20. $(D^3 + D^2 + 4D + 4)y = 0;$ when $x = 0,$ $y = 0,$ $y' = -1,$ and $y'' = 5.$

ANS. $y = e^{-x} - \cos 2x.$

21. $\dfrac{d^2x}{dt^2} + 2b\dfrac{dx}{dt} + k^2x = 0,$ $k > b > 0;$ when $t = 0,$ $x = 0$ and $\dfrac{dx}{dt} = v_0.$

ANS. $x = (v_0/a)e^{-bt} \sin at,$ where $a = \sqrt{k^2 - b^2}.$

Miscellaneous Exercises

Obtain the general solution unless otherwise instructed. Your answer can be checked by direct substitution.

1. $(9D^4 + 6D^3 + D^2)y = 0.$
2. $(4D^3 - 13D + 6)y = 0.$
3. $(D^3 + 2D^2 - 15D)y = 0.$
4. $(D^3 + 2D^2 + D + 2)y = 0.$
5. $(D^3 - 2D^2 - 3D)y = 0.$
6. $(D^3 + 3D^2 - 4)y = 0.$
7. $(4D^3 - 27D + 27)y = 0.$
8. $(10D^3 + D^2 - 7D + 2)y = 0.$
9. $(D^3 + 7D^2 + 19D + 13)y = 0;$ when $x = 0,$ $y = 0,$ $y' = 2,$ and $y'' = -12.$
10. $(D^2 - D - 6)y = 0;$ when $x = 0,$ $y = 2$ and $y' = 1.$
11. $(D^4 + 6D^3 + 9D^2)y = 0;$ when $x = 0,$ $y = 0,$ $y' = 0,$ and $y'' = 6,$ and as $x \to \infty,$ $y' \to 1.$ For this particular solution, find the value of y when $x = 1.$ ANS. $y = 1 - e^{-3}.$
12. $(D^3 + 6D^2 + 12D + 8)y = 0;$ when $x = 0,$ $y = 1,$ $y' = -2,$ and $y'' = 2.$
13. $(D^3 + 3D^2 + 3D + 1)y = 0.$
14. $(D^4 - 2D^3 - 13D^2 + 38D - 24)y = 0.$
15. $(D^6 + 9D^4 + 24D^2 + 16)y = 0.$
16. $(8D^3 - 4D^2 - 2D + 1)y = 0.$

17. $(D^4 + D^3 - 4D^2 - 4D)y = 0.$
18. $(D^4 - 2D^3 + 5D^2 - 8D + 4)y = 0.$
19. $(D^4 + 2D^2 + 1)y = 0.$
20. $(D^4 + 5D^2 + 4)y = 0.$
21. $(D^4 + 3D^3 - 4D)y = 0.$
22. $(D^5 + D^4 - 9D^3 - 13D^2 + 8D + 12)y = 0.$
23. $(D^4 - 11D^3 + 36D^2 - 16D - 64)y = 0.$
24. $(D^2 + 2D + 5)y = 0.$
25. $(D^4 + 4D^3 + 2D^2 - 8D - 8)y = 0.$
26. $(4D^4 - 24D^3 + 35D^2 + 6D - 9)y = 0.$
27. $(4D^4 + 20D^3 + 35D^2 + 25D + 6)y = 0.$
28. $(D^4 - 7D^3 + 11D^2 + 5D - 14)y = 0.$
29. $(D^3 + 5D^2 + 7D + 3)y = 0.$
30. $(D^3 - 2D^2 + D - 2)y = 0.$
31. $(D^3 - D^2 + D - 1)y = 0.$
32. $(D^3 + 4D^2 + 5D)y = 0.$
33. $(D^4 - 13D^2 + 36)y = 0.$
34. $(D^4 - 5D^3 + 5D^2 + 5D - 6)y = 0.$
35. $(4D^3 + 8D^2 - 11D + 3)y = 0.$
36. $(D^3 + D^2 - 16D - 16)y = 0.$
37. $(D^4 - D^3 - 3D^2 + D + 2)y = 0.$
38. $(D^3 - 2D^2 - 3D + 10)y = 0.$
39. $(D^5 + D^4 - 6D^3)y = 0.$
40. $(4D^3 + 28D^2 + 61D + 37)y = 0.$
41. $(4D^3 + 12D^2 + 13D + 10)y = 0.$
42. $(18D^3 - 33D^2 + 20D - 4)y = 0.$
43. $(4D^4 - 15D^2 + 5D + 6)y = 0.$
44. $(D^5 + D^4 - 7D^3 - 11D^2 - 8D - 12)y = 0.$
45. $(D^4 + 3D^3 - 6D^2 - 28D - 24)y = 0.$
46. $(4D^4 - 4D^3 - 23D^2 + 12D + 36)y = 0.$
47. $(4D^5 - 23D^3 - 33D^2 - 17D - 3)y = 0.$

CHAPTER 9

Nonhomogeneous Equations:

Undetermined Coefficients

44. Construction of a homogeneous equation from a specified solution

In Section 34 we saw that the general solution of the equation

(1) $$(b_0D^n + b_1D^{n-1} + \cdots + b_{n-1}D + b_n)y = R(x)$$

is

$$y = y_c + y_p,$$

where y_c, the complementary function, is the general solution of the homogeneous equation

(2) $$(b_0D^n + b_1D^{n-1} + \cdots + b_{n-1}D + b_n)y = 0$$

and y_p is any particular solution of the original equation (1).

Various methods for getting a particular solution of (1) when the b_0, b_1, $\cdots$, b_n are constants will be presented. In preparation for the method of undetermined coefficients it is wise to obtain proficiency in writing a homogeneous differential equation of which a given relation of proper form is a solution.

127

Recall that in solutions of homogeneous equations with constant coefficients, a term such as $c_1 e^{ax}$ occurred only when the auxiliary equation $f(m) = 0$ had a root $m = a$, and then the operator $f(D)$ had a factor $(D - a)$. In like manner, $c_2 x e^{ax}$ appeared only when $f(D)$ contained the factor $(D - a)^2$, $c_3 x^2 e^{ax}$ only when $f(D)$ contained $(D - a)^3$, etc. Such terms as $ce^{ax} \cos bx$ or $ce^{ax} \sin bx$ correspond to roots $m = a \pm ib$, or to a factor $[(D - a)^2 + b^2]$.

EXAMPLE (a): Find a homogeneous linear equation, with constant coefficients, which has as a particular solution

$$y = 7e^{3x} + 2x.$$

First note that the coefficients (7 and 2) are quite irrelevant for the present problem, so long as they are not zero. We shall obtain an equation satisfied by $y = c_1 e^{3x} + c_2 x$, no matter what the constants c_1 and c_2 may be.

A term $c_1 e^{3x}$ occurs along with a root $m = 3$ of the auxiliary equation. The term $c_2 x$ will appear if the auxiliary equation has $m = 0, 0$; that is, a double root $m = 0$. We have recognized that the equation

$$D^2(D - 3)y = 0,$$

or

$$(D^3 - 3D^2)y = 0,$$

has $y = c_1 e^{3x} + c_2 x + c_3$ as its general solution, and therefore that it also has $y = 7e^{3x} + 2x$ as a particular solution.

EXAMPLE (b): Find a homogeneous linear equation with real, constant coefficients that is satisfied by

(3) $y = 6 + 3xe^x - \cos x.$

The term 6 is associated with $m = 0$, the term $3xe^x$ with a double root $m = 1, 1$, and the term $(- \cos x)$ with the pair of imaginary roots $m = 0 \pm i$. Hence the auxiliary equation is

$$m(m - 1)^2(m^2 + 1) = 0,$$

or

$$m^5 - 2m^4 + 2m^3 - 2m^2 + m = 0.$$

Therefore the relation (3) is a solution of the differential equation

(4) $(D^5 - 2D^4 + 2D^3 - 2D^2 + D)y = 0.$

That is, from the general solution

$$y = c_1 + (c_2 + c_3 x)e^x + c_4 \cos x + c_5 \sin x$$

of equation (4), the relation (3) follows by an appropriate choice of the constants: $c_1 = 6$, $c_2 = 0$, $c_3 = 3$, $c_4 = -1$, $c_5 = 0$.

EXAMPLE (c): Find a homogeneous linear equation with real, constant coefficients which is satisfied by

$$y = 4xe^x \sin 2x.$$

The desired equation must have its auxiliary equation with roots $m = 1 \pm 2i$, $1 \pm 2i$. The roots $m = 1 \pm 2i$ correspond to factors $(m - 1)^2 + 4$, so the auxiliary equation must be

$$[(m - 1)^2 + 4]^2 = 0,$$

or

$$m^4 - 4m^3 + 14m^2 - 20m + 25 = 0.$$

Hence the desired equation is

$$(D^4 - 4D^3 + 14D^2 - 20D + 25)y = 0.$$

Note that in all such problems, a correct (but undesirable) solution may be obtained by inserting additional roots of the auxiliary equation.

Oral Exercises

In Exs. 1–14, obtain in factored form a linear differential equation, with real, constant coefficients and which is satisfied by the given relation.

1. $y = 4e^{2x} + 3e^{-x}$.　　　　　　　　ANS.　$(D - 2)(D + 1)y = 0$.
2. $y = 7 - 2x + \frac{1}{2}e^{4x}$.　　　　　　ANS.　$D^2(D - 4)y = 0$.
3. $y = -2x + \frac{1}{2}e^{4x}$.　　　　　　ANS.　$D^2(D - 4)y = 0$.
4. $y = x^2 - 5 \sin 3x$.　　　　　　　ANS.　$D^3(D^2 + 9)y = 0$.
5. $y = 2e^x \cos 3x$.

ANS.　$(D - 1 - 3i)(D - 1 + 3i)y = 0$; or $[(D - 1)^2 + 9]y = 0$; or
$$(D^2 - 2D + 10)y = 0.$$

6. $y = x^2 + 4e^x$.
7. $y = 3xe^x - 2e^{-x}$.
8. $y = 6 + 2e^{3x}$.
9. $y = 2x^2 + 1$.
10. $y = \sin 2x$.
11. $y = \sin 2x + 3 \cos 2x$.
12. $y = \cos kx$.

13. $y = x \sin 2x$.

14. $y = 2 \sinh x$.

In Exs. 15–36, state the roots of the auxiliary equation for a homogeneous linear equation with real, constant coefficients and having the given relation as a particular solution.

15. $y = 3xe^{2x}$.   ANS. $m = 2, 2$.

16. $y = x^2e^{-x} + 4e^x$.   ANS. $m = -1, -1, -1, 1$.

17. $y = e^{-x} \cos 4x$.   ANS. $m = -1 \pm 4i$.

18. $y = 3e^{-x} \cos 4x + 15e^{-x} \sin 4x$.   ANS. $m = -1 \pm 4i$.

19. $y = x(e^{2x} + 4)$.   ANS. $m = 0, 0, 2, 2$.

20. $y = 3 + 8e^{-2x}$.

21. $y = 2x^2 - e^{-3x}$.

22. $y = 4 + 2x^2 - e^{-3x}$.

23. $y = xe^x$.

24. $y = xe^x + 5e^x$.

25. $y = 4 \cos 2x$.

26. $y = 4 \cos 2x - 3 \sin 2x$.

27. $y = x \cos 2x - 3 \sin 2x$.

28. $y = x \cos 2x$.

29. $y = e^{-2x} \cos 3x$.

30. $y = e^{-2x}(\cos 3x + \sin 3x)$.

31. $y = x^2 - x + e^{-x}(x + \cos x)$.

32. $y = x^2 \sin x$.

33. $y = x^2 \sin x + x \cos x$.

34. $y = 8 \cos 4x + \sin 3x$.

35. $y = \sin^3 x$. Use the fact that $\sin^3 x = \frac{1}{4}(3 \sin x - \sin 3x)$.

36. $y = \cos^2 x$.

45. Solution of a nonhomogeneous equation

Before proceeding to the theoretical basis and the actual working technique of the useful method of undetermined coefficients, let us examine the underlying ideas as applied to a simple numerical example.

Consider the equation

(1) $$D^2(D - 1)y = 3e^x + \sin x.$$

The complementary function may be determined at once from the roots

(2) $$m = 0, 0, 1$$

of the auxiliary equation. The complementary function is

(3) $y_c = c_1 + c_2 x + c_3 e^x.$

Since the general solution of (1) is

$$y = y_c + y_p$$

where y_c is as given in (3) and y_p is any particular solution of (1), all that remains for us to do is to find a particular solution of (1).

The right-hand member of (1),

(4) $R(x) = 3e^x + \sin x,$

is a particular solution of a homogeneous linear differential equation whose auxiliary equation has the roots

(5) $m' = 1, \pm i.$

Therefore the relation (4) is a particular solution of the equation

(6) $(D - 1)(D^2 + 1)R = 0.$

We wish to convert (1) into a homogeneous linear differential equation with constant coefficients, because we know how to solve any such equation. But, by (6), the operator $(D - 1)(D^2 + 1)$ will annihilate the right member of (1). Therefore, we apply that operator to both sides of equation (1) and get

(7) $(D - 1)(D^2 + 1)D^2(D - 1)y = 0.$

Any solution of (1) must be a particular solution of (7). The general solution of (7) can be written at once from the roots of its auxiliary equation, those roots being the values $m = 0, 0, 1$ from (2) and the values $m' = 1, \pm i$ from (5). Thus the general solution of (7) is

(8) $y = c_1 + c_2 x + c_3 e^x + c_4 x e^x + c_5 \cos x + c_6 \sin x.$

But the desired general solution of (1) is

(9) $y = y_c + y_p,$

where

$$y_c = c_1 + c_2 x + c_3 e^x,$$

the c_1, c_2, c_3 being arbitrary constants as in (8). Thus there must exist a particular solution of (1) containing at most the remaining terms in (8). Using different letters as coefficients to emphasize that they are not arbitrary, we conclude that (1) has a particular solution

(10) $$y_p = Axe^x + B \cos x + C \sin x.$$

We now have only to determine the numerical coefficients A, B, C by direct use of the original equation

(1) $$D^2(D - 1)y = 3e^x + \sin x.$$

From (10) it follows that

$$Dy_p = A(xe^x + e^x) - B \sin x + C \cos x,$$

$$D^2y_p = A(xe^x + 2e^x) - B \cos x - C \sin x,$$

$$D^3y_p = A(xe^x + 3e^x) + B \sin x - C \cos x.$$

Substitution of y_p into (1) then yields

(11) $$Ae^x + (B + C) \sin x + (B - C) \cos x = 3e^x + \sin x.$$

Since (11) is to be an identity and since e^x, $\sin x$, and $\cos x$ are linearly independent, the corresponding coefficients in the two members of (11) must be equal; that is,

$$A = 3$$
$$B + C = 1$$
$$B - C = 0.$$

Therefore $A = 3$, $B = \frac{1}{2}$, $C = \frac{1}{2}$. Returning to (10), we find that a particular solution of equation (1) is

$$y_p = 3xe^x + \tfrac{1}{2} \cos x + \tfrac{1}{2} \sin x.$$

The general solution of the original equation

(1) $$D^2(D - 1)y = 3e^x + \sin x$$

is therefore obtained by adding to the complementary function the y_p found above:

(12) $$y = c_1 + c_2x + c_3e^x + 3xe^x + \tfrac{1}{2} \cos x + \tfrac{1}{2} \sin x.$$

A careful analysis of the ideas behind the process used shows that to arrive at the solution (12), we need perform only the following steps:

(a) From (1) find the values of m and m' as exhibited in (2) and (5);
(b) From the values of m and m' write y_c and y_p as in (3) and (10);
(c) Substitute y_p into (1), equate corresponding coefficients, and obtain the numerical values of the coefficients in y_p;
(d) Write the general solution of (1).

46. The method of undetermined coefficients

Let us examine the general problem of the type treated in the preceding section. Let $f(D)$ be a polynomial in the operator D. Consider the equation

$$(1) \qquad\qquad f(D)y = R(x).$$

Let the roots of the auxiliary equation $f(m) = 0$ be

$$(2) \qquad\qquad m = m_1, m_2, \cdots, m_n.$$

The general solution of (1) is

$$(3) \qquad\qquad y = y_c + y_p$$

where y_c can be obtained at once from the values of m in (2) and where $y = y_p$ is any particular solution (yet to be obtained) of (1).

Now suppose that the right member $R(x)$ of (1) is itself a particular solution of some homogeneous linear differential equation with constant coefficients,

$$(4) \qquad\qquad g(D)R = 0,$$

whose auxiliary equation has the roots

$$(5) \qquad\qquad m' = m_1', m_2', \cdots, m_k'.$$

Recall that the values of m' in (5) can be obtained by inspection from $R(x)$.

The differential equation

$$(6) \qquad\qquad g(D)f(D)y = 0$$

has as the roots of its auxiliary equation the values of m from (2) and m' from (5). Hence the general solution of (6) contains the y_c of (3) and so is of the form

$$y = y_c + y_q.$$

But also any particular solution of (1) must satisfy (6). Now, if

$$f(D)(y_c + y_q) = R(x),$$

then $f(D)y_q = R(x)$ because $f(D)y_c = 0$. Then deleting the y_c from the general solution of (6) leaves a function y_q which for some numerical values of its coefficients must satisfy (1); that is, the coefficients in y_q can be determined so that $y_q = y_p$. The determination of those numerical coefficients may be accomplished as in the examples below.

It must be kept in mind that the method of this section is applicable when, and only when, the right member of the equation is itself a particular solution of some homogeneous linear differential equation with constant coefficients. Methods which apply to equations with less restricted right-hand members will be studied in Chapter 16.

EXAMPLE (a): Solve the equation

$$(7) \qquad\qquad (D^2 + D - 2)y = 2x - 40 \cos 2x.$$

Here we have

$$m = 1, -2$$

and

$$m' = 0, 0, \pm 2i.$$

Therefore we may write

$$y_c = c_1 e^x + c_2 e^{-2x},$$

$$y_p = A + Bx + C \cos 2x + E \sin 2x,$$

in which c_1 and c_2 are arbitrary constants, while A, B, C, and E are to be determined numerically so y_p will satisfy the equation (7).

Since

$$Dy_p = B - 2C \sin 2x + 2E \cos 2x$$

and

$$D^2 y_p = -4C \cos 2x - 4E \sin 2x,$$

direct substitution of y_p into (7) yields

$$(8) \quad -4C \cos 2x - 4E \sin 2x + B - 2C \sin 2x + 2E \cos 2x - 2A$$

$$-2Bx - 2C \cos 2x - 2E \sin 2x = 2x - 40 \cos 2x.$$

But (8) is to be an identity in x, so we must equate coefficients of each of the set of linearly independent functions $\cos 2x$, $\sin 2x$, x, 1 appearing in the identity. Thus it follows that

$$-6C + 2E = -40,$$

$$-6E - 2C = 0,$$

$$-2B = 2,$$

$$B - 2A = 0.$$

The above equations determine A, B, C, and E. Indeed, they lead to

$$A = -\tfrac{1}{2}, \qquad C = 6,$$

$$B = -1, \qquad E = -2.$$

Since the general solution of (7) is $y = y_c + y_p$, we can now write the desired result,

$$y = c_1 e^x + c_2 e^{-2x} - \tfrac{1}{2} - x + 6 \cos 2x - 2 \sin 2x.$$

EXAMPLE (b): Solve the equation

$$(9) \qquad\qquad (D^2 + 1)y = \sin x.$$

At once $m = \pm i$ and $m' = \pm i$. Therefore

$$y_c = c_1 \cos x + c_2 \sin x,$$

$$y_p = Ax \cos x + Bx \sin x.$$

Now

$$y_p'' = A(-x \cos x - 2 \sin x) + B(-x \sin x + 2 \cos x),$$

so the requirement that y_p satisfy equation (9) yields

$$-2A \sin x + 2B \cos x = \sin x,$$

from which $A = -\tfrac{1}{2}$ and $B = 0$.

The general solution of (9) is

$$y = c_1 \cos x + c_2 \sin x - \tfrac{1}{2} x \cos x.$$

EXAMPLE (c): Determine y so that it will satisfy the equation

$$(10) \qquad\qquad y''' - y' = 4e^{-x} + 3e^{2x}$$

with the conditions that when $x = 0$, $y = 0$, $y' = -1$, and $y'' = 2$.

First we note that $m = 0, 1, -1$, and $m' = -1, 2$. Thus

$$y_c = c_1 + c_2 e^x + c_3 e^{-x},$$

$$y_p = Axe^{-x} + Be^{2x}.$$

Now

$$y_p' = A(-xe^{-x} + e^{-x}) + 2Be^{2x},$$

$$y_p'' = A(xe^{-x} - 2e^{-x}) + 4Be^{2x},$$

$$y_p''' = A(-xe^{-x} + 3e^{-x}) + 8Be^{2x}.$$

Then

$$y_p''' - y_p' = 2Ae^{-x} + 6Be^{2x},$$

so that from (10) we may conclude that $A = 2$ and $B = \tfrac{1}{2}$.

The general solution of (10) is therefore

$$(11) \qquad\qquad y = c_1 + c_2 e^x + c_3 e^{-x} + 2xe^{-x} + \tfrac{1}{2} e^{2x}.$$

We must determine c_1, c_2, c_3 so (11) will satisfy the conditions that when $x = 0$, $y = 0$, $y' = -1$, and $y'' = 2$.

From (11) it follows that

(12) $$y' = c_2 e^x - c_3 e^{-x} - 2xe^{-x} + 2e^{-x} + e^{2x}$$

and

(13) $$y'' = c_2 e^x + c_3 e^{-x} + 2xe^{-x} - 4e^{-x} + 2e^{2x}.$$

We put $x = 0$ in each of (11), (12), and (13) to get the equations for the determination of c_1, c_2, and c_3. These are

$$0 = c_1 + c_2 + c_3 + \tfrac{1}{2},$$
$$-1 = c_2 - c_3 + 3,$$
$$2 = c_2 + c_3 - 2,$$

from which $c_1 = -\tfrac{9}{2}$, $c_2 = 0$, $c_3 = 4$. Therefore, the final result is

$$y = -\tfrac{9}{2} + 4e^{-x} + 2xe^{-x} + \tfrac{1}{2}e^{2x}.$$

An important point, sometimes overlooked by students, is that it is the general solution, the y of (11), that must be made to satisfy the boundary conditions.

Exercises

In Exs. 1–35, obtain the general solution.

1. $(D^2 + D)y = -\cos x$.   ANS. $y = c_1 + c_2 e^{-x} + \tfrac{1}{2}\cos x - \tfrac{1}{2}\sin x$.
2. $(D^2 - 6D + 9)y = e^x$.   ANS. $y = (c_1 + c_2 x)e^{3x} + \tfrac{1}{4}e^x$.
3. $(D^2 + 3D + 2)y = 12x^2$.
    ANS. $y = c_1 e^{-x} + c_2 e^{-2x} + 6x^2 - 18x + 21$.
4. $(D^2 + 3D + 2)y = 1 + 3x + x^2$.   ANS. $y = c_1 e^{-x} + c_2 e^{-2x} + \tfrac{1}{2}x^2$.
5. $(D^2 + 9)y = 5e^x - 162x$.
    ANS. $y = c_1 \cos 3x + c_2 \sin 3x + \tfrac{1}{2}e^x - 18x$.
6. $(D^2 + 9)y = 5e^x - 162x^2$.
    ANS. $y = c_1 \cos 3x + c_2 \sin 3x + \tfrac{1}{2}e^x - 18x^2 + 4$.
7. $y'' - 3y' - 4y = 30e^x$.   ANS. $y = c_1 e^{4x} + c_2 e^{-x} - 5e^x$.
8. $y'' - 3y' - 4y = 30e^{4x}$.   ANS. $y = (c_1 + 6x)e^{4x} + c_2 e^{-x}$.
9. $(D^2 - 4)y = e^{2x} + 2$.   ANS. $y = c_1 e^{-2x} + (c_2 + \tfrac{1}{4}x)e^{2x} - \tfrac{1}{2}$.
10. $(D^2 - D - 2)y = 6x + 6e^{-x}$.
    ANS. $y = c_1 e^{-x} + c_2 e^{2x} - 3x + 3/2 - 2xe^{-x}$.
11. $y'' - 4y' + 3y = 20\cos x$.
    ANS. $y = c_1 e^x + c_2 e^{3x} + 2\cos x - 4\sin x$.

12. $y'' - 4y' + 3y = 2 \cos x + 4 \sin x$. ANS. $y = c_1 e^x + c_2 e^{3x} + \cos x$.

13. $y'' + 2y' + y = 7 + 75 \sin 2x$.

ANS. $y = e^{-x}(c_1 + c_2 x) + 7 - 12 \cos 2x - 9 \sin 2x$.

14. $(D^2 + 4D + 5)y = 50x + 13e^{3x}$.

ANS. $y = e^{-2x}(c_1 \cos x + c_2 \sin x) + 10x - 8 + \frac{1}{2}e^{3x}$.

15. $(D^2 + 1)y = \cos x$. ANS. $y = c_1 \cos x + c_2 \sin x + \frac{1}{2}x \sin x$.

16. $(D^2 - 4D + 4)y = e^{2x}$. ANS. $y = e^{2x}(c_1 + c_2 x + \frac{1}{2}x^2)$.

17. $(D^2 - 1)y = e^{-x}(2 \sin x + 4 \cos x)$.

18. $(D^2 - 1)y = 8xe^x$. ANS. $y = c_1 e^{-x} + e^x(c_2 - 2x + 2x^2)$.

19. $(D^3 - D)y = x$. ANS. $y = c_1 + c_2 e^x + c_3 e^{-x} - \frac{1}{2}x^2$.

20. $(D^3 - D^2 + D - 1)y = 4 \sin x$.

ANS. $y = c_1 e^x + (c_2 + x) \cos x + (c_3 - x) \sin x$.

21. $(D^3 + D^2 - 4D - 4)y = 3e^{-x} - 4x - 6$.

ANS. $y = c_1 e^{2x} + c_2 e^{-2x} + (c_3 - x)e^{-x} + x + \frac{1}{2}$.

22. $(D^4 - 1)y = 7x^2$.

23. $(D^4 - 1)y = e^{-x}$.

ANS. $y = c_1 e^x + (c_2 - \frac{1}{4}x)e^{-x} + c_3 \cos x + c_4 \sin x$.

24. $(D^2 - 1)y = 10 \sin^2 x$. Use the identity $\sin^2 x = \frac{1}{2}(1 - \cos 2x)$.

ANS. $y = c_1 e^x + c_2 e^{-x} - 5 + \cos 2x$.

25. $(D^2 + 1)y = 12 \cos^2 x$.

ANS. $y = c_1 \cos x + c_2 \sin x + 6 - 2 \cos 2x$.

26. $(D^2 + 4)y = 4 \sin^2 x$.

ANS. $y = c_1 \cos 2x + c_2 \sin 2x + \frac{1}{2}(1 - x \sin 2x)$.

27. $y'' - 3y' - 4y = 16x - 50 \cos 2x$.

28. $(D^3 - 3D - 2)y = 100 \sin 2x$.

29. $y'' + 4y' + 3y = 15e^{2x} + e^{-x}$.

30. $y'' - y = e^x - 4$.

31. $y'' - y' - 2y = 6x + 6e^{-x}$.

32. $y'' + 6y' + 13y = 60 \cos x + 26$.

33. $(D^3 - 3D^2 + 4)y = 6 + 80 \cos 2x$.

34. $(D^3 + D - 10)y = 29e^{4x}$.

35. $(D^3 + D^2 - 4D - 4)y = 8x + 8 + 6e^{-x}$.

In Exs. 36–44, find the particular solution indicated.

36. $(D^2 + 1)y = 10e^{2x}$; when $x = 0$, $y = 0$ and $y' = 0$.

ANS. $y = 2(e^{2x} - \cos x - 2 \sin x)$.

37. $(D^2 - 4)y = 2 - 8x$; when $x = 0$, $y = 0$ and $y' = 5$.

ANS. $y = e^{2x} - \frac{1}{2}e^{-2x} + 2x - \frac{1}{2}$.

38. $(D^2 + 3D)y = -18x$; when $x = 0$, $y = 0$ and $y' = 5$.

ANS. $y = 1 + 2x - 3x^2 - e^{-3x}$.

39. $(D^2 + 4D + 5)y = 10e^{-3x}$; when $x = 0$, $y = 4$ and $y' = 0$.

40. $\dfrac{d^2x}{dt^2} + 4\dfrac{dx}{dt} + 5x = 10$; when $t = 0$, $x = 0$ and $\dfrac{dx}{dt} = 0$.

> ANS. $x = 2(1 - e^{-2t}\cos t - 2e^{-2t}\sin t)$.

41. $\ddot{x} + 4\dot{x} + 5x = 8\sin t$; when $t = 0$, $x = 0$ and $\dot{x} = 0$. Note that $\dot{x} = \dfrac{dx}{dt}$, $\ddot{x} = \dfrac{d^2x}{dt^2}$ is a common notation when the independent variable is time.*

> ANS. $x = (1 + e^{-2t})\sin t - (1 - e^{-2t})\cos t$.

42. $y'' + 9y = 81x^2 + 14\cos 4x$; when $x = 0$, $y = 0$ and $y' = 3$.

43. $(D^3 + 4D^2 + 9D + 10)y = -24e^x$; when $x = 0$, $y = 0$, $y' = -4$ and $y'' = 10$.

44. $y'' + 2y' + 5y = 8e^{-x}$; when $x = 0$, $y = 0$ and $y' = 8$.

In Exs. 45–48, obtain from the particular solution indicated the value of y and the value of y' at $x = 2$.

45. $y'' + 2y' + y = x$; at $x = 0$, $y = -3$, and at $x = 1$, $y = -1$.

> ANS. At $x = 2$, $y = e^{-2}$ and $y' = 1$.

46. $y'' + 2y' + y = x$; at $x = 0$, $y = -2$ and $y' = 2$.

> ANS. At $x = 2$, $y = 2e^{-2}$ and $y' = 1 - e^{-2}$.

47. $4y'' + y = 2$; at $x = \pi$, $y = 0$ and $y' = 1$.

> ANS. At $x = 2$, $y = -0.7635$ and $y' = +0.3012$.

48. $2y'' - 5y' - 3y = -9x^2 - 1$; at $x = 0$, $y = 1$ and $y' = 0$.

> ANS. At $x = 2$, $y = 5.64$ and $y' = 5.68$.

49. $(D^2 + D)y = x + 1$; when $x = 0$, $y = 1$, and when $x = 1$, $y = \frac{1}{2}$. Compute the value of y at $x = 4$.

> ANS. At $x = 4$, $y = 8 - e^{-1} - e^{-2} - e^{-3}$.

50. $(D^2 + 1)y = x^3$; when $x = 0$, $y = 0$, and when $x = \pi$, $y = 0$. Show that this boundary value problem has no solution.

51. $(D^2 + 1)y = 2\cos x$; when $x = 0$, $y = 0$, and when $x = \pi$, $y = 0$. Show that this boundary value problem has an unlimited number of solutions and obtain them. ANS. $y = (c + x)\sin x$.

52. For the equation $(D^3 + D^2)y = 4$, find the solution whose graph has at the origin a point of inflection with a horizontal tangent line.

> ANS. $y = 4 - 4x + 2x^2 - 4e^{-x}$.

53. For the equation $(D^2 - D)y = 2 - 2x$, find a particular solution which has at some point (to be determined) on the x-axis an inflection point with a horizontal tangent line.

ANS. The point is $(1, 0)$; the solution is $y = x^2 + 1 - 2\exp(x - 1)$.

---

* The disadvantage of such a notation when derivatives of high order appear must be evident. Other objections can be raised; flies have been known to perform undesired differentiations.

47. Solution by inspection

It is frequently easy to obtain a particular solution of a non-homogeneous equation

$$(1) \qquad (b_0 D^n + b_1 D^{n-1} + \cdots + b_{n-1} D + b_n) y = R(x)$$

by inspection.

For example, if $R(x)$ is a constant R_0 and if $b_n \neq 0$,

$$(2) \qquad y_p = \frac{R_0}{b_n}$$

is a solution of

$$(3) \qquad (b_0 D^n + b_1 D^{n-1} + \cdots + b_n) y = R_0; \; b_n \neq 0, \; R_0 \text{ constant},$$

because all derivatives of y_p are zero, so

$$(b_0 D^n + b_1 D^{n-1} + \cdots + b_n) y_p = b_n R_0 / b_n = R_0.$$

Suppose that $b_n = 0$ in equation (3). Let $D^k y$ be the lowest-ordered derivative that actually appears in the differential equation. Then the equation may be written

$$(4) \qquad (b_0 D^n + \cdots + b_{n-k} D^k) y = R_0; \; b_{n-k} \neq 0, \; R_0 \text{ constant}.$$

Now $D^k x^k = k!$, a constant, so that all higher derivatives of x^k are zero. Thus it becomes evident that (4) has a solution

$$(5) \qquad y_p = \frac{R_0 x^k}{k! \, b_{n-k}},$$

for then $(b_0 D^n + \cdots + b_{n-k} D^k) y_p = b_{n-k} R_0 k! / (k! b_{n-k}) = R_0$.

EXAMPLE (a): Solve the equation

$$(6) \qquad (D^2 - 3D + 2) y = 16.$$

By the methods of Chapter 8 we obtain the complementary function,

$$y_c = c_1 e^x + c_2 e^{2x}.$$

By inspection a particular solution of the original equation is

$$y_p = \tfrac{16}{2} = 8.$$

Hence the general solution of (6) is

$$y = c_1 e^x + c_2 e^{2x} + 8.$$

EXAMPLE (b): Solve the equation

(7)
$$\frac{d^5y}{dx^5} + 4\frac{d^3y}{dx^3} = 7.$$

From the auxiliary equation $m^5 + 4m^3 = 0$ we get $m = 0, 0, 0, \pm 2i$. Hence

$$y_c = c_1 + c_2x + c_3x^2 + c_4\cos 2x + c_5\sin 2x.$$

A particular solution of (7) is

$$y_p = \frac{7x^3}{3!\cdot 4} = \frac{7x^3}{24}.$$

As a check, note that

$$(D^5 + 4D^3)\frac{7x^3}{24} = 0 + 4\cdot\frac{7\cdot 6}{24} = 7.$$

The general solution of equation (7) is

$$y = c_1 + c_2x + c_3x^2 + \tfrac{7}{24}x^3 + c_4\cos 2x + c_5\sin 2x,$$

in which the $c_1, \cdots, c_5$ are arbitrary constants.

Examination of

(8)
$$(D^2 + 4)y = \sin 3x$$

leads us to search for a solution proportional to $\sin 3x$, because if y is proportional to $\sin 3x$, so is D^2y. Indeed, from

(9)
$$y = A\sin 3x$$

we get

$$D^2y = -9A\sin 3x,$$

so (9) is a solution of (8) if

$$(-9 + 4)A = 1; A = -\tfrac{1}{5}.$$

Thus (8) has the general solution

$$y = c_1\cos 2x + c_2\sin 2x - \tfrac{1}{5}\sin 3x,$$

a result easily obtained mentally.

For equation (8), the general method of undetermined coefficients leads us to write

$$m = \pm 2i, m' = \pm 3i,$$

and so to write

(10)
$$y_p = A\sin 3x + B\cos 3x.$$

When the y_p of (10) is substituted into (8), it is found, of course, that

$$A = -1/5, B = 0.$$

In contrast, consider the equation

(11) $(D^2 + 4D + 4)y = \sin 3x.$

Here any attempt to find a solution proportional to $\sin 3x$ is doomed to failure because, although $D^2 y$ will also be proportional to $\sin 3x$, the term Dy will involve $\cos 3x$. There is no other term on either side of (11) to compensate for this cosine term, so no solution of the form $y = A \sin 3x$ is possible. For this equation, $m = -2, -2, m' = \pm 3i$, and in the particular solution

$$y_p = A \sin 3x + B \cos 3x,$$

it must turn out that $B \neq 0$. No labor has been saved by the inspection.

In more complicated situations such as

$$(D^2 + 4)y = x \sin 3x - 2 \cos 3x,$$

the method of inspection will save no work.

For the equation

(12) $(D^2 + 4)y = e^{5x},$

we see, since $(D^2 + 4)e^{5x} = 29e^{5x}$, that

$$y_p = \tfrac{1}{29}e^{5x}$$

is a solution.

Finally, note that if y_1 is a solution of

$$f(D)y = R_1(x)$$

and y_2 is a solution of

$$f(D)y = R_2(x),$$

then

$$y_p = y_1 + y_2$$

is a solution of

$$f(D)y = R_1(x) + R_2(x).$$

It follows readily that the task of obtaining a particular solution of

$$f(D)y = R(x)$$

may be split into parts by treating separate terms of $R(x)$ independently, if convenient. See the examples below. This is the basis of the "method of superposition" which plays a useful role in applied mathematics.

E XAMPLE (c): Find a particular solution of

(13) $$(D^2 - 9)y = 3e^x + x - \sin 4x.$$

Since $(D^2 - 9)e^x = -8e^x$, we see by inspection that

$$y_1 = -\tfrac{3}{8}e^x$$

is a particular solution of

$$(D^2 - 9)y_1 = 3e^x.$$

In a similar manner, we see that $y_2 = -\tfrac{1}{9}x$ satisfies

$$(D^2 - 9)y_2 = x$$

and that

$$y_3 = \tfrac{1}{25} \sin 4x$$

satisfies

$$(D^2 - 9)y_3 = - \sin 4x.$$

Hence

$$y_p = -\tfrac{3}{8}e^x - \tfrac{1}{9}x + \tfrac{1}{25} \sin 4x$$

is a solution of equation (13).

E XAMPLE (d): Find a particular solution of

(14) $$(D^2 + 4)y = \sin x + \sin 2x.$$

At once we see that $y_1 = \tfrac{1}{3} \sin x$ is a solution of

$$(D^2 + 4)y_1 = \sin x.$$

Then we seek a solution of

(15) $$(D^2 + 4)y_2 = \sin 2x$$

by the method of undetermined coefficients. Since $m = \pm 2i$ and

$$m' = \pm 2i,$$

we put

$$y_2 = Ax \sin 2x + Bx \cos 2x$$

into (15) and easily determine that

$$4A \cos 2x - 4B \sin 2x = \sin 2x,$$

from which $A = 0$, $B = -\tfrac{1}{4}$.

Thus a particular solution of (14) is

$$y_p = \tfrac{1}{3} \sin x - \tfrac{1}{4}x \cos 2x.$$

Exercises

1. Show that if $b \neq a$, then

$$(D^2 + a^2)y = \sin bx$$

has the particular solution $y = (a^2 - b^2)^{-1} \sin bx$.

2. Show that the equation

$$(D^2 + a^2)y = \sin ax$$

has no solution of the form $y = A \sin ax$, with A constant. Find a particular solution of the equation.   ANS. $y = -\dfrac{x}{2a} \cos ax$.

In Exs. 3–50, find a particular solution by inspection. Verify your solution.

3. $(D^2 + 4)y = 12$.

4. $(D^2 + 9)y = 18$.

5. $(D^2 + 4D + 4)y = 8$.

6. $(D^2 + 2D - 3)y = 6$.

7. $(D^3 - 3D + 2)y = -7$.

8. $(D^4 + 4D^2 + 4)y = -20$.

9. $(D^2 + 4D)y = 12$.

10. $(D^3 - 9D)y = 27$.

11. $(D^3 + D)y = 15$.

12. $(D^3 + D)y = -8$.

13. $(D^4 - 4D^2)y = 24$.

14. $(D^4 + D^2)y = -12$.

15. $(D^5 - D^3)y = 24$.

16. $(D^5 - 9D^3)y = 27$.

17. $(D^2 + 4)y = 6 \sin x$.   ANS. $y = 2 \sin x$.

18. $(D^2 + 4)y = 10 \cos 3x$.   ANS. $y = -2 \cos 3x$.

19. $(D^2 + 4)y = 8x + 1 - 15e^x$.   ANS. $y = 2x + \frac{1}{4} - 3e^x$.

20. $(D^2 + D)y = 6 + 3e^{2x}$.   ANS. $y = 6x + \frac{1}{2}e^{2x}$.

21. $(D^2 + 3D - 4)y = 18e^{2x}$.   ANS. $y = 3e^{2x}$.

22. $(D^2 + 2D + 5)y = 4e^x - 10$.   ANS. $y = \frac{1}{2}e^x - 2$.

23. $(D^2 - 1)y = 2e^{3x}$.

24. $(D^2 - 1)y = 2x + 3$.

25. $(D^2 - 1)y = \cos 2x$.

26. $(D^2 - 1)y = \sin 2x$.

27. $(D^2 + 1)y = e^x + 3x$.

28. $(D^2 + 1)y = 5e^{-3x}$.

29. $(D^2 + 1)y = -2x + \cos 2x$.

30. $(D^2 + 1)y = 4e^{-2x}$.

31. $(D^2 + 1)y = 10 \sin 4x$.

32. $(D^2 + 1)y = -6e^{-3x}$.

33. $(D^2 + 2D + 1)y = 12e^x$.

34. $(D^2 + 2D + 1)y = 7e^{-2x}$.

35. $(D^2 - 2D + 1)y = 12e^{-x}$.

36. $(D^2 - 2D + 1)y = 6e^{-2x}$.

37. $(D^2 - 2D - 3)y = e^x$.

38. $(D^2 - 2D - 3)y = e^{2x}$.

39. $(4D^2 + 1)y = 12 \sin x$.

40. $(4D^2 + 1)y = -12 \cos x$.

41. $(4D^2 + 4D + 1)y = 18e^x - 5$.

42. $(4D^2 + 4D + 1)y = 7e^{-x} + 2$.

43. $(D^3 - 1)y = e^{-x}$.

44. $(D^3 - 1)y = 4 - 3x^2$.

45. $(D^3 - D)y = e^{2x}$.

46. $(D^4 + 4)y = 5e^{2x}$.

47. $(D^4 + 4)y = 6 \sin 2x$.

48. $(D^4 + 4)y = \cos 2x$.

49. $(D^3 - D)y = 5 \sin 2x$.

50. $(D^3 - D)y = 5 \cos 2x$.

CHAPTER 10

Inverse Differential Operators

48. The exponential shift

Let $D \equiv d/dx$ as usual, and let $V(x)$ possess as many derivatives as may be encountered in the operations performed. Then

$$D[e^{-ax}V(x)] = e^{-ax}DV(x) - ae^{-ax}V(x)$$

$$= e^{-ax}(D - a)V(x).$$

Hence, operating with D again, we are led to

$$D^2[e^{-ax}V(x)] = D[e^{-ax}\{(D - a)V(x)\}]$$

$$= e^{-ax}(D - a)^2V(x).$$

Iteration of the process yields, for n any positive integer,

$$D^n[e^{-ax}V(x)] = e^{-ax}(D - a)^nV(x).$$

Using the linearity of differential operators, we conclude that when $f(D)$ is a polynomial in D with constant coefficients, then

(1) $$f(D)[e^{-ax}V(x)] = e^{-ax}f(D - a)V(x).$$

In equation (1), put $e^{-ax}V(x) = y$. Then (1) becomes

$$f(D)y = e^{-ax}f(D - a)[e^{ax}y],$$

or

144

(2) $$e^{ax}f(D)y = f(D - a)[e^{ax}y].$$

The relation (2) shows us how to shift an exponential factor from the left of a differential operator to the right of the operator. This relation has many uses, one of which is exhibited in the following examples.

EXAMPLE (a): Solve the equation

(3) $$(D^2 - 2D + 5)y = 16x^3e^{3x}.$$

Note that the complementary function is

(4) $$y_c = c_1e^x \cos 2x + c_2e^x \sin 2x.$$

We can conclude also that there is a particular solution,

(5) $$y_p = Ax^3e^{3x} + Bx^2e^{3x} + Cxe^{3x} + Ee^{3x},$$

which can be obtained by the method of Chapter 9. But the task of obtaining the derivatives of y_p and finding the numerical values of A, B, C, and E is a little tedious. It can be made easier by using the exponential shift (2).

Let us write (3) in the form

$$e^{-3x}(D^2 - 2D + 5)y = 16x^3,$$

and then apply the relation (2), with $a = -3$. In shifting the exponential e^{-3x} from the left to the right of the differential operator, we must replace D by $(D + 3)$ throughout, thus obtaining

$$[(D + 3)^2 - 2(D + 3) + 5](e^{-3x}y) = 16x^3,$$

or

(6) $$(D^2 + 4D + 8)(e^{-3x}y) = 16x^3.$$

In equation (6), the dependent variable is $(e^{-3x}y)$. We know at once that (6) has a particular solution of the form

(7) $$e^{-3x}y_p = Ax^3 + Bx^2 + Cx + E.$$

Successive differentiations of (7) are simple. Indeed,

$$D(e^{-3x}y_p) = 3Ax^2 + 2Bx + C,$$
$$D^2(e^{-3x}y_p) = 6Ax + 2B,$$

so from (6) we get

$$6Ax + 2B + 12Ax^2 + 8Bx + 4C + 8Ax^3 + 8Bx^2 + 8Cx + 8E = 16x^3.$$

Hence

$$8A = 16,$$
$$12A + 8B = 0,$$
$$6A + 8B + 8C = 0,$$
$$2B + 4C + 8E = 0,$$

from which $A = 2$, $B = -3$, $C = \frac{3}{2}$, $E = 0$.

Therefore

$$e^{-3x}y_p = 2x^3 - 3x^2 + \frac{3}{2}x,$$

or

$$y_p = (2x^3 - 3x^2 + \frac{3}{2}x)e^{3x},$$

and the general solution of the original equation (3) is

$$y = c_1e^x \cos 2x + c_2e^x \sin 2x + (2x^3 - 3x^2 + \frac{3}{2}x)e^{3x}.$$

The complementary function could also have been obtained from (6).

EXAMPLE (b): Solve the equation

(8) $$(D^2 - 2D + 1)y = xe^x + 7x - 2.$$

Here the immediate use of the exponential shift would do no good, because removing the e^x factor from the first term on the right would only insert a factor e^{-x} in the second and third terms on the right. The terms $7x - 2$ on the right give us no trouble as they stand. Therefore we break (8) into two problems, obtaining a particular solution for each of the equations

(9) $$(D^2 - 2D + 1)y_1 = xe^x$$

and

(10) $$(D^2 - 2D + 1)y_2 = 7x - 2.$$

On (9) we use the exponential shift, passing from

$$e^{-x}(D - 1)^2y_1 = x$$

to

(11) $$D^2(e^{-x}y_1) = x.$$

A particular solution of (11) is easily obtained:

$$e^{-x}y_1 = \frac{1}{6}x^3,$$

so

(12) $$y_1 = \frac{1}{6}x^3e^x.$$

Equation (10) is treated as in Chapter 9. Put

$$y_2 = Ax + B.$$

Then $Dy_2 = A$, and from (10) it is easily found that $A = 7$, $B = 12$. Thus a particular solution of (10) is

(13) $$y_2 = 7x + 12.$$

Using (12), (13), and the roots of the auxiliary equation for (8), the general solution of (8) can now be written. It is

$$y = (c_1 + c_2x)e^x + \tfrac{1}{6}x^3e^x + 7x + 12.$$

EXAMPLE (c): Solve the equation

(14) $$D^2(D + 4)^2y = 96e^{-4x}.$$

At once we have $m = 0, 0, -4, -4$ and $m' = -4$. We seek first a particular solution. Therefore we integrate each member of (14) twice before using the exponential shift. From (14) it follows that

(15) $$(D + 4)^2y_p = 6e^{-4x},$$

the constants of integration being disregarded because only a particular solution is sought. Equation (15) yields

$$e^{4x}(D + 4)^2y_p = 6,$$
$$D^2(y_pe^{4x}) = 6,$$
$$y_pe^{4x} = 3x^2,$$
$$y_p = 3x^2e^{-4x}.$$

Thus the general solution of (14) is seen to be

$$y = c_1 + c_2x + (c_3 + c_4x + 3x^2)e^{-4x}.$$

The exponential shift is particularly helpful when applied in connection with terms for which the values of m' (using the notations of Chapter 9) are repetitions of values of m.

Exercises

In Exs. 1–12, use the exponential shift to find a particular solution.

1. $(D - 3)^2y = e^{3x}$.   ANS. $y = \tfrac{1}{2}x^2e^{3x}$.
2. $(D - 1)^2y = e^x$.
3. $(D + 2)^2y = 12xe^{-2x}$.   ANS. $y = 2x^3e^{-2x}$.

4. $(D + 1)^2 y = 3xe^{-x}$.

5. $(D - 2)^3 y = 6xe^{2x}$.   ANS. $y = \frac{1}{4}x^4 e^{2x}$.

6. $(D + 4)^3 y = 8xe^{-4x}$.

7. $(D + 3)^3 y = 15x^2 e^{-3x}$.   ANS. $y = \frac{1}{4}x^5 e^{-3x}$.

8. $(D - 4)^3 y = 15x^2 e^{4x}$.

9. $D^2(D - 2)^2 y = 16e^{2x}$.   ANS. $y = 2x^2 e^{2x}$.

10. $D^2(D + 3)^2 y = 9e^{-3x}$.

11. $(D^2 - D - 2)y = 18xe^{-x}$.   ANS. $y = -(3x^2 + 2x)e^{-x}$.

12. $(D^2 - D - 2)y = 36xe^{2x}$.

In Exs. 13–18, find a particular solution, using the exponential shift in part of your work, as in Example (b) above.

13. $(D - 2)^2 y = 20 - 3xe^{2x}$.   ANS. $y = 5 - \frac{1}{2}x^3 e^{2x}$.

14. $(D - 2)^2 y = 4 - 8x + 6xe^{2x}$.

15. $y'' - 9y = 9(2x - 3 + 4xe^{3x})$.   ANS. $y = 3 - 2x + (3x^2 - x)e^{3x}$.

16. $y'' + 4y' + 4y = 4x - 6e^{-2x} + 3e^x$.

17. $(D + 1)^2 y = e^{-x} + 3x$.   ANS. $y = \frac{1}{2}x^2 e^{-x} + 3x - 6$.

18. $(D^2 - 4)y = 16xe^{-2x} + 8x + 4$.   ANS. $y = -(2x + 1)(xe^{-2x} + 1)$.

In Exs. 19–28, find the general solution.

19. $y'' - 4y = 8xe^{2x}$.   ANS. $y = c_1 e^{-2x} + (c_2 - \frac{1}{2}x + x^2)e^{2x}$.

20. $y'' - 9y = -72xe^{-3x}$.

21. $D(D + 1)^2 y = e^{-x}$.   ANS. $y = c_1 + (c_2 + c_3 x - \frac{1}{2}x^2)e^{-x}$.

22. $D^2(D - 2)^2 y = 2e^{2x}$.

23. $y'' + 2y' + y = 48e^{-x} \cos 4x$.   ANS. $y = (c_1 + c_2 x - 3 \cos 4x)e^{-x}$.

24. $y'' + 4y' + 4y = 18e^{-2x} \cos 3x$.

25. $(D - 1)^2 y = e^x \sec^2 x \tan x$.   ANS. $y = e^x(c_1 + c_2 x + \frac{1}{2} \tan x)$.

26. $(D^2 + 4D + 4)y = -x^{-2}e^{-2x}$.   ANS. $y = e^{-2x}(c_1 + c_2 x + \ln x)$.

27. $(D - a)^2 y = e^{ax} f''(x)$.   ANS. $y = e^{ax}[c_1 + c_2 x + f(x)]$.

28. $(D^2 + 7D + 12)y = e^{-3x} \sec^2 x(1 + 2 \tan x)$.

              ANS. $y = c_1 e^{-4x} + e^{-3x}(c_2 + \tan x)$.

49. The operator $1/f(D)$

In seeking a particular solution of

(1) $$f(D)y = R(x),$$

it is natural to write

(2) $$y = \frac{1}{f(D)} R(x)$$

and to try to define an operator $1/f(D)$ so that the function y of (2) will have meaning and will satisfy equation (1).

Instead of building a theory of such inverse differential operators, we shall adopt the following method of attack. Purely formal (unjustified) manipulations of the symbols will be performed, thus leading to a tentative evaluation of

$$\frac{1}{f(D)} R(x).$$

After all, the only thing which we require of our evaluation is that

(3) $$f(D) \cdot \frac{1}{f(D)} R(x) = R(x).$$

Hence the burden of proof will be placed on a direct verification of the condition (3) in each instance.

50. Evaluation of $[1/f(D)]e^{ax}$

We proved (pages 108–109) with slightly different notation that

(1) $$f(D)e^{ax} = e^{ax}f(a)$$

and

(2) $$(D - a)^n(x^n e^{ax}) = n!e^{ax}.$$

Equation (1) suggests

(3) $$\frac{1}{f(D)} e^{ax} = \frac{e^{ax}}{f(a)}, \quad f(a) \neq 0.$$

Now from (1) it follows that

$$f(D) \frac{e^{ax}}{f(a)} = \frac{f(a)e^{ax}}{f(a)} = e^{ax}.$$

Hence (3) is verified.

Now suppose that $f(a) = 0$. Then $f(D)$ contains the factor $(D - a)$. Suppose that the factor occurs precisely n times in $f(D)$; that is, let

$$f(D) = \varphi(D)(D - a)^n; \varphi(a) \neq 0.$$

With the aid of (2) we obtain

$$\varphi(D)(D - a)^n(x^n e^{ax}) = \varphi(D)n!e^{ax},$$

from which, by (1), it follows that

(4) $$\varphi(D)(D - a)^n(x^n e^{ax}) = n!\varphi(a)e^{ax}.$$

Therefore we write

(5) $$\frac{1}{\varphi(D)(D - a)^n}\, e^{ax} = \frac{x^n e^{ax}}{n!\varphi(a)}, \quad \varphi(a) \neq 0,$$

which is easily verified. Indeed,

$$\varphi(D)(D - a)^n \frac{x^n e^{ax}}{n!\varphi(a)} = \frac{n!\varphi(a)e^{ax}}{n!\varphi(a)} = e^{ax}.$$

Note that formula (3) is included in formula (5) as the special case, $n = 0$. See also Ex. 19, page 152.

EXAMPLE (a): Solve the equation

(6) $$(D^2 + 1)y = e^{2x}.$$

Here the roots of the auxiliary equation are $m = \pm i$. Further,

$$f(D) = (D^2 + 1)$$

and

$$f(2) \neq 0.$$

Hence, using (3),

$$y_p = \frac{1}{D^2 + 1}\, e^{2x} = \frac{e^{2x}}{2^2 + 1} = \frac{1}{5}e^{2x},$$

so the solution of (6) is

$$y = c_1 \cos x + c_2 \sin x + \frac{1}{5} e^{2x}.$$

EXAMPLE (b): Solve the equation

(7) $$D^2(D - 1)^3(D + 1)y = e^x.$$

Here $m = 0, 0, 1, 1, 1, -1$. To get a particular solution of (7), we use formula (5) with $a = 1$, $n = 3$, $\varphi(D) = D^2(D + 1)$. Then

$$\varphi(1) = 1^2 \cdot 2$$

and a particular solution of (7) is given by

$$y_p = \frac{1}{(D - 1)^3 D^2(D + 1)}\, e^x = \frac{x^3 e^x}{3!1^2 \cdot 2} = \frac{1}{12} x^3 e^x.$$

Then the general solution of (7) is

$$y = c_1 + c_2 x + c_3 e^{-x} + (c_4 + c_5 x + c_6 x^2 + \tfrac{1}{12}x^3)e^x.$$

51. Evaluation of $(D^2 + a^2)^{-1} \sin ax$ and $(D^2 + a^2)^{-1} \cos ax$

No special device is needed for the evaluation of

$$(D^2 + a^2)^{-1} \sin bx$$

when $b \neq a$. In fact

$$\frac{1}{D^2 + a^2} \sin bx = \frac{\sin bx}{a^2 - b^2} \; ; b \neq a,$$

as indicated in Ex. 1, page 143, and a similar result holds for the expression $(D^2 + a^2)^{-1} \cos bx$, when $b \neq a$.

Consider next the evaluation of

(1)
$$\frac{1}{D^2 + a^2} \sin ax.$$

The formulas of the preceding section can be put to good use here, since

$$\sin ax = \frac{e^{aix} - e^{-aix}}{2i} .$$

Then

$$\frac{1}{D^2 + a^2} \sin ax = \frac{1}{2i} \frac{1}{(D - ai)(D + ai)} (e^{aix} - e^{-aix})$$

$$= \frac{1}{2i} \left(\frac{xe^{aix}}{1!2ai} - \frac{xe^{-aix}}{1!(-2ai)} \right)$$

$$= -\frac{x}{2a} \frac{e^{aix} + e^{-aix}}{2} ,$$

so

(2)
$$\frac{1}{D^2 + a^2} \sin ax = -\frac{x}{2a} \cos ax.$$

The verification of (2) is left as an exercise.

Another useful result,

(3)
$$\frac{1}{D^2 + a^2} \cos ax = \frac{x}{2a} \sin ax,$$

can be obtained in the same way.

Oral Exercises

Give the general solution of each equation.

1. $(D^2 - 1)y = e^{2x}$.   ANS. $y = c_1 e^x + c_2 e^{-x} + \frac{1}{3}e^{2x}$.
2. $(D^2 - 1)y = e^x$.   ANS. $y = c_1 e^x + c_2 e^{-x} + \frac{1}{2}xe^x$.

3. $(D^2 + 1)y = \sin x.$ ANS. $y = c_1 \cos x + c_2 \sin x - \frac{1}{2}x \cos x.$
4. $(D^2 + 4)y = \cos 2x.$ ANS. $y = c_1 \cos 2x + c_2 \sin 2x + \frac{1}{4}x \sin 2x.$
5. $(D^2 + 9)y = e^{2x}.$ **6.** $(D^2 + 4)y = e^{3x}.$
7. $(4D^2 + 1)y = e^{-2x}.$ **8.** $D(D - 2)y = e^{-x}.$
9. $D(D - 2)^2 y = e^{2x}.$ **10.** $D(D + 3)^2 y = e^{-3x}.$
11. $(D^2 + 4)y = \cos 3x.$ **12.** $(D^2 + 9)y = \cos 3x.$
13. $(D^2 + 4)y = \sin 2x.$ **14.** $(D^2 + 36)y = \sin 6x.$
15. $(D^2 + 9)y = \sin 3x.$ **16.** $(D^2 + 36)y = \cos 6x.$

Exercises

1. Verify formula (2) of Section 51.
2. Obtain and verify formula (3) of Section 51.

In Exs. 3–18, find the general solution.

3. $(D^2 + 3D - 4)y = 12e^{2x}.$ ANS. $y = c_1 e^{-4x} + c_2 e^x + 2e^{2x}.$
4. $(D^2 + 3D - 4)y = 21e^{3x}.$
5. $(D^2 + 3D - 4)y = 15e^x.$ ANS. $y = c_1 e^{-4x} + (c_2 + 3x)e^x.$
6. $(D^2 + 3D - 4)y = 20e^{-4x}.$
7. $(D^2 - 3D + 2)y = e^x + e^{2x}.$ ANS. $y = (c_1 - x)e^x + (c_2 + x)e^{2x}.$
8. $(4D^2 - 1)y = e^{x/2} + 12e^x.$
9. $D^2(D - 2)^3 y = 48e^{2x}.$
     ANS. $y = c_1 + c_2 x + (c_3 + c_4 x + c_5 x^2 + 2x^3)e^{2x}.$
10. $(D^4 - 18D^2 + 81)y = 36e^{3x}.$
11. $(D^2 + 16)y = 14 \cos 3x.$ ANS. $y = c_1 \cos 4x + c_2 \sin 4x + 2 \cos 3x.$
12. $(4D^2 + 1)y = 33 \sin 3x.$
13. $y'' + 16y = 24 \sin 4x.$ ANS. $y = (c_1 - 3x) \cos 4x + c_2 \sin 4x.$
14. $y'' + 16y = 48 \cos 4x.$
15. $y'' + y = 12 \cos 2x - \sin x.$
     ANS. $y = (c_1 + \frac{1}{2}x) \cos x + c_2 \sin x - 4 \cos 2x.$
16. $y'' + y = \sin 3x + 4 \cos x.$
17. $(D^2 - 2D + 5)y = e^x \cos 2x.$ Hint: use the exponential shift followed by formula (3) of Section 51.
     ANS. $y = e^x(c_1 \cos 2x + c_2 \sin 2x) + \frac{1}{4}xe^x \sin 2x.$
18. $(D^2 + 2D + 5)y = e^{-x} \sin 2x.$
     ANS. $y = e^{-x}(c_1 \cos 2x + c_2 \sin 2x) - \frac{1}{4}xe^{-x} \cos 2x.$
19. Prove that if $f(x) = (x - a)^n \varphi(x)$, then $f^{(n)}(a) = n!\varphi(a)$. Then use equation (5) of Section 50 above to prove that

$$\frac{1}{f(D)} e^{ax} = \frac{x^n e^{ax}}{f^{(n)}(a)},$$

where n is the smallest non-negative integer for which $f^{(n)}(a) \neq 0$. See C. A. Hutchinson, "Another Note on Linear Operators," *Amer. Math. Monthly*, **46** (1939), 161.

In Exs. 20–23, use the formula of Ex. 19 above.

20. Ex. 5.   **21.** Ex. 6.
22. Ex. 9.   **23.** Ex. 10.

In Exs. 24–29, verify the formulas* stated.

24. $\dfrac{1}{f(D)} \sin ax = \dfrac{f(-D) \sin ax}{f(ai)f(-ai)} \, ; f(ai)f(-ai) \neq 0.$

25. $\dfrac{1}{f(D)} \cos ax = \dfrac{f(-D) \cos ax}{f(ai)f(-ai)} \, ; f(ai)f(-ai) \neq 0.$

26. $\dfrac{1}{f(D)} \sinh ax = \dfrac{f(-D) \sinh ax}{f(a)f(-a)} \, ; f(a)f(-a) \neq 0.$

27. $\dfrac{1}{f(D)} \cosh ax = \dfrac{f(-D) \cosh ax}{f(a)f(-a)} \, ; f(a)f(-a) \neq 0.$

28. $\dfrac{1}{(D^2 + a^2)^n} \sin ax = \dfrac{x^n}{(2a)^n n!} \sin \left(ax - \tfrac{1}{2}n\pi\right).$

29. $\dfrac{1}{(D^2 + a^2)^n} \cos ax = \dfrac{x^n}{(2a)^n n!} \cos \left(ax - \tfrac{1}{2}n\pi\right).$

In Exs. 30–33 use the formulas of Ex. 24–25 above.

30. Ex. 1, page 136.   **31.** Ex. 11, page 136.
32. Ex. 12, page 137.   **33.** Ex. 32, page 137.

52. Evaluation of $[1/f(D)]x^n$

It is proved in more advanced books† that

$$\frac{1}{f(D)} x^n$$

is correctly evaluated by replacing $1/f(D)$ by its formal series expansion in ascending powers of D and then carrying out the indicated operations.

---

* The formulas of Exs. 24–27 were obtained by C. A. Hutchinson, "An Operational Formula," *Amer. Math. Monthly*, **40** (1933), 482–483; those of Exs. 28–29 were given by C. A. Hutchinson, "Note on an Operational Formula," *Amer. Math. Monthly*, **44** (1937), 371–372.

† See E. L. Ince, *Ordinary Differential Equations* (London: Longmans, Green and Co., 1927), p. 140.

By correctly evaluated it is meant that if y_p be the result of the evaluation, then $f(D)y_p = x^n$.

The extension of this method to the evaluation of $[1/f(D)]p(x)$, where $p(x)$ is a polynomial in x, should be evident.

Two comments are in order here. First, if $f(D)$ has a factor D^k, $k > 0$, then negative powers of D will appear in the expansion. These are to be interpreted as iterated integrations, illustrated below:

$$D^{-1}x^3 = \frac{x^4}{4},$$

$$D^{-2}x^3 = D^{-1}\frac{x^4}{4} = \frac{x^5}{20}, \text{ etc.}$$

Note that in searching for a particular solution we disregard constants of integration. The presence of negative powers of D is easily avoided as is shown in Example (b) below.

Second, only a finite number of terms in the series expansion of $1/f(D)$ affect the result, since for $m > n$, $D^m x^n = 0$.

EXAMPLE (a): Find a particular solution of the equation

$$(D^2 + 1)y = x^2.$$

Now

$$\frac{1}{D^2 + 1} = 1 - D^2 + D^4 - \cdots,$$

so

$$y_p = \frac{1}{D^2 + 1}x^2 = (1 - D^2)x^2 = x^2 - 2,$$

in which all terms involving $D^m x^2$ for $m > 2$ have been dropped since each is zero.

EXAMPLE (b): Solve the equation

(1) $$D^3(D^2 - 1)y = x^2.$$

First let us integrate each member of equation (1) three times, disregarding constants of integration, thus obtaining

$$(D^2 - 1)y = \frac{x^5}{60}.$$

Then

$$y_p = \frac{1}{D^2 - 1} \cdot \frac{x^5}{60} = (-1 - D^2 - D^4 - D^6 - \cdots) \frac{x^5}{60},$$

from which

$$y_p = -\frac{x^5}{60} - \frac{x^3}{3} - 2x.$$

The general solution of (1) is

$$y = c_1 e^x + c_2 e^{-x} + c_3 + c_4 x + c_5 x^2 - \frac{x^3}{3} - \frac{x^5}{60},$$

where the term $(-2x)$ from y_p has been absorbed into the complementary function.

If we do not wish to avoid negative powers of D, we can, from (1), write at once

$$y_p = \frac{1}{D^3(D^2 - 1)} x^2 = D^{-3}(-1 - D^2 - D^4 - D^6 - \cdots)x^2$$
$$= (-D^{-3} - D^{-1} - D - D^3 - \cdots)x^2.$$

Now $D^{-1}x^2 = x^3/3$, $D^{-2}x^2 = x^4/12$, $D^{-3}x^2 = x^5/60$, $Dx^2 = 2x$, and $D^3x^2 = 0$, so

$$y_p = -\frac{x^5}{60} - \frac{x^3}{3} - 2x$$

as before.

EXAMPLE (c): Find a particular solution of the equation

(2) $(D^2 + D - 2)y = 2x - x^3.$

Here

$$y_p = \frac{1}{D^2 + D - 2}(2x - x^3).$$

By dividing $(-2 + D + D^2)$ into 1 (long division), it is found that

(3) $y_p = (-\frac{1}{2} - \frac{1}{4}D - \frac{3}{8}D^2 - \frac{5}{16}D^3 - \cdots)(2x - x^3).$

From (3) we conclude with a little labor that

(4) $y_p = \frac{1}{2}x^3 + \frac{3}{4}x^2 + \frac{5}{4}x + \frac{11}{8}.$

The formal character of the process we have just used makes imperative the verification of our final result by direct substitution into the original differential equation. That verification is left for the student.

The brevity of the solution above is due to the omission of all the actual work, the long division, and the reduction of (3) to (4). Before getting too enthusiastic about this method, a student should solve equation (2) by the method of Chapter 9 and also supply the missing steps in the solution above. Then the two processes can be compared.

There does seem to be one type of equation for which the method of this section is a vast improvement over the previous attacks. See the next example.

EXAMPLE (d): Find a particular solution of the equation

$$(D^8 - 1)y = x^{15}.$$

Here

$$y_p = \frac{1}{D^8 - 1} x^{15} = (-1 - D^8 - \cdots)x^{15}.$$

But $D^8 x^{15} = 15!x^7/7!$. Hence*

$$y_p = -x^{15} - 15!x^7/7!.$$

53. Additional notes on the operational method

Since the equation

(1) $$(D - m)y = R(x)$$

is of the first order, an integrating factor e^{-mx} is available. It follows that a particular solution of (1) is

$$y_p = e^{mx}\int e^{-mx}R(x)\, dx,$$

where the constant of integration may be omitted. Thus it is seen that

(2) $$\frac{1}{D - m} R(x) = e^{mx}\int e^{-mx}R(x)\, dx.$$

Suppose $f(D) = (D - m_1)(D - m_2) \cdots (D - m_n)$, in which the factors are all distinct. Then there exists the partial fractions expansion

(3) $$\frac{1}{f(D)} = \frac{A_1}{D - m_1} + \frac{A_2}{D - m_2} + \cdots + \frac{A_n}{D - m_n},$$

the $A_1, A_2, \cdots, A_n$ being constants. It can be shown† that in

---

* For those who must live life the hard way, it is admitted that

$$15!/7! = 259\ 459\ 200.$$

† E. L. Ince, *Ordinary Differential Equations* (London: Longmans, Green and Co., 1927), pp. 140–141.

$[1/f(D)]R(x)$, the operator $1/f(D)$ may be replaced by the right member in (3). Then formula (2), or any other suitable tool, may be used to evaluate each term of the type $A_k(D - m_k)^{-1}R(x)$.

Even if $f(D)$ involves repeated factors, an evaluation similar to that above may be accomplished. The partial fractions expansion then requires the evaluation of terms of the kind $(D - m)^{-n}R(x)$ with $n > 1$. Put

$$y_p = (D - m)^{-n}R(x),$$

then

$$(D - m)^n y_p = R(x),$$

on which the exponential shift works neatly. Thus from

$$e^{-mx}(D - m)^n y_p = e^{-mx}R(x)$$

it follows that

$$D^n(e^{-mx}y_p) = e^{-mx}R(x),$$

so the value of y_p can be obtained with n integrations.

At one stage of the derivation of the exponential shift formula we showed (page 144) that for any y

$$f(D)y = e^{ax}f(D + a)(e^{-ax}y).$$

Let us choose

$$y = e^{ax}\frac{1}{f(D + a)}V(x).$$

Then

$$f(D)y = e^{ax}f(D + a)\left[\frac{1}{f(D + a)}V(x)\right]$$
$$= e^{ax}V(x).$$

Therefore

$$\frac{1}{f(D)}e^{ax}V(x) = y,$$

or

(4) $$\frac{1}{f(D)}[e^{ax}V(x)] = e^{ax}\frac{1}{f(D + a)}V(x).$$

The relation (4) may be used to perform the exponential shift automatically in solving an equation such as

(5) $$(D^2 - 2D + 5)y = e^x \cos 2x.$$

Here

$$y_p = \frac{1}{D^2 - 2D + 5}(e^x \cos 2x),$$

which, because of (4), can be written

$$y_p = e^x \frac{1}{(D + 1)^2 - 2(D + 1) + 5} \cos 2x$$

or

$$y_p = e^x \frac{1}{D^2 + 4} \cos 2x.$$

Then, using (3), page 151, we get

$$y_p = \tfrac{1}{4}xe^x \sin 2x.$$

Exercises

In each exercise, find a particular solution and verify your result.

1. $(D^2 - 1)y = x^3$.   ANS. $y = -x^3 - 6x$.

2. $(D^2 - 1)y = x^4$.   ANS. $y = -x^4 - 12x^2 - 24$.

3. $(4D^2 + 1)y = x^3$.   ANS. $y = x^3 - 24x$.

4. $(4D^2 + 1)y = x^4$.   ANS. $y = x^4 - 48x^2 + 384$.

5. $(D - 1)^2 y = x^2$.   ANS. $y = x^2 + 4x + 6$.

6. $(D + 1)^2 y = x^2 + 3x + 3$.   ANS. $y = x^2 - x + 3$.

7. $(D - 1)^2 y = x^3 - 4x^2$.   ANS. $y = x^3 + 2x^2 + 2x$.

8. $(D + 1)^2 y = x^3 + 6x^2$.   ANS. $y = x^3 - 6x + 12$.

9. $D(D^2 + 4)y = 4x^3 + 2x$.   ANS. $y = \tfrac{1}{4}x^4 - \tfrac{1}{2}x^2$.

10. $D^2(D^2 + 4)y = 12x$.   ANS. $y = \tfrac{1}{2}x^3$.

11. $D^2(D + 1)y = 12x - 2$.   ANS. $y = 2x^3 - 7x^2$.

12. $D^2(D - 1)y = 12x - 2$.   ANS. $y = -2x^3 - 5x^2$.

13. $(D^2 - 3D + 2)y = 6x^2 - 6x - 11$.   ANS. $y = 3x^2 + 6x + \tfrac{1}{2}$.

14. $(D^2 - 3D + 2)y = 2x^3 - 9x^2 + 2x - 16$.   ANS. $y = x^3 - 2x - 11$.

15. $(D^6 - 1)y = x^{10}$.   ANS. $y = -x^{10} - \dfrac{10!}{4!}x^4$.

16. $(D^3 + 3D^2 - 4)y = 16x^3 + 20x^2$.   ANS. $y = -4x^3 - 5x^2 - 18x - \tfrac{27}{2}$.

Miscellaneous Exercises

In Exs. 1–18, find a particular solution.

1. $(D^2 - 4D + 4)y = 6x^2 e^{2x}$.   ANS. $y = \tfrac{1}{2}x^4 e^{2x}$.

2. $(D - 3)^2 y = e^{3x}$.   ANS. $y = \tfrac{1}{2}x^2 e^{3x}$.

3. $D(D - 2)y = e^{2x}$.   ANS. $y = \tfrac{1}{2}xe^{2x}$.

4. $D^2(D + 1)y = e^{-x}$.   ANS. $y = xe^{-x}$.

5. $(D^2 + 4)y = 8x^5$.   ANS. $y = 2x^5 - 10x^3 + 15x$.

6. $(D^2 + 4)y = 16xe^{2x}$.   ANS. $y = (2x - 1)e^{2x}$.

7. $(D^2 + 4D + 5)y = 4e^{-2x} \cos x.$ ANS. $y = 2xe^{-2x} \sin x.$

8. $(D^2 - D - 2)y = 4x^2 - 3e^{-x}.$ ANS. $y = xe^{-x} - 2x^2 + 2x - 3.$

9. $(D^2 - 4D + 13)y = 24e^{2x} \sin 3x.$ ANS. $y = -4xe^{2x} \cos 3x.$

10. $(D^2 - 4D + 13)y = 24e^{2x} \sin x.$ ANS. $y = 3e^{2x} \sin x.$

11. $(D^2 - 3D + 2)y = (x - 2)e^x.$ ANS. $y = -\frac{1}{2}(x^2 - 2x)e^x.$

12. $(D^2 - 3D + 2)y = 72xe^{-x}.$ ANS. $y = 2(6x + 5)e^{-x}.$

13. $(D^2 + 4)y = 12(\sin x + \sin 2x).$ ANS. $y = 4 \sin x - 3x \cos 2x.$

14. $(D^2 + 4)y = 20(e^x - \cos 2x).$ ANS. $y = 4e^x - 5x \sin 2x.$

15. $(D^2 + 16)y = 8(x + \sin 4x).$ ANS. $y = x(\frac{1}{2} - \cos 4x).$

16. $(D^2 + 4)y = 8 \sin x \cos x.$ ANS. $y = -x \cos 2x.$

17. $(D^2 + 4)y = 8 \cos^2 x.$ ANS. $y = 1 + x \sin 2x.$

18. $(D^4 - 1)y = x^6.$ ANS. $y = -x^6 - 360x^2.$

In Exs. 19–28, find the general solution.

19. $(D^2 - 4D + 13)y = 24e^{2x} \cos x.$
$\quad$ ANS. $y = e^{2x}(c_1 \cos 3x + c_2 \sin 3x + 3 \cos x).$

20. $(D^2 - 4D + 13)y = 24e^{2x} \cos 3x.$
$\quad$ ANS. $y = e^{2x}(c_1 \cos 3x + c_2 \sin 3x + 4x \sin 3x).$

21. $(D^2 + 25)y = \sin 5x.$ ANS. $y = c_1 \cos 5x + c_2 \sin 5x - 0.1x \cos 5x.$

22. $D(D^2 + 1)y = \sin x.$ ANS. $y = c_1 + c_2 \cos x + (c_3 - \frac{1}{2}x) \sin x.$

23. $D^2(D^2 + 1)y = \sin x.$
$\quad$ ANS. $y = c_1 + c_2 x + (c_3 + \frac{1}{2}x) \cos x + c_4 \sin x.$

24. $(D^2 - 3D + 2)y = x^2 - 2x.$

25. Ex. 8, page 136.

26. Ex. 10, page 136.

27. Ex. 18, page 137.

28. Ex. 19, page 137.

In Exs. 29–34, find the particular solution indicated.

29. $(D^2 + 1)y = 4e^x;$ when $x = 0$, $y = 0$ and $y' = 0.$
$\quad$ ANS. $y = 2(e^x - \cos x - \sin x).$

30. $(D^2 + 4)y = 2x - 8;$ when $x = 0$, $y = 1$ and $y' = 0.$
$\quad$ ANS. $4y = 12 \cos 2x - \sin 2x + 2x - 8.$

31. $(D^2 + 3D + 2)y = 4x^2;$ when $x = 0$, $y = 0$ and $y' = 0.$
$\quad$ ANS. $y = 2x^2 - 6x + 7 - 8e^{-x} + e^{-2x}.$

32. $(D^2 - 1)y = \sin 2x;$ when $x = 0$, $y = 0$ and $y' = 1.$
$\quad$ ANS. $10y = 7(e^x - e^{-x}) - 2 \sin 2x;$
$\quad$ or $5y = 7 \sinh x - \sin 2x.$

33. $(D^2 + 2D)y = 2x;$ when $x = 0$, $y = 0$, and when $x = 1$, $y = 0.$
$\quad$ ANS. $2y = x^2 - x.$

34. The equation of Ex. 33 with the conditions that when $x = 0$, $y = 0$ and
$y' = 0$.   ANS. $4y = 2x^2 - 2x + 1 - e^{-2x}$.

In Exs. 35–37, obtain from the particular solution indicated the value
of y and the value of y' at $x = 1$.

35. $y'' + 2y' + y = x + 2$; when $x = 0$, $y = 1$ and $y' = 0$.
                    ANS.   At $x = 1$, $y = (e + 1)/e$ and $y' = (e - 1)/e$.
36. $y'' + 2y' + y = x + 2$; when $x = 0$, $y = 0$ and $y' = 0$.
                    ANS.   At $x = 1$, $y = (e - 1)/e$ and $y' = 1$.
37. $(D^2 + 1)y = 3$; when $x = \pi/2$, $y = 0$ and $y' = 0$.
                    ANS.   At $x = 1$, $y = 0.4756$ and $y' = -1.6209$.

CHAPTER 11

The Laplace Transform

54. The transform concept

The reader is already familiar with some operators that transform functions into functions. An outstanding example is the differential operator D which transforms each function of a large class (those possessing a derivative) into another function.

We have already found that the operator D is useful in the treatment of linear differential equations with constant coefficients. In this chapter we study another transformation (a mapping of functions onto functions) which has played an increasingly important role in both pure and applied mathematics in the past few decades. The operator L, to be introduced in Section 55, is particularly effective in the study of boundary value problems involving linear differential equations with constant coefficients.

One class of transformations, which are called integral transforms, may be defined by

$$(1) \qquad T\{F(t)\} = \int_{-\infty}^{\infty} K(s, t) F(t) \, dt = f(s).$$

Given a function $K(s, t)$, called the kernel of the transformation, equation (1) associates with each $F(t)$ of the class of functions for which the above integral exists a function $f(s)$ defined by (1). Generalizations and abstractions of (1), as well as studies of special cases, are to be found in profusion in mathematical literature.

161

Various particular choices of $K(s, t)$ in (1) have led to special transforms, each with its own properties to make it useful in specific circumstances. The transform defined by choosing

$$K(s, t) = 0, \quad \text{for } t < 0,$$
$$= e^{-st}, \quad \text{for } t \geq 0,$$

is the one to which this chapter is devoted.

55. Definition of the Laplace transform

Let $F(t)$ be any function such that the integrations encountered may be legitimately performed on $F(t)$. The *Laplace transform* of $F(t)$ is denoted by $L\{F(t)\}$ and is defined by

$$(1) \qquad L\{F(t)\} = \int_0^\infty e^{-st}F(t)\, dt.$$

The integral in (1) is a function of the parameter s; call that function $f(s)$. We may write

$$(2) \qquad L\{F(t)\} = \int_0^\infty e^{-st}F(t)\, dt = f(s).$$

It is customary to refer to $f(s)$, as well as to the symbol $L\{F(t)\}$, as the transform, or the Laplace transform, of $F(t)$.

We may also look upon (2) as a definition of a Laplace operator L, which transforms each function $F(t)$ of a certain set of functions into some function $f(s)$.

It is easy to show that if the integral in (2) does converge, it will do so for all s greater than* some fixed value s_0. That is, equation (2) will define $f(s)$ for $s > s_0$. In extreme cases the integral may converge for all finite s.

It is important that the operator L, like the differential operator D, is a linear operator. If $F_1(t)$ and $F_2(t)$ have Laplace transforms and if c_1 and c_2 are any constants,

$$(3) \qquad L\{c_1F_1(t) + c_2F_2(t)\} = c_1L\{F_1(t)\} + c_2L\{F_2(t)\}.$$

Using elementary properties of definite integrals, the student can easily show the validity of equation (3).

We shall hereafter employ the relation (3) without restating the fact that the operator L is a linear one.

---

* If s is not to be restricted to real values, the convergence takes place for all s with real part greater than some fixed value.

56. Transforms of elementary functions

The transforms of certain exponential and trigonometric functions and of polynomials will now be obtained. These results enter our work frequently.

EXAMPLE (a):   Find $L\{e^{kt}\}$.

We proceed as follows:

$$L\{e^{kt}\} = \int_0^\infty e^{-st} \cdot e^{kt}\, dt = \int_0^\infty e^{-(s-k)t}\, dt.$$

For $s \leqq k$, the exponent on e is positive or zero and the integral diverges. For $s > k$, the integral converges.

Therefore, for $s > k$,

$$\begin{aligned}
L\{e^{kt}\} &= \int_0^\infty e^{-(s-k)t}\, dt \\
&= \left[\frac{-e^{-(s-k)t}}{s-k}\right]_0^\infty \\
&= 0 + \frac{1}{s-k}.
\end{aligned}$$

Thus we find that

(1) $$L\{e^{kt}\} = \frac{1}{s-k}, \qquad s > k.$$

Note the special case $k = 0$:

(2) $$L\{1\} = \frac{1}{s}, \qquad s > 0.$$

EXAMPLE (b): Obtain $L\{\sin kt\}$.

From any elementary calculus,* or by employing integration by parts twice, we obtain

$$\int e^{ax} \sin mx\, dx = \frac{e^{ax}(a \sin mx - m \cos mx)}{a^2 + m^2} + C.$$

Since

$$L\{\sin kt\} = \int_0^\infty e^{-st} \sin kt\, dt,$$

---

* For example, E. D. Rainville, *Unified Calculus and Analytic Geometry* (New York: The Macmillan Co., 1961), p. 345.

it follows that

$$(3) \qquad L\{\sin kt\} = \left[\frac{e^{-st}(-s \sin kt - k \cos kt)}{s^2 + k^2}\right]_0^\infty.$$

For positive s, $e^{-st} \to 0$ as $t \to \infty$. Furthermore, $\sin kt$ and $\cos kt$ are bounded as $t \to \infty$. Therefore (3) yields

$$L\{\sin kt\} = 0 - \frac{1(0 - k)}{s^2 + k^2},$$

or

$$(4) \qquad L\{\sin kt\} = \frac{k}{s^2 + k^2}, \qquad s > 0.$$

The result

$$(5) \qquad L\{\cos kt\} = \frac{s}{s^2 + k^2}, \qquad s > 0,$$

can be obtained in a similar manner from the elementary formula

$$(6) \qquad \int e^{ax} \cos mx \, dx = \frac{e^{ax}(a \cos mx + m \sin mx)}{a^2 + m^2} + C.$$

EXAMPLE (c): Obtain $L\{t^n\}$ for n a positive integer.

By definition

$$L\{t^n\} = \int_0^\infty e^{-st}t^n \, dt.$$

Let us attack the integral using integration by parts with the choice exhibited in the table.

t^n	$e^{-st} \, dt$
$nt^{n-1} \, dt$	$-\dfrac{1}{s} e^{-st}$

We thus obtain

$$(7) \qquad \int_0^\infty e^{-st}t^n \, dt = \left[\frac{-t^n e^{-st}}{s}\right]_0^\infty + \frac{n}{s} \int_0^\infty e^{-st}t^{n-1} \, dt.$$

For $s > 0$ and $n > 0$, the first term on the right in (7) is zero, and we are left with

$$\int_0^\infty e^{-st}t^n \, dt = \frac{n}{s} \int_0^\infty e^{-st}t^{n-1} \, dt, \qquad s > 0,$$

or

$$(8) \qquad L\{t^n\} = \frac{n}{s} L\{t^{n-1}\}, \qquad s > 0.$$

From (8) we may conclude that, for $n > 1$,

$$L\{t^{n-1}\} = \frac{n-1}{s} L\{t^{n-2}\}$$

so

(9) $$L\{t^n\} = \frac{n(n-1)}{s^2} L\{t^{n-2}\}.$$

Iteration of this process yields

$$L\{t^n\} = \frac{n(n-1)(n-2) \cdots 2 \cdot 1}{s^n} L\{t^0\}.$$

From Example (a) above, we have

$$L\{t^0\} = L\{1\} = s^{-1}.$$

Hence, for n a positive integer,

(10) $$L\{t^n\} = \frac{n!}{s^{n+1}}, \qquad s > 0.$$

The Laplace transform of $F(t)$ will exist even if the object function $F(t)$ is discontinuous, provided the integral in the definition of $L\{F(t)\}$ exists. Little will be done at this time with specific discontinuous $F(t)$, because more efficient methods for obtaining such transforms are to be developed later.

EXAMPLE (d): Find the Laplace transform of $H(t)$ where

$$H(t) = t, \qquad 0 < t < 4,$$
$$= 5, \qquad t > 4.$$

Note that the fact that $H(t)$ is not defined at $t = 0$ and $t = 4$ has no bearing whatever on the existence, or the value, of $L\{H(t)\}$. We turn to the definition of $L\{H(t)\}$ to obtain

$$L\{H(t)\} = \int_0^\infty e^{-st} H(t)\, dt$$

$$= \int_0^4 e^{-st} t\, dt + \int_4^\infty e^{-st}\, 5\, dt.$$

Using integration by parts on the next-to-last integral above, we soon arrive, for $s > 0$, at

$$L\{H(t)\} = \left[-\frac{t}{s} e^{-st} - \frac{1}{s^2} e^{-st} \right]_0^4 + \left[-\frac{5}{s} e^{-st} \right]_4^\infty.$$

Thus

$$L\{H(t)\} = -\frac{4e^{-4s}}{s} - \frac{e^{-4s}}{s^2} + 0 + \frac{1}{s^2} - 0 + \frac{5e^{-4s}}{s}$$

$$= \frac{1}{s^2} + \frac{e^{-4s}}{s} - \frac{e^{-4s}}{s^2}.$$

Exercises

1. Using equation (6) above, show that

$$L\{\cos kt\} = \frac{s}{s^2 + k^2}, \quad s > 0.$$

2. Obtain $L\{t^2 - 3t + 5\}$ ·   ANS. $\dfrac{2}{s^3} - \dfrac{3}{s^2} + \dfrac{5}{s}, \quad s > 0.$

3. Obtain $L\{\frac{1}{2}t^3 + t^2 - 1\}$ ·   ANS. $\dfrac{3}{s^4} + \dfrac{2}{s^3} - \dfrac{1}{s}, \quad s > 0.$

4. Evaluate $L\{e^{-4t} + 3e^{-2t}\}$ ·   ANS. $\dfrac{2(2s + 7)}{(s + 2)(s + 4)}, \quad s > -2.$

5. Evaluate $L\{2e^{3t} - e^{-3t}\}$ ·   ANS. $\dfrac{s + 9}{s^2 - 9}, \quad s > 3.$

6. Show that $L\{\cosh kt\} = \dfrac{s}{s^2 - k^2}, \quad s > |k|.$

7. Show that $L\{\sinh kt\} = \dfrac{k}{s^2 - k^2}, \quad s > |k|.$

8. Use the trigonometric identity $\cos^2 A = \frac{1}{2}(1 + \cos 2A)$ and equation
(5), Section 56, to evaluate $L\{\cos^2 kt\}$.   ANS. $\dfrac{s^2 + 2k^2}{s(s^2 + 4k^2)}, \quad s > 0.$

9. Parallel the method suggested in Ex. 8 to obtain $L\{\sin^2 kt\}$.

           ANS. $\dfrac{2k^2}{s(s^2 + 4k^2)}, \quad s > 0.$

10. Obtain $L\{\sin^2 kt\}$ directly from the answer to Ex. 8.

11. Evaluate $L\{\sin kt \cos kt\}$ with the aid of a trigonometric identity.

           ANS. $\dfrac{k}{s^2 + 4k^2}, \quad s > 0.$

12. Evaluate $L\{e^{-at} - e^{-bt}\}$.   ANS. $\dfrac{b - a}{(s + a)(s + b)}, \quad s > \text{Max}(-a, -b)$ ·

13. Find $L\{\psi(t)\}$ where

$$\psi(t) = 4, \quad 0 < t < 1,$$
$$= 3, \quad t > 1.$$

           ANS. $\dfrac{1}{s}(4 - e^{-s}), \quad s > 0.$

14. Find $L\{\varphi(t)\}$ where

$$\varphi(t) = 1, \qquad 0 < t < 2,$$
$$= t, \qquad t > 2.$$

ANS. $\dfrac{1}{s} + \dfrac{e^{-2s}}{s} + \dfrac{e^{-2s}}{s^2}, \quad s > 0.$

15. Find $L\{A(t)\}$ where

$$A(t) = 0, \qquad 0 < t < 1,$$
$$= t, \qquad 1 < t < 2,$$
$$= 0, \qquad t > 2.$$

ANS. $\left(\dfrac{1}{s^2} + \dfrac{1}{s}\right) e^{-s} - \left(\dfrac{1}{s^2} + \dfrac{2}{s}\right) e^{-2s}, \quad s > 0.$

16. Find $L\{B(t)\}$ where

$$B(t) = \sin 2t, \qquad 0 < t < \pi,$$
$$= 0, \qquad t > \pi.$$

ANS. $\dfrac{2(1 - e^{-\pi s})}{s^2 + 4}, \quad s > 0.$

57. Sectionally continuous functions

It soon becomes tiresome to test each $F(t)$ we encounter to determine whether the integral

$$(1) \qquad \int_0^\infty e^{-st} F(t) \, dt$$

exists for some range of values of s. We therefore seek a fairly large class of functions for which we can prove once and for all that the integral (1) exists.

One of our avowed interests in the Laplace transform is in its usefulness as a tool in solving problems in more or less elementary applications, particularly boundary value problems in differential equations. Therefore we do not hesitate to restrict our study to functions $F(t)$ that are continuous or even differentiable, except possibly at a discrete set of points, in the semi-infinite range $t \geqq 0$.

For such functions, the existence of the integral (1) can be endangered only at points of discontinuity of $F(t)$ or by divergence due to behavior of the integrand as $t \to \infty$.

In elementary calculus we found that finite discontinuities, or finite jumps, of the integrand did not interfere with the existence of the integral. We therefore introduce a term to describe functions that are continuous except for such jumps.

DEFINITION: *The function $F(t)$ is said to be sectionally continuous over the closed interval $a \leqq t \leqq b$ if that interval can be divided into a finite number of subintervals $c \leqq t \leqq d$ such that in each subinterval:*

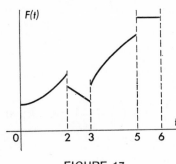

FIGURE 17

1. $F(t)$ is continuous in the open interval $c < t < d$,

2. $F(t)$ approaches a limit as t approaches each endpoint from within the interval; that is, $\underset{t \to c^+}{\mathrm{Lim}}\, F(t)$ and $\underset{t \to d^-}{\mathrm{Lim}}\, F(t)$ exist.

Figure 17 shows an $F(t)$ that is sectionally continuous over the interval

$$0 \leqq t \leqq 6.$$

The student should realize that there is no implication that $F(t)$ must be sectionally continuous for $L\{F(t)\}$ to exist. Indeed, we shall meet several counterexamples to any such notion. The concept of sectionally continuous functions will, in Section 59, play a role in a set of conditions sufficient for the existence of the transform.

58. Functions of exponential order

If the integral of $e^{-st}F(t)$ between the limits 0 and t_0 exists for every finite positive t_0, the only remaining threat to the existence of the transform

$$(1) \qquad \int_0^\infty e^{-st}F(t)\,dt$$

is the behavior of the integrand as $t \to \infty$.

We know that

$$(2) \qquad \int_0^\infty e^{-ct}\,dt$$

converges for $c > 0$. This arouses our interest in functions $F(t)$ that are, for large $t(t \geqq t_0)$, essentially bounded by some exponential e^{bt} so that the integrand in (1) will behave like the integrand in (2) for s large enough.

DEFINITION: *The function $F(t)$ is said to be of exponential order as $t \to \infty$ if there exist constants M and b and a fixed t-value t_0 such that*

$$(3) \qquad |F(t)| < Me^{bt}, \qquad for\ t \geqq t_0.$$

If b is to be emphasized, we say that $F(t)$ is of the order of e^{bt} as $t \to \infty$. We also write

(4) $$F(t) = O(e^{bt}), \qquad t \to \infty,$$

to mean that $F(t)$ is of exponential order, the exponential being e^{bt}, as $t \to \infty$. That is, (4) is another way of expressing (3).

The integral in (1) may be split into parts as follows:

(5) $$\int_0^\infty e^{-st}F(t)\,dt = \int_0^{t_0} e^{-st}F(t)\,dt + \int_{t_0}^\infty e^{-st}F(t)\,dt.$$

If $F(t)$ is of exponential order, $F(t) = O(e^{bt})$, the last integral in equation (5) exists because from the inequality (3) it follows that for $s > b$,

(6) $$\int_{t_0}^\infty |e^{-st}F(t)|\,dt < M \int_{t_0}^\infty e^{-st} \cdot e^{bt}\,dt = \frac{M \exp\left[-t_0(s-b)\right]}{s-b}.$$

For $s > b$, the last member of (6) approaches zero as $t_0 \to \infty$. Therefore the last integral in (5) is absolutely convergent* for $s > b$. We have proved the following result.

THEOREM 5: *If the integral of $e^{-st}F(t)$ between the limits 0 and t_0 exists for every finite positive t_0, and if $F(t)$ is of exponential order, $F(t) = O(e^{bt})$ as $t \to \infty$, the Laplace transform*

(7) $$L\{F(t)\} = \int_0^\infty e^{-st}F(t)\,dt = f(s)$$

exists for $s > b$.

We know that a function that is sectionally continuous over an interval is integrable over that interval. This leads us to the following useful special case of Theorem 5.

THEOREM 6: *If $F(t)$ is sectionally continuous over every finite interval in the range $t \geq 0$, and if $F(t)$ is of exponential order, $F(t) = O(e^{bt})$ as $t \to \infty$, the Laplace transform $L\{F(t)\}$ exists for $s > b$.*

Functions of exponential order play a dominant role throughout our work. It is therefore wise to develop proficiency in determining whether or not a specified function is of exponential order.

Surely if a constant b exists such that

(8) $$\operatorname*{Lim}_{t \to \infty} \left[e^{-bt}|F(t)|\right]$$

---

* If complex s is to be used, the integral converges for $\operatorname{Re}(s) > b$.

exists, the function $F(t)$ is of exponential order, indeed of the order of e^{bt}. To see this, let the value of the limit (8) be $K \neq 0$. Then, for t large enough, $|e^{-bt}F(t)|$ can be made as close to K as is desired, so certainly

$$|e^{-bt}F(t)| < 2K.$$

Therefore, for t sufficiently large,

(9) $$|F(t)| < Me^{bt},$$

with $M = 2K$. If the limit in (8) is zero, we may write (9) with $M = 1$.
   On the other hand, if for every fixed c,

(10) $$\lim_{t \to \infty} [e^{-ct}|F(t)|] = \infty,$$

the function $F(t)$ is not of exponential order. For, assume b exists such that

(11) $$|F(t)| < Me^{bt}, \qquad t \geqq t_0;$$

then the choice $c = 2b$ would yield, by (11),

$$|e^{-2bt}F(t)| < Me^{-bt},$$

so $e^{-2bt}F(t) \to 0$ as $t \to \infty$, which disagrees with (10).

EXAMPLE (a): Show that t^3 is of exponential order as $t \to \infty$.
   We consider, with b as yet unspecified,

(12) $$\lim_{t \to \infty} (e^{-bt}t^3) = \lim_{t \to \infty} \frac{t^3}{e^{bt}}.$$

If $b > 0$, the limit in (12) is of a type treated in calculus. In fact,

$$\lim_{t \to \infty} \frac{t^3}{e^{bt}} = \lim_{t \to \infty} \frac{3t^2}{be^{bt}} = \lim_{t \to \infty} \frac{6t}{b^2e^{bt}} = \lim_{t \to \infty} \frac{6}{b^3e^{bt}} = 0.$$

Therefore t^3 is of exponential order,

$$t^3 = O(e^{bt}), \qquad t \to \infty,$$

for any fixed positive b.

EXAMPLE (b): Show that $\exp(t^2)$ is not of exponential order as $t \to \infty$.
   Consider

(13) $$\lim_{t \to \infty} \frac{\exp(t^2)}{\exp(bt)}.$$

If $b \leqq 0$, the limit in (13) is infinite. If $b > 0$,

$$\operatorname*{Lim}_{t \to \infty} \frac{\exp{(t^2)}}{\exp{(bt)}} = \operatorname*{Lim}_{t \to \infty} \exp{[t(t - b)]} = \infty.$$

Thus, no matter what fixed b we use, the limit in (13) is infinite and $\exp{(t^2)}$ cannot be of exponential order.

The exercises at the end of the next section give additional opportunities for practice in determining whether or not a function is of exponential order.

59. Functions of class A

For brevity we shall hereafter use the term "a function of class A" for any function that

(a) is sectionally continuous over every finite interval in the range $t \geqq 0$, and

(b) is of exponential order as $t \to \infty$.

We may then reword Theorem 6 as follows.

THEOREM 7: *If $F(t)$ is a function of class A, $L\{F(t)\}$ exists.*

It is important to realize that Theorem 7 states only that for $L\{F(t)\}$ to exist, it is sufficient that $F(t)$ be of class A. The condition is not necessary. A classic example showing that functions other than those of class A do have Laplace transforms is

$$F(t) = t^{-\frac{1}{2}}.$$

This function is not sectionally continuous in every finite interval in the range $t \geqq 0$, because $F \to \infty$ as $t \to 0^+$. But $t^{-\frac{1}{2}}$ is integrable from 0 to any positive t_0. Also $t^{-\frac{1}{2}} \to 0$ as $t \to \infty$, so $t^{-\frac{1}{2}}$ is of exponential order, with $M = 1$ and $b = 0$ in the inequality (3), page 168. Hence, by Theorem 5, page 169, $L\{t^{-\frac{1}{2}}\}$ exists.

Indeed, for $s > 0$,

$$L\{t^{-\frac{1}{2}}\} = \int_0^\infty e^{-st}t^{-\frac{1}{2}}\, dt,$$

in which the change of variable $t^{\frac{1}{2}} = \beta$ leads to

$$L\{t^{-\frac{1}{2}}\} = 2 \int_0^\infty \exp{(-s\beta^2)}\, d\beta, \qquad s > 0.$$

Another change of variable of integration, $s^{\frac{1}{2}}\beta = y$, yields

$$L\{t^{-\frac{1}{2}}\} = 2s^{-\frac{1}{2}} \int_0^\infty \exp(-y^2)\, dy, \qquad s > 0.$$

In elementary calculus* we found that $\int_0^\infty \exp(-y^2)\, dy = \frac{1}{2}\sqrt{\pi}$.
   Therefore

(1)
$$L\{t^{-\frac{1}{2}}\} = 2s^{-\frac{1}{2}} \cdot \frac{1}{2}\sqrt{\pi}$$
$$= \left(\frac{\pi}{s}\right)^{\frac{1}{2}}, \qquad s > 0,$$

even though $t^{-\frac{1}{2}} \to \infty$ as $t \to 0^+$. Additional examples are easily constructed and we shall meet some of them later in the book.

   If $F(t)$ is of class A, $F(t)$ is bounded over the range $0 \leq t \leq t_0$,

(2)
$$|F(t)| < M_1, \qquad 0 \leq t \leq t_0.$$

But $F(t)$ is also of exponential order,

(3)
$$|F(t)| < M_2 e^{bt}, \qquad t \geq t_0.$$

If we choose M as the larger of M_1 and M_2 and c as the larger of b and zero, we may write

(4)
$$|F(t)| < M e^{ct}, \qquad t \geq 0.$$

Therefore, for any function $F(t)$ of class A,

(5)
$$\left| \int_0^\infty e^{-st}F(t)\, dt \right| < M \int_0^\infty e^{-st} \cdot e^{ct}\, dt = \frac{M}{s-c}, \qquad s > c.$$

Since the right member of (5) approaches zero as $s \to \infty$, we have proved the following useful result.

THEOREM 8: *If $F(t)$ is of class A and if $L\{F(t)\} = f(s)$,*

$$\lim_{s \to \infty} f(s) = 0.$$

   From (5) we may also conclude the stronger result that the transform $f(s)$ of a function $F(t)$ of class A must be such that $sf(s)$ is bounded as $s \to \infty$.

---

   * E. D. Rainville, *Unified Calculus and Analytic Geometry* (New York: The Macmillan Co., 1961), p. 531.

Exercises

1. Prove that if $F_1(t)$ and $F_2(t)$ are each of exponential order as $t \to \infty$, then $F_1(t) \cdot F_2(t)$ and $F_1(t) + F_2(t)$ are also of exponential order as $t \to \infty$.
2. Prove that if $F_1(t)$ and $F_2(t)$ are of class A, page 171, then $F_1(t) + F_2(t)$ and $F_1(t) \cdot F_2(t)$ are also of class A.
3. Show that t^x is of exponential order as $t \to \infty$ for all real x.

In Exs. 4–17, show that the given function is of class A. In these exercises, n denotes a non-negative integer, k any real number.

4. $\sin kt$.

5. $\cos kt$.

6. $\cosh kt$.

7. $\sinh kt$.

8. t^n.

9. $t^n e^{kt}$.

10. $t^n \sin kt$.

11. $t^n \cos kt$.

12. $t^n \sinh kt$.

13. $t^n \cosh kt$.

14. $\dfrac{\sin kt}{t}$.

15. $\dfrac{1 - \exp(-t)}{t}$.

16. $\dfrac{1 - \cos kt}{t}$.

17. $\dfrac{\cos t - \cosh t}{t}$.

60. Transforms of derivatives

Any function of class A, page 171, has a Laplace transform, but the derivative of such a function may or may not be of class A. For the function

$$F_1(t) = \sin[\exp(t)]$$

with derivative

$$F_1'(t) = \exp(t) \cos[\exp(t)],$$

both F_1 and F_1' are of exponential order as $t \to \infty$. Here F_1 is bounded so it is of the order of $\exp(0 \cdot t)$; F_1' is of the order of $\exp(t)$. On the other hand, the function

$$F_2(t) = \sin[\exp(t^2)]$$

with derivative

$$F_2'(t) = 2t \exp(t^2) \cos[\exp(t^2)]$$

is such that F_2 is of the order of $\exp(0 \cdot t)$, but F_2' is not of exponential order. From Example (b), page 170,

$$\lim_{t \to \infty} \frac{\exp(t^2)}{\exp(bt)} = \infty$$

for any real b. Since the factors $2t \cos [\exp (t^2)]$ do not even approach zero as $t \to \infty$, the product $F'_2 \exp (-ct)$ cannot be bounded as $t \to \infty$ no matter how large a fixed c is chosen.

Therefore, in studying the transforms of derivatives, we shall stipulate that the derivatives themselves be of class A.

If $F(t)$ is continuous for $t \geqq 0$ and of exponential order as $t \to \infty$, and if $F'(t)$ is of class A, the integral in

$$(1) \qquad L\{F'(t)\} = \int_0^\infty e^{-st}F'(t) \, dt$$

may be simplified by integration by parts with the choice exhibited in the table.

e^{-st}	$F'(t) \, dt$
$-se^{-st} \, dt$	$F(t)$

We thus obtain, for s greater than some fixed s_0,

$$\int_0^\infty e^{-st}F'(t) \, dt = \left[e^{-st}F(t) \right]_0^\infty + s \int_0^\infty e^{-st}F(t) \, dt,$$

or

$$(2) \qquad L\{F'(t)\} = -F(0) + sL\{F(t)\}.$$

THEOREM 9: *If $F(t)$ is continuous for $t \geqq 0$ and of exponential order as $t \to \infty$, and if $F'(t)$ is of class A, page 171, it follows from $L\{F(t)\} = f(s)$ that*

$$(3) \qquad L\{F'(t)\} = sf(s) - F(0).$$

In treating a differential equation of order n, we seek solutions for which the highest-ordered derivative present is reasonably well behaved, say sectionally continuous. The integral of a sectionally continuous function is continuous. Hence, we lose nothing by requiring continuity for all derivatives of order lower than n. The requirement that the various derivatives be of exponential order is forced upon us by our desire to use the Laplace transform as a tool. For our purposes, iteration of Theorem 9 to obtain transforms of higher derivatives makes sense.

From (3) we obtain, if F, F', F'' are suitably restricted,

$$L\{F''(t)\} = sL\{F'(t)\} - F'(0),$$

or

$$(4) \qquad L\{F''(t)\} = s^2f(s) - sF(0) - F'(0),$$

and the process can be repeated as many times as we wish.

THEOREM 10: *If $F(t), F'(t), \cdots, F^{(n-1)}(t)$ are continuous for $t \geqq 0$ and of exponential order as $t \to \infty$, and if $F^{(n)}(t)$ is of class A, then from*

$$L\{F(t)\} = f(s)$$

it follows that

$$(5) \qquad L\{F^{(n)}(t)\} = s^n f(s) - \sum_{k=0}^{n-1} s^{n-1-k} F^{(k)}(0).$$

Thus

$$L\{F^{(3)}(t)\} = s^3 f(s) - s^2 F(0) - s F'(0) - F''(0),$$

$$L\{F^{(4)}(t)\} = s^4 f(s) - s^3 F(0) - s^2 F'(0) - s F''(0) - F^{(3)}(0), \text{ etc.}$$

Theorem 10 is basic in employing the Laplace transform to solve linear differential equations with constant coefficients. The theorem permits us to transform such differential equations into algebraic ones.

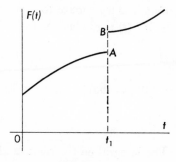

The restriction that $F(t)$ be continuous can be relaxed, but discontinuities in $F(t)$ bring in additional terms in the transform of $F'(t)$. As an example, consider an $F(t)$ that is continuous for $t \geqq 0$ except for a finite jump at $t = t_1$, as in Figure 18. If $F(t)$ is also of exponential order as $t \to \infty$, and if $F'(t)$ is of class A, we may write

FIGURE 18

$$L\{F'(t)\} = \int_0^\infty e^{-st} F'(t)\, dt$$
$$= \int_0^{t_1} e^{-st} F'(t)\, dt + \int_{t_1}^\infty e^{-st} F'(t)\, dt.$$

Then, integration by parts applied to the last two integrals yields

$$L\{F'(t)\} = \left[e^{-st} F(t) \right]_0^{t_1} + s \int_0^{t_1} e^{-st} F(t)\, dt + \left[e^{-st} F(t) \right]_{t_1}^\infty$$
$$+ s \int_{t_1}^\infty e^{-st} F(t)\, dt$$

$$= s \int_0^\infty e^{-st} F(t)\, dt + \exp(-st_1) F(t_1{}^-) - F(0) + 0$$
$$- \exp(-st_1) F(t_1{}^+)$$

$$= s L\{F(t)\} - F(0) - \exp(-st_1)[F(t_1{}^+) - F(t_1{}^-)].$$

In Figure 18 the directed distance AB is of length $[F(t_1{}^+) - F(t_1{}^-)]$.

THEOREM 11: *If $F(t)$ is of exponential order as $t \to \infty$ and $F(t)$ is continuous for $t \geq 0$ except for a finite jump at $t = t_1$, and if $F'(t)$ is of class A, then from*

$$L\{F(t)\} = f(s)$$

it follows that

(6) $\qquad L\{F'(t)\} = sf(s) - F(0) - \exp(-st_1)[F(t_1^+) - F(t_1^-)].$

If $F(t)$ has more than one finite discontinuity, additional terms, similar to the last term in (6), enter the formula for $L\{F'(t)\}$.

61. Derivatives of transforms

For functions of class A, the methods of advanced calculus show that it is legitimate to differentiate the Laplace transform integral. That is, if $F(t)$ is of class A, from

(1) $$f(s) = \int_0^\infty e^{-st} F(t) \, dt$$

it follows that

(2) $$f'(s) = \int_0^\infty (-t) e^{-st} F(t) \, dt.$$

The integral on the right in (2) is the transform of the function $(-t) F(t)$.

THEOREM 12: *If $F(t)$ is a function of class A, it follows from*

$$L\{F(t)\} = f(s)$$

that

(3) $$f'(s) = L\{-tF(t)\}.$$

When $F(t)$ is of class A, $(-t)^k F(t)$ is also of class A for any positive integer k.

THEOREM 13: *If $F(t)$ is of class A, it follows from $L\{F(t)\} = f(s)$ that for any positive integer n,*

(4) $$\frac{d^n}{ds^n} f(s) = L\{(-t)^n F(t)\}.$$

These theorems are useful in several ways. One immediate application is to add to our list of transforms with very little labor. We know that

(5) $$\frac{k}{s^2 + k^2} = L\{\sin kt\},$$

and therefore, by Theorem 12,

$$\frac{-2ks}{(s^2 + k^2)^2} = L\{-t \sin kt\}.$$

Thus we obtain

(6) $$\frac{s}{(s^2 + k^2)^2} = L\left\{\frac{t}{2k} \sin kt\right\}.$$

From the known formula

$$\frac{s}{s^2 + k^2} = L\{\cos kt\}$$

we obtain, by differentiation with respect to s,

(7) $$\frac{k^2 - s^2}{(s^2 + k^2)^2} = L\{-t \cos kt\}.$$

Let us add to each side of (7) the corresponding member of

$$\frac{1}{s^2 + k^2} = L\left\{\frac{1}{k} \sin kt\right\}$$

to get

$$\frac{s^2 + k^2 + k^2 - s^2}{(s^2 + k^2)^2} = L\left\{\frac{1}{k} \sin kt - t \cos kt\right\},$$

from which it follows that

(8) $$\frac{1}{(s^2 + k^2)^2} = L\left\{\frac{1}{2k^3}(\sin kt - kt \cos kt)\right\}.$$

62. The gamma function

For obtaining the Laplace transform of nonintegral powers of t, we need a function not usually discussed in elementary mathematics.

The Gamma function $\Gamma(x)$ is defined by

(1) $$\Gamma(x) = \int_0^\infty e^{-\beta}\beta^{x-1}\, d\beta, \qquad x > 0.$$

Substitution of $(x + 1)$ for x in (1) gives

(2) $$\Gamma(x + 1) = \int_0^\infty e^{-\beta}\beta^x\, d\beta.$$

An integration by parts, integrating $e^{-\beta} \, d\beta$ and differentiating β^x, yields

(3) $$\Gamma(x+1) = \left[-e^{-\beta}\beta^x \right]_0^{\infty} + x \int_0^{\infty} e^{-\beta}\beta^{x-1} \, d\beta.$$

Since $x > 0$, $\beta^x \to 0$ as $\beta \to 0$. Since x is fixed, $e^{-\beta}\beta^x \to 0$ as $\beta \to \infty$. Thus

(4) $$\Gamma(x+1) = x \int_0^{\infty} e^{-\beta}\beta^{x-1} \, d\beta = x\Gamma(x).$$

THEOREM 14: *For $x > 0$, $\Gamma(x+1) = x\Gamma(x)$.*

Suppose n is a positive integer. Iteration of Theorem 14 gives us

$$\Gamma(n+1) = n\Gamma(n)$$
$$= n(n-1)\Gamma(n-1)$$
$$\cdots$$
$$= n(n-1)(n-2) \cdots 2 \cdot 1 \cdot \Gamma(1).$$
$$= n!\Gamma(1).$$

But, by definition,

$$\Gamma(1) = \int_0^{\infty} e^{-\beta}\beta^0 \, d\beta = \left[-e^{-\beta} \right]_0^{\infty} = 1.$$

THEOREM 15: *For positive integral n, $\Gamma(n+1) = n!$.*

In the integral for $\Gamma(x+1)$ in (2), let us put $\beta = st$ with $s > 0$ and t as the new variable of integration. This yields, since $t \to 0$ as $\beta \to 0$ and $t \to \infty$ as $\beta \to \infty$,

(5) $$\Gamma(x+1) = \int_0^{\infty} e^{-st}s^x t^x s \, dt = s^{x+1} \int_0^{\infty} e^{-st}t^x \, dt,$$

which is valid for $x + 1 > 0$. We thus obtain

$$\frac{\Gamma(x+1)}{s^{x+1}} = \int_0^{\infty} e^{-st}t^x \, dt, \qquad s > 0, \, x > -1,$$

which in our Laplace transform notation says that

(6) $$L\{t^x\} = \frac{\Gamma(x+1)}{s^{x+1}}, \qquad s > 0, \quad x > -1.$$

If in (6) we put $x = -\frac{1}{2}$, we get

$$L\{t^{-\frac{1}{2}}\} = \frac{\Gamma(\frac{1}{2})}{s^{\frac{1}{2}}}.$$

But we already know that $L\{t^{-\frac{1}{2}}\} = \left(\dfrac{\pi}{s}\right)^{\frac{1}{2}}$. Hence

(7) $$\Gamma(\tfrac{1}{2}) = \sqrt{\pi}.$$

63. Periodic functions

Suppose the function $F(t)$ is periodic with period ω:

(1) $$F(t + \omega) = F(t).$$

The function is completely determined by (1) once the nature of $F(t)$ throughout one period, $0 \leqq t < \omega$, is given. If $F(t)$ has a transform,

(2) $$L\{F(t)\} = \int_0^\infty e^{-st}F(t)\, dt,$$

the integral can be written as a sum of integrals,

(3) $$L\{F(t)\} = \sum_{n=0}^\infty \int_{n\omega}^{(n+1)\omega} e^{-st}F(t)\, dt.$$

Let us put $t = n\omega + \beta$. Then (3) becomes

$$L\{F(t)\} = \sum_{n=0}^\infty \int_0^\omega \exp\left(-sn\omega - s\beta\right)F(\beta + n\omega)\, d\beta.$$

But $F(\beta + n\omega) = F(\beta)$, by iteration of (1). Hence

(4) $$L\{F(t)\} = \sum_{n=0}^\infty \exp\left(-sn\omega\right) \int_0^\omega \exp\left(-s\beta\right)F(\beta)\, d\beta.$$

The integral on the right in (4) is independent of n and we can sum the series on the right;

$$\sum_{n=0}^\infty \exp\left(-sn\omega\right) = \sum_{n=0}^\infty [\exp\left(-s\omega\right)]^n = \frac{1}{1 - e^{-s\omega}}.$$

THEOREM 16: *If $F(t)$ has a Laplace transform and if $F(t + \omega) = F(t)$,*

(5) $$L\{F(t)\} = \frac{\displaystyle\int_0^\omega e^{-s\beta}F(\beta)\, d\beta}{1 - e^{-s\omega}}.$$

Next suppose that a function $H(t)$ has a period $2c$ and that we demand that $H(t)$ be zero throughout the right half of each period. That is,

(6) $H(t + 2c) = H(t),$

(7) $H(t) = g(t), \qquad 0 \leqq t < c,$
                                 $\qquad\quad = 0, \qquad c \leqq t < 2c.$

Then we say that $H(t)$ is a half-wave rectification of $g(t)$. Using (5) we may conclude that for the $H(t)$ defined by (6) and (7),

(8) $$L\{H(t)\} = \frac{\int_0^c \exp(-s\beta)g(\beta)\, d\beta}{1 - \exp(-2cs)}.$$

EXAMPLE (a): Find the transform of the function $\psi(t, c)$ shown in Figure 19 and defined by

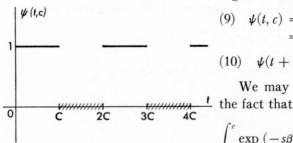

(9) $\psi(t, c) = 1, \qquad 0 < t < c,$
      $\qquad\quad = 0, \qquad c < t < 2c;$

(10) $\psi(t + 2c, c) = \psi(t, c).$

We may use equation (8) and the fact that

$$\int_0^c \exp(-s\beta)\, d\beta = \frac{1 - \exp(-sc)}{s}$$

FIGURE 19

to conclude that

(11) $L\{\psi(t, c)\} = \dfrac{1}{s} \cdot \dfrac{1 - \exp(-sc)}{1 - \exp(-2sc)} = \dfrac{1}{s} \cdot \dfrac{1}{1 + \exp(-sc)}.$

EXAMPLE (b): Find the transform of the square-wave function $Q(t, c)$ shown in Figure 20 and defined by

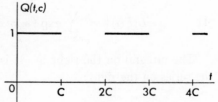

(12) $Q(t, c) = 1, \qquad 0 < t < c,$
       $\qquad\quad = -1, \qquad c < t < 2c;$

(13) $Q(t + 2c, c) = Q(t, c).$

This transform can be obtained by using Theorem 16, but also

FIGURE 20

(14) $Q(t, c) = 2\psi(t, c) - 1;$

hence, from (11),

(15) $L\{Q(t, c)\} = \dfrac{1}{s}\left[\dfrac{2}{1 + \exp(-sc)} - 1\right] = \dfrac{1}{s} \cdot \dfrac{1 - \exp(-sc)}{1 + \exp(-sc)}.$

By multiplying numerator and denominator of the last fraction above by exp $(\frac{1}{2}sc)$, we may put (15) in the form

(16) $$L\{Q(t, c)\} = \frac{1}{s} \tanh \frac{cs}{2}.$$

Exercises

1. Show that $L\{t^{\frac{1}{2}}\} = \dfrac{1}{2s}\left(\dfrac{\pi}{s}\right)^{\frac{1}{2}}, \quad s > 0.$

2. Show that $L\{t^{\frac{5}{2}}\} = \dfrac{15}{8s^3}\left(\dfrac{\pi}{s}\right)^{\frac{1}{2}}, \quad s > 0.$

3. Use equation (4), page 174, to derive $L\{\sin kt\}$.

4. Use equation (4), page 174, to derive $L\{\cos kt\}$.

5. Check the known transforms of sin kt and cos kt against one another by using Theorem 9, page 174.

6. If n is a positive integer, obtain $L\{t^n e^{kt}\}$ from the known $L\{e^{kt}\}$ by using Theorem 13, page 176. ANS. $\dfrac{n!}{(s-k)^{n+1}}, \quad s > k.$

7. Find $L\{t^2 \sin kt\}$. ANS. $\dfrac{2k(3s^2 - k^2)}{(s^2 + k^2)^3}, \quad s > 0.$

8. Find $L\{t^2 \cos kt\}$. ANS. $\dfrac{2s(s^2 - 3k^2)}{(s^2 + k^2)^3}, s > 0.$

9. For the function

$$F(t) = t + 1, \qquad 0 \leq t \leq 2,$$
$$\quad\;\; = 3, \qquad\qquad t > 2,$$

graph $F(t)$ and $F'(t)$. Find $L\{F(t)\}$. Find $L\{F'(t)\}$ in two ways. ANS. $L\{F'(t)\} = s^{-1}(1 - e^{-2s}), \quad s > 0.$

10. For the function

$$H(t) = t + 1, \qquad 0 \leq t \leq 2,$$
$$\quad\;\; = 6, \qquad\qquad t > 2,$$

parallel Ex. 9 above.

11. Define a triangular-wave function $T(t, c)$ by

$$T(t, c) = t, \qquad 0 \leq t \leq c,$$
$$\qquad\quad = 2c - t, \quad c < t < 2c;$$
$$T(t + 2c, c) = T(t, c).$$

Sketch $T(t, c)$ and find its Laplace transform. ANS. $\dfrac{1}{s^2} \tanh \dfrac{cs}{2}.$

12. Show that the derivative of the function $T(t, c)$ of Ex. 11 is, except at certain points, the function $Q(t, c)$ of Example (b), Section 63. Obtain $L\{T(t, c)\}$ from $L\{Q(t, c)\}$.

13. Sketch a half-wave rectification of the function $\sin \omega t$, as described below, and find its transform.

$$F(t) = \sin \omega t, \qquad 0 \leqq t \leqq \frac{\pi}{\omega},$$

$$= 0, \qquad \frac{\pi}{\omega} < t < \frac{2\pi}{\omega} \; ;$$

$$F\left(t + \frac{2\pi}{\omega}\right) = F(t).$$

ANS. $\dfrac{\omega}{s^2 + \omega^2} \cdot \dfrac{1}{1 - \exp\left(-\dfrac{s\pi}{\omega}\right)}$.

14. Find $L\{F(t)\}$ where $F(t) = t$ for $0 < t < \omega$ and $F(t + \omega) = F(t)$.

ANS. $\dfrac{1}{s^2} - \dfrac{\omega}{s} \dfrac{\exp(-s\omega)}{1 - \exp(-s\omega)} = \dfrac{1}{s^2} + \dfrac{\omega}{2s}\left(1 - \coth\dfrac{\omega s}{2}\right)$.

15. Prove that if $L\{F(t)\} = f(s)$ and if $\dfrac{F(t)}{t}$ is of class A,

$$L\left\{\frac{F(t)}{t}\right\} = \int_s^\infty f(\beta) \, d\beta.$$

Hint: Use Theorem 12, page 176.

CHAPTER 12

Inverse Transforms

64. Definition of an inverse transform

Suppose the function $F(t)$ is to be determined from a differential equation with boundary conditions. The Laplace operator L is used to transform the original problem into a new problem from which the transform $f(s)$ is to be found. If the Laplace transformation is to be effective, the new problem must be simpler than the original problem. We first find $f(s)$ and then must obtain $F(t)$ from $f(s)$. It is therefore desirable to develop methods for finding the object function $F(t)$ when its transform $f(s)$ is known.

If

(1) $$L\{F(t)\} = f(s),$$

we say that $F(t)$ is an *inverse Laplace transform*, or an inverse transform, of $f(s)$ and we write

(2) $$F(t) = L^{-1}\{f(s)\}.$$

Since (1) means that

(3) $$\int_0^\infty e^{-st}F(t)\,dt = f(s),$$

it follows at once that an inverse transform is not unique. For example, if $F_1(t)$ and $F_2(t)$ are identical except at a discrete set of points and differ at

183

those points, the value of the integral in (3) is the same for the two functions; their transforms are identical.

Let us employ the term *null function* for any function $N(t)$ for which

$$(4) \qquad \int_0^{t_0} N(t) \, dt = 0$$

for every positive t_0. Lerch's theorem (not proved here) states that if $L\{F_1(t)\} = L\{F_2(t)\}$, then $F_1(t) - F_2(t) = N(t)$. That is, an inverse Laplace transform is unique except for the addition of an arbitrary null function.

The only continuous null function is zero. If an $f(s)$ has a continuous inverse $F(t)$, then $F(t)$ is the only continuous inverse of $f(s)$. If $f(s)$ has an inverse $F_1(t)$ continuous over a specified closed interval, every inverse that is also continuous over that interval is identical with $F_1(t)$ on that interval. Essentially, inverses of the same $f(s)$ differ at most at their points of discontinuity.

In applications, failure of uniqueness caused by addition of a null function is not vital, because the effect of that null function on physical properties of the solution is null. In the problems we treat, the inverse $F(t)$ is required either to be continuous for $t \geq 0$ or to be sectionally continuous with the values of $F(t)$ at the points of discontinuity specified by each problem. The $F(t)$ is then unique.

A crude, but sometimes effective, method for finding inverse Laplace transforms is to construct a table of transforms (page 210) and then to use it in reverse to find inverse transforms.

We know from Ex. 1, page 166, that

$$(5) \qquad L\{\cos kt\} = \frac{s}{s^2 + k^2}.$$

Therefore

$$(6) \qquad L^{-1}\left\{\frac{s}{s^2 + k^2}\right\} = \cos kt.$$

We shall refine the above method, and actually make it quite powerful, by developing theorems by which a given $f(s)$ may be expanded into component parts whose inverses are known (found in the table). Other theorems will permit us to write $f(s)$ in alternate forms which yield the desired inverse. The most fundamental of such theorems is one that states that the inverse transformation is a linear operation.

THEOREM 17: *If c_1 and c_2 are constants,*

$$L^{-1}\{c_1 f_1(s) + c_2 f_2(s)\} = c_1 L^{-1}\{f_1(s)\} + c_2 L^{-1}\{f_2(s)\}.$$

Next let us prove a simple, but extremely useful, theorem on the manipulation of inverse transforms. From

(7) $$f(s) = \int_0^\infty e^{-st}F(t)\,dt,$$

we obtain

$$f(s - a) = \int_0^\infty e^{-(s-a)t}F(t)\,dt$$
$$= \int_0^\infty e^{-st}[e^{at}F(t)]\,dt.$$

Thus, from $L^{-1}\{f(s)\} = F(t)$ it follows that

$$L^{-1}\{f(s - a)\} = e^{at}F(t),$$

or

(8) $$L^{-1}\{f(s - a)\} = e^{at}L^{-1}\{f(s)\}.$$

Equation (8) may be rewritten with the exponential transferred to the other side of the equation. We thus obtain the following result.

THEOREM 18: $L^{-1}\{f(s)\} = e^{-at}L^{-1}\{f(s - a)\}.$

EXAMPLE (a): Find $L^{-1}\left\{\dfrac{15}{s^2 + 4s + 13}\right\}.$

First complete the square in the denominator.

$$L^{-1}\left\{\frac{15}{s^2 + 4s + 13}\right\} = L^{-1}\left\{\frac{15}{(s + 2)^2 + 9}\right\}.$$

Since we know that $L^{-1}\left\{\dfrac{k}{s^2 + k^2}\right\} = \sin kt$, we proceed as follows:

$$L^{-1}\left\{\frac{15}{s^2 + 4s + 13}\right\} = 5L^{-1}\left\{\frac{3}{(s + 2)^2 + 9}\right\} = 5e^{-2t}L^{-1}\left\{\frac{3}{s^2 + 9}\right\}$$
$$= 5e^{-2t}\sin 3t,$$

in which we have used Theorem 18.

EXAMPLE (b): Evaluate $L^{-1}\left\{\dfrac{s + 1}{s^2 + 6s + 25}\right\}.$

We write

$$L^{-1}\left\{\frac{s + 1}{s^2 + 6s + 25}\right\} = L^{-1}\left\{\frac{s + 1}{(s + 3)^2 + 16}\right\}.$$

Then

$$L^{-1}\left\{\frac{s+1}{s^2+6s+25}\right\} = e^{-3t}L^{-1}\left\{\frac{s-2}{s^2+16}\right\}$$

$$= e^{-3t}\left[L^{-1}\left\{\frac{s}{s^2+16}\right\} - \tfrac{1}{2}L^{-1}\left\{\frac{4}{s^2+16}\right\}\right]$$

$$= e^{-3t}(\cos 4t - \tfrac{1}{2}\sin 4t).$$

Exercises

In Exs. 1–10, obtain $L^{-1}\{f(s)\}$ from the given $f(s)$.

1. $\dfrac{1}{s^2+2s+5}$.　　　　　　　　　　　　　　　ANS.　$\tfrac{1}{2}e^{-t}\sin 2t$.

2. $\dfrac{1}{s^2-6s+10}$.　　　　　　　　　　　　　　ANS.　$e^{3t}\sin t$.

3. $\dfrac{s}{s^2+2s+5}$.　　　　　　　　　　ANS.　$e^{-t}(\cos 2t - \tfrac{1}{2}\sin 2t)$.

4. $\dfrac{s}{s^2-6s+13}$.　　　　　　　　　ANS.　$e^{3t}(\cos 2t + \tfrac{3}{2}\sin 2t)$.

5. $\dfrac{1}{s^2+8s+16}$.　　　　　　　　　　　　　　ANS.　te^{-4t}.

6. $\dfrac{s}{s^2+8s+16}$.　　　　　　　　　　　　ANS.　$e^{-4t}(1-4t)$.

7. $\dfrac{s-5}{s^2+6s+13}$.　　　　　　　　　ANS.　$e^{-3t}(\cos 2t - 4\sin 2t)$.

8. $\dfrac{2s-1}{s^2+4s+29}$.　　　　　　　　　ANS.　$e^{-2t}(2\cos 5t - \sin 5t)$.

9. $\dfrac{3s+1}{(s+1)^4}$.　　　　　　　　　ANS.　$e^{-t}\left(\dfrac{3}{2}t^2 - \dfrac{1}{3}t^3\right)$.

10. $\dfrac{s^2}{(s+2)^3}$.　　　　　　　　　ANS.　$e^{-2t}(1-4t+2t^2)$.

11. Show that for n a non-negative integer

$$L^{-1}\left\{\frac{1}{(s+a)^{n+1}}\right\} = \frac{t^n e^{-at}}{n!}.$$

12. Show that for $m > -1$,

$$L^{-1}\left\{\frac{1}{(s+a)^{m+1}}\right\} = \frac{t^m e^{-at}}{\Gamma(m+1)}.$$

13. Show that

$$L^{-1}\left\{\frac{1}{(s+a)^2+b^2}\right\} = \frac{1}{b}e^{-at}\sin bt.$$

14. Show that

$$L^{-1}\left\{\frac{s}{(s+a)^2+b^2}\right\} = \frac{1}{b}e^{-at}(b\cos bt - a\sin bt).$$

15. For $a > 0$, show that from $L^{-1}\{f(s)\} = F(t)$ it follows that

$$L^{-1}\{f(as)\} = \frac{1}{a}F\left(\frac{t}{a}\right).$$

16. For $a > 0$, show that from $L^{-1}\{f(s)\} = F(t)$ it follows that

$$L^{-1}\{f(as+b)\} = \frac{1}{a}\exp\left(-\frac{bt}{a}\right)F\left(\frac{t}{a}\right).$$

65. A step function

Applications frequently deal with situations that change abruptly at specified times. We need a notation for a function that will suppress a given term up to a certain value of t and insert the term for all larger t. The function we are about to introduce leads us to a powerful tool for the constructing of inverse transforms.

Let us define function $\alpha(t)$ by

$$(1) \qquad \begin{aligned} \alpha(t) &= 0, \quad t < 0, \\ &= 1, \quad t \geqq 0. \end{aligned}$$

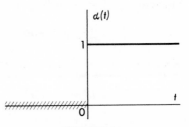

The graph of $\alpha(t)$ is shown in Figure 21.

The definition (1) says that $\alpha(t)$ is zero when the argument is negative and $\alpha(t)$ is unity when the argument is positive or is zero. It follows that

FIGURE 21

$$(2) \qquad \begin{aligned} \alpha(t-c) &= 0, \quad t < c, \\ &= 1, \quad t \geqq c. \end{aligned}$$

The α function permits easy designation of the result of translating the graph of $F(t)$. If the graph of

$$(3) \qquad y = F(t), \quad t \geqq 0,$$

is as shown in Figure 22, page 188, the graph of

$$(4) \qquad y = \alpha(t-c)F(t-c), \quad t \geqq c,$$

is that shown in Figure 23. Furthermore, if $F(x)$ is defined for $-c \leqq x < 0$, $F(t - c)$ is defined for $0 \leqq t < c$ and the y of (4) is zero for $0 \leqq t < c$

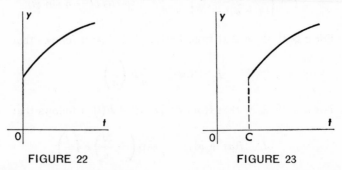

FIGURE 22   FIGURE 23

because of the negative argument in $\alpha(t - c)$. Notice that the values of $F(x)$ for negative x have no bearing on this result because each value is multiplied by zero (from the α); only the existence of F for negative arguments is needed.

The Laplace transform of $\alpha(t - c)F(t - c)$ is related to that of $F(t)$. Consider

$$L\{\alpha(t - c)F(t - c)\} = \int_0^\infty e^{-st}\alpha(t - c)F(t - c)\, dt.$$

Since $\alpha(t - c) = 0$ for $0 \leqq t < c$ and $\alpha(t - c) = 1$ for $t \geqq c$, we get

$$L\{\alpha(t - c)F(t - c)\} = \int_c^\infty e^{-st}F(t - c)\, dt.$$

Now put $t - c = v$ in the integral to obtain

$$L\{\alpha(t - c)F(t - c)\} = \int_0^\infty e^{-s(c+v)}F(v)\, dv$$

$$= e^{-cs}\int_0^\infty e^{-sv}F(v)\, dv.$$

Since a definite integral is independent of the variable of integration,

$$\int_0^\infty e^{-sv}F(v)\, dv = \int_0^\infty e^{-st}F(t)\, dt = L\{F(t)\} = f(s).$$

Therefore we have shown that

(5) $$L\{\alpha(t - c)F(t - c)\} = e^{-cs}L\{F(t)\} = e^{-cs}f(s).$$

THEOREM 19: *If $L^{-1}\{f(s)\} = F(t)$, if $c \geqq 0$, and if $F(t)$ be assigned values (no matter what ones) for $-c \leqq t < 0$,*

(6) $$L^{-1}\{e^{-cs}f(s)\} = F(t - c)\alpha(t - c).$$

EXAMPLE (a): Find $L\{y(t)\}$ where (Figure 24)

$$y(t) = t^2, \qquad 0 < t < 2,$$
$$= 6, \qquad t > 2.$$

Here, direct use of the definition of a transform yields

$$L\{y(t)\} = \int_0^2 t^2 e^{-st}\, dt + \int_2^\infty 6e^{-st}\, dt.$$

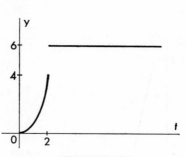

FIGURE 24

Although the above integrations are not difficult, one of them may (or may not, depending on the skill of the operator) involve two integrations by parts. We prefer to use the α function.

Since $\alpha(t - 2) = 0$ for $t < 2$ and $\alpha(t - 2) = 1$ for $t \geq 2$, we build the $y(t)$ in the following way. The crude trial

$$y_1 = t^2$$

works for $0 < t < 2$, but we wish to knock out the t^2 when $t > 2$. Hence we write

$$y_2 = t^2 - t^2\alpha(t - 2).$$

This gives t^2 for $t < 2$ and zero for $t > 2$. Then we add the term $6\alpha(t - 2)$ and finally arrive at

(7) $$y(t) = t^2 - t^2\alpha(t - 2) + 6\alpha(t - 2).$$

The y of (7) is the y of our example and, of course, it can be written at once after a little practice with the α function. No intermediate steps such as forming y_1 and y_2 need be used.

Unfortunately, the y of (7) is not yet in the best form for our purpose. The theorem we wish to use gives us

$$L\{F(t - c)\alpha(t - c)\} = e^{-cs}f(s).$$

Therefore we must have the coefficient of $\alpha(t - 2)$ expressed as a function of $(t - 2)$. Since

$$-t^2 + 6 = -(t^2 - 4t + 4) - 4(t - 2) + 2,$$

(8) $$y(t) = t^2 - (t - 2)^2\alpha(t - 2) - 4(t - 2)\alpha(t - 2) + 2\alpha(t - 2),$$

from which it follows at once that

$$L\{y(t)\} = \frac{2}{s^3} - \frac{2e^{-2s}}{s^3} - \frac{4e^{-2s}}{s^2} + \frac{2e^{-2s}}{s}.$$

EXAMPLE (b): Find and sketch a function $g(t)$ for which

$$g(t) = L^{-1} \left\{ \frac{3}{s} - \frac{4e^{-s}}{s^2} + \frac{4e^{-3s}}{s^2} \right\}.$$

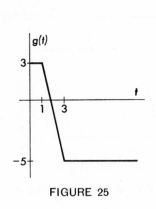

FIGURE 25

We know that $L^{-1} \left\{ \dfrac{4}{s^2} \right\} = 4t$. By Theorem 19 we then get

$$L^{-1} \left\{ \frac{4e^{-s}}{s^2} \right\} = 4(t - 1)\alpha(t - 1)$$

and

$$L^{-1} \left\{ \frac{4e^{-3s}}{s^2} \right\} = 4(t - 3)\alpha(t - 3).$$

We may therefore write

(9) $\qquad g(t) = 3 - 4(t - 1)\alpha(t - 1) + 4(t - 3)\alpha(t - 3).$

To write $g(t)$ without the α function, consider first the interval

$$0 \leq t < 1$$

in which $\alpha(t - 1) = 0$ and $\alpha(t - 3) = 0$. We find

(10) $\qquad\qquad\qquad g(t) = 3, \qquad 0 \leq t < 1.$

For $1 \leq t < 3$, $\alpha(t - 1) = 1$, and $\alpha(t - 3) = 0$. Hence

(11) $\qquad g(t) = 3 - 4(t - 1) = 7 - 4t, \qquad 1 \leq t < 3.$

For $t \geq 3$, $\alpha(t - 1) = 1$ and $\alpha(t - 3) = 1$, so

(12) $\qquad g(t) = 3 - 4(t - 1) + 4(t - 3) = -5, \qquad t \geq 3.$

Equations (10), (11), and (12) are equivalent to equation (9). The graph of $g(t)$ is shown in Figure 25.

Exercises

In Exs. 1–8, express $F(t)$ in terms of the α function and find $L\{F(t)\}$.

1. $F(t) = 2, \qquad 0 < t < 1,$
$\qquad = t, \qquad\qquad t > 1.$ ANS. $\dfrac{2}{s} + e^{-s} \left(\dfrac{1}{s^2} - \dfrac{1}{s} \right).$

2. $F(t) = 6, \qquad 0 < t < 4,$
$\qquad = 2t + 1, \qquad t > 4.$ ANS. $\dfrac{6}{s} + e^{-4s} \left(\dfrac{2}{s^2} + \dfrac{3}{s} \right).$

3. $F(t) = t^2, \qquad 0 < t < 1,$
$\qquad = 4, \qquad\qquad t > 1.$ ANS. $\dfrac{2}{s^3} + e^{-s} \left(\dfrac{3}{s} - \dfrac{2}{s^2} - \dfrac{2}{s^3} \right).$

4. $F(t) = t^2,$ $0 < t < 2,$

     $= 4,$ $2 \leqq t \leqq 4,$

     $= 0,$ $t > 4.$ ANS. $\dfrac{2}{s^3} - e^{-2s}\left(\dfrac{4}{s^2} + \dfrac{2}{s^3}\right) - \dfrac{4}{s}\, e^{-4s}.$

5. $F(t) = t^2,$ $0 < t < 2,$

     $= t - 1,$ $2 < t < 3,$

     $= 7,$ $t > 3.$

ANS. $\dfrac{2}{s^3} - e^{-2s}\left(\dfrac{3}{s} + \dfrac{3}{s^2} + \dfrac{2}{s^3}\right) + e^{-3s}\left(\dfrac{5}{s} - \dfrac{1}{s^2}\right).$

6. $F(t) = e^{-t},$ $0 < t < 2,$ ANS. $\dfrac{1 - \exp{(-2s - 2)}}{s + 1}.$

     $= 0,$ $t > 2.$

7. $F(t) = \sin 3t,$ $0 < t < \tfrac{1}{2}\pi,$ ANS. $\dfrac{3 + s\exp{(-\tfrac{1}{2}\pi s)}}{s^2 + 9}.$

     $= 0,$ $t > \tfrac{1}{2}\pi.$

8. $F(t) = \sin 3t,$ $0 < t < \pi,$

     $= 0,$ $t > \pi.$ ANS. $\dfrac{3(1 + e^{-\pi s})}{s^2 + 9}.$

9. Find and sketch an inverse Laplace transform of

$$\frac{5e^{-3s}}{s} - \frac{e^{-s}}{s}.$$

ANS. $F(t) = 5\alpha(t - 3) - \alpha(t - 1).$

10. Evaluate $L^{-1}\left\{\dfrac{e^{-4s}}{(s + 2)^3}\right\}.$

ANS. $\tfrac{1}{2}(t - 4)^2 \exp{[-2(t - 4)]}\, \alpha(t - 4).$

11. If $F(t)$ is to be continuous for $t \geqq 0$ and

$$F(t) = L^{-1}\left\{\frac{e^{-3s}}{(s + 1)^3}\right\},$$

evaluate $F(2), F(5), F(7).$

ANS. $F(2) = 0, F(5) = 2e^{-2}, F(7) = 8e^{-4}.$

12. If $F(t)$ is to be continuous for $t \geqq 0$ and

$$F(t) = L^{-1}\left\{\frac{(1 - e^{-2s})(1 - 3e^{-2s})}{s^2}\right\},$$

evaluate $F(1), F(3), F(5).$ ANS. $F(1) = 1, F(3) = -1, F(5) = -4.$

13. Prove that $\psi(t, c) = \displaystyle\sum_{n=0}^{\infty} (-1)^n \alpha(t - nc)$ is the same function as was

used in Example (a), Section 63. Note that for any specific t, the series is finite; no question of convergence is involved.

14. Obtain the transform of the half-wave rectification $F(t)$ of $\sin t$ by writing

$$F(t) = \sin t\, \psi\,(t, \pi)$$

in terms of the ψ of Ex. 13 above. Use the fact that

$$(-1)^n \sin t = \sin (t - n\pi).$$

Check your result with that in Ex. 13, page 182.

66. A convolution theorem

We now seek a formula for the inverse transform of a product of transforms. Given

(1) $$L^{-1}\{f(s)\} = F(t), \qquad L^{-1}\{g(s)\} = G(t),$$

in which $F(t)$ and $G(t)$ are assumed to be functions of class A, we shall obtain a formula for

(2) $$L^{-1}\{f(s)g(s)\}.$$

Since $f(s)$ is the transform of $F(t)$, we may write

(3) $$f(s) = \int_0^\infty e^{-st}F(t)\,dt.$$

Since $g(s)$ is the transform of $G(t)$,

(4) $$g(s) = \int_0^\infty e^{-s\beta}G(\beta)\,d\beta,$$

in which, to avoid confusion, we have used β (rather than t) as the variable of integration in the definite integral.

By equation (4), we have

(5) $$f(s)g(s) = \int_0^\infty e^{-s\beta}f(s)G(\beta)\,d\beta.$$

On the right in (5) we encounter the product $e^{-s\beta}f(s)$. By Theorem 19, page 188, we know that from

(6) $$L^{-1}\{f(s)\} = F(t)$$

it follows that

(7) $$L^{-1}\{e^{-s\beta}f(s)\} = F(t - \beta)\alpha(t - \beta),$$

in which α is the step function discussed in Section 65. Equation (7) means that

(8) $$e^{-s\beta}f(s) = \int_0^\infty e^{-st}F(t - \beta)\alpha(t - \beta)\,dt.$$

With the aid of (8) we may put equation (5) in the form

$$(9) \qquad f(s)g(s) = \int_0^\infty \int_0^\infty e^{-st}G(\beta)F(t - \beta)\alpha(t - \beta) \, dt \, d\beta.$$

Since $\alpha(t - \beta) = 0$ for $0 < t < \beta$ and $\alpha(t - \beta) = 1$ for $t \geqq \beta$, equation (9) may be rewritten as

$$(10) \qquad f(s)g(s) = \int_0^\infty \int_\beta^\infty e^{-st}G(\beta)F(t - \beta) \, dt \, d\beta.$$

In (10), the integration in the $t\beta$-plane covers the shaded region shown in Figure 26. The elements are summed from $t = \beta$ to $t = \infty$ and then from $\beta = 0$ to $\beta = \infty$.

By the methods of advanced calculus it can be shown that, because $F(t)$ and $G(t)$ are functions of class A, it is legitimate to interchange the order of integration on the right in equation (10). From Figure 26 we see that in the new order of integration, the elements are to be summed from $\beta = 0$ to $\beta = t$ and then from $t = 0$ to $t = \infty$. We thus obtain

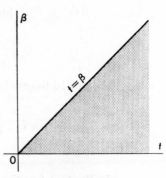

FIGURE 26

$$f(s)g(s) = \int_0^\infty \int_0^t e^{-st}G(\beta)F(t - \beta) \, d\beta \, dt,$$

or

$$(11) \qquad f(s)g(s) = \int_0^\infty e^{-st} \left[\int_0^t G(\beta)F(t - \beta) \, d\beta \right] dt.$$

Since the right member of (11) is precisely the Laplace transform of

$$\int_0^t G(\beta)F(t - \beta) \, d\beta,$$

we have arrived at the desired result, which is called the convolution theorem for the Laplace transform.

THEOREM 20: *If $L^{-1}\{f(s)\} = F(t)$, if $L^{-1}\{g(s)\} = G(t)$, and if $F(t)$ and $G(t)$ are functions of class A, page* 171, *then*

$$(12) \qquad L^{-1}\{f(s)g(s)\} = \int_0^t G(\beta)F(t - \beta) \, d\beta.$$

It is easy to show that the right member of equation (12) is also a function of class A.

Of course F and G are interchangeable in (12), since f and g enter (12) symmetrically. We may replace (12) by

$$(13) \qquad L^{-1}\{f(s)g(s)\} = \int_0^t F(\beta)G(t - \beta) \, d\beta,$$

a result which also follows from (12) by a change of variable of integration.

EXAMPLE: Evaluate $L^{-1}\left\{\dfrac{f(s)}{s}\right\}$.

Let $L^{-1}\{f(s)\} = F(t)$. Since

$$L^{-1}\left\{\frac{1}{s}\right\} = 1,$$

we use Theorem 20 to conclude that

$$L^{-1}\left\{\frac{f(s)}{s}\right\} = \int_0^t F(\beta) \, d\beta.$$

67. Partial fractions

In using the Laplace transform to solve differential equations, we often need to obtain the inverse transform of a rational fraction

$$(1) \qquad \frac{N(s)}{D(s)}.$$

The numerator and denominator in (1) are polynomials in s and the degree of $D(s)$ is larger than the degree of $N(s)$. The fraction (1) has the partial fractions expansion used in calculus.* Because of the linearity of the inverse operator L^{-1}, the partial fractions expansion of (1) permits us to replace a complicated problem in obtaining an inverse transform with a set of simpler problems.

EXAMPLE (a): Obtain $L^{-1}\left\{\dfrac{s^2 - 6}{s^3 + 4s^2 + 3s}\right\}$.

Since the denominator is a product of distinct linear factors, we know that constants A, B, C exist such that

---

* See, for example, E. D. Rainville, *Unified Calculus and Analytic Geometry* (New York: The Macmillan Co., 1961), pp. 357–364.

$$\frac{s^2 - 6}{s^3 + 4s^2 + 3s} = \frac{s^2 - 6}{s(s + 1)(s + 3)} = \frac{A}{s} + \frac{B}{s + 1} + \frac{C}{s + 3}.$$

Multiplying each term by the lowest common denominator, we obtain the identity

(2) $\qquad s^2 - 6 = A(s + 1)(s + 3) + Bs(s + 3) + Cs(s + 1),$

from which we need to determine A, B, and C. Using the values $s = 0$, -1, -3 successively in (2), we get

$$\begin{aligned}
s = 0: && -6 &= A(1)(3), \\
s = -1: && -5 &= B(-1)(2), \\
s = -3: && 3 &= C(-3)(-2),
\end{aligned}$$

from which $A = -2$, $B = \frac{5}{2}$, $C = \frac{1}{2}$. Therefore

$$\frac{s^2 - 6}{s^3 + 4s^2 + 3s} = \frac{-2}{s} + \frac{\frac{5}{2}}{s + 1} + \frac{\frac{1}{2}}{s + 3}.$$

Since $L^{-1}\left\{\frac{1}{s}\right\} = 1$ and $L^{-1}\left\{\frac{1}{s + a}\right\} = e^{-at}$, we get the desired result,

$$L^{-1}\left\{\frac{s^2 - 6}{s^3 + 4s^2 + 3s}\right\} = -2 + \tfrac{5}{2}e^{-t} + \tfrac{1}{2}e^{-3t}.$$

EXAMPLE (b): Obtain $L^{-1}\left\{\dfrac{5s^3 - 6s - 3}{s^3(s + 1)^2}\right\}$.

Since the denominator contains repeated linear factors, we must assume partial fractions of the form shown:

(3) $\qquad \dfrac{5s^3 - 6s - 3}{s^3(s + 1)^2} = \dfrac{A_1}{s} + \dfrac{A_2}{s^2} + \dfrac{A_3}{s^3} + \dfrac{B_1}{s + 1} + \dfrac{B_2}{(s + 1)^2}.$

Corresponding to a denominator factor $(x - \gamma)^r$, we must in general assume r partial fractions of the form

$$\frac{A_1}{x - \gamma} + \frac{A_2}{(x - \gamma)^2} + \cdots + \frac{A_r}{(x - \gamma)^r}.$$

From (3) we get

(4) $\quad 5s^3 - 6s - 3 = A_1 s^2(s + 1)^2 + A_2 s(s + 1)^2$
$$\qquad\qquad\qquad + A_3(s + 1)^2 + B_1 s^3(s + 1) + B_2 s^3,$$

which must be an identity in s. To get the necessary five equations for the determination of A_1, A_2, A_3, B_1, B_2, two elementary methods are popular.

Specific values of s can be used in (4), or the coefficients of like powers of s in the two members of (4) may be equated. We employ whatever combination of these methods yields simple equations to be solved for A_1, A_2, $\cdots$. B_2. From (4) we obtain

$$s = 0: \qquad\qquad -3 = A_3(1),$$
$$s = -1: \qquad\qquad -2 = B_2(-1),$$
$$\text{coeff. of } s^4: \qquad\qquad 0 = A_1 + B_1,$$
$$\text{coeff. of } s^3: \qquad\qquad 5 = 2A_1 + A_2 + B_1 + B_2,$$
$$\text{coeff. of } s: \qquad\qquad -6 = A_2 + 2A_3.$$

The above equations yield $A_1 = 3, A_2 = 0, A_3 = -3, B_1 = -3, B_2 = 2$. Therefore we find that

$$L^{-1}\left\{\frac{5s^3 - 6s - 3}{s^3(s+1)^2}\right\} = L^{-1}\left\{\frac{3}{s} - \frac{3}{s^3} - \frac{3}{s+1} + \frac{2}{(s+1)^2}\right\}$$

$$= 3 - \tfrac{3}{2}t^2 - 3e^{-t} + 2te^{-t}.$$

EXAMPLE (c): Obtain $L^{-1}\left\{\dfrac{16}{s(s^2+4)^2}\right\}$.

Since quadratic factors require the corresponding partial fractions to have linear numerators, we start with an expansion of the form

$$\frac{16}{s(s^2+4)^2} = \frac{A}{s} + \frac{B_1s + C_1}{s^2+4} + \frac{B_2s + C_2}{(s^2+4)^2}.$$

From the identity

$$16 = A(s^2+4)^2 + (B_1s + C_1)s(s^2+4) + (B_2s + C_2)s,$$

it is not difficult to find the values $A = 1, B_1 = -1, B_2 = -4, C_1 = 0$, $C_2 = 0$. We thus obtain

$$L^{-1}\left\{\frac{16}{s(s^2+4)^2}\right\} = L^{-1}\left\{\frac{1}{s} - \frac{s}{s^2+4} - \frac{4s}{(s^2+4)^2}\right\}$$

$$= 1 - \cos 2t - t\sin 2t.$$

It is possible to obtain formulas for the partial fractions expansion of the rational fractions being treated in this section. Such formulas are useful in theory and not particularly inefficient in practice. The elementary techniques above, if used intelligently, are efficient in numerical problems and are the only partial fractions methods presented in this short treatment of the subject.

Exercises

In Exs. 1–10, find an inverse transform of the given $f(s)$.

1. $\dfrac{1}{s^2 + as}$.　　　　　　　　　　　ANS.　$\dfrac{1}{a}(1 - e^{-at})$.

2. $\dfrac{s + 2}{s^2 - 6s + 8}$.　　　　　　　　　ANS.　$3e^{4t} - 2e^{2t}$.

3. $\dfrac{2s^2 + 5s - 4}{s^3 + s^2 - 2s}$.　　　　　　　ANS.　$2 + e^t - e^{-2t}$.

4. $\dfrac{2s^2 + 1}{s(s + 1)^2}$.　　　　　　　　ANS.　$1 + e^{-t} - 3te^{-t}$.

5. $\dfrac{4s + 4}{s^2(s - 2)}$.　　　　　　　　ANS.　$3e^{2t} - 3 - 2t$.

6. $\dfrac{1}{s^3(s^2 + 1)}$.　　　　　　　　ANS.　$\frac{1}{2}t^2 - 1 + \cos t$.

7. $\dfrac{5s - 2}{s^2(s + 2)(s - 1)}$.　　　　　　ANS.　$t - 2 + e^t + e^{-2t}$.

8. $\dfrac{1}{(s^2 + a^2)(s^2 + b^2)}$,　$a^2 \neq b^2,\ ab \neq 0$.　ANS.　$\dfrac{b \sin at - a \sin bt}{ab(b^2 - a^2)}$.

9. $\dfrac{s}{(s^2 + a^2)(s^2 + b^2)}$,　$a^2 \neq b^2,\ ab \neq 0$.　ANS.　$\dfrac{\cos at - \cos bt}{b^2 - a^2}$.

10. $\dfrac{s^2}{(s^2 + a^2)(s^2 + b^2)}$,　$a^2 \neq b^2,\ ab \neq 0$.　ANS.　$\dfrac{a \sin at - b \sin bt}{a^2 - b^2}$.

11. Obtain the answers to Exs. 9 and 10 from that for Ex. 8.

12. Use equation (8), page 177, and the convolution, Theorem 20, to obtain

$$L^{-1}\left\{\frac{16}{s(s^2 + 4)^2}\right\} = \int_0^t (\sin 2\beta - 2\beta \cos 2\beta)\, d\beta,$$

and then perform the integration to check the answer to Example (c), page 196.

68. Simple boundary value problems

Because of Theorem 10, page 175, the Laplace operator will transform a differential equation with constant coefficients into an algebraic equation in the transformed function. Several examples will be treated in detail so that we can get some feeling for the advantages and disadvantages of the transform method. One fact is apparent from the start: this method is at its best when the boundary conditions are actually initial conditions, those giving the value of the function and its derivatives at time zero.

EXAMPLE (a): Solve the problem

(1) $y''(t) + \beta^2 y(t) = A \sin \omega t;$ $y(0) = 1,$ $y'(0) = 0.$

Here A, β, ω are constants. Since $\beta = 0$ would make the problem one of elementary calculus and since a change in sign of β or ω would not alter the character of the problem, we may assume that β and ω are positive.

Let $L\{y(t)\} = u(s).$

Then $L\{y'(t)\} = su(s) - 1,$
                       $L\{y''(t)\} = s^2u(s) - s \cdot 1 - 0,$

and application of the operator L transforms the problem (1) into

$$s^2u(s) - s + \beta^2 u(s) = \frac{A\omega}{s^2 + \omega^2},$$

from which

(2) $$u(s) = \frac{s}{s^2 + \beta^2} + \frac{A\omega}{(s^2 + \beta^2)(s^2 + \omega^2)}.$$

We need the inverse transform of the right member of (2). The form of that inverse depends upon whether β and ω are equal or unequal.
   If $\omega \neq \beta$,

$$u(s) = \frac{s}{s^2 + \beta^2} + \frac{A\omega}{\beta^2 - \omega^2}\left(\frac{1}{s^2 + \omega^2} - \frac{1}{s^2 + \beta^2}\right)$$

$$= \frac{s}{s^2 + \beta^2} + \frac{A}{\beta(\beta^2 - \omega^2)}\left(\frac{\omega\beta}{s^2 + \omega^2} - \frac{\omega\beta}{s^2 + \beta^2}\right).$$

Now $y(t) = L^{-1}\{u(s)\}$ so, for $\omega \neq \beta$,

(3) $$y(t) = \cos \beta t + \frac{A}{\beta(\beta^2 - \omega^2)}(\beta \sin \omega t - \omega \sin \beta t).$$

If $\omega = \beta$, the transform (2) becomes

(4) $$u(s) = \frac{s}{s^2 + \beta^2} + \frac{A\beta}{(s^2 + \beta^2)^2}.$$

We know that

$$L^{-1}\left\{\frac{1}{(s^2 + \beta^2)^2}\right\} = \frac{1}{2\beta^3}(\sin \beta t - \beta t \cos \beta t).$$

Hence, for $\omega = \beta$,

(5) $$y(t) = \cos \beta t + \frac{A}{2\beta^2}(\sin \beta t - \beta t \cos \beta t).$$

Note that the initial conditions were satisfied automatically by this method when Theorem 10 was applied. We get, not the general soultion with arbitrary constants still to be determined, but that particular solution which satisfies the desired initial conditions. The transform method also gives us some insight into the reason that the solution takes different forms according to whether ω and β are equal or unequal.

EXAMPLE (b): Solve the problem

(6) $\qquad x''(t) + 2x'(t) + x(t) = 3te^{-t}; \qquad x(0) = 4, \quad x'(0) = 2.$

Let $L\{x(t)\} = y(s)$. Then the operator L converts (6) into

$$s^2 y(s) - 4s - 2 + 2[sy(s) - 4] + y(s) = \frac{3}{(s+1)^2},$$

or

(7) $\qquad y(s) = \frac{4s + 10}{(s+1)^2} + \frac{3}{(s+1)^4}.$

We may write

$$y(s) = \frac{4(s+1) + 6}{(s+1)^2} + \frac{3}{(s+1)^4}$$

$$= \frac{4}{s+1} + \frac{6}{(s+1)^2} + \frac{3}{(s+1)^4}.$$

Employing the inverse transform, we obtain

(8) $\qquad x(t) = (4 + 6t + \tfrac{1}{2}t^3)e^{-t}.$

Again the presence of initial conditions contributed to the efficiency of our method. In obtaining and in using equation (7), those terms that came from the initial values $x(0)$ and $x'(0)$ were not combined with the term that came from the transform of the right member of the differential equation. To combine such terms rarely simplifies and frequently complicates the task of obtaining the inverse transform.

From the solution

(8) $\qquad x(t) = (4 + 6t + \tfrac{1}{2}t^3)e^{-t}$

the student should obtain the derivatives

$$x'(t) = (2 - 6t + \tfrac{3}{2}t^2 - \tfrac{1}{2}t^3)e^{-t},$$

$$x''(t) = (-8 + 9t - 3t^2 + \tfrac{1}{2}t^3)e^{-t},$$

and thus verify that the x of (8) satisfies both the differential equation and the initial conditions of the problem (6). Such verification not only checks our work but also removes any need to justify temporary assumptions about the right to use the Laplace transform theorems on the function $x(t)$ during the time that the function is still unknown.

EXAMPLE (c): Solve the problem

$$(9) \qquad x''(t) + 4x(t) = \psi(t); \qquad x(0) = 1, \qquad x'(0) = 0,$$

in which $\psi(t)$ is defined by

$$(10) \qquad\qquad \psi(t) = 4t, \qquad 0 \leqq t \leqq 1,$$
$$= 4, \qquad t > 1.$$

We seek, of course, a solution valid in the range $t \geqq 0$ in which the right member $\psi(t)$ is defined.

In this problem another phase of the power of the Laplace transform method begins to emerge. The fact that the function $\psi(t)$ in the differential equation has discontinuous derivatives makes the use of the classical method of undetermined coefficients somewhat awkward, but such discontinuities do not interfere at all with the simplicity of the Laplace transform method.

In attacking this problem, let us put $L\{x(t)\} = h(s)$. We need to obtain $L\{\psi(t)\}$. In terms of the α function we may write, from (10),

$$(11) \qquad\qquad \psi(t) = 4t - 4(t - 1)\alpha(t - 1), \qquad t \geqq 0.$$

From (11) it follows that

$$L\{\psi(t)\} = \frac{4}{s^2} - \frac{4e^{-s}}{s^2}.$$

Therefore the application of the operator L transforms problem (9) into

$$s^2h(s) - s - 0 + 4h(s) = \frac{4}{s^2} - \frac{4e^{-s}}{s^2},$$

from which

$$(12) \qquad h(s) = \frac{s}{s^2 + 4} + \frac{4}{s^2(s^2 + 4)} - \frac{4e^{-s}}{s^2(s^2 + 4)}.$$

Now

$$\frac{4}{s^2(s^2 + 4)} = \frac{1}{s^2} - \frac{1}{s^2 + 4},$$

so (12) becomes

$$(13) \qquad h(s) = \frac{s}{s^2 + 4} + \frac{1}{s^2} - \frac{1}{s^2 + 4} - \left(\frac{1}{s^2} - \frac{1}{s^2 + 4}\right)e^{-s}.$$

Since $x(t) = L^{-1}\{h(s)\}$, we obtain the desired solution

(14) $x(t) = \cos 2t + t - \frac{1}{2} \sin 2t - [(t-1) - \frac{1}{2} \sin 2(t-1)] \alpha(t-1)$.

It is easy to verify our solution. From (14) it follows that

(15) $x'(t) = -2 \sin 2t + 1 - \cos 2t - [1 - \cos 2(t-1)] \alpha(t-1)$,

(16) $x''(t) = -4 \cos 2t + 2 \sin 2t - 2 \sin 2(t-1) \alpha(t-1)$.

Therefore $x(0) = 1$ and $x'(0) = 0$, as desired. Also, from (14), and (16), we get

$$x''(t) + 4x(t) = 4t -- 4(t-1)\alpha(t-1) = \psi(t), \qquad t \geqq 0.$$

EXAMPLE (d): Solve the problem

(17) $x''(t) + k^2 x(t) = F(t); \qquad x(0) = A, \qquad x'(0) = B.$

Here k, A, B are constants and $F(t)$ is a known but unstipulated function. For the time being, think of $F(t)$ as a function whose Laplace transform exists. Let

$$L\{x(t)\} = u(s), \qquad L\{F(t)\} = f(s).$$

Then the Laplace operator transforms problem (17) into

$$s^2 u(s) - As - B + k^2 u(s) = f(s),$$

(18) $u(s) = \dfrac{As + B}{s^2 + k^2} + \dfrac{f(s)}{s^2 + k^2}.$

To get the inverse transform of the last term in (18), we use the convolution theorem. Thus we arrive at

$$x(t) = A \cos kt + \frac{B}{k} \sin kt + \frac{1}{k} \int_0^t F(t - \beta) \sin k\beta \, d\beta,$$

or

(19) $x(t) = A \cos kt + \dfrac{B}{k} \sin kt + \dfrac{1}{k} \displaystyle\int_0^t F(\beta) \sin k(t - \beta) \, d\beta.$

For the student who has had advanced calculus and knows how to differentiate a definite integral with respect to a parameter (Leibniz' rule), verification of the solution (19) is simple. Once that check has been performed, the need for the assumption that $F(t)$ has a Laplace transform is removed. It does not matter what method we use to get a solution (with certain exceptions naturally imposed during college examinations) if the validity of the result can be verified from the result itself.

EXAMPLE (e): Solve the problem

$$(20) \quad w''(x) + 2w'(x) + w(x) = x; \qquad w(0) = -3, \qquad w(1) = -1.$$

In this example the boundary conditions are not both of the initial condition type. Using x, rather than t, as independent variable, let

$$(21) \qquad\qquad L\{w(x)\} = g(s).$$

We know $w(0) = -3$, but we also need $w'(0)$ in order to write the transform of $w''(x)$. Hence we put

$$(22) \qquad\qquad w'(0) = B$$

and expect to determine B later by using the condition that $w(1) = -1$.

The transformed problem is

$$s^2g(s) - s(-3) - B + 2[sg(s) - (-3)] + g(s) = \frac{1}{s^2}.$$

from which

$$(23) \qquad g(s) = \frac{-3(s+1) + B - 3}{(s+1)^2} + \frac{1}{s^2(s+1)^2}.$$

But, by the usual partial fractions expansion,

$$\frac{1}{s^2(s+1)^2} = -\frac{2}{s} + \frac{1}{s^2} + \frac{2}{s+1} + \frac{1}{(s+1)^2},$$

so

$$(24) \qquad g(s) = \frac{1}{s^2} - \frac{2}{s} - \frac{1}{s+1} + \frac{B-2}{(s+1)^2},$$

from which we obtain

$$(25) \qquad w(x) = x - 2 - e^{-x} + (B-2)xe^{-x}.$$

We have yet to impose the condition that $w(1) = -1$. From (25) with $x = 1$, we get

$$-1 = 1 - 2 - e^{-1} + (B-2)e^{-1},$$

so $B = 3$.

Thus our final result is

$$(26) \qquad w(x) = x - 2 - e^{-x} + xe^{-x}.$$

The problem in Example (e) may be solved efficiently by the methods of Chapter 9. See also Exs. 21–42 below.

Exercises

In Exs. 1–14, solve the problem by the Laplace transform method. Verify that your solution satisfies the differential equation and the boundary conditions.

1. $x''(t) + 4x'(t) + 4x(t) = 4e^{-2t}$; $x(0) = -1$, $x'(0) = 4$.

ANS. $x(t) = e^{-2t}(2t^2 + 2t - 1)$.

2. $x''(t) + x(t) = 6 \cos 2t$; $x(0) = 3$, $x'(0) = 1$.

ANS. $x(t) = 5 \cos t + \sin t - 2 \cos 2t$.

3. $y''(t) - y(t) = 5 \sin 2t$; $y(0) = 0$, $y'(0) = 1$.

ANS. $y(t) = 3 \sinh t - \sin 2t$.

4. $y''(t) + 6y'(t) + 9y(t) = 6t^2e^{-3t}$; $y(0) = 0$, $y'(0) = 0$.

ANS. $y(t) = \frac{1}{2}t^4e^{-3t}$.

5. $x''(t) + 4x(t) = 2t - 8$; $x(0) = 1$, $x'(0) = 0$.

ANS. $x(t) = 3 \cos 2t - \frac{1}{4} \sin 2t + \frac{1}{2}t - 2$.

6. $x''(t) + 2x'(t) = 8t$; $x(0) = 0$, $x'(0) = 0$.

ANS. $x(t) = 2t^2 - 2t + 1 - e^{-2t}$.

7. $u''(t) + 4u(t) = 15e^t$; $u(0) = 1$, $u'(0) = 3$.

ANS. $u(t) = 3e^t - 2 \cos 2t$.

8. $u''(t) + 4u'(t) + 3u(t) = 12$; $u(0) = 7$, $u'(0) = 1$.

ANS. $u(t) = 4 + 5e^{-t} - 2e^{-3t}$.

9. $y''(x) + 9y(x) = 40e^x$; $y(0) = 5$, $y'(0) = -2$.

ANS. $y(x) = 4e^x + \cos 3x - 2 \sin 3x$.

10. $y''(x) + y(x) = 4e^x$; $y(0) = 0$, $y'(0) = 0$.

ANS. $y(x) = 2(e^x - \cos x - \sin x)$.

11. $x''(t) + 3x'(t) + 2x(t) = 4t^2$; $x(0) = 0$, $x'(0) = 0$.

ANS. $x(t) = 2t^2 - 6t + 7 - 8e^{-t} + e^{-2t}$.

12. $x''(t) - 4x'(t) + 4x(t) = 4 \cos 2t$; $x(0) = 2$, $x'(0) = 5$.

ANS. $x(t) = 2e^{2t}(1 + t) - \frac{1}{2} \sin 2t$.

13. $x''(t) + x(t) = F(t)$; $x(0) = 0$, $x'(0) = 0$, in which

$$F(t) = 4, \qquad 0 \leq t \leq 2,$$
$$= t + 2, \qquad t > 2.$$

ANS. $x(t) = 4 - 4 \cos t + [(t - 2) - \sin (t - 2)] \alpha(t - 2)$.

14. $x''(t) + x(t) = H(t)$; $x(0) = 1$, $x'(0) = 0$, in which

$$H(t) = 3, \qquad 0 \leq t \leq 4,$$
$$= 2t - 5, \qquad t > 4.$$

ANS. $x(t) = 3 - 2 \cos t + 2[t - 4 - \sin (t - 4)] \alpha(t - 4)$.

15. Compute $y(\tfrac{1}{2}\pi)$ and $y(2 + \tfrac{1}{2}\pi)$ for the function $y(x)$ that satisfies the boundary value problem

$$y''(x) + y(x) = (x - 2)\alpha(x - 2); \; y(0) = 0, \; y'(0) = 0.$$

ANS. $y(\tfrac{1}{2}\pi) = 0, \; y(2 + \tfrac{1}{2}\pi) = \tfrac{1}{2}\pi - 1.$

16. Compute $x(1)$ and $x(4)$ for the function $x(t)$ that satisfies the boundary value problem

$$x''(t) + 2x'(t) + x(t) = 2 + (t - 3)\alpha(t - 3); \; x(0) = 2, \; x'(0) = 1.$$

ANS. $x(1) = 2 + e^{-1}, \; x(4) = 1 + 3e^{-1} + 4e^{-4}.$

17. Solve the problem

$$x''(t) + 2x'(t) + x(t) = F(t); \; x(0) = 0, \; x'(0) = 0.$$

ANS. $x(t) = \int_0^t \beta e^{-\beta} F(t - \beta) \, d\beta.$

18. Solve the problem

$$y''(t) - k^2 y(t) = H(t); \; y(0) = 0, \; y'(0) = 0.$$

ANS. $y(t) = \dfrac{1}{k} \int_0^t H(t - \beta)\sinh k\beta \, d\beta.$

19. Solve the problem

$$y''(t) + 4y'(t) + 13y(t) = F(t); \; y(0) = 0, \; y'(0) = 0.$$

20. Solve the problem

$$x''(t) + 6x'(t) + 9x(t) = F(t); \; x(0) = A, \; x'(0) = B.$$

ANS. $x(t) = e^{-3t}[A + (B + 3A)t] + \int_0^t \beta e^{-3\beta} F(t - \beta) \, d\beta.$

In Exs. 21–42, use the Laplace transform method with the realization that these exercises were not constructed with the Laplace transform technique in mind. Compare your work with that done in solving the same problems by the methods of Chapter 9.

21. Ex. 1, page 136.   **22.** Ex. 2, page 136.
23. Ex. 3, page 136.   **24.** Ex. 11, page 136.
25. Ex. 14, page 137.   **26.** Ex. 20, page 137.
27. Ex. 21, page 137.   **28.** Ex. 22, page 137.
29. Ex. 23, page 137.   **30.** Ex. 36, page 137.
31. Ex. 37, page 137.   **32.** Ex. 38, page 137.
33. Ex. 39, page 138.   **34.** Ex. 40, page 138.
35. Ex. 41, page 138.   **36.** Ex. 42, page 138.
37. Ex. 43, page 138.   **38.** Ex. 44, page 138.

39. Ex. 45, page 138.   **40.** Ex. 46, page 138.

41. Solve the problem

$$x''(t) - 4x'(t) + 4x(t) = e^{2t}; \ x'(0) = 0, \ x(1) = 0.$$

ANS. $x(t) = \frac{1}{2}(1 - t)^2 e^{2t}.$

42. Solve the problem

$$x''(t) + 4x(t) = -8t^2; \ x(0) = 3, \ x(\tfrac{1}{4}\pi) = 0.$$

ANS. $x(t) = 2 \cos 2t + \left(\frac{1}{8}\pi^2 - 1\right) \sin 2t + 1 - 2t^2.$

69. Special integral equations

A differential equation may be loosely described as one that contains a derivative of a dependent variable; the equation contains a dependent variable under a derivative sign. An equation that contains a dependent variable under an integral sign is called an integral equation.

Because of the convolution theorem, the Laplace transform is an excellent tool for solving a very special class of integral equations. We know from Theorem 20 that if

$$L\{F(t)\} = f(s)$$

and

$$L\{G(t)\} = g(s),$$

then

(1) $$L\left\{\int_0^t F(\beta)G(t - \beta) \, d\beta\right\} = f(s)g(s).$$

The relation (1) suggests the use of the Laplace transform on equations that contain convolution integrals.

EXAMPLE (a): Find $F(t)$ from the integral equation

(2) $$F(t) = 4t - 3\int_0^t F(\beta) \sin (t - \beta) \, d\beta.$$

The integral in (2) is in precisely the right form to permit the use of the convolution theorem. Let

$$L\{F(t)\} = f(s).$$

Then, since

$$L\{\sin t\} = \frac{1}{s^2 + 1},$$

application of Theorem 20, page 193, yields

$$L\left\{\int_0^t F(\beta) \sin (t - \beta)\, d\beta\right\} = \frac{f(s)}{s^2 + 1}.$$

Therefore, the Laplace operator converts equation (2) into

(3) $$f(s) = \frac{4}{s^2} - \frac{3f(s)}{s^2 + 1}.$$

We need to obtain $f(s)$ from (3) and then $F(t)$ from $f(s)$. From (3) we get

$$\left(1 + \frac{3}{s^2 + 1}\right) f(s) = \frac{4}{s^2},$$

or

$$f(s) = \frac{4(s^2 + 1)}{s^2(s^2 + 4)}.$$

Then, by the methods of Section 67, or by inspection,

$$f(s) = \frac{1}{s^2} + \frac{3}{s^2 + 4}.$$

Therefore

$$F(t) = L^{-1}\left\{\frac{1}{s^2} + \frac{3}{s^2 + 4}\right\},$$

(4) $$F(t) = t + \tfrac{3}{2} \sin 2t.$$

That the $F(t)$ of (4) is a solution of equation (2) may be verified directly. Such a check is frequently tedious. We shall show that for the F of (4), the right-hand side of equation (2) reduces to the left-hand side of (2). Since

$$RHS = 4t - 3\int_0^t (\beta + \tfrac{3}{2} \sin 2\beta) \sin (t - \beta)\, d\beta,$$

we integrate by parts with the choice shown in the table.

$(\beta + \tfrac{3}{2} \sin 2\beta)$	$\sin (t - \beta)\, d\beta$
$(1 + 3 \cos 2\beta)\, d\beta$	$\cos (t - \beta)$

It thus follows that

$$RHS = 4t - 3\left[(\beta + \tfrac{3}{2} \sin 2\beta) \cos (t - \beta)\right]_0^t$$
$$+ 3\int_0^t (1 + 3 \cos 2\beta) \cos (t - \beta)\, d\beta,$$

from which

$$RHS = 4t - 3(t + \tfrac{3}{2} \sin 2t) + 3 \int_0^t \cos (t - \beta) \, d\beta$$

$$+ 9 \int_0^t \cos 2\beta \cos (t - \beta) \, d\beta,$$

or

$$RHS = t - \tfrac{9}{2} \sin 2t - 3 \left[\sin (t - \beta) \right]_0^t$$

$$+ \tfrac{9}{2} \int_0^t [\cos (t + \beta) + \cos (t - 3\beta)] \, d\beta.$$

This leads us to the result

$$RHS = t - \tfrac{9}{2} \sin 2t + 3 \sin t + \tfrac{9}{2} \left[\sin (t + \beta) - \tfrac{1}{3} \sin (t - 3\beta) \right]_0^t$$

$$= t - \tfrac{9}{2} \sin 2t + 3 \sin t + \tfrac{9}{2} \sin 2t + \tfrac{3}{2} \sin 2t - \tfrac{9}{2} \sin t + \tfrac{3}{2} \sin t,$$

or

$$RHS = t + \tfrac{3}{2} \sin 2t = F(t) = LHS,$$

as desired.

It is important to realize that the original equation

$$(2) \qquad\qquad F(t) = 4t - 3 \int_0^t F(\beta) \sin (t - \beta) \, d\beta$$

could equally well have been encountered in the equivalent form

$$F(t) = 4t - 3 \int_0^t F(t - \beta) \sin \beta \, d\beta.$$

An essential ingredient for the success of the method being used is that the integral involved be in exactly the convolution integral form. We must have zero to the independent variable as limits of integration, and an integrand that is the product of a function of the variable of integration by a function of the difference between the independent variable and the variable of integration. The fact that integrals of that form appear with some frequency in physical problems is all that keeps the topic of this section from being relegated to the role of a mathematical parlor game.

EXAMPLE (b): Solve the equation

$$(5) \qquad\qquad g(x) = \tfrac{1}{2}x^2 - \int_0^x (x - y)g(y) \, dy.$$

Again the integral involved is one of the convolution type with x playing the role of the independent variable. Let the Laplace transform of $g(x)$ be some as yet unknown function $h(z)$:

(6) $$L\{g(x)\} = h(z).$$

Since $L\{\frac{1}{2}x^2\} = \dfrac{1}{z^3}$ and $L\{x\} = \dfrac{1}{z^2}$, we may apply the operator L throughout (5) and obtain

$$h(z) = \frac{1}{z^3} - \frac{h(z)}{z^2},$$

from which

$$\left(1 + \frac{1}{z^2}\right) h(z) = \frac{1}{z^3},$$

or

$$h(z) = \frac{1}{z(z^2 + 1)} = \frac{z^2 + 1 - z^2}{z(z^2 + 1)} = \frac{1}{z} - \frac{z}{z^2 + 1}.$$

Then

$$g(x) = L^{-1} \left\{ \frac{1}{z} - \frac{z}{z^2 + 1} \right\}$$

or

(7) $$g(x) = 1 - \cos x.$$

Verification of (7) is simple. For the right member of (5) we get

$$RHS = \tfrac{1}{2}x^2 - \int_0^x (x - y)(1 - \cos y)\, dy$$

$$= \tfrac{1}{2}x^2 - \left[(x - y)(y - \sin y) \right]_0^x - \int_0^x (y - \sin y)\, dy$$

$$= \tfrac{1}{2}x^2 - 0 - \left[\tfrac{1}{2}y^2 + \cos y \right]_0^x$$

$$= \tfrac{1}{2}x^2 - \tfrac{1}{2}x^2 - \cos x + 1 = 1 - \cos x = LHS.$$

Exercises

In Exs. 1–4, solve the given equation and verify your solution.

1. $F(t) = 1 + 2 \displaystyle\int_0^t F(t - \beta)e^{-2\beta}\, d\beta.$ ANS. $F(t) = 1 + 2t.$

2. $F(t) = 1 + \displaystyle\int_0^t F(\beta) \sin (t - \beta)\, d\beta.$ ANS. $F(t) = 1 + \tfrac{1}{2}t^2.$

3. $F(t) = t + \displaystyle\int_0^t F(t - \beta)e^{-\beta}\, d\beta.$ ANS. $F(t) = t + \tfrac{1}{2}t^2.$

4. $F(t) = 4t^2 - \displaystyle\int_0^t F(t - \beta)e^{-\beta}\, d\beta.$

     ANS. $F(t) = -1 + 2t + 2t^2 + e^{-2t}.$

In Exs. 5–8, solve the given equation. If sufficient time is available, verify your solution.

5. $F(t) = t^3 + \int_0^t F(\beta) \sin (t - \beta) \, d\beta.$ ANS. $\quad F(t) = t^3 + \dfrac{1}{20} t^5.$

6. $F(t) = 8t^2 - 3 \int_0^t F(\beta) \sin (t - \beta) \, d\beta.$

7. $F(t) = t^2 - 2 \int_0^t F(t - \beta) \sinh 2\beta \, d\beta.$ ANS. $\quad F(t) = t^2 - \dfrac{1}{3} t^4.$

8. $F(t) = 1 + 2 \int_0^t F(t - \beta) \cos \beta \, d\beta.$ ANS. $\quad F(t) = 1 + 2te^t.$

In Exs. 9–12, solve the given equation.

9. $H(t) = 9e^{2t} - 2 \int_0^t H(t - \beta) \cos \beta \, d\beta.$

10. $H(y) = y^2 + \int_0^y H(x) \sin (y - x) \, dx.$ ANS. $\quad H(y) = y^2 + \dfrac{1}{12} y^4.$

11. $g(x) = e^{-x} - 2 \int_0^x g(\beta) \cos (x - \beta) \, d\beta.$ ANS. $\quad g(x) = e^{-x}(1 - x)^2.$

12. $y(t) = 6t + 4 \int_0^t (\beta - t)^2 y(\beta) \, d\beta.$

ANS. $\quad y(t) = e^{2t} - e^{-t} (\cos \sqrt{3}\, t - \sqrt{3} \sin \sqrt{3}\, t).$

13. Solve the following equation for $F(t)$ with the condition that $F(0) = 4$:

$F'(t) = t + \int_0^t F(t - \beta) \cos \beta \, d\beta.$ ANS. $\quad F(t) = 4 + \dfrac{5}{2} t^2 + \dfrac{1}{24} t^4.$

14. Solve the following equation for $F(t)$ with the condition that $F(0) = 0$:

$F'(t) = \sin t + \int_0^t F(t - \beta) \cos \beta \, d\beta.$ ANS. $\quad F(t) = \frac{1}{2}t^2.$

15. Show that the equation of Ex. 3 above can be put in the form

(A) $\qquad\qquad e^t F(t) = te^t + \int_0^t e^\beta F(\beta) \, d\beta.$

Differentiate each member of (A) with respect to t and thus replace the integral equation with a differential equation. Note that $F(0) = 0$. Find $F(t)$ by this method.

16. Solve the equation

$$\int_0^t F(t - \beta) e^{-\beta} \, d\beta = t$$

by two methods; use the convolution theorem and the basic idea introduced in Ex. 15. Note that no differential equation need be solved in this instance.

Table of Transforms

Whenever n is used, it denotes a non-negative integer.

The range of validity may be determined from the appropriate text material. Many other transforms will be found in the examples and exercises.

$f(s) = L\{F(t)\}$	$F(t)$
$f(s - a)$	$e^{at}F(t)$
$f(as + b)$	$\dfrac{1}{a}\exp\left(-\dfrac{bt}{a}\right)F\left(\dfrac{t}{a}\right)$
$\dfrac{1}{s}e^{-cs}, \quad c > 0$	$\alpha(t - c) = 0, \quad 0 \leq t < c,$ $= 1, t \geq c$
$e^{-cs}f(s), \quad c > 0$	$F(t - c)\alpha(t - c)$
$f_1(s)\,f_2(s)$	$\displaystyle\int_0^t F_1(\beta)\,F_2(t - \beta)\,d\beta$
$\dfrac{1}{s}$	1
$\dfrac{1}{s^{n+1}}$	$\dfrac{t^n}{n!}$
$\dfrac{1}{s^{x+1}}, \quad x > -1$	$\dfrac{t^x}{\Gamma(x + 1)}$
$s^{-\frac{1}{2}}$	$(\pi t)^{-\frac{1}{2}}$
$\dfrac{1}{s + a}$	e^{-at}

$f(s) = L\{F(t)\}$	$F(t)$
$\dfrac{1}{(s+a)^{n+1}}$	$\dfrac{t^n e^{-at}}{n!}$
$\dfrac{k}{s^2+k^2}$	$\sin kt$
$\dfrac{s}{s^2+k^2}$	$\cos kt$
$\dfrac{k}{s^2-k^2}$	$\sinh kt$
$\dfrac{s}{s^2-k^2}$	$\cosh kt$
$\dfrac{2k^3}{(s^2+k^2)^2}$	$\sin kt - kt\cos kt$
$\dfrac{2ks}{(s^2+k^2)^2}$	$t\sin kt$
$\ln\left(1+\dfrac{1}{s}\right)$	$\dfrac{1-e^{-t}}{t}$
$\ln\dfrac{s+k}{s-k}$	$\dfrac{2\sinh kt}{t}$
$\ln\left(1-\dfrac{k^2}{s^2}\right)$	$\dfrac{2}{t}(1-\cosh kt)$
$\ln\left(1+\dfrac{k^2}{s^2}\right)$	$\dfrac{2}{t}(1-\cos kt)$
$\text{Arctan}\ \dfrac{k}{s}$	$\dfrac{\sin kt}{t}$

CHAPTER 13

Applications

70. Vibration of a spring

Consider a steel spring attached to a support and hanging downward. Within certain elastic limits the spring will obey Hooke's law: if the spring is stretched or compressed, its change in length will be proportional to the force exerted upon the spring and, when that force is removed, the spring will return to its original position with its length and other physical properties unchanged. There is, therefore, associated with each spring a numerical constant, the ratio of the force exerted to the displacement produced by that force. If a force of magnitude Q pounds stretches the spring c feet, the relation

$$(1) \qquad Q = kc$$

defines the spring constant k in units of pounds per foot.

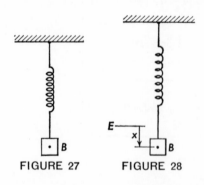

FIGURE 27   FIGURE 28

Let a body B weighing w pounds be attached to the lower end of a spring (Figure 27) and brought to the point of equilibrium where it can remain at rest. Once the weight B is moved from the point of equilibrium E in Figure 28, the motion of B will be determined by a differential equation and associated boundary conditions.

Let t be time measured in seconds after some initial moment when the motion begins. Let x, in feet, be distance measured positive downward (negative upward) from the point of equilibrium, as in Figure 28. We assume that the motion of B takes place entirely in a vertical line, so the velocity and acceleration are given by the first and second derivatives of x with respect to t.

In addition to the force proportional to displacement (Hooke's law), there will in general be a retarding force caused by resistance of the medium in which the motion takes place or by friction. We are interested here in only such retarding forces as can be well approximated by a term proportional to the velocity because we restrict our study to problems involving linear differential equations. Such a retarding force will con-tribute to the total force acting on B a term $bx'(t)$, in which b is a constant to be determined experimentally for the medium in which the motion takes place. Some common retarding forces, such as one proportional to the cube of the velocity, lead to nonlinear differential equations which are not amenable to treatment by the Laplace transform.

The weight of the spring is usually negligible compared to the weight B, so we use for the mass of our system the weight of B divided by g, the constant acceleration of gravity. If no forces other than those described above act upon the weight, the displacement x must satisfy the equation

$$(2) \qquad \frac{w}{g} x''(t) + bx'(t) + kx(t) = 0.$$

Suppose an additional vertical force, due to the motion of the support or to presence of a magnetic field, etc., is imposed upon the system. The new, impressed force, will depend upon time and we may use $F(t)$ to denote the acceleration which it alone would impart to the weight B. Then the impressed force is $\frac{w}{g} F(t)$ and equation (2) is replaced by

$$(3) \qquad \frac{w}{g} x''(t) + bx'(t) + kx(t) = \frac{w}{g} F(t).$$

At time zero, let the weight be displaced by an amount x_0 from the equilibrium point and let the weight be given an initial velocity v_0. Either or both of x_0 and v_0 may be zero in specific instances. The problem of determining the position of the weight at any time t becomes that of solving the boundary value problem consisting of the differential equation

$$(4) \qquad \frac{w}{g} x''(t) + bx'(t) + kx(t) = \frac{w}{g} F(t), \qquad \text{for } t > 0,$$

and the initial conditions

(5) $$x(0) = x_0, \qquad x'(0) = v_0.$$

It is convenient to rewrite equation (4) in the form

(6) $$x''(t) + 2\gamma x'(t) + \beta^2 x(t) = F(t),$$

in which we have put

$$\frac{bg}{w} = 2\gamma, \qquad \frac{kg}{w} = \beta^2.$$

We may choose $\beta > 0$ and we know $\gamma \geqq 0$. Note that $\gamma = 0$ corresponds to a negligible retarding force.

Impressed forces so ill-behaved that their Laplace transforms do not exist are hardly worth considering. We therefore let

(7) $$L\{x(t)\} = u(s), \quad L\{F(t)\} = f(s),$$

and obtain from the problem (5) and (6) the transformed problem

$$s^2 u(s) - sx_0 - v_0 + 2\gamma[su(s) - x_0] + \beta^2 u(s) = f(s),$$

$$u(s) = \frac{sx_0 + v_0 + 2\gamma x_0}{s^2 + 2\gamma s + \beta^2} + \frac{f(s)}{s^2 + 2\gamma s + \beta^2},$$

which we write as

(8) $$u(s) = \frac{x_0(s + \gamma) + v_0 + \gamma x_0}{(s + \gamma)^2 + \beta^2 - \gamma^2} + \frac{f(s)}{(s + \gamma)^2 + \beta^2 - \gamma^2}.$$

The desired $x(t)$ is the inverse transform of $u(s)$.

Here we begin to reap benefits from our use of the Laplace transform. Even before we get $x(t)$ we can see that its form will depend upon whether the denominator in (8) has distinct real linear factors, or equal factors, or is the sum of two squares. That is, the form of $x(t)$ will depend upon whether $\beta < \gamma$, $\beta = \gamma$, or $\beta > \gamma$. Furthermore, if $\gamma \neq 0$, we can predict the presence of a damping factor $e^{-\gamma t}$ in $x(t)$.

The inverse of the $u(s)$ of equation (8) can be obtained with our standard methods, including the convolution theorem. When the $F(t)$ is reasonably simple, one of the types which occur frequently in practice, the convolution theorem leads to forms less desirable than those obtained by the other methods in Chapter 12.

We shall now consider separately the various situations that arise according to the choice of parameters β and γ and the forcing function $F(t)$ in this problem of the vibrating spring.

In treating spring problems we are particularly interested in impressed forces that lead to $F(t)$ of forms such as those listed:

(a) No impressed force: $F(t) = 0$;

(b) Simple harmonic forcing function:

$$F(t) = A_1 \sin \omega t + A_2 \cos \omega t;$$

(c) Temporary constant force:

$$\begin{aligned} F(t) &= A, \quad 0 < t < t_0, \\ &= 0, \qquad t > t_0; \end{aligned}$$

(d) A delayed form of (c):

$$\begin{aligned} F(t) &= 0, \quad 0 < t < t_0, \\ &= A, \quad t_0 < t < t_1, \\ &= 0, \qquad t > t_1; \end{aligned}$$

(e) $F(t) =$ the half-wave rectification of a sine curve.

It will become apparent when we study electric circuits in Section 78 that all of our present work carries over to simple circuit problems with new meanings attached to the parameters and functions involved. In circuit theory we shall add to the forms of $F(t)$ listed above both $F(t)$ equal to a constant and $F(t)$ equal to the square-wave function that appeared in Section 63.

71. Undamped vibrations

If $\gamma = 0$ in the problem of Section 70, the transform becomes

$$(1) \qquad u(s) = \frac{x_0 s + v_0}{s^2 + \beta^2} + \frac{f(s)}{s^2 + \beta^2}.$$

The inverse transform of the first term on the right in (1) is

$$x_0 \cos \beta t + \frac{v_0}{\beta} \sin \beta t,$$

which contributes to $x(t)$ a simple harmonic motion, called the *natural component* of the motion, natural because it is independent of the forcing function $F(t)$. From the last term in (1) we obtain the forced component, the form of which is dependent upon $F(t)$.

Instead of jumping from (1) to the general solution

$$(2) \qquad x(t) = x_0 \cos \beta t + v_0 \beta^{-1} \sin \beta t + \beta^{-1} \int_0^t F(t - v) \sin \beta v \, dv,$$

we prefer to obtain $x(t)$ without a convolution integral for the specific types of $F(t)$ which occur often. Equation (2) was easily obtained but it leaves all the labor of simplification to the unfortunate user who has a particular $F(t)$ with which to deal.

EXAMPLE (a): Solve the spring problem with no damping but with a forcing function $F(t) = A \sin \omega t$.

The differential equation of motion is

$$\frac{w}{g} x''(t) + kx(t) = \frac{w}{g} A \sin \omega t$$

and is readily put into the form

$$(3) \qquad x''(t) + \beta^2 x(t) = A \sin \omega t$$

with the introduction of $\beta^2 = kg/w$. We shall assume initial conditions

$$(4) \qquad x(0) = x_0, \quad x'(0) = v_0.$$

Let $L\{x(t)\} = u(s)$. Then (3) and (4) yield

$$s^2 u(s) - sx_0 - v_0 + \beta^2 u(s) = \frac{A\omega}{s^2 + \omega^2},$$

or

$$(5) \qquad u(s) = \frac{sx_0 + v_0}{s^2 + \beta^2} + \frac{A\omega}{(s^2 + \beta^2)(s^2 + \omega^2)}.$$

The last term in (5) will lead to different inverse transforms according to whether $\omega = \beta$ or $\omega \neq \beta$. The case $\omega = \beta$ leads to resonance, which will be discussed in the next section.

If $\omega \neq \beta$, equation (5) yields

$$(6) \qquad u(s) = \frac{sx_0 + v_0}{s^2 + \beta^2} + \frac{A\omega}{\omega^2 - \beta^2}\left(\frac{1}{s^2 + \beta^2} - \frac{1}{s^2 + \omega^2}\right).$$

From (6) it follows at once that

$$(7) \quad x(t) = x_0 \cos \beta t + v_0 \beta^{-1} \sin \beta t + \frac{A\omega}{\beta(\omega^2 - \beta^2)} \sin \beta t - \frac{A}{\omega^2 - \beta^2} \sin \omega t.$$

That the x of (7) is a solution of the problem (3) and (4) is easily verified. A study of (7) is simple and leads at once to conclusions such as that $x(t)$ is bounded, etc. The first two terms on the right in (7) yield the natural harmonic component of the motion, the last two terms form the forced component.

EXAMPLE (b): A spring is such that it would be stretched 6 inches by a 12-pound weight. Let the weight be attached to the spring and pulled down 4 inches below the equilibrium point. If the weight is started with an upward velocity of 2 feet per second, describe the motion. No damping or impressed force is present.

We know that the acceleration of gravity enters our work in the expression for the mass. We wish to use the value $g = 32$ ft. per sec. per sec. and we must use consistent units, so we put all lengths into feet.

First we determine the spring constant k from the fact that the 12-pound weight stretches the spring 6 inches, $\frac{1}{2}$ ft. Thus $12 = \frac{1}{2}k$ so that $k = 24$ lb. per ft.

The differential equation of the motion is therefore

$$(8) \qquad\qquad \tfrac{12}{32}x''(t) + 24x(t) = 0.$$

At time zero the weight is 4 inches ($\frac{1}{3}$ ft.) below the equilibrium point, so $x(0) = \frac{1}{3}$. The initial velocity is negative (upward), so $x'(0) = -2$. Thus our problem is that of solving

$$(9) \qquad x''(t) + 64x(t) = 0; \qquad x(0) = \tfrac{1}{3}, \quad x'(0) = -2.$$

We let $L\{x(t)\} = u(s)$ and conclude at once that

$$s^2u(s) - \tfrac{1}{3}s + 2 + 64u(s) = 0,$$

from which

$$u(s) = \frac{\tfrac{1}{3}s - 2}{s^2 + 64}.$$

Then

$$(10) \qquad\qquad x(t) = \tfrac{1}{3}\cos 8t - \tfrac{1}{4}\sin 8t.$$

A detailed study of the motion is straightforward once (10) has been obtained. The amplitude of the motion is

$$\sqrt{(\tfrac{1}{3})^2 + (\tfrac{1}{4})^2} = \tfrac{5}{12};$$

that is, the weight oscillates between points 5 inches above and below E. The period is $\frac{1}{4}\pi$ sec.

EXAMPLE (c): A spring, with spring constant 0.75 lb. per ft., lies on a long smooth (frictionless) table. A 6-lb. weight is attached to the spring and is at rest (velocity zero) at the equilibrium position. A 1.5-lb. force is applied to the support along the line of action of the spring for 4 seconds and is then removed. Discuss the motion.

We must solve the problem

(11) $\qquad \frac{6}{32}x''(t) + \frac{3}{4}x(t) = H(t); \qquad x(0) = 0, \quad x'(0) = 0,$

in which

$$H(t) = 1.5, \qquad 0 < t < 4,$$
$$= 0, \qquad\qquad t > 4.$$

Now $H(t) = 1.5[1 - \alpha(t - 4)]$ in terms of the α function of Section 65. Therefore we rewrite our problem (11) in the form

(12) $\qquad x''(t) + 4x(t) = 8[1 - \alpha(t - 4)]; \quad x(0) = 0, \quad x'(0) = 0.$

Let $L\{x(t)\} = u(s)$. Then (12) yields

$$s^2 u(s) + 4u(s) = \frac{8}{s}(1 - e^{-4s}),$$

or

$$u(s) = \frac{8(1 - e^{-4s})}{s(s^2 + 4)}$$

$$= 2\left(\frac{1}{s} - \frac{s}{s^2 + 4}\right)(1 - e^{-4s}).$$

The desired solution is

(13) $\qquad x(t) = 2(1 - \cos 2t) - 2[1 - \cos 2(t - 4)]\alpha(t - 4).$

Of course, the solution (13) can be broken down into the two relations

(14)   For $0 \leq t \leq 4,$ $x(t) = 2(1 - \cos 2t),$

(15)   For $t > 4,$ $x(t) = 2[\cos 2(t - 4) - \cos 2t],$

if those forms seem simpler to use.

Verification of the solution (13), or (14) and (15), is direct. The student should show that

$$\operatorname*{Lim}_{t \to 4^-} x(t) = \operatorname*{Lim}_{t \to 4^+} x(t) = 2(1 - \cos 8) = 2.29$$

and

$$\operatorname*{Lim}_{t \to 4^-} x'(t) = \operatorname*{Lim}_{t \to 4^+} x'(t) = 4 \sin 8 = 3.96.$$

From (13) or (14) we see that in the range $0 < t < 4$, the maximum deviation of the weight from the starting point is $x = 4$ ft. and occurs at $t = \frac{1}{2}\pi = 1.57$ sec. At $t = 4$, $x = 2.29$ ft. as shown above. For $t > 4$, equation (15) takes over and thereafter the motion is simple harmonic with a maximum x of 3.03 ft. Indeed, for $t > 4$,

$$\max |x(t)| = 2 \sqrt{(1 - \cos 8)^2 + \sin^2 8}$$
$$= 2 \sqrt{2} \sqrt{1 - \cos 8}$$
$$= 2 \sqrt{2.2910} = 3.03.$$

Example (c) is one type of problem for which the Laplace transform technique is particularly useful. Such problems can be solved by the older classical methods, but with much less simplicity and dispatch.

72. Resonance

In the problem of undamped vibrations of a spring, one of the examples we encountered was

(1) $x''(t) + \beta^2 x(t) = A \sin \omega t;$ $x(0) = x_0, \quad x'(0) = v_0.$

The solution of (1) was obtained by putting $L\{x(t)\} = u(s)$ and getting

(2) $$u(s) = \frac{sx_0 + v_0}{s^2 + \beta^2} + \frac{A\omega}{(s^2 + \beta^2)(s^2 + \omega^2)}.$$

From (2) we see that the inverse transform differs according to whether $\omega = \beta$ or $\omega \neq \beta$. The latter has been studied. Let us now assume $\omega = \beta$.
   Our problem is to solve

(3) $x''(t) + \beta^2 x(t) = A \sin \beta t;$ $x(0) = x_0, \quad x'(0) = v_0,$

with the aid of

(4) $$u(s) = \frac{sx_0 + v_0}{s^2 + \beta^2} + \frac{A\beta}{(s^2 + \beta^2)^2}.$$

We already know, from page 177, that

$$L^{-1}\left\{\frac{1}{(s^2 + \beta^2)^2}\right\} = \frac{1}{2\beta^3}(\sin \beta t - \beta t \cos \beta t).$$

Therefore (4) leads us to the solution

(5) $$x(t) = x_0 \cos \beta t + \frac{v_0}{\beta} \sin \beta t + \frac{A}{2\beta^2}(\sin \beta t - \beta t \cos \beta t).$$

That (5) satisfies all the conditions of (3) is readily verified.
   In the solution (5) the terms proportional to $\cos \beta t$ and $\sin \beta t$ are bounded, but the term with $\beta t \cos \beta t$ can be made as large as we wish by proper choice of t. This building up of large amplitudes in the vibration when $\omega = \beta$ in (1) is called *resonance*.

Exercises

1. A spring is such that a 5-pound weight stretches it 6 inches. The 5-pound weight is attached, the spring reaches equilibrium, then the weight is pulled down 3 inches below the equilibrium point and started off with an upward velocity of 6 ft. per sec. Find an equation giving the position of the weight at all subsequent times.

ANS. $x = \frac{1}{4}(\cos 8t - 3 \sin 8t)$.

2. A spring is stretched 1.5 inches by a 2-pound weight. Let the weight be pushed up 3 inches above E and then released. Describe the motion.

ANS. $x = -\frac{1}{4} \cos 16t$.

3. For the spring and weight of Ex. 2, let the weight be pulled down 4 inches below E and given a downward initial velocity of 8 ft. per sec. Describe the motion. ANS. $x = \frac{1}{3} \cos 16t + \frac{1}{2} \sin 16t$.

4. Show that the answer to Ex. 3 can be written $x = 0.60 \sin (16t + \varphi)$ where $\varphi = $ Arctan $\frac{2}{3}$.

5. A spring is such that a 4-pound weight stretches it 6 inches. An impressed force $\frac{1}{2} \cos 8t$ is acting on the spring. If the 4-pound weight is started from the equilibrium point with an imparted upward velocity of 4 ft. per sec., determine the position of the weight as a function of time. ANS. $x = \frac{1}{4}(t - 2) \sin 8t$.

6. A spring is such that it is stretched 6 inches by a 12-pound weight. The 12-pound weight is pulled down 3 inches below the equilibrium point and then released. If there is an impressed force of magnitude $9 \sin 4t$ pounds, describe the motion. Assume that the impressed force acts downward for very small t.

ANS. $x = \frac{1}{4} \cos 8t - \frac{1}{4} \sin 8t + \frac{1}{2} \sin 4t$.

7. Show that the answer to Ex. 6 can be written

$$x = \frac{1}{4} \sqrt{2} \cos (8t + \pi/4) + \frac{1}{2} \sin 4t.$$

8. A spring is such that a 2-pound weight stretches it $\frac{1}{2}$ ft. An impressed force $\frac{1}{4} \sin 8t$ is acting upon the spring. If the 2-pound weight is released from a point 3 inches below the equilibrium point, determine the equation of motion. ANS. $x = \frac{1}{4}(1 - t) \cos 8t + \frac{1}{32} \sin 8t$ (ft.).

9. For the motion of Ex. 8, find the first four times at which stops occur and find the position at each stop. ANS. $t = \pi/8, \pi/4, 1, 3\pi/8$ (sec.) and $x = -0.15, +0.05, +0.03, +0.04$ (ft.), respectively.

10. Determine the position to be expected, if nothing such as breakage interferes, at the time of the 65th stop, when $t = 8\pi$ (sec.), in Ex. 8.

ANS. $x = -6.0$ (ft.).

11. A spring is such that a 16-pound weight stretches it 1.5 inches. The weight is pulled down to a point 4 inches below the equilibrium point and given an initial downward velocity of 4 ft. per sec. There is an impressed force of 360 cos $4t$ pounds. Find the position and velocity of the weight at time $t = \pi/8$ seconds.

ANS. At $t = \pi/8$(sec.), $x = -\frac{8}{3}$ (ft.), $v = -8$ (ft./sec.).

12. A spring is stretched 3 inches by a 5-pound weight. Let the weight be started from E with an upward velocity of 12 ft. per sec. Describe the motion.   ANS. $x = -1.06 \sin 11.3t$.

13. For the spring and weight of Ex. 12, let the weight be pulled down 4 inches below E and then given an upward velocity of 8 ft. per sec. Describe the motion.   ANS. $x = 0.33 \cos 11.3t - 0.71 \sin 11.3t$.

14. Find the amplitude of the motion in Ex. 13.   ANS. 0.78 ft.

15. A 20-pound weight stretches a certain spring 10 inches. Let the spring first be compressed 4 inches, and then the 20-pound weight attached and given an initial downward velocity of 8 ft. per sec. Find how far the weight would drop.   ANS. 35 in.

16. A spring is such that an 8-pound weight would stretch it 6 inches. Let a 4-pound weight be attached to the spring, pushed up 2 inches above its equilibrium point and then released. Describe the motion.

ANS. $x = -\frac{1}{6} \cos 11.3t$.

17. If the 4-pound weight of Ex. 16 starts at the same point, 2 inches above E, but with an upward velocity of 15 ft. per sec., when will the weight reach its lowest point?   ANS. At $t =$ approximately 0.4 sec.

18. A spring is such that it is stretched 4 inches by a 10-pound weight. Suppose the 10-pound weight to be pulled down 5 inches below E and then given a downward velocity of 15 ft. per sec. Describe the motion.

ANS. $x = 0.42 \cos 9.8t + 1.53 \sin 9.8t$
$= 1.59 \cos (9.8t - \varphi)$, where $\varphi =$ Arctan 3.64.

19. A spring is such that it is stretched 4 inches by an 8-pound weight. Suppose the weight to be pulled down 6 inches below E and then given an upward velocity of 8 ft. per sec. Describe the motion.

ANS. $x = 0.50 \cos 9.8t - 0.82 \sin 9.8t$.

20. Show that the answer to Ex. 19 can be written $x = 0.96 \cos (9.8t + \varphi)$ where $\varphi =$ Arctan 1.64.

21. A spring is such that a 4-pound weight stretches it 6 inches. The 4-pound weight is attached to the vertical spring and reaches its equilibrium point. The weight is then $(t = 0)$ drawn downward 3 inches and released. There is a simple harmonic exterior force equal to sin $8t$ impressed upon the whole system. Find the time for each of the first

four stops following $t = 0$. Put the stops in chronological order.

ANS. $t = \pi/8, \frac{1}{2}, \pi/4, 3\pi/8$ (sec.).

22. A spring is stretched 1.5 inches by a 4-pound weight. Let the weight be pulled down 3 inches below equilibrium and released. If there is an impressed force $8 \sin 16t$ acting upon the spring, describe the motion.

ANS. $x = \frac{1}{4}(1 - 8t) \cos 16t + \frac{1}{8} \sin 16t$.

23. For the motion of Ex. 22, find the first four times at which stops occur and find the position at each stop.

ANS. $t = \frac{1}{8}, \pi/16, \pi/8, 3\pi/16$ (sec.) and $x = +0.11, +0.14, -0.54, +0.93$ (ft.), respectively.

73. Damped vibrations

In the general linear spring problem of Section 70, we were confronted with

$$(1) \quad x''(t) + 2\gamma x'(t) + \beta^2 x(t) = F(t); \qquad x(0) = x_0, \quad x'(0) = v_0,$$

in which $\gamma = \dfrac{bg}{w}$ and $\beta^2 = \dfrac{kg}{w}$, $\beta > 0$. We let

$$L\{x(t)\} = u(s), \qquad L\{F(t)\} = f(s)$$

and obtained

$$(2) \quad u(s) = \frac{x_0(s + \gamma) + v_0 + \gamma x_0}{(s + \gamma)^2 + \beta^2 - \gamma^2} + \frac{f(s)}{(s + \gamma)^2 + \beta^2 - \gamma^2}.$$

We are now concerned with $\gamma > 0$; a non-negligible retarding force is present. We know that the form of the inverse transform of $u(s)$ depends upon whether $\beta > \gamma$, $\beta = \gamma$, or $\beta < \gamma$.

If $\beta > \gamma$, $\beta^2 - \gamma^2 > 0$, so let us put

$$(3) \qquad \beta^2 - \gamma^2 = \delta^2.$$

Then (2) becomes

$$(4) \qquad u(s) = \frac{x_0(s + \gamma) + v_0 + \gamma x_0}{(s + \gamma)^2 + \delta^2} + \frac{f(s)}{(s + \gamma)^2 + \delta^2}$$

and we arrive at

$$(5) \qquad x(t) = e^{-\gamma t}[x_0 \cos \delta t + (v_0 + \gamma x_0)\delta^{-1} \sin \delta t] + \psi_1(t)$$

in which $\psi_1(t)$ is an inverse transform of the last term in (4). The function $\psi_1(t)$ can always be written in terms of $F(t)$ by the convolution theorem, but that leads to undesirable complications for the most common choices of $F(t)$. In the solution (5), the presence of the damping factor $e^{-\gamma t}$ shows that the natural component of the motion approaches zero as $t \to \infty$.

If in (1) and (2) we have $\beta = \gamma$, the transform

$$(6) \qquad u(s) = \frac{x_0(s + \gamma) + v_0 + \gamma x_0}{(s + \gamma)^2} + \frac{f(s)}{(s + \gamma)^2}$$

leads us to the solution

$$(7) \qquad x(t) = e^{-\gamma t}[x_0 + (v_0 + \gamma x_0)t] + \psi_2(t),$$

in which $\psi_2(t)$ is an inverse of $(s + \gamma)^{-2}f(s)$ and is easily determined once $F(t)$ is stipulated. Again the natural component has the damping factor $e^{-\gamma t}$ in it.

If in (1) and (2) we have $\beta < \gamma$, $\gamma^2 - \beta^2 > 0$, and we put

$$(8) \qquad \gamma^2 - \beta^2 = \sigma^2.$$

Then (2) becomes

$$(9) \qquad u(s) = \frac{x_0(s + \gamma) + v_0 + \gamma x_0}{(s + \gamma)^2 - \sigma^2} + \frac{f(s)}{(s + \gamma)^2 - \sigma^2},$$

which leads to the solution

$$(10) \qquad x(t) = e^{-\gamma t}[x_0 \cosh \sigma t + (v_0 + \gamma x_0)\sigma^{-1} \sinh \sigma t] + \psi_3(t),$$

in which $\psi_3(t)$ is an inverse of the last term in (9). By (8) we see that $\gamma > \sigma$, so that once more the natural component of the $x(t)$ in (10) approaches zero as $t \to \infty$.

Suppose for the moment that we have $F(t) \equiv 0$, so the natural component of the motion is all that is under consideration. If $\beta > \gamma$, equation (5) holds and the motion is a *damped oscillatory* one. If $\beta = \gamma$, equation (7) holds and the motion is not oscillatory; it is called *critically damped* motion. If $\beta < \gamma$, (10) holds and the motion is said to be *overdamped;* the parameter γ is larger than it needs to be to remove the oscillations. Figure 29 shows a representative graph of each type

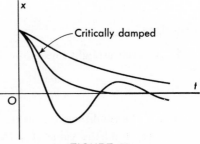

FIGURE 29

of motion mentioned in this paragraph, a damped oscillatory motion, a critically damped motion, and an overdamped motion.

EXAMPLE: Solve the problem of Example (b), Section 71, with an added damping force of magnitude $0.6|v|$. Such a damping force can be realized by immersing the weight B in a thick liquid.

The boundary value problem to be solved is

(11) $\frac{12}{32}x''(t) + 0.6x'(t) + 24x(t) = 0; \qquad x(0) = \frac{1}{3}, \quad x'(0) = -2.$

Put $L\{x(t)\} = u(s)$. Then (11) yields

$$(s^2 + 1.6s + 64)u(s) = \tfrac{1}{3}(s - 4.4),$$

from which we obtain

$$x(t) = \tfrac{1}{3}L^{-1}\left\{\frac{s - 4.4}{(s + 0.8)^2 + 63.36}\right\}$$

$$= \tfrac{1}{3}\exp(-0.8t)L^{-1}\left\{\frac{s - 5.2}{s^2 + 63.36}\right\}.$$

Therefore the desired solution is

(12) $x(t) = \exp(-0.8t)(0.33\cos 8.0t - 0.22\sin 8.0t),$

a portion of its graph being shown in Figure 30.

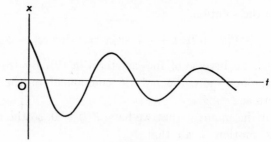

FIGURE 30

Exercises

1. A certain straight-line motion is determined by the differential equation

$$\frac{d^2x}{dt^2} + 2\gamma\frac{dx}{dt} + 169x = 0$$

and the conditions that when $t = 0$, $x = 0$ and $v = 8$ ft. per sec.

(a) Find the value of γ that leads to critical damping, determine x in terms of t, and draw the graph for $0 \leqq t \leqq 0.2$.

ANS. $\gamma = 13(1/\text{sec.})$, $x = 8te^{-13t}$.

(b) Use $\gamma = 12$. Find x in terms of t and draw the graph.

ANS. $x = 1.6e^{-12t}\sin 5t$.

(c) Use $\gamma = 14$. Find x in terms of t and draw the graph.

ANS. $x = 0.77(e^{-8.8t} - e^{-19.2t})$.

2. A spring is such that a 2-pound weight stretches it $\frac{1}{2}$ foot. An impressed force $\frac{1}{4} \sin 8t$ and a damping force of magnitude $|v|$ are both acting on the spring. The weight starts $\frac{1}{4}$ foot below the equilibrium point with an imparted upward velocity of 3 ft. per sec. Find a formula for the position of the weight at time t.

ANS. $x = \frac{3}{32}e^{-8t}(3 - 8t) - \frac{1}{32}\cos 8t$.

3. A spring is such that a 4-pound weight stretches it 0.64 feet. The 4-pound weight is pushed up $\frac{1}{3}$ foot above the point of equilibrium and then started with a downward velocity of 5 ft. per sec. The motion takes place in a medium which furnishes a damping force of magnitude $\frac{1}{4}|v|$ at all times. Find the equation describing the position of the weight at time t.
ANS. $x = \frac{1}{3}e^{-t}(2 \sin 7t - \cos 7t)$.

4. A spring is such that a 4-pound weight stretches it 0.32 feet. The weight is attached to the spring and moves in a medium which furnishes a damping force of magnitude $\frac{3}{2}|v|$. The weight is drawn down $\frac{1}{2}$ foot below the equilibrium point and given an initial upward velocity of 4 ft. per sec. Find the position of the weight thereafter.

ANS. $x = \frac{1}{8}e^{-6t}(4 \cos 8t - \sin 8t)$.

5. A spring is such that a 4-pound weight stretches the spring 0.4 feet. The 4-pound weight is attached to the spring (suspended from a fixed support) and the system is allowed to reach equilibrium. Then the weight is started from equilibrium position with an imparted upward velocity of 2 ft. per sec. Assume that the motion takes place in a medium which furnishes a retarding force of magnitude numerically equal to the speed, in feet per second, of the moving weight. Determine the position of the weight as a function of time.

ANS. $x = -\frac{1}{4}e^{-4t} \sin 8t$.

6. A spring is stretched 6 inches by a 3-pound weight. The 3-pound weight is attached to the spring and then started from equilibrium with an imparted upward velocity of 12 ft. per sec. Air resistance furnishes a retarding force equal in magnitude to $0.03|v|$. Find the equation of motion.
ANS. $x = -1.5e^{-0.16t} \sin 8t$.

7. A spring is such that a 2-pound weight stretches it 6 inches. There is a damping force present, with magnitude the same as the magnitude of the velocity. An impressed force $(2 \sin 8t)$ is acting on the spring. If, at $t = 0$, the weight is released from a point 3 inches below the equilibrium point, find its position for $t > 0$.

ANS. $x = (\frac{1}{2} + 4t)e^{-8t} - \frac{1}{4}\cos 8t$.

8. A spring is stretched 10 inches by a 4-pound weight. The weight is started 6 inches below the equilibrium point with an upward velocity of 8 ft. per sec. If a resisting medium furnishes a retarding force of magnitude $\frac{1}{4}|v|$, describe the motion.

ANS. $x = e^{-t}[0.50 \cos 6.1t - 1.23 \sin 6.1t]$.

9. For Ex. 8, find the times of the first three stops and the position (to the nearest inch) of the weight at each stop.

ANS. $t_1 = 0.3$ sec., $x_1 = -12$ in.; $t_2 = 0.8$ sec.,
$x_2 = +6$ in.; $t_3 = 1.3$ sec., $x_3 = -4$ in.

10. A spring is stretched 4 inches by a 2-pound weight. The 2-pound weight is started from the equilibrium point with a downward velocity of 12 ft. per sec. If air resistance furnishes a retarding force of magnitude 0.02 of the velocity, describe the motion.

ANS. $x = 1.22e^{-0.16t} \sin 9.8t$.

11. For Ex. 10, find how long it takes the damping factor to drop to one-tenth its initial value.   ANS. 14.4 sec.

12. For Ex. 10, find the position of the weight at: (a) the first stop; (b) the second stop.   ANS. (a) $x = 1.2$ ft.; (b) $x = -1.1$ ft.

13. Let the motion of Ex. 8, page 220, be retarded by a damping force of magnitude $0.6|v|$. Find the equation of motion.

ANS. $x = 0.30e^{-4.8t} \cos 6.4t + 0.22e^{-4.8t} \sin 6.4t - 0.05 \cos 8t$ (ft.).

14. Show that whenever $t > 1$ (sec.), the solution of Ex. 13 can be replaced (to the nearest 0.01 ft.) by $x = -0.05 \cos 8t$.

15. Let the motion of Ex. 8, page 220, be retarded by a damping force of magnitude $|v|$. Find the equation of motion and also determine its form (to the nearest 0.01 ft.) for $t > 1$ (sec.).

ANS. $x = \frac{9}{32}(8t + 1)e^{-8t} - \frac{1}{32} \cos 8t$ (ft.); for $t > 1$, $x = -\frac{1}{32} \cos 8t$.

16. Let the motion of Ex. 8, page 220, be retarded by a damping force of magnitude $\frac{5}{3}|v|$. Find the equation of motion.

ANS. $x = 0.30e^{-(8/3)t} - 0.03e^{-24t} - 0.02 \cos 8t$.

17. Alter Ex. 6, page 220, by inserting a damping force of magnitude one-half that of the velocity and then determine x.

ANS. $x = \exp\left(-\frac{2}{3}t\right)(0.30 \cos 8.0t - 0.22 \sin 8.0t)$
$- 0.05 \cos 4t + 0.49 \sin 4t$

18. A spring is stretched 6 inches by a 4-pound weight. Let the weight be pulled down 6 inches below equilibrium and given an initial upward velocity of 7 ft. per sec. Assuming a damping force twice the magnitude of the velocity, describe the motion and sketch the graph at intervals of 0.05 sec. for $0 \le t \le 0.3$ (sec.).   ANS. $x = \frac{1}{2}e^{-8t}(1 - 6t)$.

19. An object weighing w pounds is dropped from a height h feet above the

earth. At time t (sec.) after the object is dropped, let its distance from the starting point be x (ft.), measured positive downward. Assuming air resistance to be negligible, show that x must satisfy the equation

$$\frac{w}{g}\frac{d^2x}{dt^2} = w$$

as long as $x < h$. Find x.   ANS. $x = \frac{1}{2}gt^2$.

20. Let the weight of Ex. 19 be given an initial velocity v_0. Let v be the velocity at time t. Determine v and x.

ANS. $v = gt + v_0$, $x = \frac{1}{2}gt^2 + v_0 t$.

21. From the results in Ex. 20, find a relation that does not contain t explicitly.   ANS. $v^2 = v_0^2 + 2gx$.

22. If air resistance furnishes an additional force proportional to the velocity in the motion studied in Ex. 19 and 20, show that the equation of motion becomes

(A) $$\frac{w}{g}\frac{d^2x}{dt^2} + b\frac{dx}{dt} = w.$$

Solve equation (A) given the conditions

(B)   when $t = 0$, $x = 0$ and $v = v_0$.

Use $a = bg/w$.   ANS. $x = a^{-1}gt + a^{-2}(av_0 - g)(1 - e^{-at})$.

23. To compare the results of Ex. 20 and 22 when $a = bg/w$ is small, use the power series for e^{-at} in the answer for Ex. 22 and discard all terms involving a^n for $n \geq 3$.

ANS. $x = \frac{1}{2}gt^2 + v_0 t - \frac{1}{6}at^2(3v_0 + gt) + \frac{1}{24}a^2t^3(4v_0 + gt)$.

24. The equation of motion of the vertical fall of a man with a parachute may be roughly approximated by equation (A) of Ex. 22. Suppose a 180-pound man drops from a great height and attains a velocity of 20 miles per hour after a long time. Determine the implied coefficient b of equation (A).   ANS.   6.1 (lb.)(sec.) per ft.

25. A particle is moving along the x-axis according to the law

$$\frac{d^2x}{dt^2} + 6\frac{dx}{dt} + 25x = 0.$$

If the particle started at $x = 0$ with an initial velocity of 12 ft. per sec. to the left, determine: (a) x in terms of t; (b) the times at which stops occur; and (c) the ratio between the numerical values of x at successive stops.   ANS.   (a) $x = -3e^{-3t}\sin 4t$,
(b) $t = 0.23 + \frac{1}{4}n\pi$, $n = 0, 1, 2, 3, \cdots$, (c) 0.095.

74. The simple pendulum

A rod of length C feet is suspended by one end so it can swing freely in a vertical plane. Let a weight B (the bob) of w pounds be attached to the free end of the rod, and let the weight of the rod be negligible compared to the weight of the bob.

Let θ (radians) be the angular displacement from the vertical, as shown in Figure 31, of the rod at time t (sec.). The tangential component of the force w (lb.) is $w \sin \theta$ and it tends to decrease θ. Then, neglecting the weight of the rod and using $S = C\theta$ as a measure of arc length from the vertical position, we may conclude that

$$(1) \qquad \frac{w}{g} \frac{d^2S}{dt^2} = -w \sin \theta.$$

Since $S = C\theta$ and C is constant, (1) becomes

FIGURE 31 (2) $\qquad \frac{d^2\theta}{dt^2} + \frac{g}{C} \sin \theta = 0.$

The solution of equation (2) is not elementary; it involves an elliptic integral. If θ is small, however, $\sin \theta$ and θ are nearly equal and (2) is closely approximated by the much simpler equation

$$(3) \qquad \frac{d^2\theta}{dt^2} + \beta^2\theta = 0; \beta^2 = \frac{g}{C}.$$

The solution of (3) with pertinent boundary conditions gives usable results whenever those conditions are such that θ remains small, say $|\theta| < 0.3$ (radians).

75. Beams

Consider a beam of length $2c$, as shown in Figure 32. Denote distance from one end of the beam by x, the deflection of the beam by y. If the beam is subjected to a vertical load $W(x)$, the deflection y must satisfy the equation

$$(1) \qquad EI \frac{d^4y}{dx^4} = W(x), \qquad \text{for } 0 < x < 2c,$$

in which E, the modulus of elasticity, and I, a moment of inertia, are known constants associated with the particular beam.

The slope of the curve of deflection is $y'(x)$, the bending moment is $EIy''(x)$, and the shearing force is $EIy'''(x)$. Common boundary conditions are of the following types:

   (a) Beam imbedded in a support: $y = 0$ and $y' = 0$ at the point;

   (b) Beam simply supported: $y = 0$ and $y'' = 0$ at the point;

   (c) Beam free: $y'' = 0$ and $y''' = 0$ at the point.

Problems in the transverse displacement of a beam take the form of the differential equation (1) with boundary conditions at each end of the beam. Such problems can be solved by integration with the use of a little algebra. There are however two reasons for employing our transform method in such problems. Frequently the load function, or its derivative, is discontinuous. Beam problems also give us a chance to examine a useful device in which a problem over a finite range is solved with the aid of an associated problem over an infinite range.

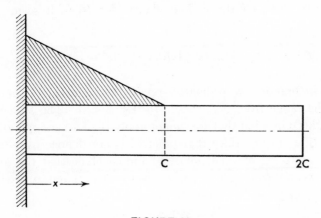

FIGURE 32

EXAMPLE: Find the displacement y throughout the beam of Figure 32, in which the load is assumed to decrease uniformly from w_0 at $x = 0$ to zero at $x = c$ and to remain zero from $x = c$ to $x = 2c$. The weight of the beam is to be negligible. The beam is imbedded at $x = 0$ and free at $x = 2c$.

We are to solve the problem

$$(2) \qquad EI\frac{d^4y}{dx^4} = \frac{w_0}{c}[c - x + (x - c)\alpha(x - c)], \qquad \text{for } 0 < x < 2c;$$

$$(3) \qquad\qquad\qquad y(0) = 0, \qquad y'(0) = 0;$$

$$(4) \qquad\qquad\qquad y''(2c) = 0, \qquad y'''(2c) = 0.$$

The student should verify that the right member of (2) is the stipulated load function

(5)
$$W(x) = \frac{w_0}{c}(c - x), \qquad \text{for } 0 \leq x \leq c,$$
$$= 0, \qquad\qquad \text{for } c < x \leq 2c.$$

To apply the transform technique, with x playing the role for which we usually employ t, we need first to extend the range of x so it will run from 0 to ∞. That is, instead of the problem (2), (3), (4), we shall solve the problem consisting of

(6)
$$EI\frac{d^4y}{dx^4} = H(x), \qquad \text{for } 0 < x < \infty,$$

and the conditions (3) and (4). In (6) the function $H(x)$ is to be chosen by us except that $H(x)$ must agree with $W(x)$ over the range $0 < x < 2c$. The solution of the problem (6), (3), (4) will then be used only in the range $0 \leq x \leq 2c$. Of the various choices for $H(x)$, it seems simplest to use

(7)
$$H(x) = \frac{w_0}{c}[c - x + (x - c)\alpha(x - c)], \qquad \text{for } 0 < x < \infty.$$

That is, in practice we ordinarily retain the equation (2) and merely extend the range from $0 < x < 2c$ to $0 < x < \infty$. The student must, however, keep in mind that we cannot apply the Laplace operator to the function $W(x)$ of (5), since that function is not defined over the entire range $0 < x < \infty$. We shall solve (6) and conclude that the solution is valid for (2) on the range $0 \leq x \leq 2c$, over which (2) and (6) are identical.

Let

$$L\{EIy(x)\} = u(s);$$
(8)
$$u(s) = EI\int_0^\infty e^{-sx}y(x)\, dx.$$

To transform $EIy^{(4)}(x)$ we need to use the values of $EIy(x)$ and its first three derivatives at $x = 0$. From (3) we know that

$$EIy(0) = 0, \qquad EIy'(0) = 0.$$
Put

(9)
$$EIy''(0) = A, \qquad EIy'''(0) = B.$$

The constants A and B must be determined by using the conditions (4).

By our usual methods we obtain, for the $H(x)$ of (7),

$$L\{H(x)\} = \frac{w_0}{c} L\{c - x + (x - c)\alpha(x - c)\}$$

$$= \frac{w_0}{c} \left(\frac{c}{s} - \frac{1}{s^2} + \frac{e^{-cs}}{s^2} \right).$$

Thus the differential equation (6) is transformed into

$$s^4 u(s) - s^3 \cdot 0 - s^2 \cdot 0 - s \cdot A - B = \frac{w_0}{c} \left(\frac{c}{s} - \frac{1}{s^2} + \frac{e^{-cs}}{s^2} \right),$$

from which we get

$$(10) \qquad u(s) = \frac{A}{s^3} + \frac{B}{s^4} + \frac{w_0}{c} \left(\frac{c}{s^5} - \frac{1}{s^6} + \frac{e^{-cs}}{s^6} \right).$$

Now $L^{-1}\{u(s)\} = EIy(x)$. Hence

$$(11) \quad EIy(x) = \tfrac{1}{2}Ax^2 + \tfrac{1}{6}Bx^3 + \frac{w_0}{120c} [5cx^4 - x^5 + (x - c)^5\alpha(x - c)].$$

From (11) we obtain

$$(12) \quad EIy'(x) = Ax + \tfrac{1}{2}Bx^2 + \frac{w_0}{24c} [4cx^3 - x^4 + (x - 4)^4\alpha(x - c)],$$

$$(13) \quad EIy''(x) = A + Bx + \frac{w_0}{6c} [3cx^2 - x^3 + (x - c)^3\alpha(x - c)],$$

$$(14) \qquad EIy'''(x) = B + \frac{w_0}{2c} [2cx - x^2 + (x - c)^2\alpha(x - c)].$$

By differentiating both members of equation (14), we can see that the y of (11) is a solution of (6) over the infinite range and, more important, a solution of (2) over the range $0 < x < 2c$.

With the aid of equations (11) through (14) we can now determine A and B to make the y satisfy appropriate conditions at $x = 2c$, whether the beam be free, imbedded, or pin-supported there. In our example the beam is to be free at $x = 2c$; the solution is to satisfy the conditions

$$(4) \qquad\qquad y''(2c) = 0, \qquad y'''(2c) = 0.$$

Using (13) and (14), and a little work, we find that (4) requires $A = \tfrac{1}{6}w_0 c^2$, $B = -\tfrac{1}{2}w_0 c$. We are thus led to the solution

$$(15) \quad EIy(x) = \tfrac{1}{12}w_0 c^2 x^2 - \tfrac{1}{12}w_0 c x^3$$

$$+ \frac{w_0}{120c} [5cx^4 - x^5 + (x - c)^5\alpha(x - c)],$$

for $0 \leqq x \leqq 2c$.

The student should verify by differentiations and appropriate substitutions that the y of (15) satisfies the original differential equation (2)
and boundary conditions (3) and (4).

From (15) we can obtain whatever information we wish. For example,
at $x = \frac{1}{2}c$ the bending moment is

$$EIy''(\tfrac{1}{2}c) = w_0c^2[\tfrac{1}{6} - \tfrac{1}{4} + \tfrac{1}{6}(-\tfrac{1}{8} + \tfrac{3}{4} + 0)] = \tfrac{1}{48}w_0c^2.$$

Exercises

1. A clock has a 6-inch pendulum. The clock ticks once for each time that
   the pendulum completes a swing, returning to its original position.
   How many times does the clock tick in 30 seconds?   ANS.   38 times.
2. A 6-inch pendulum is released from rest at an angle one-tenth of a
   radian from the vertical. Using $g = 32$ (ft. per sec. per sec.), describe
   the motion.   ANS. $\theta = 0.1 \cos 8t$ (radians).
3. For the pendulum of Ex. 2, find the maximum angular speed and its
   first time of occurrence.   ANS.   0.8 (rad. per sec.) at 0.2 sec.
4. A 6-inch pendulum is started with a velocity of one radian per second,
   toward the vertical, from a position one-tenth radian from the vertical.
   Describe the motion.   ANS. $\theta = \tfrac{1}{10} \cos 8t - \tfrac{1}{8} \sin 8t$ (radians).
5. For Ex. 4, find to the nearest degree the maximum angular displace-
   ment from the vertical.   ANS.   9°.
6. Interpret as a pendulum problem and solve:

   (A) $\dfrac{d^2\theta}{dt^2} + \beta^2\theta = 0: \beta^2 = \dfrac{g}{C}$,

   (B)   when $t = 0$, $\theta = \theta_0$ and $\omega = \dfrac{d\theta}{dt} = \omega_0$.

                        ANS. $\theta = \theta_0 \cos \beta t + \beta^{-1}\omega_0 \sin \beta t$ (radians).
7. Find the maximum angular displacement from the vertical for the
   pendulum of Ex. 6.   ANS. $\theta_{\max} = (\theta_0^2 + \beta^{-2}\omega_0^2)^{\frac{1}{2}}$.

In Exs. 8–11, find the y that satisfies equation (1), page 228, with the
given load function $W(x)$ and the given conditions at the ends of the beam.
(See (a), (b), (c), page 229.) Verify your solutions.

8. $W(x)$ as in the example introduced on page 229; beam imbedded at
   both $x = 0$ and $x = 2c$.
   ANS. $EIy(x) = \tfrac{23}{480}w_0c^2x^2 - \tfrac{3}{40}w_0cx^3$
   $$+ \frac{w_0}{120c} [5cx^4 - x^5 + (x - c)^5\alpha(x - c)].$$

9. $W(x) = 0,$ for $0 < x < \frac{1}{2}c,$

       $= w_0,$ for $\frac{1}{2}c < x < \frac{3}{2}c,$

       $= 0,$ for $\frac{3}{2}c < x < 2c;$

beam imbedded at $x = 0$, free at $x = 2c$.

     ANS. $EIy(x) = \frac{1}{2}w_0c^2x^2 - \frac{1}{6}w_0cx^3$

$$+ \tfrac{1}{24}w_0[(x - \tfrac{1}{2}c)^4\alpha(x - \tfrac{1}{2}c) - (x - \tfrac{3}{2}c)^4\alpha(x - \tfrac{3}{2}c)].$$

10. $W(x) = w_0[1 - \alpha(x - c)]$ (describe the load); beam to be imbedded at $x = 0$ and pin-supported (simply supported) at $x = 2c$.

   ANS. $EIy(x) = \frac{9}{64}w_0c^2x^2 - \frac{19}{128}w_0cx^3 + \frac{1}{24}w_0[x^4 - (x - \cdot c)^4\alpha(x - c)].$

11. $W(x) = \dfrac{w_0}{c}(2c - x),$ for $0 < x < c,$

       $= w_0,$ for $c < x < 2c;$

beam to be imbedded at $x = 0$ and free at $x = 2c$.

     ANS. $EIy(x) = \frac{13}{12}w_0c^2x^2 - \frac{5}{12}w_0cx^3 + \frac{1}{24}w_0x^4$

$$+ \frac{w_0}{120c}[5cx^4 - x^5 + (x - c)^5\alpha(x - c)].$$

CHAPTER 14

Systems of Equations

76. The Laplace transform method

The Laplace operator can be used to transform a system of linear differential equations with constant coefficients into a system of algebraic equations.

EXAMPLE: Solve the system of equations

$$(1) \qquad x''(t) - x(t) + 5y'(t) = t,$$

$$(2) \qquad y''(t) - 4y(t) - 2x'(t) = -2,$$

with the initial conditions

$$(3) \qquad x(0) = 0, \quad x'(0) = 0, \quad y(0) = 0, \quad y'(0) = 0.$$

Let $L\{x(t)\} = u(s)$ and $L\{y(t)\} = v(s)$. Then, application of the Laplace operator transforms the problem into that of solving a pair of simultaneous algebraic equations:

$$(4) \qquad (s^2 - 1)u(s) + 5sv(s) = \frac{1}{s^2},$$

$$(5) \qquad -2su(s) + (s^2 - 4)v(s) = -\frac{2}{s}.$$

We solve equations (4) and (5) to obtain

(6)
$$u(s) = \frac{11s^2 - 4}{s^2(s^2 + 1)(s^2 + 4)},$$

(7)
$$v(s) = \frac{-2s^2 + 4}{s(s^2 + 1)(s^2 + 4)}.$$

Seeking the inverse transforms of u and v, we first expand the right members of (6) and (7) into partial fractions:

(8)
$$u(s) = -\frac{1}{s^2} + \frac{5}{s^2 + 1} - \frac{4}{s^2 + 4},$$

(9)
$$v(s) = \frac{1}{s} - \frac{2s}{s^2 + 1} + \frac{s}{s^2 + 4}.$$

Since $x(t) = L^{-1}\{u(s)\}$ and $y(t) = L^{-1}\{v(s)\}$, we get the desired results

(10)
$$x(t) = -t + 5 \sin t - 2 \sin 2t,$$

(11)
$$y(t) = 1 - 2 \cos t + \cos 2t,$$

which are easily verified by direct substitution into (1), (2), and (3).

The above procedure is simple in concept and powerful in theoretical studies, but of only moderate efficiency for numerical problems. The student should not overlook the sometimes tedious algebra used in passing from (6) and (7) to (8) and (9). The example was deliberately constructed to make the work simple.

77. The differential operator method

In solving systems of simultaneous linear equations, the differential operator notation is another convenient tool. Consider the system

(1)
$$y'' - y + 5v' = x,$$
$$2y' - v'' + 4v = 2,$$

with independent variable x and dependent variables y and v. It is natural to attack the system (1) by eliminating one dependent variable to obtain a single equation for the other dependent variable. Using $D = \dfrac{d}{dx}$, write the system (1) in the form

(2)
$$(D^2 - 1)y + 5Dv = x,$$
$$2Dy - (D^2 - 4)v = 2.$$

Then, elimination of one dependent variable is straightforward. We may, for instance, operate upon the first equation with $2D$ and upon the second equation with $(D^2 - 1)$, and then subtract one from the other, obtaining

$$[10D^2 + (D^2 - 1)(D^2 - 4)]v = 2Dx - (D^2 - 1)2,$$

or

(3) $(D^4 + 5D^2 + 4)v = 4.$

In a similar manner v may be eliminated; the resultant equation for y is

$$[(D^2 - 1)(D^2 - 4) + 10D^2]y = (D^2 - 4)x + 5D(2),$$

or

(4) $(D^4 + 5D^2 + 4)y = -4x.$

From equations (3) and (4) it follows at once that

(5) $v = 1 + a_1 \cos x + a_2 \sin x + a_3 \cos 2x + a_4 \sin 2x$

and

(6) $y = -x + b_1 \cos x + b_2 \sin x + b_3 \cos 2x + b_4 \sin 2x.$

The a's and b's have yet to be adjusted to make (5) and (6) satisfy the original equations, rather than just the equations (3) and (4), which resulted from the original ones after certain eliminations were performed.

Combining (by substitution) the v of (5) and the y of (6) with the first equation of the system (2) leads to the identity

(7) $x - 2b_1 \cos x - 2b_2 \sin x - 5b_3 \cos 2x - 5b_4 \sin 2x$

          $- 5a_1 \sin x + 5a_2 \cos x - 10a_3 \sin 2x + 10a_4 \cos 2x \equiv x.$

That (7) be an identity in x demands that

(8) $-2b_1 + 5a_2 = 0,$

                                 $-2b_2 - 5a_1 = 0,$

                                 $-5b_3 + 10a_4 = 0,$

                                 $-5b_4 - 10a_3 = 0.$

Relations between the a's and b's equivalent to the relations (8) follow from substitution of the v of (5) and the y of (6) into the second equation of the system (2).

We conclude that the general solution of the system (2) is

(9) $v = 1 + a_1 \cos x + a_2 \sin x + a_3 \cos 2x + a_4 \sin 2x,$

$\qquad y = -x + \tfrac{5}{2}a_2 \cos x - \tfrac{5}{2}a_1 \sin x + 2a_4 \cos 2x - 2a_3 \sin 2x,$

in which a_1, a_2, a_3, a_4 are arbitrary constants.

The equations (3) and (4) for v and y can be written with the aid of determinants. From the system (2) above we may write at once

$$\begin{vmatrix} (D^2 - 1) & 5D \\ 2D & -(D^2 - 4) \end{vmatrix} v = \begin{vmatrix} (D^2 - 1) & x \\ 2D & 2 \end{vmatrix},$$

which reduces to equation (3) above, if care is used in the interpretation of the right-hand member. The determinant on the right is to be interpreted as

$$(D^2 - 1)(2) - 2D(x),$$

not as the differential operator $2(D^2 - 1) - x(2D)$.

Determinants are extremely useful in any treatment of the theory of systems of linear equations. For many simple systems which arise in practice, no such powerful tool is needed.

There are other techniques for treating a system such as (2). For example, we may first obtain (3) and from it v as in equation (5). Next we wish to find an equation giving y in terms of v; that is, we seek to eliminate from the system (2) those terms that involve derivatives of y. From (2) we obtain the two equations

(10) $(2D^2 - 2)y + 10Dv = 2x,$

(11) $2D^2y - (D^3 - 4D)v = 0,$

the latter by operating with D on each member of the second equation of the system (2). From (10) and (11) it follows at once that

$$2y - D^3v - 6Dv = -2x,$$

or

(12) $y = -x + \tfrac{1}{2}D^3v + 3Dv.$

The v of equation (5) may now be used in (12) to compute the y which was given in the solution (9). In this method of solution there is no need to obtain (4), (6), (7), or (8).

Both methods outlined here are available whenever the system is linear with constant coefficients. Such systems appear naturally in the study of electric networks, which will be discussed in the next chapter.

Systems of nonlinear equations and systems of linear equations with variable coefficients will not be studied in this book.

Exercises

In Exs. 1–8, use the Laplace transform method.

1. $x''(t) - 3x'(t) - y'(t) + 2y(t) = 14t + 3$,
$x'(t) - 3x(t) + y'(t) = 1$; $x(0) = 0$, $x'(0) = 0$, $y(0) = 6.5$.

$$\text{ANS.} \quad x(t) = 2 - \tfrac{1}{2}e^t - \tfrac{1}{2}e^{3t} - e^{-2t},$$
$$y(t) = 7t + 5 - e^t + \tfrac{5}{2}e^{-2t}.$$

2. $2x'(t) + 2x(t) + y'(t) - y(t) = 3t$,
$x'(t) + x(t) + y'(t) + y(t) = 1$; $x(0) = 1$, $y(0) = 3$.

$$\text{ANS.} \quad x(t) = t + 3e^{-t} - 2e^{-3t},$$
$$y(t) = 1 - t + 2e^{-3t}.$$

3. $x'(t) - 2x(t) - y'(t) - y(t) = 6e^{3t}$,
$2x'(t) - 3x(t) + y'(t) - 3y(t) = 6e^{3t}$; $x(0) = 3$, $y(0) = 0$.

$$\text{ANS.} \quad x(t) = (1 + 2t)e^t + 2e^{3t},$$
$$y(t) = (1 - t)e^t - e^{3t}.$$

4. $x''(t) + 2x(t) - y'(t) = 2t + 5$,
$x'(t) - x(t) + y'(t) + y(t) = -2t - 1$; $x(0) = 3$, $x'(0) = 0$, $y(0) = -3$.

$$\text{ANS.} \quad x(t) = t + 2 + e^{-2t} + \sin t,$$
$$y(t) = 1 - t - 3e^{-2t} - \cos t.$$

5. The equations of the example of Section 76, page 234, with initial conditions $x(0) = 0$, $x'(0) = 0$, $y(0) = 1$, $y'(0) = 0$.

$$\text{ANS.} \quad x(t) = -t - \tfrac{5}{3}\sin t + \tfrac{4}{3}\sin 2t,$$
$$y(t) = 1 + \tfrac{2}{3}\cos t - \tfrac{2}{3}\cos 2t.$$

6. The equations of the example of Section 76, page 234, with initial conditions $x(0) = 9$, $x'(0) = 2$, $y(0) = 1$, $y'(0) = 0$.

$$\text{ANS.} \quad x(t) = -t + 15\cos t - 5\sin t - 6\cos 2t + 4\sin 2t,$$
$$y(t) = 1 + 2\cos t + 6\sin t - 2\cos 2t - 3\sin 2t.$$

7. $x''(t) + y'(t) - y(t) = 0$,
$2x'(t) - x(t) + z'(t) - z(t) = 0$,
$x'(t) + 3x(t) + y'(t) - 4y(t) + 3z(t) = 0$;
$x(0) = 0$, $x'(0) = 1$, $y(0) = 0$, $z(0) = 0$.

8. $x''(t) - x(t) + 5y'(t) = \beta(t)$,
$y''(t) - 4y(t) - 2x'(t) = 0$,
in which $\beta(t) = 6t$, $0 \leq t \leq 2$,
             $= 12$, $t > 2$;
$x(0) = 0$, $x'(0) = 0$, $y(0) = 0$, $y'(0) = 0$.

$$\text{ANS.} \quad x(t) = -2(3t - 5\sin t + \sin 2t)$$
$$+ 2[3(t - 2) - 5\sin(t - 2) + \sin 2(t - 2)]\alpha(t - 2),$$
$$y(t) = 3 - 4\cos t + \cos 2t$$
$$- [3 - 4\cos(t - 2) + \cos 2(t - 2)]\alpha(t - 2).$$

In Exs. 9–12, use the differential operator method.

9. Ex. 1.   10. Ex. 2.
11. Ex. 3.   12. Ex. 4.

In Exs. 13–24, use whichever method you prefer. Obtain the general solution except where otherwise directed.

13. $v' - 2v + 2w' = 2 - 4e^{2x}$,
    $2v' - 3v + 3w' - w = 0.$ ANS. $v = a_1e^x + a_2e^{-2x} + 5e^{2x} - 1$,
                                            $w = \frac{1}{2}a_1e^x - a_2e^{-2x} - e^{2x} + 3.$

14. $(3D + 2)v + (D - 6)w = 5e^x$,
    $(4D + 2)v + (D - 8)w = 5e^x + 2x - 3.$
                            ANS. $v = a_1 \cos 2x + a_2 \sin 2x + 2e^x - 3x + 5$,
                                    $w = a_2 \cos 2x - a_1 \sin 2x + e^x - x.$

15. $(D^2 + 6)y + Dv = 0$,
    $(D + 2)y + (D - 2)v = 2.$
                            ANS. $y = c_1e^{3x} + c_2 \cos 2x + c_3 \sin 2x$,
                                    $v = -1 - 5c_1e^{3x} + c_3 \cos 2x - c_2 \sin 2x.$

16. $D^2y - (2D - 1)v = 1$,
    $(2D + 1)y + (D^2 - 4)v = 0.$
    ANS. $v = 1 + a_1e^x + a_2e^{-x} + a_3 \cos x + a_4 \sin x$,
            $y = 4 + a_1e^x - 3a_2e^{-x} + (a_3 - 2a_4) \cos x + (2a_3 + a_4) \sin x.$

17. $(D^2 - 3D)y - (D - 2)z = 14x + 7$,
    $(D - 3)y + Dz = 1.$
                            ANS. $y = 2 + a_1e^x + a_2e^{3x} + a_3e^{-2x}$,
                                    $z = 7 + 7x + 2a_1e^x - \frac{5}{2}a_3e^{-2x}.$

18. $(D^3 + D^2 - 1)u + (D^3 + 2D^2 + 3D + 1)v = 3 - x$,
    $(D - 1)u + (D + 1)v = 3 - x.$
                            ANS. $u = 2x + a_1 + a_2 \cos x + a_3 \sin x$,
                                    $v = x + a_1 - a_3 \cos x + a_2 \sin x.$

19. $(D^2 + 1)y + 4(D - 1)v = 4e^x$,
    $(D - 1)y + (D + 9)v = 0$; when $x = 0$, $y = 5$, $y' = 0$, $v = \frac{1}{2}$.
                            ANS. $y = 2e^x + 2e^{-x} + e^{-2x}(\cos x + 2 \sin x)$,
                                    $v = \frac{1}{2}e^{-x} + e^{-2x} \sin x.$

20. $\dfrac{d^2x}{dt^2} + x - 2\dfrac{dy}{dt} = 2t$,

    $2\dfrac{dx}{dt} - x + \dfrac{dy}{dt} - 2y = 7.$

                            ANS. $x = 2t - 2 + b_1e^t + b_2e^{-t} + b_3e^{-2t}$,
                                    $y = -t - 1 + b_1e^t - b_2e^{-t} - \frac{5}{4}b_3e^{-2t}.$

21. $2(D + 1)y + (D - 1)w = x + 1,$
$(D + 3)y + (D + 1)w = 4x + 14.$

ANS. $y = x + 2 + c_1e^{-x}\cos 2x + c_2e^{-x}\sin 2x,$
$w = x + 6 + (c_2 - c_1)e^{-x}\cos 2x - (c_1 + c_2)e^{-x}\sin 2x.$

22. $(D + 1)y + (D - 4)v = 6\cos x,$
$(D - 1)y + (D^2 + 4)v = -6\sin x.$

ANS. $y = 3\cos x + 3\sin x + a_1 + a_2\cos 3x + a_3\sin 3x,$
$v = \frac{1}{4}a_1 - \frac{1}{5}(a_2 - 3a_3)\cos 3x - \frac{1}{5}(3a_2 + a_3)\sin 3x.$

23. $2Du + (D - 1)v + (D + 2)w = 0,$
$(D + 2)u + (2D - 3)v - (D - 6)w = 0,$
$2Du - (D + 3)v - Dw = 0.$

ANS. $u = 3c_1e^{2x} + 3c_2e^{-x} + 3c_3e^{x/2},$
$v = 4c_1e^{2x} - 5c_2e^{-x} + c_3e^{x/2},$
$w = -4c_1e^{2x} - 4c_2e^{-x} - c_3e^{x/2}.$

24. $D^2y + (D - 1)v = 0,$
$(2D - 1)y + (D - 1)w = 0,$
$(D + 3)y + (D - 4)v + 3w = 0.$

ANS. $y = a_1 + a_2e^x + 3a_3e^{4x},$
$v = b_2e^x - a_2xe^x - 16a_3e^{4x},$
$w = -a_1 + (b_2 - a_2)e^x - a_2xe^x - 7a_3e^{4x}.$

25. Solve the problem of Section 77 by the method of Section 76.

CHAPTER 15

Electric Circuits and Networks

78. Circuits

The basic laws governing the flow of electric current in a circuit or a network will be given here without derivation. The notation used is common to most texts in electrical engineering and is:

t (sec.) = time
Q (coulombs) = quantity of electricity; e.g., charge on a capacitor
I (amperes) = current, time rate of flow of electricity
E (volts) = electromotive force or voltage
R (ohms) = resistance
L (henrys) = inductance
C (farads) = capacitance.

By the definition of Q and I it follows that

$$I(t) = Q'(t).$$

The current at each point in a network may be determined by solving the equations that result from applying Kirchhoff's laws:

(a) *The sum of the currents into (or away from) any point is zero,* and

(b) *Around any closed path the sum of the instantaneous voltage drops in a specified direction is zero.*

241

A circuit is treated as a network containing only one closed path. Figure 33 exhibits an "*RLC* circuit" with some of the customary conventions for indicating various elements.

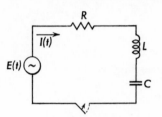

For a circuit, Kirchhoff's current law (a) indicates merely that the current is the same throughout. That law plays a larger role in networks, as we shall see later.

To apply Kirchhoff's voltage law (b), it is necessary to know the contributions of each of the idealized elements in Figure 33.

FIGURE 33

The voltage drop across the resistance is RI, that across the inductance is $LI'(t)$, and that across the capacitor is $C^{-1}Q(t)$. The impressed electromotive force $E(t)$ is contributing a voltage rise.

Assume that at time $t = 0$ the switch shown in Figure 33 is to be closed. At $t = 0$ there is no current flowing, $I(0) = 0$, and if the capacitor is initially without charge, $Q(0) = 0$. From Kirchhoff's law (b), we get the differential equation

$$(1) \qquad LI'(t) + RI(t) + C^{-1}Q(t) = E(t),$$

in which

$$(2) \qquad I(t) = Q'(t).$$

Equations (1) and (2), with the initial conditions

$$(3) \qquad I(0) = 0, \qquad Q(0) = 0,$$

constitute the problem to be solved.

To retain the conventional symbol L for the number of henrys inductance of the circuit, we shall in this section denote by L_t the Laplace operator for which L is used in all other sections of the book.

Let the transforms of $I(t)$, $Q(t)$, $E(t)$ be denoted by lower case letters:

$$(4) \qquad L_t\{I(t)\} = i(s), \qquad L_t\{Q(t)\} = q(s), \qquad L_t\{E(t)\} = e(s).$$

The problem (1), (2), and (3) is then transformed into

$$(5) \qquad L\, si(s) + Ri(s) + C^{-1}q(s) = e(s),$$
$$(6) \qquad i(s) = sq(s).$$

From (5) and (6) we find either or both of $i(s)$ and $q(s)$,

$$(7) \qquad i(s) = \frac{se(s)}{Ls^2 + Rs + C^{-1}},$$

(8)
$$q(s) = \frac{e(s)}{Ls^2 + Rs + C^{-1}}.$$

Then $I(t)$ and $Q(t)$ are obtained as inverse transforms from (7) and (8).
   From (7), (8), or the differential equation

(9)
$$LQ''(t) + RQ'(t) + C^{-1}Q(t) = E(t),$$

it follows that the circuit problem is equivalent to a problem in damped
vibrations of a spring (Section 73). The resistance term $RQ'(t)$ parallels
the damping term in vibration problems. The analogies between electrical
and mechanical systems are useful in practice.

EXAMPLE: In the RL circuit with the schematic diagram shown in Figure 34, let the
switch be closed at $t = 0$. At some later time,
$t = t_0$, the direct current element, the constant
E, is to be removed from the circuit, which remains closed. Find the current for all $t > 0$.
   The boundary value problem to be solved is

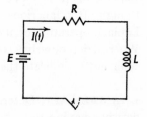

FIGURE 34

(10) $LI'(t) + RI(t) = E(t); \quad I(0) = 0,$
(11) $\quad E(t) = E[1 - \alpha(t - t_0)].$

Let the transform of $I(t)$ be $i(s)$. We know the transform of $E(t)$. Therefore we obtain the transformed problem

(12)
$$sL\, i(s) + Ri(s) = \frac{E}{s}[1 - \exp(-t_0 s)],$$

from which

(13)
$$i(s) = \frac{E[1 - \exp(-t_0 s)]}{s(sL + R)}.$$

   Now

$$\frac{1}{s(sL + R)} = \frac{1}{R}\left(\frac{1}{s} - \frac{1}{s + RL^{-1}}\right),$$

so

$$i(s) = \frac{E}{R}\left(\frac{1}{s} - \frac{1}{s + RL^{-1}}\right)[1 - \exp(-t_0 s)].$$

Therefore

(14) $$I(t) = \frac{E}{R}\Bigg[1 - \alpha(t - t_0) - \exp\left(-\frac{R}{L}t\right)$$
$$+ \exp\left\{-\frac{R}{L}(t - t_0)\right\}\alpha(t - t_0)\Bigg].$$

The student should verify (14) and show that it can be written

(15)   For $0 \leqq t \leqq t_0$, $I(t) = \dfrac{E}{R}\left[1 - \exp\left(-\dfrac{Rt}{L}\right)\right];$

(16)   For $t > t_0$, $I(t) = I(t_0) \exp\left[-\dfrac{R}{L}(t - t_0)\right].$

79. Simple networks

Systems of differential equations occur naturally in the application of Kirchhoff's laws, page 241, to electric networks. The use of the Laplace operator makes the solution of such systems a straightforward, though often laborious, process. For the general theory of networks the Laplace operator (or its Heaviside equivalent) is a tool of great value. We restrict ourselves to extremely simple situations which should be sufficient to indicate the procedure commonly used.

EXAMPLE (a): Determine the character of the current $I_1(t)$ in the network having the schematic diagram in Figure 35, under the assumption that when the switch is closed the currents are each zero.

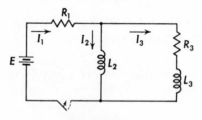

FIGURE 35

In a network, we apply Kirchhoff's laws, page 241, to obtain a system of equations to determine the currents. Since there are three dependent variables, I_1, I_2, I_3, we need three equations.

From the current law it follows that

(1) $I_1 = I_2 + I_3.$

Application of the voltage law to the circuit on the left in Figure 35 yields

(2) $R_1 I_1 + L_2 I_2' = E.$

Using the voltage law on the outside circuit, we get

(3) $R_1 I_1 + R_3 I_3 + L_3 I_3' = E.$

Still another equation can be obtained from the circuit on the right in Figure 35:

(4) $$R_3 I_3 + L_3 I_3' - L_2 I_2' = 0.$$

Equation (4) also follows at once from equations (2) and (3); it may be used instead of either (2) or (3).

We wish to obtain $I_1(t)$ from the boundary value problem consisting of equations (1), (2), (3), and the conditions $I_1(0) = 0$, $I_2(0) = 0$, $I_3(0) = 0$. One of the three initial conditions is redundant because of equation (1).

Let $L\{I_k(t)\} = i_k(s)$ for each of $k = 1, 2, 3$. Then use of the operator L transforms our problem into the algebraic one of solving the equations

(5) $$i_1 - i_2 - i_3 = 0,$$

(6) $$R_1 i_1 + s L_2 i_2 = \frac{E}{s}$$

(7) $$R_1 i_1 + (R_3 + s L_3) i_3 = \frac{E}{s}.$$

Since we desire only $i_1(s)$, let us use determinants to write the solution

(8) $$i_1(s) = \frac{\begin{vmatrix} 0 & -1 & -1 \\ \dfrac{E}{s} & sL_2 & 0 \\ \dfrac{E}{s} & 0 & (R_3 + sL_3) \end{vmatrix}}{\Delta} = \frac{E}{s} \cdot \frac{R_3 + s(L_2 + L_3)}{\Delta},$$

in which

$$\Delta = \begin{vmatrix} 1 & -1 & -1 \\ R_1 & sL_2 & 0 \\ R_1 & 0 & (R_3 + sL_3) \end{vmatrix} = \begin{vmatrix} 1 & 0 & 0 \\ R_1 & (sL_2 + R_1) & R_1 \\ R_1 & R_1 & (R_1 + R_3 + sL_3) \end{vmatrix}.$$

Then

(9) $$\Delta = L_2 L_3 s^2 + (R_1 L_2 + R_3 L_2 + R_1 L_3)s + R_1 R_3.$$

We are interested in the factors of Δ. Consider the equation

(10) $$\Delta = 0.$$

Equation (10) has no positive roots. Its discriminant

$$(R_1 L_2 + R_3 L_2 + R_1 L_3)^2 - 4 L_2 L_3 R_1 R_3$$

may be written

$$(R_1L_2)^2 + 2R_1L_2(R_3L_2 + R_1L_3) + (R_3L_2 + R_1L_3)^2 - 4L_2L_3R_1R_3,$$

which equals

$$(R_1L_2)^2 + 2R_1L_2(R_3L_2 + R_1L_3) + (R_3L_2 - R_1L_3)^2$$

and is therefore positive. Thus we see that equation (10) has two distinct negative roots. Call them $(-a_1)$ and $(-a_2)$. It follows that

$$\Delta = L_2L_3(s + a_1)(s + a_2),$$

and we have, from (8),

(11) $$i_1(s) = \frac{E}{s} \frac{R_3 + s(L_2 + L_3)}{L_2L_3(s + a_1)(s + a_2)}.$$

The right member of equation (11) has a partial fractions expansion

(12) $$i_1(s) = \frac{A_0}{s} + \frac{A_1}{s + a_1} + \frac{A_2}{s + a_2},$$

so

$$I_1(t) = A_0 + A_1 \exp(-a_1t) + A_2 \exp(-a_2t).$$

EXAMPLE (b): For the network shown in Figure 36, set up the equations for the determination of the currents I_1, I_2, I_3, and the charge Q_3. Assume that when the switch is closed all currents and charges are zero. Obtain the transformed problem.

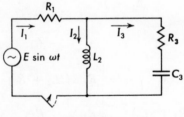

FIGURE 36

Using Kirchhoff's laws we write the equations

(13) $$I_1 = I_2 + I_3,$$

(14) $$R_1I_1 + L_2\frac{dI_2}{dt} = E \sin \omega t,$$

(15) $$R_1I_1 + R_3I_3 + \frac{1}{C_3} Q_3 = E \sin \omega t;$$

and the definition of current as time rate of change of charge yields

(16) $$I_3 = \frac{dQ_3}{dt}.$$

Our problem consists of the four equations (13) through (16) with the initial conditions that

(17) $$I_2(0) = 0, \qquad I_3(0) = 0, \qquad Q_3(0) = 0.$$

Let $L\{I_k(t)\} = i_k(s)$, $k = 1, 2, 3$, and $L\{Q_3(t)\} = q_3(s)$. Then the transformed problem is the problem of solving the algebraic system

(18) $$i_1 - i_2 - i_3 = 0,$$

(19) $$R_1i_1 + sL_2i_2 = \frac{E\omega}{s^2 + \omega^2},$$

(20) $$R_1i_1 + R_3i_3 + \frac{1}{C_3}q_3 = \frac{E\omega}{s^2 + \omega^2},$$

(21) $$i_3 = sq_3.$$

Exercises

1. For the RL circuit of Figure 34, page 243, find the current I if the direct current element E is not removed from the circuit.
   ANS. $I = ER^{-1}[1 - \exp(-RtL^{-1})]$.
2. Solve Ex. 1 if the direct-current element is replaced by an alternating-current element $E \cos \omega t$. For convenience, use the notation

   $$Z^2 = R^2 + \omega^2 L^2,$$

   in which Z is called the steady-state impedance of this circuit.
   ANS. $I = EZ^{-2}[\omega L \sin \omega t + R \cos \omega t - R \exp(-RtL^{-1})]$.
3. Solve Ex. 2, replacing $E \cos \omega t$ with $E \sin \omega t$.
4. Figure 37 shows an RC circuit with an alternating-current element inserted. Assume that the switch is closed at $t = 0$ at which time $Q = 0$ and $I = 0$. Use the notation

   $$Z^2 = R^2 + (\omega C)^{-2},$$

   where Z is the steady-state impedance of this circuit. Find I for $t > 0$.
   ANS. $I = EZ^{-2}[R \sin \omega t + (\omega C)^{-1} \cos \omega t - (\omega C)^{-1} \exp(-tR^{-1}C^{-1})]$.

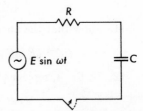

FIGURE 37

5. In Figure 37, replace the alternating-current element with a direct-current element $E = 50$ volts and use $R = 10$ ohms, $C = 4(10)^{-4}$ farad. Assume that when the switch is closed (at $t = 0$) the charge on the capacitor is 0.015 coulomb. Find the initial current in the circuit and the current for $t > 0$.

ANS. $I(0) = 1.25$(amp), $I(t) = 1.25 \exp(-250t)$(amp.).

6. In Figure 33, page 242, find $I(t)$ if $E(t) = 60$ volts, $R = 40$ ohms, $C = 5(10)^{-5}$ farad, $L = 0.02$ henry. Assume $I(0) = 0$, $Q(0) = 0$.

ANS. $I = 3000t \exp(-1000t)$(amp.).

7. In Ex. 6, find the maximum current.   ANS. $I_{\max} = 3e^{-1}$ (amp.).

In Exs. 8–11, use Figure 33, page 242, with $E(t) = E \sin \omega t$ and with the following notations used to simplify the appearance of the formulas:

$$a = \frac{R}{2L}, \; b^2 = a^2 - \frac{1}{LC}, \; \beta^2 = \frac{1}{LC} - a^2,$$

$$\gamma = \omega L - \frac{1}{\omega C}, \; Z^2 = R^2 + \gamma^2.$$

The quantity Z is the steady-state impedance for an RLC circuit. In each of Exs. 8–11, find $I(t)$ assuming that $I(0) = 0$ and $Q(0) = 0$.

8. Assume that $4L < R^2C$.

ANS. $I = EZ^{-2}(R \sin \omega t - \gamma \cos \omega t) + \frac{1}{2}Eb^{-1}Z^{-2}[\{\gamma(a + b)$
$- \omega R\}\exp\{-(a - b)t\} + \{\omega R - \gamma(a - b)\}\exp\{-(a + b)t\}]$.

9. Assume that $R^2C < 4L$.

ANS. $I = EZ^{-2}(R \sin \omega t - \gamma \cos \omega t)$
$+ E\beta^{-1}Z^{-2}e^{-at}[\beta\gamma \cos \beta t - a(\gamma + 2\omega^{-1}C^{-1}) \sin \beta t]$.

10. Assume that $R^2C = 4L$.

ANS. $I = EZ^{-2}(R \sin \omega t - \gamma \cos \omega t)$
$+ E\omega^{-1}Z^{-2}e^{-at}[\gamma\omega - a(\gamma\omega + aR)t]$.

11. Show that the answer to Ex. 10 can be put in the form

$$I = EZ^{-2}(R \sin \omega t - \gamma \cos \omega t) + EZ^{-2}e^{-at}[\gamma + (a\gamma - R\omega)t].$$

12. In Ex. 4, replace the alternating current element $E \sin \omega t$ with

$$E[\alpha(t - t_0) - \alpha(t - t_1)], \quad t_1 > t_0 > 0.$$

Graph the new emf. Determine the current in the circuit.

ANS. $I(t) = \dfrac{E}{R}\left[\exp\left(-\dfrac{t - t_0}{RC}\right)\alpha(t - t_0) - \exp\left(-\dfrac{t - t_1}{RC}\right)\alpha(t - t_1)\right]$.

13. In Figure 38, let $E = 60$ volts, $R_1 = 10$ ohms, $R_3 = 20$ ohms, and $C_2 = 5(10)^{-4}$ farad. Determine the currents if when the switch is closed the capacitor carries a charge of 0.03 coulomb.

ANS. $I_1 = 2(1 - e^{-300t})$, $I_2 = -3e^{-300t}$, $I_3 = 2 + e^{-300t}$.

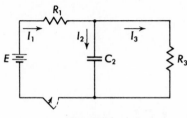

FIGURE 38

14. In Ex. 13, let the initial charge on the capacitor be 0.01 coulomb, but leave the rest of the problem unchanged.

ANS. $I_1 = 2(1 + e^{-300t})$, $I_2 = 3e^{-300t}$, $I_3 = 2 - e^{-300t}$.

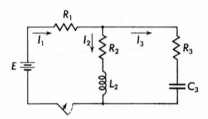

FIGURE 39

15. For the network in Figure 39, set up the equations for the determination of the charge Q_3 and the currents I_1, I_2, I_3. Assume all four of those quantities to be zero at time zero. Transform the problem into algebraic form.

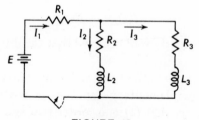

FIGURE 40

16. For the network in Figure 40, set up the equations for the determination of the currents. Assume all currents to be zero at time zero. Find $i_1(s) = L\{I_1(t)\}$ and discuss the character of $I_1(t)$ without explicitly finding the function.

CHAPTER 16

Variation of Parameters
and Other Methods

80. Variation of parameters

In this chapter, three methods will be presented, any one of which will lead to the general solution of a linear differential equation with constant coefficients.

This time all that need be assumed about the right-hand member $R(x)$ in the equation

$$(1) \qquad\qquad f(D)y = R(x)$$

is that $R(x)$ be sufficiently well behaved that the integrals we encounter will exist.

For equation (1), once the roots of the auxiliary equation $f(m) = 0$ are known, the complementary function is written by inspection. Suppose, for instance, that (1) is of order two and its complementary function is given by

$$(2) \qquad\qquad y_c = c_1\varphi_1(x) + c_2\varphi_2(x),$$

where c_1 and c_2 are arbitrary constants (or parameters) and the $\varphi_1(x)$ and $\varphi_2(x)$ are, of course, known functions.

Then the method of variation of parameters is as follows. First replace the constants c_1 and c_2 by unknown functions of x, say A and B. That is, put

$$(3) \qquad\qquad y = A\varphi_1(x) + B\varphi_2(x),$$

where A and B should now be looked upon as two new dependent variables. Here A and B replace the parameters c_1 and c_2 of (2), and now A and B are being permitted to vary. That is where the method got its name.

Now three dependent variables, A, B, and y, are present. They must satisfy equations (1) and (3). But, in general, three variables can be made to satisfy three equations. Hence we are free to impose one more condition upon A, B, and y.

From (3) it follows that

$$(4) \qquad y' = A\varphi_1'(x) + B\varphi_2'(x) + A'\varphi_1(x) + B'\varphi_2(x).$$

Now let us impose a third condition by demanding that

$$(5) \qquad\qquad A'\varphi_1(x) + B'\varphi_2(x) = 0.$$

Then (4) becomes

$$(6) \qquad\qquad y' = A\varphi_1'(x) + B\varphi_2'(x),$$

from which

$$(7) \qquad y'' = A\varphi_1''(x) + B\varphi_2''(x) + A'\varphi_1'(x) + B'\varphi_2'(x),$$

involving nothing higher than first-order derivatives of A and B.

Finally, (3), (6), and (7) can be used to eliminate y from (1), and we can thus get an equation in A' and B' to go with (5). Thus A' and B' can be found, and then we can determine A and B by integration. Once A and B are known, equation (3) gives us the desired y. See the examples below.

The method is easily extended to equations of order higher than two, but no essentially new ideas appear and the details can get tedious. In this section, only second-order equations will be treated.

EXAMPLE (a): Solve the equation

$$(8) \qquad\qquad (D^2 + 1)y = \sec x \tan x.$$

Of course,

$$y_c = c_1 \cos x + c_2 \sin x.$$

Let us seek a particular solution by variation of parameters. Put

(9) $$y = A \cos x + B \sin x,$$

from which

$$y' = -A \sin x + B \cos x + A' \cos x + B' \sin x.$$

Next set

(10) $$A' \cos x + B' \sin x = 0,$$

so

$$y' = -A \sin x + B \cos x.$$

  Then

(11) $$y'' = -A \cos x - B \sin x - A' \sin x + B' \cos x.$$

Next we eliminate y by combining equations (9) and (11) with the original equation (8). Thus we get the relation

(12) $$-A' \sin x + B' \cos x = \sec x \tan x.$$

  From (12) and (10), A' is easily eliminated. The result is

$$B' = \tan x,$$

so

(13) $$B = \ln \sec x,$$

in which the arbitrary constant has been disregarded because we are seeking only a particular solution to add to our previously determined complementary function y_c.

  From equations (12) and (10) it also follows easily that

$$A' = -\sin x \sec x \tan x,$$

or

$$A' = -\tan^2 x.$$

Then

$$A = -\int \tan^2 x \, dx = \int (1 - \sec^2 x) \, dx,$$

so

(14) $$A = x - \tan x,$$

again disregarding the arbitrary constant.

  Returning to equation (9) with the known A from (14) and the known B from (13), we write the particular solution

$$y_p = (x - \tan x) \cos x + \sin x \ln \sec x,$$

or

$$y_p = x \cos x - \sin x + \sin x \ln \sec x.$$

Then the general solution of (8) is

(15) $y = c_1 \cos x + c_3 \sin x + x \cos x + \sin x \ln \sec x,$

where the term $(-\sin x)$ in y_p has been absorbed in the complementary function term $c_3 \sin x$, since c_3 is an arbitrary constant.

The solution (15) can, as usual, be verified by direct substitution into the original differential equation.

EXAMPLE (b): Solve the equation

(16) $(D^2 - 3D + 2)y = \dfrac{1}{1 + e^{-x}}.$

Here

$$y_c = c_1 e^x + c_2 e^{2x},$$

so we put

(17) $y = Ae^x + Be^{2x}.$

Since

$$y' = Ae^x + 2Be^{2x} + A'e^x + B'e^{2x},$$

we impose the condition

(18) $A'e^x + B'e^{2x} = 0.$

Then

(19) $y' = Ae^x + 2Be^{2x},$

from which it follows that

(20) $y'' = Ae^x + 4Be^{2x} + A'e^x + 2B'e^{2x}.$

Combining (17), (19), (20), and the original equation (16), we find that

(21) $A'e^x + 2B'e^{2x} = \dfrac{1}{1 + e^{-x}}.$

Elimination of B' from equations (18) and (21) yields

$$A'e^x = -\frac{1}{1 + e^{-x}},$$

$$A' = -\frac{e^{-x}}{1 + e^{-x}}.$$

Then

$$A = \ln(1 + e^{-x}).$$

Similarly,

$$B'e^{2x} = \frac{1}{1 + e^{-x}}$$

so

$$B = \int \frac{e^{-2x}}{1 + e^{-x}} \, dx = \int \left[e^{-x} - \frac{e^{-x}}{1 + e^{-x}} \right] dx,$$

or

$$B = -e^{-x} + \ln (1 + e^{-x}).$$

Then, from (17),

$$y_p = e^x \ln (1 + e^{-x}) - e^x + e^{2x} \ln (1 + e^{-x}).$$

The term $(-e^x)$ in y_p can be absorbed into the complementary function. The general solution of equation (16) is

$$y = c_3 e^x + c_2 e^{2x} + (e^x + e^{2x}) \ln (1 + e^{-x}).$$

Equation (16) can equally well be solved without variation of parameters by a judicious use of the exponential shift of Section 48.

81. Solution of $y'' + y = f(x)$

Consider next the equation

(1) $$(D^2 + 1)y = f(x),$$

in which all that we require of $f(x)$ is that it be integrable in the interval on which we seek a solution. For instance, $f(x)$ may be any continuous function or any function with only a finite number of finite discontinuities on the interval $a \leq x \leq b$.

The method of variation of parameters will now be applied to the solution of (1). Put

(2) $$y = A \cos x + B \sin x.$$

Then

$$y' = -A \sin x + B \cos x + A' \cos x + B' \sin x,$$

and if we choose

(3) $$A' \cos x + B' \sin x = 0,$$

we obtain

(4) $$y'' = -A \cos x - B \sin x - A' \sin x + B' \cos x.$$

From (1), (2), and (4) it follows that

(5) $$-A' \sin x + B' \cos x = f(x).$$

Equations (3) and (5) may be solved for A' and B', yielding

$$A' = -f(x) \sin x, \quad B' = f(x) \cos x.$$

We may now write

(6) $$A = -\int_a^x f(\beta) \sin \beta \, d\beta,$$

(7) $$B = \int_a^x f(\beta) \cos \beta \, d\beta,$$

for any x in $a \leq x \leq b$. It is here that we use the integrability of $f(x)$ on the interval $a \leq x \leq b$.

The A and B of (6) and (7) may be inserted in (2) to give us the particular solution

$$y_p = -\cos x \int_a^x f(\beta) \sin \beta \, d\beta + \sin x \int_a^x f(\beta) \cos \beta \, d\beta$$

$$= \int_a^x f(\beta)[\sin x \cos \beta - \cos x \sin \beta] \, d\beta.$$

Hence we have

(8) $$y_p = \int_a^x f(\beta) \sin (x - \beta) \, d\beta,$$

and we can now write the general solution of equation (1):

(9) $$y = c_1 \cos x + c_2 \sin x + \int_a^x f(\beta) \sin (x - \beta) \, d\beta.$$

See Section 68 for a simpler, but less elementary, method for obtaining the solution (9).

82. A general second-order linear equation

The method used in Section 80 applies equally well to the equation

(1) $$y'' + p(x)y' + q(x)y = f(x),$$

where $p(x)$ and $q(x)$ need not be constants, as long as we know two linearly independent solutions $y = y_1(x)$ and $y = y_2(x)$ of the corresponding homogeneous equation

(2) $$y'' + p(x)y' + q(x)y = 0.$$

Let the Wronskian (page 99) of $y_1(x)$ and $y_2(x)$ be denoted by $W(x)$,

(3) $$W(x) = \begin{vmatrix} y_1(x) & y_2(x) \\ y_1'(x) & y_2'(x) \end{vmatrix},$$

and let $W(x) \neq 0$ on the interval $a \leq x \leq b$. Then the method of variation of parameters yields the following particular solution of equation (1).

(4) $$y_p = \int_a^x \frac{f(\beta)[y_1(\beta)y_2(x) - y_1(x)y_2(\beta)] \, d\beta}{W(\beta)}.$$

The general solution of (1) is, of course,

(5) $$y = c_1 y_1(x) + c_2 y_2(x) + y_p(x).$$

Since we have as yet no methods for obtaining y_1 and y_2 unless equation (1) has constant coefficients, the solution (5) is at present of purely theoretical interest to us. In general, power series methods are used to find y_1 and y_2 when equation (1) has variable coefficients.

For the Wronskian (3) of any two linearly independent solutions y_1 and y_2 of equation (1), it is not difficult* to derive Abel's formula

(6) $$W(x) = c \exp\left[-\int p(x) \, dx\right],$$

where c is constant.

Exercises

In Exs. 1–20, use variation of parameters, Section 80.

1. $(D^2 + 1)y = \csc x \cot x.$
ANS. $y = c_1 \cos x + c_2 \sin x - x \sin x - \cos x \ln \sin x.$

2. $(D^2 + 1)y = \cot x.$ ANS. $y = y_c - \sin x \ln (\csc x + \cot x).$

3. $(D^2 + 1)y = \sec x.$
ANS. $y = c_1 \cos x + c_2 \sin x + x \sin x + \cos x \ln \cos x.$

4. $(D^2 + 1)y = \sec^2 x.$ ANS. $y = y_c - 1 + \sin x \ln (\sec x + \tan x).$

5. $(D^2 + 1)y = \sec^3 x.$ ANS. $y = y_c + \frac{1}{2} \sec x.$

6. $(D^2 + 1)y = \sec^4 x.$
ANS. $y = y_c - \frac{1}{2} + \frac{1}{6} \sec^2 x + \frac{1}{2} \sin x \ln (\sec x + \tan x).$

7. $(D^2 + 1)y = \tan x.$ ANS. $y = y_c - \cos x \ln (\sec x + \tan x).$

8. $(D^2 + 1)y = \tan^2 x.$
ANS. $y = y_1 - 1$, where y_1 is the solution of Ex. 4 above.

---

* See, for example, E. D. Rainville, *Intermediate Differential Equations*, 2nd ed. (New York: The Macmillan Co., 1964), p. 274.

9. $(D^2 + 1)y = \sec x \csc x$.

     ANS. $y = y_c - \cos x \ln (\sec x + \tan x) - \sin x \ln (\csc x + \cot x)$.

10. $(D^2 + 1)y = \sec^2 x \csc x$.   ANS. $y = y_c - \sin x \ln (\csc 2x + \cot 2x)$.

11. $(D^2 - 2D + 1)y = e^{2x}(e^x + 1)^{-2}$.   ANS. $y = y_c + e^x \ln (1 + e^x)$.

12. $(D^2 - 3D + 2)y = e^{2x}/(1 + e^{2x})$.

     ANS. $y = y_c + e^x \operatorname{Arctan} (e^{-x}) - \frac{1}{2}e^{2x} \ln (1 + e^{-2x})$.

13. $(D^2 - 3D + 2)y = \cos (e^{-x})$.   ANS. $y = y_c - e^{2x} \cos (e^{-x})$.

14. $(D^2 - 1)y = 2(1 - e^{-2x})^{-\frac{1}{2}}$.

     ANS. $y = c_1 e^x + c_2 e^{-x} - e^x \operatorname{Arcsin} (e^{-x}) - (1 - e^{-2x})^{\frac{1}{2}}$.

15. $(D^2 - 1)y = e^{-2x} \sin e^{-x}$.   ANS. $y = y_c - \sin e^{-x} - e^x \cos e^{-x}$.

16. $(D^2 - 5D + 4)y = 6/(1 + e^{-2x})$.

     ANS. $y = y_c + 2e^x \operatorname{Arctan} e^{-x} - e^{2x} + e^{4x} \ln (1 + e^{-2x})$.

17. $(D^2 - 1)y = (1 + e^{-x})^{-2}$.

     ANS. $y = y_c - 1 + xe^{-x} + e^{-x} \ln (1 + e^{-x})$.

18. $(D - 1)(D - 3)y = \cos e^{-x}$.

     ANS. $y = y_c + e^{3x} \sin e^{-x} - e^{2x} \cos e^{-x}$.

19. $(D^2 - 3D + 2)y = 15(1 + e^{-x})^{\frac{1}{2}}$.

     ANS. $y = c_1 e^x + c_2 e^{2x} + 4(e^x + e^{2x})(1 + e^{-x})^{\frac{3}{2}}$; or

                                  $y = y_c + 4e^{2x}(1 + e^{-x})^{\frac{5}{2}}$.

20. $(D^2 - 3D + 2)y = (1 + e^{-2x})^{-\frac{1}{2}}$.

     ANS. $y = y_c + e^x \ln [e^{-x} + (1 + e^{-2x})^{\frac{1}{2}}] - e^{2x}(1 + e^{-2x})^{\frac{1}{2}}$.

In Exs. 21–28 use the exponential shift once or twice, as needed, to solve the equation without variation of parameters.

21. Ex. 11.   **22.** Ex. 12.

23. Ex. 13.   **24.** Ex. 15.

25. Ex. 16.   **26.** Ex. 17.

27. Ex. 18.   **28.** Ex. 19.

29. Use variation of parameters to obtain the solution (4), Section 82.

30. Use variation of parameters to solve the equation

$$y'' + 4y' + 4y = f(x).$$

     ANS. $y = c_1 e^{-2x} + c_2 x e^{-2x} + \int_0^x f(\beta)(x - \beta) \exp [-2(x - \beta)] \, d\beta$.

83. Reduction of order by using factors of the operator

Consider the equation

(1) $(D - a)(D - b)y = R(x)$.

The change of dependent variable

(2) $$(D - b)y = w$$

leads us to the equation

(3) $$(D - a)w = R(x),$$

which is linear of the first order. Then (3) can be written in standard form (page 36)

$$dw - aw\, dx = R(x)\, dx$$

and so solved with the aid of the integrating factor e^{-ax}.

Once w is known we revert to equation (2) to find y. Equation (2) is also of the first order, so it can be solved just as (3) was solved.

The problem of solving the equation (1) of order two is thus replaced by a succession of two problems, each the solving of an equation of order one. In general this device permits us to replace a linear equation of order n (with constant coefficients) with n successive linear equations of order one. The only difficulty is that of performing the integrations. In practice, that difficulty is often quite serious.

EXAMPLE: Solve the equation

(4) $$(D^2 - 1)y = \frac{2}{e^x + e^{-x}}.$$

Thinking of equation (4) in the form

$$(D + 1)(D - 1)y = \frac{2}{e^x + e^{-x}},$$

we put

(5) $$(D - 1)y = w.$$

Then we need to solve

$$(D + 1)w = \frac{2}{e^x + e^{-x}},$$

which may be written

(6) $$dw + w\, dx = \frac{2\, dx}{e^x + e^{-x}}.$$

An integrating factor for (6) is e^x. Therefore

$$e^x\, dw + we^x\, dx = \frac{2e^x\, dx}{e^x + e^{-x}}$$

is exact. Hence

$$e^x w = \int \frac{2e^x \, dx}{e^x + e^{-x}} = \int \frac{2e^{2x}}{e^{2x} + 1} \, dx,$$

from which

$$e^x w = \ln (e^{2x} + 1),$$

the arbitrary constant being disregarded as usual when searching for a particular solution.

Next the expression for w is inserted in equation (5), which then becomes

$$(D - 1)y = e^{-x} \ln (e^{2x} + 1),$$

$$dy - y \, dx = e^{-x} \ln (e^{2x} + 1) \, dx.$$

Here an integrating factor is e^{-x}, so we write

$$e^{-x} \, dy - y e^{-x} \, dx = e^{-2x} \ln (e^{2x} + 1) \, dx,$$

$$e^{-x} y = \int e^{-2x} \ln (e^{2x} + 1) \, dx.$$

Integration by parts can be used to reduce the above to the form

(7) $$e^{-x} y = -\tfrac{1}{2} e^{-2x} \ln (e^{2x} + 1) + \int \frac{dx}{e^{2x} + 1}.$$

Then we write

$$e^{-x} y = -\tfrac{1}{2} e^{-2x} \ln (e^{2x} + 1) + \int \left[1 - \frac{e^{2x}}{e^{2x} + 1} \right] dx$$

and thus find that

$$e^{-x} y = -\tfrac{1}{2} e^{-2x} \ln (e^{2x} + 1) + x - \tfrac{1}{2} \ln (e^{2x} + 1),$$

(8) $$y = xe^x - \tfrac{1}{2}(e^x + e^{-x}) \ln (e^{2x} + 1).$$

Equation (8) is a particular solution of the original equation (4). The general solution of the differential equation (4) is therefore

$$y = c_1 e^x + c_2 e^{-x} + xe^x - \tfrac{1}{2}(e^x + e^{-x}) \ln (e^{2x} + 1).$$

84. A third method: change of dependent variable

Consider the general second-order linear equation

(1) $$y'' + py' + qy = R.$$

Suppose we know a solution $y = y_1$ of the corresponding homogeneous equation

(2) $$y'' + py' + qy = 0.$$

Then the introduction of a new dependent variable v by the substitution

(3) $$y = y_1v$$

will lead to a solution of equation (1) in the following way.

From (3) it follows that

$$y' = y_1v' + y_1'v,$$
$$y'' = y_1v'' + 2y_1'v' + y_1''v,$$

so substitution of (3) into (1) yields

$$y_1v'' + 2y_1'v' + y_1''v + py_1v' + py_1'v + qy_1v = R,$$

or

(4) $$y_1v'' + (2y_1' + py_1)v' + (y_1'' + py_1' + qy_1)v = R.$$

But $y = y_1$ is a solution of (2). That is,

$$y_1'' + py_1' + qy_1 = 0$$

and equation (4) reduces to

(5) $$y_1v'' + (2y_1' + py_1)v' = R.$$

Now let $v' = w$ so equation (5) becomes

(6) $$y_1w' + (2y_1' + py_1)w = R,$$

a linear equation of the first order in w.

By the usual method (integrating factor) we can find w from (6). Then we can get v from $v' = w$ by an integration. Finally $y = y_1v$.

Note that the method is not restricted to equations with constant coefficients. It depends only upon our knowing a particular solution of equation (2); that is, upon our knowledge of the complementary function. For practical purposes, the method depends also upon our being able to effect the integrations.

EXAMPLE: Solve the equation

(7) $$(D^2 + 1)y = \csc x.$$

The complementary function is

(8) $$y_c = c_1 \cos x + c_2 \sin x.$$

We may use any special case of (8) as the y_1 in the theory above. Let us then put

$$y = v \sin x.$$

We find that

$$y' = v' \sin x + v \cos x$$

and

$$y'' = v'' \sin x + 2v' \cos x - v \sin x.$$

The equation for v is

$$v'' \sin x + 2v' \cos x = \csc x,$$

or

(9) $$v'' + 2v' \cot x = \csc^2 x.$$

Put $v' = w$; then equation (9) becomes

$$w' + 2w \cot x = \csc^2 x,$$

or

$$dw + 2w \cot x \, dx = \csc^2 x \, dx,$$

for which an integrating factor is $\sin^2 x$. Thus

(10) $$\sin^2 x \, dw + 2w \sin x \cos x \, dx = dx$$

is exact. From (10) we get

$$w \sin^2 x = x,$$

seeking, as usual, only a particular solution.
Then

$$w = x \csc^2 x$$

or

$$v' = x \csc^2 x.$$

Hence

$$v = \int x \csc^2 x \, dx,$$

or

$$v = -x \cot x + \ln \sin x,$$

a result easily obtained using integration by parts.
Now

$$y = v \sin x,$$

so the particular solution which we sought is

$$y_p = -x \cos x + \sin x \ln \sin x.$$

Finally, the complete solution of (7) is seen to be

$$y = c_1 \cos x + c_2 \sin x - x \cos x + \sin x \ln \sin x.$$

Exercises

In Exs. 1–4, use the method of Section 83.

1. $(D^2 + 2D + 1)y = (e^x - 1)^{-2}$.

ANS. $y = e^{-x}[c_1 + c_2x - \ln(1 - e^{-x})]$.

2. $(D^2 + 2D + 1)y = (e^x + 1)^{-2}$.

ANS. $y = e^{-x}[c_1 + c_2x + \ln(1 + e^{-x})]$.

3. $(D - 1)(D - 3)y = \sin e^{-x}$.

ANS. $y = y_c - e^{2x} \sin e^{-x} - e^{3x} \cos e^{-x}$.

4. $(D^2 - 1)y = 2e^x(1 + e^x)^{-2}$.

ANS. $y = y_c + 1 + xe^x - (e^x + e^{-x}) \ln(1 + e^x)$.

In Exs. 5–9, use the method of Section 84.

5. Use the substitution $y = v \cos x$ to solve the equation of the example of Section 84.

6. $(D^2 + 1)y = \sec x$.   ANS.   See Ex. 3, page 256.

7. $(D^2 + 1)y = \sec^3 x$. Use $y = v \sin x$.   ANS.   See Ex. 5, page 256.

8. $(D^2 + 1)y = \csc^3 x$. Take a hint from Ex. 7. Use $y = v \cos x$, since $\cos x$ is complementary to $\sin x$ just as $\csc x$ is complementary to $\sec x$.

9. $(D^2 - 3D + 2)y = (1 + e^{-2x})^{-\frac{1}{2}}$.   ANS.   See Ex. 20, page 257.

10. $y'' + 4y' + 4y = x^{-2}e^{-2x}$. Use the exponential shift.

ANS. $y = e^{-2x}(c_1 + c_2x - \ln x)$.

11. In the example of Section 83, perform the integration needed in equation (7) by using the trick below.

$$\int \frac{dx}{e^{2x} + 1} = \int \frac{e^{-2x}\,dx}{1 + e^{-2x}} = -\tfrac{1}{2}\ln(1 + e^{-2x}).$$

Thus obtain for equation (4) a particular solution in the form

$$y = -\tfrac{1}{2}e^{-x}\ln(e^{2x} + 1) - \tfrac{1}{2}e^x\ln(1 + e^{-2x})$$

and show that this solution is equivalent to that given in equation (8).

Miscellaneous Exercises

1. $(D^2 - 1)y = 2e^{-x}(1 + e^{-2x})^{-2}$.

ANS. $y = y_c - xe^{-x} - \tfrac{1}{2}e^{-x}\ln(1 + e^{-2x})$.

2. $(D^2 - 1)y = (1 - e^{2x})^{-\frac{1}{2}}$.   ANS. $y = y_c - (1 - e^{2x})^{\frac{1}{2}}$.

3. $(D^2 - 1)y = e^{2x}(3 \tan e^x + e^x \sec^2 e^x)$.   ANS. $y = y_c + e^x \ln \sec e^x$.

4. $(D^2 + 1)y = \sec^2 x \tan x$.

ANS. $y = y_c + \tfrac{1}{2}\tan x + \tfrac{1}{2}\cos x \ln(\sec x + \tan x)$.

5. Do Ex. 4 by another method.

6. $(D^2 + 1)y = \csc x$. Use variation of parameters.

ANS.   See the example of Section 84.

7. $(D^2 - 3D + 2)y = \sec^2 (e^{-x})$.

ANS. $y = c_1 e^x + c_2 e^{2x} + e^{2x} \ln \sec (e^{-x})$.

8. Do Ex. 7 by another method.

9. $(D^2 - 1)y = 2/(1 + e^x)$.

ANS. $y = y_c - 1 - xe^x + (e^x - e^{-x}) \ln (1 + e^x)$.

10. $(D^3 + D)y = \sec^2 x$. Hint: integrate once first.

ANS. $y = c_1 + c_2 \cos x + c_3 \sin x - \cos x \ln (\sec x + \tan x)$.

11. $(D^2 - 1)y = 2/(e^x - e^{-x})$.

ANS. $y = y_c - xe^{-x} + \frac{1}{2}(e^x - e^{-x}) \ln (1 - e^{-2x})$.

12. $(D^2 - 3D + 2)y = \sin e^{-x}$.   ANS. $y = y_c - e^{2x} \sin e^{-x}$.

13. $(D^2 - 1)y = 1/(e^{2x} + 1)$.   ANS. $y = y_c - \frac{1}{2} - \cosh x \operatorname{Arctan} e^{-x}$.

14. $y'' + y = \sec^3 x \tan x$.   ANS. $y = y_c + \frac{1}{6} \sec x \tan x$.

15. $y'' + y = \sec x \tan^2 x$. Verify your answer.

16. $y'' + 4y' + 3y = \sin e^x$.   ANS. $y = y_c - e^{-2x} \sin e^x - e^{-3x} \cos e^x$.

17. $y'' + y = \csc^3 x \cot x$.   ANS. $y = y_c + \frac{1}{6} \cot x \csc x$.

CHAPTER 17

The Existence of Solutions

85. Preliminary remarks

The methods of Chapter 2 are strictly dependent upon certain special properties (variables separable, exactness, etc.), which may or may not be possessed by an individual equation. It is intuitively plausible that no collection of methods can be found that would permit the explicit solution, in the sense of Chapter 2, of all differential equations. We may seek solutions in other forms, employing infinite series or other limiting processes; we may resort to numerical approximations.

Confronted with this situation, the pure mathematician frequently reacts by searching for what is known as an existence theorem. He seeks to determine conditions that are sufficient to insure the existence of a solution with certain properties. It may happen that in discovering such a theorem and a proof of it, the mathematician will hit upon a method, practical or not, for constructing a solution of the equation.

86. Nature of solutions of a particular equation

Before proceeding to a statement of an existence theorem, let us examine in some detail the solutions of a simple equation,

(1) $$2y\,dx - x\,dy = 0.$$

Equation (1) has the general solution $y = cx^2$, including the solution $x = 0$ by our usual convention. This family of curves consists of the two axes and all parabolas that have the origin as vertex and have their foci on the y-axis, as shown in Figure 41, page 265.

Additional solutions of equation (1) may be formed by combining parts of different elements of the family of solutions given above. Since we need to retain continuity of y and dy/dx, we permit ourselves to pass from one element of the family to another only where the two intersect and have a common tangent. In this case the elements intersect only at the origin.

As an example, the curve defined by

$$y = x^2, \qquad 0 \leqq x,$$
$$y = -4x^2, \quad x < 0,$$

is a solution of equation (1). Note the continuity of its slope at the origin.

Given any point in the xy-plane, we can find a solution that passes through that point. If the given point is not the origin, then the solution that passes through the given point is unique in the vicinity of that point. See Section 33.

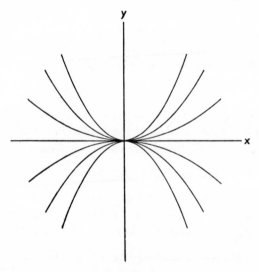

FIGURE 41

Now write equation (1) in the form

(2)
$$\frac{dy}{dx} = \frac{2y}{x}.$$

The right member of equation (2) is discontinuous at each point where $x = 0$ and is continuous elsewhere. Through each point where the right member of equation (2) is continuous there is a solution unique near that point. At the origin, trouble is to be expected because of the clustering of solutions there as indicated earlier. In searching for solutions through a point $x = 0$, $y = y_0 \neq 0$, it is more natural to write equation (2) in the form

$$(3) \qquad \frac{dx}{dy} = \frac{x}{2y},$$

and to consider x as the dependent variable. Then the slope is dx/dy and it is continuous at $(0, y_0)$, $y_0 \neq 0$. Again a solution passing through the point in question exists and is unique near that point.

87. An existence theorem

We now state without proof an existence theorem for certain first-order equations. A proof of this theorem can be found in Ince.*

Consider the equation of order one and degree one,

$$(1) \qquad \frac{dy}{dx} = f(x, y).$$

Let T denote the rectangular region defined by

$$|x - x_0| \leq a, \quad |y - y_0| \leq b,$$

a region with the point (x_0, y_0) at its center. Let the function $f(x, y)$ in equation (1) be single-valued and continuous in T and let $f(x, y)$ satisfy the "Lipschitz condition" that there exists a constant K such that

$$|f(x, y_1) - f(x, y_2)| < K|y_1 - y_2|$$

for every pair of points (x, y_1) and (x, y_2), of the same abscissa, in T.

Under the conditions imposed on $f(x, y)$ above, there exists an interval about x_0, $|x - x_0| \leq h$, and a function $y(x)$ which has the properties:

    (a) $y = y(x)$ is a solution of equation (1) on the interval $|x - x_0| \leq h$;

    (b) On the interval $|x - x_0| \leq h$, $y(x)$ satisfies the inequality $|y(x) - y_0| \leq b$;

    (c) At $x = x_0$, $y = y(x_0) = y_0$;

    (d) $y(x)$ is unique on the interval $|x - x_0| \leq h$ in the sense that it is the only function that has all of the properties (a), (b), and (c).

---

* E. L. Ince, *Ordinary Differential Equations* (London: Longmans, Green and Co., 1927), pp. 62–66.

The interval $|x - x_0| \leq h$ may or may not need to be smaller than the interval $|x - x_0| \leq a$ over which conditions were imposed upon $f(x, y)$.

In rough language, the theorem states that if $f(x, y)$ is sufficiently well behaved near the point (x_0, y_0), then the differential equation

$$(1) \qquad \frac{dy}{dx} = f(x, y)$$

has a solution that passes through the point (x_0, y_0) and that solution is unique near (x_0, y_0).

It is important that the solution under discussion can actually be exhibited. The function $y(x)$ is the limit of a sequence of functions $y_n(x)$; $n = 1, 2, \cdots$, defined as follows:

$$y = y(x) = \operatorname*{Lim}_{n \to \infty} y_n(x),$$

where

$$y_1(x) = y_0 + \int_{x_0}^{x} f(t, y_0)\, dt,$$

$$y_2(x) = y_0 + \int_{x_0}^{x} f[t, y_1(t)]\, dt,$$

$$y_3(x) = y_0 + \int_{x_0}^{x} f[t, y_2(t)]\, dt,$$

$$\cdots$$

$$y_n(x) = y_0 + \int_{x_0}^{x} f[t, y_{n-1}(t)]\, dt.$$

The student should use this process to construct a solution of the boundary value problem

$$(2) \qquad \frac{dy}{dx} = \frac{2y}{x}; \text{ when } x = 1, y = 1.$$

It will be found that

$$y_1(x) = 1 + 2 \ln x,$$
$$y_2(x) = 1 + 2 \ln x + 2 \ln^2 x,$$
$$y_3(x) = 1 + 2 \ln x + 2 \ln^2 x + \tfrac{4}{3} \ln^3 x,$$
$$\cdots$$

$$y_n(x) = 1 + \sum_{k=1}^{n} \frac{2^k \ln^k x}{k!},$$

and that

$$y = \exp (2 \ln x) = x^2.$$

CHAPTER 18

Equations of Order One

and Higher Degree

88. Factoring the left member

If an equation

(1) $$f(x, y, y') = 0$$

is of degree higher than one, it may be possible to factor the left member into parts, each of degree one. The problem of solving (1) is then replaced by two or more problems of simpler type. The latter may be capable of solution by the methods of Chapters 2 and 4.

Since y' will be raised to powers in the example and exercises, let us simplify the printing and writing by a common device, using p for y':

$$p = \frac{dy}{dx}.$$

EXAMPLE: Solve the differential equation

(2) $$xyp^2 + (x + y)p + 1 = 0.$$

The left member of equation (2) is readily factored. Thus (2) leads to

$$(xp + 1)(yp + 1) = 0,$$

from which it follows that either

(3) $$yp + 1 = 0$$

or

(4) $$xp + 1 = 0.$$

From equation (3) in the form

$$y \, dy + dx = 0$$

it follows that

(5) $$y^2 = -2(x - c_1).$$

Equation (4) may be written

$$x \, dy + dx = 0$$

from which, for $x \neq 0$,

$$dy + \frac{dx}{x} = 0,$$

so

(6) $$y = - \ln (c_2 x).$$

Equation (2) may be rewritten

$$xy(dy)^2 + (x + y)(dx)(dy) + (dx)^2 = 0,$$

in which form $x = 0$ is seen to be a solution. But (6) may be written
in the form $x = c_3 e^{-y}$ where $c_3 = 1/c_2$. Then $x = 0$ is a special case
of this latter solution and need not be listed separately.

We say, and it is very rough language, that the general solution of
(2) is (5) and (6). Particular solutions may be made up from this general
solution; they may be drawn from (5) alone, from (6) alone, or conceivably pieced together by using (5) in some intervals and (6) in others. At
a point where a solution from (5) is to be joined with a solution from (6),
the slope must remain continuous, so (see Ex. 21 below) the piecing
together must take place along the line $y = x$. Note (see Ex. 23) that the
second derivative, which does not enter the differential equation, need
not be continuous.

The existence of these three sets of particular solutions of (2), that is,
solutions from (5), from (6), or from (5) and (6), leads to an interesting
phenomenon in boundary value problems. Consider the problem of finding
a solution of (2) such that the solution passes through the point $(-\frac{1}{2}, 2)$.

If the result is to be valid for the interval $-1 < x < -\frac{1}{4}$, there are two answers, which will be found in Ex. 24, following. If the result is to be valid for $-1 < x < \frac{1}{2}$, there is only one answer (Ex. 25), one of the two answers to Ex. 24. If the result is to be valid in $-1 < x < 2$, there is only one answer (Ex. 26), and it is different from either of the answers to Ex. 24.

Exercises

In Exs. 1–18, find the general solution in the sense of (5) and (6) above.

1. $x^2p^2 - y^2 = 0.$ ANS. $y = c_1x, \; xy = c_2.$

2. $xp^2 - (2x + 3y)p + 6y = 0.$ ANS. $y = c_1x^3, \; y = 2x + c_2.$

3. $x^2p^2 - 5xyp + 6y^2 = 0.$ ANS. $y = c_1x^2, \; y = c_2x^3.$

4. $x^2p^2 + xp - y^2 - y = 0.$ ANS. $y = c_1x, \; x(y + 1) = c_2.$

5. $xp^2 + (1 - x^2y)p - xy = 0.$

          ANS. $y = c_1 \exp\left(\frac{1}{2}x^2\right), \; y = -\ln(c_2x).$

6. $p^2 - (x^2y + 3)p + 3x^2y = 0.$ ANS. $y = 3x + c_1, \; x^3 = 3\ln(c_2y).$

7. $xp^2 - (1 + xy)p + y = 0.$ ANS. $y = \ln(c_1x), \; x = \ln(c_2y).$

8. $p^2 - x^2y^2 = 0.$ ANS. $x^2 = 2\ln(c_1y), \; x^2 = -2\ln(c_2y).$

9. $(x + y)^2p^2 = y^2.$ ANS. $x = y\ln(c_1y), \; y(2x + y) = c_2.$

10. $yp^2 + (x - y^2)p - xy = 0.$ ANS. $x^2 + y^2 = c_1{}^2, \; y = c_2e^x.$

11. $p^2 - xy(x + y)p + x^3y^3 = 0.$

          ANS. $y(x^2 + c_1) = -2, \; x^3 = 3\ln(c_2y).$

12. $(4x - y)p^2 + 6(x - y)p + 2x - 5y = 0.$

          ANS. $x + y = c_1, \; (2x + y)^2 = c_2(y - x).$

13. $(x - y)^2p^2 = y^2.$ ANS. $x = -y\ln(c_1y), \; y(2x - y) = c_2.$

14. $xyp^2 + (xy^2 - 1)p - y = 0.$ ANS. $y^2 = 2\ln(c_1x), \; x = -\ln(c_2y).$

15. $(x^2 + y^2)^2p^2 = 4x^2y^2.$ ANS. $y^2 - x^2 = c_1y, \; y(3x^2 + y^2) = c_2.$

16. $(y + x)^2p^2 + (2y^2 + xy - x^2)p + y(y - x) = 0.$

          ANS. $y^2 + 2xy = c_1, \; y^2 + 2xy - x^2 = c_2.$

17. $xy(x^2 + y^2)(p^2 - 1) = p(x^4 + x^2y^2 + y^4).$

          ANS. $y^2(y^2 + 2x^2) = c_1, \; y^2 = 2x^2\ln(c_2x).$

18. $xp^3 - (x^2 + x + y)p^2 + (x^2 + xy + y)p - xy = 0.$

          ANS. $y = c_1x, \; y = x + c_2, \; x^2 = 2(y - c_3).$

Exs. 19–26 refer to the example of this section. There the differential equation

(2) $xyp^2 + (x + y)p + 1 = 0$

was shown to have the general solution

(5) $$y^2 = -2(x - c_1)$$

and

(6) $$y = -\ln(c_2 x).$$

19. Show that of the family (5) above, the only curve that passes through the point $(1, 1)$ is $y = (3 - 2x)^{\frac{1}{2}}$ and that this solution is valid for $x < \frac{3}{2}$.

20. Show that of the family (6) above, the only curve that passes through the point $(1, 1)$ is $y = 1 - \ln x$ and that this solution is valid for $0 < x$.

21. Show that if a solution of (2) is to be pieced together from (5) and (6), then the slopes of the curves must be equal where the pieces join. Show that the pieces must therefore be joined at a point on the line $y = x$.

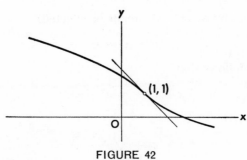

FIGURE 42

22. Show that the curve determined by

$$y = (3 - 2x)^{\frac{1}{2}} \quad \text{for } x \leq 1,$$
$$y = 1 - \ln x \quad \text{for } 1 \leq x$$

is a solution of equation (2) and is valid for all x. The interesting portion of this curve is shown in Figure 42.

23. Show for the solution given in Ex. 22 that y'' is not continuous at $x = 1$. Show that as $x \to 1^-$, $y'' \to -1$, and as $x \to 1^+$, $y'' \to +1$.

24. Find those solutions of (2) which are valid in $-1 < x < -\frac{1}{4}$ and each of which has its graph passing through the point $(-\frac{1}{2}, 2)$.
    ANS. $y = (3 - 2x)^{\frac{1}{2}}$; and $y = 2 - \ln 2 - \ln(-x)$.

25. Find that solution of (2) which is valid for $-1 < x < \frac{1}{2}$ and has its graph passing through the point $(-\frac{1}{2}, 2)$. ANS. $y = (3 - 2x)^{\frac{1}{2}}$.

26. Find that solution of (2) which is valid for $-1 < x < 2$ and has its graph passing through the point $(-\frac{1}{2}, 2)$.
    ANS. $y = (3 - 2x)^{\frac{1}{2}}$ for $x \leq 1$,
    $y = 1 - \ln x$ for $1 \leq x$.

89. Singular solutions

Let us solve the differential equation

(1) $$y^2 p^2 - a^2 + y^2 = 0.$$

Here

$$yp = \pm \sqrt{a^2 - y^2},$$

so we may write

(2) $$\frac{y\,dy}{\sqrt{a^2 - y^2}} = dx,$$

or

(3) $$-\frac{y\,dy}{\sqrt{a^2 - y^2}} = dx,$$

or (if the division by $\sqrt{a^2 - y^2}$ cannot be effected)

(4) $$a^2 - y^2 = 0.$$

From (2) it follows that

(5) $$x = c_1 - \sqrt{a^2 - y^2},$$

while from (3) that

(6) $$x = c_2 + \sqrt{a^2 - y^2},$$

and from (4) that

(7) $$y = a \quad \text{or} \quad y = -a.$$

Graphically, the solutions (5) are left-hand semicircles with radius a and centered on the x-axis; the solutions (6) are right-hand semicircles of radius a, centered on the x-axis. We may combine (5) and (6) into

(8) $$(x - c)^2 + y^2 = a^2,$$

which is called the general solution of (1).

From either of equations (7) we get $p = 0$, so they too satisfy the differential equation (1). But neither of equations (7) is a special case of (8). Then $y = a$ and $y = -a$ are called singular solutions.

A *singular solution* of a nonlinear first-order differential equation is any solution that

(a) is not a special case of the general solution, and

(b) is, at each of its points, tangent to some element of the one-parameter family that is the general solution.

A linear equation cannot have a singular solution.

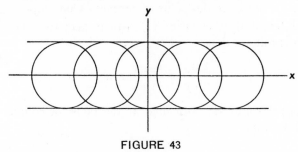

Figure 43 shows several elements of the family of circles given by equation (8) and also shows the two lines representing $y = a$ and $y = -a$. At each point of either line, the line is tangent to an element of the family of circles. A curve which at each of its points is tangent to an element of a one-parameter family of curves is called an *envelope* of that family.

90. The c-discriminant equation

Consider the differential equation of the first order,

(1) $$f(x, y, p) = 0; \quad p = \frac{dy}{dx},$$

in which the left member is a polynomial in x, y, and p. It may not be possible to factor the left member into factors which are themselves polynomials in x, y, and p. Then the equation is said to be irreducible.

The general solution of (1) will be a one-parameter family of curves,

(2) $$\varphi(x, y, c) = 0.$$

A singular solution, if it exists, for equation (1) must be an envelope of the family (2). Each point on the envelope is a point of tangency of the envelope with some element of the family (2) and is determined by the value of c that identifies that element of the family. Then the envelope has parametric equations, $x = x(c)$ and $y = y(c)$, with the c of equation (2) as the parameter. The functions $x(c)$ and $y(c)$ are as yet unknown to us. But the x and y of the point of contact must also satisfy equation (2), from which we get, by differentiation with respect to c, the equation

(3) $$\frac{\partial \varphi}{\partial x} \frac{dx}{dc} + \frac{\partial \varphi}{\partial y} \frac{dy}{dc} + \frac{\partial \varphi}{\partial c} = 0.$$

The slope of the envelope and the slope of the family element concerned must be equal at the point of contact. That slope can be determined by differentiating equation (2) with respect to x, keeping c constant. Thus it follows that

$$(4) \qquad \frac{\partial \varphi}{\partial x} + \frac{\partial \varphi}{\partial y} \frac{dy}{dx} = 0.$$

Equations (3) and (4) both hold at the point of contact and from them it follows that

$$(5) \qquad \frac{\partial \varphi}{\partial c} = 0.$$

We now have two equations, $\varphi = 0$ and $\dfrac{\partial \varphi}{\partial c} = 0$, which must be satisfied by x, y, and c. These two equations may be taken as the desired parametric equations. They contain any envelope which may exist for the original family of curves, $\varphi = 0$. Fortunately, there is no need for us to put these equations into the form $x = x(c)$, $y = y(c)$.

The equation that results from the elimination of c from the equations $\varphi = 0$ and $\dfrac{\partial \varphi}{\partial c} = 0$ is called the *c-discriminant equation** of the family $\varphi = 0$. It is a necessary and sufficient condition that the equation

$$(2) \qquad \varphi(x, y, c) = 0,$$

considered as an equation in c, have at least two of its roots equal.

There is nothing in our work to guarantee that the c-discriminant equation, or any part of it, will be a solution of the differential equation. To get the c-discriminant equation we need the general solution. During the process of obtaining the general solution, we find also the singular solution, if there is one.

91. The *p*-discriminant equation

Suppose that in the irreducible differential equation

$$(1) \qquad f(x, y, p) = 0$$

the polynomial f is of degree n in p. There will be n roots of equation (1),

---

* The c-discriminant equation may contain a locus of cusps of the elements of the general solution and a locus of nodes of those elements, as well as the envelope which aroused our interest in it.

each yielding a result of the form

$$(2) \qquad\qquad p = g(x, y).$$

If at a point (x_0, y_0) the equation (1) has, as an equation in p, all its roots distinct, then near (x_0, y_0) there will be n distinct equations of the type of equation (2). Near (x_0, y_0) the right members of these n equations will be single-valued and may satisfy the conditions of the existence theorem described in Chapter 17. But if at (x_0, y_0) equation (1) has at least two of its roots equal, then at least two of the n equations like (2) will have right members assuming the same value at (x_0, y_0). For such equations there is no region, no matter how small, surrounding (x_0, y_0) in which the right member is single-valued. Hence the existence theorem of Chapter 17 cannot be applied when equation (1) has two or more equal roots as an equation in p. Therefore we must give separate consideration to the locus of points (x, y) for which (1) has at least two of its roots equal.

The condition that equation (1) have at least two equal roots as an equation in p is that both $f = 0$ and $\dfrac{\partial f}{\partial p} = 0$. These two equations in the three variables x, y, and p are parametric equations of a curve in the xy-plane with p playing the role of parameter. The equation that results when p is eliminated from the parametric equations $f = 0$ and $\dfrac{\partial f}{\partial p} = 0$ is called the *p-discriminant equation*.

If an envelope of the general solution of $f = 0$ exists, it will be contained in the p-discriminant equation. No proof is included here.[*] For us the p-discriminant equation is useful in two ways. When a singular solution is obtained in the natural course of solving an equation, as occurs in Sections 92–94, the p-discriminant equation furnishes us with a check. If none of our methods of attack leads to a general solution, then the p-discriminant equation offers curves which may be particular (including singular) solutions of the differential equation. Then the p-discriminant equation should be tested for possible solutions of the differential equation. Such particular solutions make, of course, no contribution toward finding the general solution.

The p-discriminant equation may contain singular solutions, solutions that are not singular, and curves that are not solutions at all.

---

[*] For more detail on singular solutions and the discriminants see E. L. Ince, *Ordinary Differential Equations* (London: Longmans, Green and Co., 1927), pp. 82–92.

Exercises

1. For the quadratic equation

$$f = Ap^2 + Bp + C = 0,$$

with A, B, C functions of x and y, show that the p-discriminant obtained by eliminating p from $f = 0$ and $\dfrac{\partial f}{\partial p} = 0$ is the familiar equation

$$B^2 - 4AC = 0.$$

2. For the cubic $p^3 + Ap + B = 0$, show that the p-discriminant equation is $4A^3 + 27B^2 = 0$.

3. For the cubic $p^3 + Ap^2 + B = 0$, show that the p-discriminant equation is $B(4A^3 + 27B) = 0$.

4. Set up the condition that the equation $x^3p^2 + x^2yp + 4 = 0$ (Ex. 1, page 287) have equal roots as a quadratic in p. Compare with the singular solution $xy^2 = 16$.

5. Show that the condition that the equation $xyp^2 + (x + y)p + 1 = 0$ of the example of Section 88 have equal roots in p is $(x - y)^2 = 0$ and that the latter equation does not yield a solution of the differential equation. Was there a singular solution?

6. For the equation $y^2p^2 - a^2 + y^2 = 0$ of Section 89, find the condition for equal roots in p and compare with the singular solution.

7. For the differential equation of Ex. 6 show that the curve defined by

$$y = [a^2 - (x + 2a)^2]^{\frac{1}{2}} \quad \text{for} \; -3a < x \leqq -2a,$$
$$y = a \quad\quad\quad\quad\quad\quad\quad \text{for} \; -2a \leqq x \leqq 2a,$$
$$y = [a^2 - (x - 2a)^2]^{\frac{1}{2}} \quad \text{for} \;\;\; 2a \leqq x < 3a,$$

is a solution. Sketch the curve and show how it was pieced together from the general solution and the singular solution given in equations (5), (6), and (7) of Section 89.

In Ex. 8–16, obtain (a) the p-discriminant equation and (b) those solutions of the differential equation that are contained in the p-discriminant.

8. $xp^2 - 2yp + 4x = 0.$ ANS.   (a) $y^2 - 4x^2 = 0$; (b) $y = 2x$, $y = -2x$.

9. $3x^4p^2 - xp - y = 0.$ ANS.   (a) $x^2(1 + 12x^2y) = 0$; (b) $x = 0$, $12x^2y = -1$.

10. $p^2 - xp - y = 0.$ ANS.   (a) $x^2 + 4y = 0$; (b) None.

11. $p^2 - xp + y = 0.$ ANS.   (a) $x^2 - 4y = 0$; (b) $x^2 - 4y = 0$.

12. $p^2 + 4x^5p - 12x^4y = 0.$ ANS.   (a) $x^4(x^6 + 3y) = 0$; (b) $3y = -x^6.$

13. $4y^3p^2 - 4xp + y = 0.$ ANS.   (a) $(y^2 - x)(y^2 + x) = 0$;
                                        (b) Same as (a).

14. $4y^3p^2 + 4xp + y = 0.$ See also Ex. 13.
                        ANS.   (a) $(y^2 - x)(y^2 + x) = 0$;
                                        (b) None.

15. $p^3 + xp^2 - y = 0.$ ANS.   (a) $y(4x^3 - 27y) = 0$; (b) $y = 0.$

16. $y^4p^3 - 6xp + 2y = 0.$ ANS.   (a) $y^8(y^2 - 2x)(y^4 + 2xy^2 + 4x^2) = 0$;
                                        (b) $y = 0,\ y^2 = 2x.$

17. For the differential equation of Ex. 4 above, the general solution will be found to be $cxy + 4x + c^2 = 0$. Find the condition that this quadratic equation in c have equal roots. Compare that condition with the singular solution.

18. For the general solution

$$(x^2 - 1)c^2 - 2xyc + y^2 - 1 = 0$$

of Example (b), Section 93, find the condition that the equation have equal roots when considered as a quadratic in c. Compare that condition with the singular solution given in that example.

19. Consider the differential equation $xp^2 - 3yp + 9x^2 = 0$ of Example (a), Section 92. Verify that the singular solution $y^2 = 4x^3$ is the envelope of the family of curves given by the general solution

$$x^3 = c(y - c).$$

That is, show that the last two equations have the common solution $x = c^{\frac{1}{2}}, y = 2c$, counted twice. Then obtain the slopes of the two curves at the point of intersection. Each slope turns out to be $3c^{\frac{1}{2}}$.

92. Eliminating the dependent variable

Suppose the equation

(1) $$f(x, y, p) = 0; \ p = \frac{dy}{dx},$$

is of a form such that we can readily solve it for the dependent variable y and write

(2) $$y = g(x, p).$$

We can differentiate equation (2) with respect to x and, since $\frac{dy}{dx} = p$, get an equation

(3) $$h\left(x,\ p,\ \frac{dp}{dx}\right) = 0$$

involving only x and p. If we can solve equation (3), we will have two equations relating x, y, and p, namely, equation (2) and the solution of (3). These together form parametric equations of the solution of (1) with p now considered a parameter. Or, if p be eliminated between (2) and the solution of (3), then a solution in the nonparametric form is obtained.

EXAMPLE (a): Solve the differential equation

(4) $$xp^2 - 3yp + 9x^2 = 0.$$

Rewrite (4) as

(5) $$3y = xp + 9x^2/p.$$

Then differentiate both members of (5) with respect to x, using the fact that $\dfrac{dy}{dx} = p$, thus getting

$$3p = p + \frac{18x}{p} + \left(x - \frac{9x^2}{p^2}\right)\frac{dp}{dx},$$

or

(6) $$2p\left(1 - \frac{9x}{p^2}\right) = x\left(1 - \frac{9x}{p^2}\right)\frac{dp}{dx}.$$

From (6) it follows that either

(7) $$1 - \frac{9x}{p^2} = 0$$

or

(8) $$2p = x\frac{dp}{dx}.$$

First consider (8), which leads to

$$2\frac{dx}{x} = \frac{dp}{p}$$

so

(9) $$p = cx^2.$$

Therefore equations (4) and (9), with p as a parameter, constitute a solution of (4) looked upon as a differential equation with $p = dy/dx$.

In this example it is easy to eliminate p from equations (4) and (9), so we perform that elimination. The result is

$$x \cdot c^2 x^4 - 3y \cdot cx^2 + 9x^2 = 0.$$

Disregarding for the moment the possibility that $x = 0$, we can write our solution as

$$c^2 x^3 - 3cy + 9 = 0,$$

or

$$3cy = c^2 x^3 + 9.$$

Now put $c = 3k$ to get

(10) $$ky = k^2 x^3 + 1.$$

Equation (10) with k as an arbitrary constant is called the general solution of the differential equation (4).

It can be seen, rewriting (4) in the form

$$x(dy)^2 - 3y(dy)(dx) + 9x^2(dx)^2 = 0,$$

that $x = 0$ is also a solution of the differential equation. This solution can be fitted into the general solution by a simple device. In equation (10) replace k by $1/c_1$, thus obtaining

(11) $$c_1 y = x^3 + c_1^2.$$

Putting $c_1 = 0$ in (11) yields the solution $x = 0$.

We have yet to deal with equation (7). Note that (7) is an algebraic relation between x and p in contrast to the differential relation (8) which we have already used. We reason that the elimination of p from (7) and (4) may lead to a solution of the differential equation (4) and that the solution will not involve an arbitrary constant. From (7) it is seen that $p = 3x^{\frac{1}{2}}$ or $p = -3x^{\frac{1}{2}}$. Either of these expressions for p may be substituted into (4) and will lead to

(12) $$y^2 = 4x^3.$$

It is not difficult to show that equation (12) is a solution of the differential equation. This solution is not a special case of the general solution (10) or (11). It is a singular solution. Equation (12) has for its graph the envelope of the family of curves given by equation (11). The solution (12) is also easily obtained from the p-discriminant equation.

EXAMPLE (b): Solve the differential equation

(13) $$xp^2 - yp - x = 0.$$

The equation is readily solved for y, yielding

$$y = xp - \frac{x}{p}.$$

Then differentiation with respect to x gives

$$p = p - \frac{1}{p} + \left(x + \frac{x}{p^2}\right)\frac{dp}{dx},$$

or

$$\frac{1}{p} = x\left(1 + \frac{1}{p^2}\right)\frac{dp}{dx}.$$

Thus we are led to the differential equation

$$\frac{dx}{x} = \frac{p^2 + 1}{p}\,dp,$$

from which

$$\ln x = \tfrac{1}{2}p^2 + \ln p + \ln c,$$

or

(14) $$x = cp \exp\left(\tfrac{1}{2}p^2\right).$$

From equation (13) we get

$$y = x(p^2 - 1)/p.$$

Therefore, using (14), we find y in the form

(15) $$y = c(p^2 - 1) \exp\left(\tfrac{1}{2}p^2\right).$$

Equations (14) and (15) are parametric equations of the general solution of the original differential equation. In sketching a curve of the family of solutions, for each value of p inserted in (14) and (15) a pair of values x and y is obtained. Thus for each p used we get a point on the desired curve.

The parameter p could have been eliminated by solving the quadratic (13) for p and substituting in (14). The result would be more difficult to sketch than the same curve in parametric form, (14) and (15).

The student should use the p-discriminant equation to show that equation (13) has no singular solution.

It frequently happens, as exhibited in answers to some of the exercises below that it is inconvenient, even out of the question, to obtain y in terms of p and c alone. It may be best to leave the solution in the form

(16) $$\varphi(x, p) = 0$$

and

(17) $$y = g(x, p).$$

Then, in computation we would choose p and determine x from equation (16), after which y would be found from equation (17), using the values of both x and p.

93. Clairaut's equation

Any differential equation of the form

(1) $$y = px + f(p),$$

where $f(p)$ contains neither x nor y explicitly, can be solved at once by the method of Section 92. Equation (1) is called *Clairaut's equation*.

Let us differentiate both members of (1) with respect to x, thus getting

$$p = p + [x + f'(p)]p',$$

(2) $$[x + f'(p)]\frac{dp}{dx} = 0.$$

Then either

(3) $$\frac{dp}{dx} = 0$$

or

(4) $$x + f'(p) = 0.$$

The solution of the differential equation (3) is, of course, $p = c$, where c is an arbitrary constant. Returning to the differential equation (1), we can now write its general solution as

(5) $$y = cx + f(c),$$

a result easily verified by direct substitution into the differential equation (1). Note that (5) is the equation of a family of straight lines.

Now consider equation (4). Since $f(p)$ and $f'(p)$ are known functions of p, equations (4) and (1) together constitute a set of parametric equations giving x and y in terms of the parameter p. Indeed, from equation (4) it follows that

(6) $$x = -f'(p),$$

which, combined with equation (1), yields

(7) $$y = f(p) - pf'(p).$$

If $f(p)$ is not a linear function of p and not a constant, it can be shown (Exs. 1 and 2 below) that (6) and (7) are parametric equations of a nonlinear solution of the differential equation (1). Since the general solution (5) represents a straight line for each value of c, the solution (6) and (7) cannot be a special case of (5); it is a singular solution.

EXAMPLE (a): Solve the differential equation

(8) $y = px + p^3.$

Since (8) is a Clairaut equation, we can write its general solution

$$y = cx + c^3$$

at once.

Then using (6) and (7) we obtain the parametric equations

(9) $x = -3p^2,\ y = -2p^3,$

of the singular solution. The parameter p may be eliminated from equa-

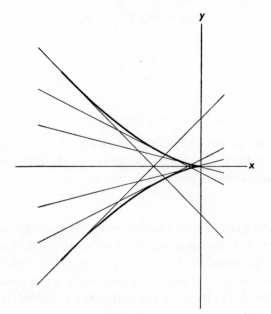

FIGURE 44

tions (9), yielding the form

(10) $27y^2 = -4x^3$

for the singular solution. See Figure 44.

EXAMPLE (b): Solve the differential equation

(11) $$(x^2 - 1)p^2 - 2xyp + y^2 - 1 = 0.$$

Rewrite (11) as

$$x^2p^2 - 2xyp + y^2 - 1 - p^2 = 0.$$

Then it is clear that the equation is of the form

(12) $$(y - xp)^2 - 1 - p^2 = 0$$

and so could be broken up into two equations, each of Clairaut's form. Then the general solution of (11) is obtained by replacing p everywhere in it by an arbitrary constant c. That is,

(13) $$(x^2 - 1)c^2 - 2xyc + y^2 - 1 = 0$$

is the general solution of (11). The solution (13) is composed of two families of straight lines,

(14) $$y = c_1 x + \sqrt{1 + c_1^2}$$

and

(15) $$y = c_2 x - \sqrt{1 + c_2^2}.$$

From the p-discriminant equation for (11) we obtain at once the singular solution

(16) $$x^2 + y^2 = 1.$$

Exercises

1. Let α be a parameter and prove that if $f''(\alpha)$ exists, then

(17) $$x = -f'(\alpha), \quad y = f(\alpha) - \alpha f'(\alpha)$$

is a solution of the differential equation $y = px + f(p)$. Hint: use dx and dy to get p in terms of α and then show that $y - px - f(p)$ vanishes identically.

2. Prove that if $f''(\alpha) \neq 0$, then (17) above is not a special case of the general solution $y = cx + f(c)$. Hint: show that the slope of the graph of one solution depends upon x whereas the slope of the graph of the other does not depend upon x.

In Exs. 3–30, find the general solution and also the singular solution, if it exists.

3. $p^2 + x^3 p - 2x^2 y = 0$.   ANS. $c^2 + cx^2 = 2y$; sing. sol., $8y = -x^4$.

4. $p^2 + 4x^5 p - 12x^4 y = 0.$

ANS. $12y = c(c + 4x^3)$; sing. sol., $3y = -x^6.$

5. $2xp^3 - 6yp^2 + x^4 = 0.$ ANS. $2c^3 x^3 = 1 - 6c^2 y$; sing. sol., $2y = x^2.$

6. $p^2 - xp + y = 0.$ ANS. $y = cx - c^2$; sing. sol., $x^2 = 4y.$

7. $y = px + kp^2.$ ANS. $y = cx + kc^2$; sing. sol., $x^2 = -4ky.$

8. $x^8 p^2 + 3xp + 9y = 0.$

ANS. $x^3(y + c^2) + c = 0$; sing. sol., $4x^6 y = 1.$

9. $x^4 p^2 + 2x^3 yp - 4 = 0.$ ANS. $x^2(1 + cy) = c^2.$

10. $xp^2 - 2yp + 4x = 0.$

ANS. $x^2 = c(y - c)$; sing. sol., $y = 2x$ and $y = -2x.$

11. $3x^4 p^2 - xp - y = 0.$ ANS. $xy = c(3cx - 1)$; sing. sol., $12x^2 y = -1.$

12. $xp^2 + (x - y)p + 1 - y = 0.$

ANS. $xc^2 + (x - y)c + 1 - y = 0$; sing. sol., $(x + y)^2 = 4x.$

13. $p(xp - y + k) + a = 0.$

ANS. $c(xc - y + k) + a = 0$; sing. sol., $(y - k)^2 = 4ax.$

14. $x^6 p^3 - 3xp - 3y = 0.$ ANS. $3xy = c(xc^2 - 3)$; sing. sol., $9x^3 y^2 = 4.$

15. $y = x^6 p^3 - xp.$ ANS. $xy = c(c^2 x - 1)$; sing. sol., $27x^3 y^2 = 4.$

16. $xp^4 - 2yp^3 + 12x^3 = 0.$

ANS. $2c^3 y = c^4 x^2 + 12$; sing. sol., $3y^2 = \pm 8x^3.$

17. $xp^3 - yp^2 + 1 = 0.$

ANS. $xc^3 - yc^2 + 1 = 0$; sing. sol., $4y^3 = 27x^2.$

18. $y = px + p^n$, for $n \neq 0$, $n \neq 1.$

ANS. $y = cx + c^n$; sing. sol., $\left(\dfrac{x}{n}\right)^n = -\left(\dfrac{y}{n - 1}\right)^{n-1}.$

19. $p^2 - xp - y = 0.$ ANS. $3x = 2p + cp^{-\frac{1}{2}}$ and $3y = p^2 - cp^{\frac{1}{2}}.$

20. $2p^3 + xp - 2y = 0.$ ANS. $x = 2p(3p + c)$ and $y = p^2(4p + c).$

21. $2p^2 + xp - 2y = 0.$ ANS. $x = 4p \ln (pc)$ and $y = p^2[1 + 2 \ln (pc)].$

22. $p^3 + 2xp - y = 0.$

ANS. $4x = -3p^2 + cp^{-2}$ and $2y = -p^3 + cp^{-1}.$

23. $4xp^2 - 3yp + 3 = 0.$

ANS. $2x = 3p^{-2} + cp^{-4}$ and $3y = 9p^{-1} + 2cp^{-3}.$

24. $p^3 - xp + 2y = 0.$ ANS. $x = p(c - 3p)$ and $2y = p^2(c - 4p).$

25. $5p^2 + 6xp - 2y = 0.$ ANS. $p^3(x + p)^2 = c$ and $2y = 6xp + 5p^2.$

26. $2xp^2 + (2x - y)p + 1 - y = 0.$

ANS. $p^2 x = (1 + p)^{-1} + \ln [c(1 + p)]$ and
$py = 1 + (1 + p)^{-1} + 2 \ln [c(1 + p)].$

27. $5p^2 + 3xp - y = 0.$ ANS. $p^3(x + 2p)^2 = c$ and $y = 3xp + 5p^2.$

28. $p^2 + 3xp - y = 0.$ ANS. $p^3(5x + 2p)^2 = c$ and $y = 3xp + p^2.$

29. $y = xp + x^3 p^2.$ ANS. $x^2 = cp^{-\frac{3}{2}} - 2p^{-1}$ and $y = xp + x^3 p^2.$

30. $8y = 3x^2 + p^2.$ ANS. $(p - 3x)^3 = c(p - x)$ and $8y = 3x^2 + p^2.$

94. Eliminating the independent variable

Suppose that a differential equation

(1) $$f(x, y, p) = 0; \quad p = \frac{dy}{dx},$$

can readily be solved for the independent variable x. Then we can proceed very much as we did in Section 92, but this time differentiating with respect to y and using the fact that

$$\frac{dx}{dy} = \frac{1}{p}.$$

This is, of course, nothing new at all. Since (1) is a first-order equation, the roles of independent and dependent variable can be interchanged at will using the relation

$$\frac{dy}{dx} = \left(\frac{dx}{dy}\right)^{-1}.$$

EXAMPLE: Solve the differential equation

(2) $$yp^2 - xp + 2y = 0.$$

First solve for x, obtaining

(3) $$x = yp + \frac{2y}{p},$$

and then differentiate both members of equation (3) with respect to y. The resulting relation is

$$\frac{1}{p} = p + \frac{2}{p} + \left(y - \frac{2y}{p^2}\right)\frac{dp}{dy}$$

or

$$\frac{1}{p} + p + y\left(1 - \frac{2}{p^2}\right)\frac{dp}{dy} = 0.$$

Therefore we are led to the equation

(4) $$\frac{dy}{y} + \frac{p^2 - 2}{p(1 + p^2)}\,dp = 0,$$

from which

$$\frac{dy}{y} + \frac{3p\,dp}{1 + p^2} - \frac{2\,dp}{p} = 0.$$

Hence
$$\ln y = -\tfrac{3}{2}\ln (1 + p^2) + 2 \ln p + \ln c,$$
so

(5) $$y = cp^2(1 + p^2)^{-\frac{3}{2}}.$$

From equation (3) it follows that
$$x = p^{-1}y(p^2 + 2).$$
Therefore, using (5) we may write

(6) $$x = cp(p^2 + 2)(1 + p^2)^{-\frac{3}{2}}.$$

Equations (5) and (6) are a set of parametric equations for the general solution of (2). There is no singular solution of (2).

Exercises

In Exs. 1–10, find the general solution and the singular solution in non-parametric form. That is, eliminate the parameter after obtaining the solutions in parametric form.

1. $xp^2 + yp = 3y^4$.   ANS. $3y = c(1 + cxy)$; sing. sol., $12xy^2 = -1$.

2. $9xp^2 + 3yp + y^8 = 0$. ANS. $c^2xy^3 + c + y^3 = 0$; sing. sol., $4xy^6 = 1$.

3. $p^2 + xy^2p + y^3 = 0$.   ANS. $cy(x - c) = 1$; sing. sol., $x^2y = 4$.

4. $4xp^2 + 4yp - y^4 = 0$. ANS. $y(c^2x - 1) = 2c$; sing. sol., $xy^2 = -1$.

5. $4yp^2 - 2xp + y = 0$.   ANS. $cx = y^2 + c^2$; sing. sols., $x = \pm 2y$.

6. $9p^2 + 12xy^4p + 4y^5 = 0$.

　　　　　　　　ANS. $c^2y^3 + 4cxy^3 + 4 = 0$; sing. sol., $x^2y^3 = 1$.

7. $2xy^2p^2 - y^3p - 1 = 0$.   ANS. $2c^2x = cy^2 + 1$; sing. sol., $y^4 = -8x$.

8. $p^2 + 2xy^3p + y^4 = 0$.   ANS. $4cy^2(x - c) = 1$; sing. sol., $xy = -1$.

9. $9y^2p^2 - 3xp + y = 0$.   ANS. $y^3 = c(x - c)$; sing. sol., $x^2 = 4y^3$.

10. $y^4p^3 - 6xp + 2y = 0$.   ANS. $y^3 = 18c(x - 6c^2)$; sing. sol., $y^2 = 2x$.

In Exs. 11–15, find the general solution in parametric form.

11. $xp^2 - yp - y = 0$.   ANS. $x = c(p + 1)e^p$ and $y = cp^2e^p$.

12. $y^2p^3 - xp + y = 0$.   ANS. $y = cp^{-1} - \tfrac{1}{4}p^{-3}$ and $px = y(yp^3 + 1)$.

13. $yp^2 - xp + y = 0$.

　　　　　　ANS. $x = c(p^{-2} + 1)e^{-1/(2p^2)}$ and $y = cp^{-1}e^{-1/(2p^2)}$.

14. $yp^3 - 3xp + 3y = 0$.

　　　　　　ANS. $\ln y = c - p^{-3} - 2 \ln p$ and $3px = y(p^3 + 3)$.

15. $y^3p^3 - xp + y = 0$.

　　　　　　ANS. $5y^2 = cp^{-\frac{3}{2}} - 2p^{-3}$ and $5px = y(3 + cp^{\frac{3}{2}})$.

Miscellaneous Exercises

1. $x^3p^2 + x^2yp + 4 = 0$. ANS. $cxy + 4x + c^2 = 0$; sing. sol., $xy^2 = 16$.

2. $6xp^2 - (3x + 2y)p + y = 0$.   ANS. $y^3 = c_1x$, $2y = x + c_2$.

3. $9p^2 + 3xy^4p + y^5 = 0$. ANS. $cy^3(x - c) = 1$; sing. sol., $x^2y^3 = 4$.

4. $4y^3p^2 - 4xp + y = 0$.   ANS. $y^4 = 4c(x - c)$; sing. sol., $y^2 = x$.

5. $x^6p^2 - 2xp - 4y = 0$. ANS. $x^2(y - c^2) = c$; sing. sol., $4x^4y = -1$.

6. $5p^2 + 6xp - 2y = 0$. ANS. $x = cp^{-\frac{3}{2}} - p$ and $2y = 6cp^{-\frac{1}{2}} - p^2$.

7. Do Ex. 6 by another method.

8. $y^2p^2 - y(x + 1)p + x = 0$.   ANS. $x^2 - y^2 = c_1$, $y^2 = 2(x - c_2)$.

9. $4x^5p^2 + 12x^4yp + 9 = 0$. ANS. $x^3(2cy - 1) = c^2$; sing. sol., $x^3y^2 = 1$.

10. $4y^2p^3 - 2xp + y = 0$.

ANS. $y^2 = 2c(x - 2c^2)$; sing. sol., $8x^3 = 27y^4$.

11. $p^4 + xp - 3y = 0$. ANS. $5x = 4p^3 + cp^{\frac{1}{2}}$ and $15y = 9p^4 + cp^{\frac{3}{2}}$.

12. Do Ex. 11 by another method.

13. $xp^2 + (k - x - y)p + y = 0$, the equation of Ex. 5, p. 13.

ANS. $xc^2 + (k - x - y)c + y = 0$;

sing. sol., $(x - y)^2 - 2k(x + y) + k^2 = 0$.

14. $x^2p^3 - 2xyp^2 + y^2p + 1 = 0$.

ANS. $x^2c^3 - 2xyc^2 + y^2c + 1 = 0$; sing. sol., $27x = -4y^3$.

15. $16xp^2 + 8yp + y^6 = 0$. ANS. $y^2(c^2x + 1) = 2c$; sing. sol., $xy^4 = 1$.

16. $xp^2 - (x^2 + 1)p + x = 0$.   ANS. $x^2 = 2(y - c_1)$, $y = \ln(c_2x)$.

17. $p^3 - 2xp - y = 0$.   ANS. $8x = 3p^2 + cp^{-\frac{1}{3}}$ and $4y = p^3 - cp^{\frac{1}{3}}$.

18. Do Ex. 17 by another method.

19. $9xy^4p^2 - 3y^5p - 1 = 0$. ANS. $cy^3 = c^2x - 1$; sing. sol., $y^6 = -4x$.

20. $x^2p^2 - (2xy + 1)p + y^2 + 1 = 0$.

ANS. $x^2c^2 - (2xy + 1)c + y^2 + 1 = 0$; sing. sol., $4x^2 - 4xy - 1 = 0$.

21. $x^6p^2 = 8(2y + xp)$. ANS. $c^2x^2 = 8(2x^2y - c)$; sing. sol., $x^4y = -1$.

22. $x^2p^2 = (x - y)^2$.   ANS. $x(x - 2y) = c_1$, $y = -x\ln(c_2x)$.

23. $xp^3 - 2yp^2 + 4x^2 = 0$. See Ex. 10 above.

ANS. $x^2 = 4c(y - 8c^2)$; sing. sol., $8y^3 = 27x^4$.

24. $(p + 1)^2(y - px) = 1$.

ANS. $(c + 1)^2(y - cx) = 1$; sing. sol., $4(x + y)^3 = 27x^2$.

25. $p^3 - p^2 + xp - y = 0$.

ANS. $y = cx + c^3 - c^2$; sing. sol. with parametric equations,

$x = 2\alpha - 3\alpha^2$ and $y = \alpha^2 - 2\alpha^3$.

26. $xp^2 + y(1 - x)p - y^2 = 0$.   ANS. $xy = c_1$, $x = \ln(c_2y)$.

27. $yp^2 - (x + y)p + y = 0$.

ANS. $py = c\exp(p^{-1})$ and $px = y(p^2 - p + 1)$; sing. sol., $y = x$.

CHAPTER 19

Special Equations of Order Two

95. Dependent variable missing

Consider a second-order equation,

(1) $$f(x, y', y'') = 0,$$

which does not contain the dependent variable y explicitly. Let us put

$$y' = p.$$

Then

$$y'' = \frac{dp}{dx}$$

and equation (1) may be replaced by

(2) $$f\left(x, p, \frac{dp}{dx}\right) = 0,$$

an equation of order one in p. If we can find p from equation (2), then y can be obtained from $y' = p$ by an integration.

EXAMPLE: Solve the equation

(3) $$xy'' - (y')^3 - y' = 0$$

of Example (b), page 13.

Since y does not appear explicitly in the differential equation (3), put $y' = p$. Then

$$y'' = \frac{dp}{dx},$$

so equation (3) becomes

$$x\frac{dp}{dx} - p^3 - p = 0.$$

Separation of variables leads to

$$\frac{dp}{p(p^2 + 1)} = \frac{dx}{x}$$

or

$$\frac{dp}{p} - \frac{p\,dp}{p^2 + 1} = \frac{dx}{x},$$

from which

(4) $$\ln p - \tfrac{1}{2}\ln(p^2 + 1) + \ln c_1 = \ln x$$

follows.

Equation (4) yields

(5) $$c_1 p(p^2 + 1)^{-\frac{1}{2}} = x,$$

which we wish to solve for p. From (5) we conclude that

$$c_1^2 p^2 = x^2(1 + p^2),$$

$$p^2 = \frac{x^2}{c_1^2 - x^2}.$$

But $p = y'$, so we have

(6) $$dy = \pm \frac{x\,dx}{\sqrt{c_1^2 - x^2}}.$$

The solution of (6) is

$$y - c_2 = \mp(c_1^2 - x^2)^{\frac{1}{2}},$$

or

(7) $$x^2 + (y - c_2)^2 = c_1^2.$$

Equation (7) is the desired general solution of the differential equation (3). Note that in dividing by p early in the work we might have discarded the solutions $y = k\,(p = 0)$, where k is constant. But (7) can be put in the form

(8) $$c_3(x^2 + y^2) + c_4 y + 1 = 0,$$

with new arbitrary constants c_3 and c_4. Then the choice $c_3 = 0, c_4 = -1/k$ yields the solution $y = k$.

96. Independent variable missing

A second-order equation

(1) $$f(y, y', y'') = 0$$

in which the independent variable x does not appear explicitly can be reduced to a first-order equation in y and y'. Put

$$y' = p,$$

then

$$y'' = \frac{dp}{dx} = \frac{dy}{dx}\frac{dp}{dy} = p\frac{dp}{dy},$$

so equation (1) becomes

(2) $$f\left(y, p, p\frac{dp}{dy}\right) = 0.$$

We try to determine p in terms of y from equation (2) and then substitute the result into $y' = p$.

EXAMPLE: Solve the equation

(3) $$yy'' + (y')^2 + 1 = 0$$

of Ex. 8, page 14.

Since the independent variable does not appear explicitly in equation (3), we put $y' = p$ and obtain

$$y'' = p\frac{dp}{dy}$$

as before. Then equation (3) becomes

(4) $$yp\frac{dp}{dy} + p^2 + 1 = 0,$$

in which the variables p and y are easily separated.

From (4) it follows that

$$\frac{p\,dp}{p^2 + 1} + \frac{dy}{y} = 0,$$

from which

$$\tfrac{1}{2}\ln(p^2 + 1) + \ln y = \ln c_1,$$

so

(5) $$p^2 + 1 = c_1{}^2 y^{-2}.$$

We solve equation (5) for p and find that

$$p = \pm \frac{(c_1{}^2 - y^2)^{\frac{1}{2}}}{y}.$$

Therefore

$$\frac{dy}{dx} = \pm \frac{(c_1{}^2 - y^2)^{\frac{1}{2}}}{y}$$

or

$$\pm y(c_1{}^2 - y^2)^{-\frac{1}{2}} \, dy = dx.$$

Then

$$\mp (c_1{}^2 - y^2)^{\frac{1}{2}} = x - c_2.$$

from which we obtain the final result

$$(x - c_2)^2 + y^2 = c_1{}^2.$$

Exercises

1. $y'' = x(y')^3.$ ANS. $x = c_1 \sin (y + c_2).$

2. $x^2 y'' + (y')^2 - 2xy' = 0$; when $x = 2$, $y = 5$ and $y' = -4$.
ANS. $y = \frac{1}{2}x^2 + 3x - 3 + 9 \ln (3 - x).$

3. $x^2 y'' + (y')^2 - 2xy' = 0$; when $x = 2$, $y = 5$ and $y' = 2$.
ANS. $x^2 = 2(y - 3).$

4. $yy'' + (y')^2 = 0.$ ANS. See Ex. 20, page 14.

5. $y^2 y'' + (y')^3 = 0.$ ANS. $x = c_1 y - \ln (c_2 y).$

6. $(y + 1)y'' = (y')^2.$ ANS. $y + 1 = c_2 e^{c_1 x}.$

7. $2ay'' + (y')^3 = 0.$ ANS. $(y - c_2)^2 = 4a(x - c_1).$

8. Do Ex. 7 by another method.

9. $xy'' = y' + x^5$; when $x = 1$, $y = \frac{1}{2}$ and $y' = 1$.
ANS. $24y = x^6 + 9x^2 + 2.$

10. $xy'' + y' + x = 0$; when $x = 2$, $y = -1$ and $y' = -\frac{1}{2}$.
ANS. $y = -\frac{1}{4}x^2 + \ln (\frac{1}{2}x).$

11. $y'' = 2y(y')^3.$ ANS. $y^3 = 3(c_2 - x - c_1 y).$

12. $yy'' + (y')^3 - (y')^2 = 0.$ ANS. $x = y - c_1 \ln (c_2 y).$

13. $y'' + \beta^2 y = 0.$ Check your result by solving the equation in two ways.

14. $yy'' + (y')^3 = 0.$ ANS. $x = c_1 + y \ln (c_2 y).$

15. $y'' \cos x = y'.$ ANS. $y = c_2 + c_1 \ln (1 - \sin x).$

16. $y'' = x(y')^2$; when $x = 2$, $y = \frac{1}{4}\pi$ and $y' = -\frac{1}{4}$. ANS. $x = 2 \cot y.$

17. $y'' = x(y')^2$; when $x = 0$, $y = 1$ and $y' = \frac{1}{2}$.
ANS. $y = 1 + \frac{1}{2} \ln \dfrac{2 + x}{2 - x}.$

18. $y'' = -e^{-2y}$; when $x = 3$, $y = 0$ and $y' = 1$. ANS. $y = \ln (x - 2).$

19. $y'' = -e^{-2y}$; when $x = 3$, $y = 0$ and $y' = -1$.

ANS. $y = \ln (4 - x)$.

20. $2y'' = \sin 2y$; when $x = 0$, $y = \pi/2$ and $y' = 1$.

ANS. $x = -\ln (\csc y + \cot y)$.

21. $2y'' = \sin 2y$; when $x = 0$, $y = -\pi/2$ and $y' = 1$.

ANS. $x = \ln (-\csc y - \cot y)$.

22. Show that if you can perform the integrations encountered, then you can solve any equation of the form $y'' = f(y)$.

23. $x^3 y'' - x^2 y' = 3 - x^2$.   ANS. $y = x^{-1} + x + c_1 x^2 + c_2$.

24. $y'' = (y')^2$.   ANS. $y = -\ln [c_2(c_1 - x)]$; or $x = c_1 + c_3 e^{-y}$.

25. $y'' = e^x (y')^2$.   ANS. $c_1 y + c_2 = -\ln (c_1 e^{-x} - 1)$.

26. $2y'' = (y')^3 \sin 2x$; when $x = 0$, $y = 1$ and $y' = 1$.

ANS. $y = 1 + \ln (\sec x + \tan x)$.

27. $x^2 y'' + (y')^2 = 0$.   ANS. $c_1{}^2 y = c_1 x + \ln [c_2(c_1 x - 1)]$.

28. $y'' = 1 + (y')^2$.   ANS. $e^y \cos (x + c_1) = c_2$.

29. Do Ex. 28 by another method.

30. $y'' = [1 + (y')^2]^{\frac{3}{2}}$. Solve in three ways, by considering the geometric significance of the equation, and by the methods of this chapter.

31. $yy'' = (y')^2[1 - y' \sin y - yy' \cos y]$.   ANS. $x = c_1 \ln (c_2 y) - \cos y$.

32. $(1 + y^2)y'' + (y')^3 + y' = 0$.

ANS. $x = c_2 + c_1 y - (1 + c_1{}^2) \ln (y + c_1)$.

33. $[yy'' + 1 + (y')^2]^2 = [1 + (y')^2]^3$.   ANS. $(y - c_1)^2 + (x - c_2)^2 = c_1{}^2$.

34. $x^2 y'' = y'(2x - y')$; when $x = -1$, $y = 5$ and $y' = 1$.

ANS. $2y - 1 = (x - 2)^2 + 8 \ln (x + 2)$.

35. $x^2 y'' = y'(3x - 2y')$.   ANS. $2y = x^2 + c_2 - c_1 \ln (x^2 + c_1)$.

36. $xy'' = y'(2 - 3xy')$.   ANS. $3y = c_2 + \ln (x^3 + c_1)$.

37. $x^4 y'' = y'(y' + x^3)$; when $x = 1$, $y = 2$ and $y' = 1$.

ANS. $y = 1 + x^2 - \ln \left(\dfrac{1 + x^2}{2} \right)$.

38. $y'' = 2x + (x^2 - y')^2$.   ANS. $3y = x^3 + c_2 - 3 \ln (x + c_1)$.

39. $(y'')^2 - 2y'' + (y')^2 - 2xy' + x^2 = 0$; when $x = 0$, $y = \frac{1}{2}$ and $y' = 1$.

ANS. $2y = 1 + x^2 + 2 \sin x$.

40. $(y'')^2 - xy'' + y' = 0$.

ANS.   General solution: $2y = c_1 x^2 - 2c_1{}^2 x + c_2$; family of singular solutions: $12y = x^3 + k$.

41. $(y'')^3 = 12y'(xy'' - 2y')$.

ANS.   General solution: $y = c_1(x - c_1)^3 + c_2$; family of singular solutions: $9y = x^4 + k$.

42. $3yy'y'' = (y')^3 - 1$.   ANS. $27c_1(y + c_1)^2 = 8(x + c_2)^3$.

43. $4y(y')^2 y'' = (y')^4 + 3$.   ANS. $256c_1(y - c_1)^3 = 243(x - c_2)^4$.

97. The catenary

Let a cable of uniformly distributed weight w (lb. per ft.) be suspended between two supports at points A and B as indicated in Figure 45. The cable will sag and there will be a lowest point V as indicated in the figure. We wish to determine the curve formed by the suspended cable. That curve is called the *catenary*.

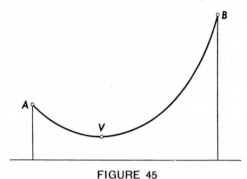

FIGURE 45

Choose coordinate axes as shown in Figure 46, the y-axis vertical through the point V and the x-axis horizontal and passing at a distance y_0 (to be chosen later) below V. Let s represent length (ft.) of the cable

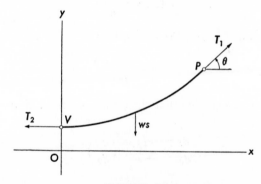

FIGURE 46

measured from V to the variable point P with coordinates (x, y). Then the portion of the cable from V to P is subject to the three forces shown in Figure 46. Those forces are: (a) the gravitational force ws (lb.) acting downward through the center of gravity of the portion of the cable from V to P, (b) the tension T_1 (lb.) acting tangentially at P, and (c) the tension T_2 (lb.) acting horizontally (again tangentially) at V. The tension T_1 is a variable; the tension T_2 is constant.

Since equilibrium is assumed, the algebraic sum of the vertical components of these forces is zero and the algebraic sum of the horizontal components of these forces is also zero. Therefore, if θ is the angle of inclination, from the horizontal, of the tangent to the curve at the point (x, y), we have

$$(1) \qquad\qquad T_1 \sin \theta - ws = 0$$

and

$$(2) \qquad\qquad T_1 \cos \theta - T_2 = 0.$$

But $\tan \theta$ is the slope of the curve of the cable, so

$$(3) \qquad\qquad \tan \theta = \frac{dy}{dx}.$$

We may eliminate the variable tension T_1 from equations (1) and (2) and obtain

$$(4) \qquad\qquad \tan \theta = \frac{ws}{T_2}.$$

The constant T_2/w has the dimension of a length. Put $T_2/w = a$ (ft.). Then equation (4) becomes

$$(5) \qquad\qquad \tan \theta = \frac{s}{a}.$$

From equations (3) and (5) we see that

$$(6) \qquad\qquad \frac{s}{a} = \frac{dy}{dx}.$$

Now we know from calculus that since s is the length of arc of the curve, then

$$(7) \qquad\qquad \frac{ds}{dx} = \sqrt{1 + \left(\frac{dy}{dx}\right)^2}.$$

From (6) we get $\dfrac{1}{a}\dfrac{ds}{dx} = \dfrac{d^2y}{dx^2}$, so the elimination of s yields the differential equation

$$(8) \qquad\qquad \frac{d^2y}{dx^2} = \frac{1}{a}\sqrt{1 + \left(\frac{dy}{dx}\right)^2}.$$

The desired equation of the curve assumed by the suspended cable is that solution of the differential equation (8) which also satisfies the boundary conditions

(9)   when $x = 0$, $y = y_0$ and $\dfrac{dy}{dx} = 0$.

Equation (8) fits into either of the types studied in this chapter. It is left as an exercise for the student to solve the differential equation (8) with the conditions (9) and arrive at the result

(10) $$y = a \cosh \frac{x}{a} + y_0 - a.$$

Then, of course, the sensible choice $y_0 = a$ is made, so the equation of the desired curve (the catenary) is

$$y = a \cosh \frac{x}{a}.$$

CHAPTER 20

The Power Series Method

98. Linear equations and power series

The solution of linear equations with constant coefficients can be accomplished by the methods developed earlier in the book. The general linear equation of the first order yields to an integrating factor as was seen in Chapter 2. For linear ordinary differential equations with variable coefficients and of order greater than one, probably the most generally effective method of attack yet devised is that based upon the use of power series.

To simplify the work and the statement of theorems, the equations treated here will be restricted to those with polynomial coefficients. The difficulties to be encountered, the methods of attack, and the results accomplished all remain essentially unchanged when the coefficients are permitted to be functions that have power series expansions valid about some point. (Such functions are called *analytic functions*.)

Consider the homogeneous linear equation of the second order,

$$(1) \qquad b_0(x)y'' + b_1(x)y' + b_2(x)y = 0,$$

with polynomial coefficients. If $b_0(x)$ does not vanish at $x = 0$, then in some interval about $x = 0$, staying away from the nearest point where $b_0(x)$ does vanish, it is safe to divide throughout by $b_0(x)$. Thus we replace equation (1) by

$$(2) \qquad y'' + p(x)y' + q(x)y = 0,$$

in which the coefficients $p(x)$, $q(x)$ are rational functions of x with denominators that do not vanish at $x = 0$.

We shall now show that it is reasonable to expect* a solution of (2) that is a power series in x and that contains two arbitrary constants. Let $y = y(x)$ be a solution of equation (2). We assign arbitrarily the values of y and y' at $x = 0$; $y(0) = A$, $y'(0) = B$.

Equation (2) yields

$$(3) \qquad y''(x) = -p(x)y'(x) - q(x)y(x),$$

so $y''(0)$ may be computed directly, because $p(x)$ and $q(x)$ are well behaved at $x = 0$. From equation (3) we get

$$(4) \quad y'''(x) = -p(x)y''(x) - p'(x)y'(x) - q(x)y'(x) - q'(x)y(x),$$

so $y'''(0)$ can be computed once $y''(0)$ is known.

The above process can be continued as long as we wish, and therefore we can determine successively $y^{(n)}(0)$ for as many integral values of n as may be desired. Now, by Maclaurin's formula in calculus,

$$(5) \qquad y(x) = y(0) + \sum_{n=1}^{\infty} y^{(n)}(0) \frac{x^n}{n!};$$

that is, the right member of (5) will converge to the value $y(x)$ throughout some interval about $x = 0$ if $y(x)$ is sufficiently well behaved at and near $x = 0$. Thus we can determine the function $y(x)$ and are led to a solution in power series form.

For actually obtaining the solutions for specific equations, we shall study another method, to be illustrated in examples, a technique far superior to the brute-force method used above. What we have gained from the present discussion is the knowledge that it is reasonable to seek a power series solution. Once we know that, it remains only to develop good methods for finding the solution and theorems regarding the validity of the results so found.

99. Equations of higher order and degree

Careful examination of the procedure used in Section 98 shows that the method was dependent only upon our being able to solve the original equation for y'' and upon the existence of the various derivatives

---

* This is no proof. For proof see, for instance, E. D. Rainville, *Intermediate Differential Equations*, 2nd ed. (New York: The Macmillan Co., 1964), pp. 67–71.

of the right member of equation (3) of that section. Hence, if we have at hand an equation of the form

(1) $y^{(k)} = f(x, y, y', \cdots, y^{(k-1)})$

of order k and of any degree, then we can anticipate the existence of a power series solution under the following conditions. Suppose the right member f in equation (1) is such that it, and its various derivatives with respect to x, exist at $x = 0$. Then we may expect to assign arbitrarily the values of y and its first $(k - 1)$ derivatives at $x = 0$ (thus having k arbitrary constants), and proceed to determine $y^{(n)}(0)$ for $n \geq k$ from equation (1).

100. Convergence of power series

From calculus we know that the power series

$$\sum_{n=0}^{\infty} a_n x^n$$

converges either at $x = 0$ only, or for all finite x, or the series converges in an interval $-R < x < R$ and diverges outside that interval. Unless the series converges at only one point, it represents, where it does converge, a function $f(x)$ in the sense that the series has at each value x the sum $f(x)$.

If

$$f(x) = \sum_{n=0}^{\infty} a_n x^n, \quad -R < x < R,$$

then also

$$f'(x) = \sum_{n=0}^{\infty} n a_n x^{n-1}, \quad -R < x < R,$$

and

$$\int_0^x f(y)\, dy = \sum_{n=0}^{\infty} \frac{a_n x^{n+1}}{n+1}, \quad -R < x < R.$$

That is, the series is termwise differentiable and integrable in the sense that the series of the derivatives of the separate terms converges to the derivative of the sum of the original series and similarly for integration.

It is important that the interval of convergence remains unchanged. We are not concerned here with convergence behavior at the endpoints of that interval.

Let us look more closely into the reason that a series has a particular interval of convergence rather than some other one. An elementary example from calculus is

$$(1) \qquad \frac{1}{1-x} = \sum_{n=0}^{\infty} x^n, \quad -1 < x < 1.$$

It is reasonable to suspect that the misbehavior of the function $1/(1-x)$ at $x=1$ is what lies behind the fact that the interval of convergence terminates at $x=1$. That it must extend that far is not so evident. The point $x=-1$ has no bearing in this instance; the interval is terminated at that end by the requirement that it be symmetric about $x=0$.

Now let us replace x in (1) by $(-x^2)$ to get

$$(2) \qquad \frac{1}{1+x^2} = \sum_{n=0}^{\infty} (-1)^n x^{2n}, \quad -1 < x < 1.$$

Again the interval of convergence is $-1 < x < 1$, but the function $f(x) = 1/(1+x^2)$ is well behaved for all real x. What stopped the interval of convergence at $x=1$ is not so clear. The fact is that we need to consider x as a complex variable to understand what is going on here.

We use the ordinary Argand diagram for complex numbers. Let $x = a + ib$, a and b real, with $i = \sqrt{-1}$, and associate with the point (a, b) in the plane the number $a + ib$. Now mark on the diagram those points (values of x) for which the function $1/(1+x^2)$ does not exist. The points are $x = i$, $x = -i$, where the denominator $(1 + x^2)$ vanishes. In books on functions of a complex variable it is shown that the series in (2) converges for all values of x inside the circle shown in Figure 47. The interval of convergence given

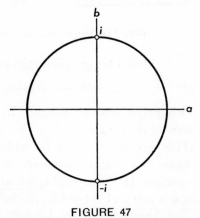

FIGURE 47

in (2) is merely a cross-section of the region of convergence in the complex plane.

A power series in a complex variable x always has as its region of convergence the interior of a circle, if we are willing to admit the extreme cases in which the circle degenerates into a single point or expands over the whole complex plane.

Points at which the denominator of a rational function vanishes are the most elementary examples of singularities of an analytic function.

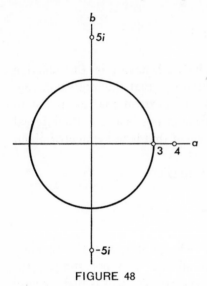

The circle of convergence of a power series cannot have inside it a singularity of the function represented by the series. The circle of convergence has its center at the origin and passes through the singularity nearest the origin.

The function

$$\frac{x - 2}{(x - 3)(x - 4)(x^2 + 25)}$$

has a denominator which vanishes at $x = 3, 4, 5i, -5i$. The function then has a power series expansion valid inside a circle (Figure 48) with center at $x = 0$ and extending as far as the nearest ($x = 3$) of the points

FIGURE 48

where the function misbehaves. For real x, the interval of convergence is $-3 < x < 3$.

101. Ordinary points and singular points

For a linear differential equation

$$(1) \qquad b_0(x)y^{(n)} + b_1(x)y^{(n-1)} + \cdots + b_n(x)y = R(x)$$

with polynomial coefficients, the point $x = x_0$ is called an *ordinary point* of the equation if $b_0(x_0) \neq 0$. A *singular point* of the linear equation (1) is any point $x = x_1$ for which $b_0(x_1) = 0$. In this chapter we shall obtain power series solutions valid near an ordinary point of a linear equation. In the next chapter we shall get power series solutions valid near a certain kind of singular point of the equation.

A knowledge of the location of the singular points of a differential equation will be useful to us later. Any point that is not a singular point is an ordinary point, so we list only the former.

We have left undiscussed the matter of a "point at infinity" in the complex plane, a concept of great utility. It is not necessary for this elementary discussion. As a result of this omission, however, it is necessary for us to attach the words "in the finite plane" to any statement purporting to list all singular points of a differential equation. The concept of a point at infinity will be introduced in Section 125.

The differential equation

$$(2) \qquad (1 - x^2)y'' - 6xy' - 4y = 0$$

has $x = 1$ and $x = -1$ as its only singular points in the finite complex plane. The equation

$$y'' + 2xy' + y = 0$$

has no singular points in the finite plane. The equation

$$xy'' + y' + xy = 0$$

has the origin, $x = 0$, as the only singular point in the finite plane.

Exercises

For each equation, list all of the singular points in the finite plane.

1. $(x^2 + 4)y'' - 6xy' + 3y = 0.$ ANS. $x = 2i, -2i.$
2. $x(3 - x)y'' - (3 - x)y' + 4xy = 0.$ ANS. $x = 0, 3.$
3. $4y'' + 3xy' + 2y = 0.$ ANS.   None.
4. $x(x - 1)^2 y'' + 3xy' + (x - 1)y = 0.$ ANS. $x = 0, 1.$
5. $x^2 y'' + xy' + (1 - x^2)y = 0.$
6. $x^4 y'' + y = 0.$
7. $(1 + x^2)y'' - 2xy' + 6y = 0.$
8. $(x^2 - 4x + 3)y'' + x^2 y' - 4y = 0.$
9. $x^2(1 - x)^3 y'' + (1 + 2x)y = 0.$
10. $6xy'' + (1 - x^2)y' + 2y = 0.$
11. $4xy'' + y = 0.$
12. $4y'' + y = 0.$
13. $x^2(x^2 - 9)y'' + 3xy' - y = 0.$
14. $x^2(1 + 4x^2)y'' - 4xy' + y = 0.$
15. $(2x + 1)(x - 3)y'' - y' + (2x + 1)y = 0.$
16. $x^3(x^2 - 4)^2 y'' + 2(x^2 - 4)y' - xy = 0.$
17. $x(x^2 + 1)^2 y'' - y = 0.$
18. $(x^2 + 6x + 8)y'' + 3y = 0.$
19. $(4x + 1)y'' + 3xy' + y = 0.$

102. Validity of the solutions near an ordinary point

Suppose $x = 0$ is an ordinary point of the linear equation

(1) $$b_0(x)y'' + b_1(x)y' + b_2(x)y = 0.$$

It is proved in more advanced books that there is a solution

(2) $$y = \sum_{n=0}^{\infty} a_n x^n$$

which contains two arbitrary constants, namely, a_0 and a_1, and which converges inside a circle with center at $x = 0$ and extending out to the singular point (or points) nearest $x = 0$. If the differential equation has no singular points in the finite plane, then the solution (2) is valid for all finite x. There remains, of course, the job of finding a_n for $n \geq 2$. That is a major part of our work in solving a particular equation.

It is necessary to realize that the theorem quoted states that the series involved converges inside a certain circle. It does not state that the series diverges outside that circle. In a particular instance it may be that the circle of convergence happens to extend farther than the minimum given by the theorem. In any case, the circle of convergence passes through a singular point of the equation—it may not be the nearest singular point.

103. Solutions near an ordinary point

In solving numerical equations, the technique employed in the following examples will be found useful.

EXAMPLE (a): Solve the equation

(1) $$(1 - x^2)y'' - 6xy' - 4y = 0$$

near the ordinary point $x = 0$.

The only singular points that this equation has in the finite plane are $x = 1$ and $x = -1$. Hence we know in advance that there is a solution

(2) $$y = \sum_{n=0}^{\infty} a_n x^n$$

valid in $|x| < 1$ and with a_0 and a_1 arbitrary.

To determine the a_n, $n > 1$, we substitute the y of equation (2) into the left member of (1). We get

$$\sum_{n=0}^{\infty} n(n-1)a_n x^{n-2} - \sum_{n=0}^{\infty} n(n-1)a_n x^n - \sum_{n=0}^{\infty} 6na_n x^n - \sum_{n=0}^{\infty} 4a_n x^n = 0,$$

or

$$(3) \qquad \sum_{n=0}^{\infty} n(n-1)a_n x^{n-2} - \sum_{n=0}^{\infty} (n^2 + 5n + 4)a_n x^n = 0,$$

in which we have combined series that contained the same powers of x.

Next let us factor the coefficient in the second series in equation (3), writing

$$(4) \qquad \sum_{n=0}^{\infty} n(n-1)a_n x^{n-2} - \sum_{n=0}^{\infty} (n+1)(n+4)a_n x^n = 0.$$

Relations for the determination of the a_n will be obtained by using the fact that for a power series to vanish identically over any interval, each coefficient in the series must be zero. Therefore we wish next to write the two series in equation (4) in a form in which the exponents on x will be the same so we can easily pick off the coefficient of each power of x.

Let us shift the index in the second series, replacing n everywhere by $(n-2)$. Then the summation which started with the old $n = 0$ will now start with $n - 2 = 0$, or the new $n = 2$. Thus we obtain

$$(5) \qquad \sum_{n=0}^{\infty} n(n-1)a_n x^{n-2} - \sum_{n=2}^{\infty} (n-1)(n+2)a_{n-2} x^{n-2} = 0.$$

In equation (5) the coefficient of each separate power of x must be zero. For $n = 0$ and $n = 1$, the second series has not yet started, so we get contributions from the first series only. In detail, we have

$$n = 0: \quad 0 \cdot a_0 = 0,$$
$$n = 1: \quad 0 \cdot a_1 = 0,$$
$$n \geq 2: \quad n(n-1)a_n - (n-1)(n+2)a_{n-2} = 0.$$

As was expected, a_0 and a_1 are arbitrary. The relation for $n \geq 2$ can be used to determine the other a's in terms of a_0 and a_1. Since

$$n(n-1) \neq 0$$

for $n \geq 2$, we can write

(6) $n \geq 2: \quad a_n = \dfrac{n + 2}{n} a_{n-2}.$

Equation (6) is called a *recurrence relation*. It gives a_n in terms of preceding a's. In this particular case, each a is determined by the a with subscript two lower than its own and consequently, eventually, by either a_0 or a_1, according to whether the original a had an even or an odd subscript.

A recurrence relation is a special kind of *difference equation*. In difference equations the arguments of the unknown function (the subscripts in our relations) need not differ by integers. There are books and courses on difference equations and the calculus of finite differences paralleling the books and courses on differential equations and calculus.

It is convenient to arrange the iterated instances of the relation (6) in two vertical columns [two columns because the subscripts in (6) differ by two], thus using successively $n = 2, 4, 6, \cdots$, and $n = 3, 5, 7, \cdots$, to obtain

$$a_2 = \frac{4}{2} a_0 \qquad\qquad a_3 = \frac{5}{3} a_1$$

$$a_4 = \frac{6}{4} a_2 \qquad\qquad a_5 = \frac{7}{5} a_3$$

$$a_6 = \frac{8}{6} a_4 \qquad\qquad a_7 = \frac{9}{7} a_5$$

$$\vdots \qquad\qquad\qquad \vdots$$

$$a_{2k} = \frac{2k + 2}{2k} a_{2k-2} \qquad a_{2k+1} = \frac{2k + 3}{2k + 1} a_{2k-1}.$$

Next, obtain the product of corresponding members of the equations in the first column. The result,

$$k \geq 1: \quad a_2 a_4 a_6 \cdots a_{2k} = \frac{4 \cdot 6 \cdot 8 \cdots (2k + 2)}{2 \cdot 4 \cdot 6 \cdots (2k)} a_0 a_2 a_4 \cdots a_{2k-2},$$

simplifies at once to

$$k \geq 1: \quad a_{2k} = (k + 1) a_0,$$

thus giving us each a with an even subscript in terms of a_0.

Similarly, from the right column in the array above we get

$$k \geq 1: \quad a_{2k+1} = \frac{5 \cdot 7 \cdot 9 \cdots (2k + 3)}{3 \cdot 5 \cdot 7 \cdots (2k + 1)} a_1.$$

or

$$k \geq 1: \quad a_{2k+1} = \frac{2k+3}{3} a_1,$$

thus giving us each a with an odd subscript in terms of a_1.

We need next to substitute the expressions we have obtained for the a's into the assumed series for y,

$$(2) \qquad\qquad y = \sum_{n=0}^{\infty} a_n x^n.$$

The nature of our expressions for the a's, depending on whether the subscript is odd or even, dictates that we should first split the series in (2) into two series, one containing all the terms with even subscripts, and the other containing all the terms with odd subscripts. We write

$$y = \left[a_0 + \sum_{k=1}^{\infty} a_{2k} x^{2k} \right] + \left[a_1 x + \sum_{k=1}^{\infty} a_{2k+1} x^{2k+1} \right],$$

and then use our known results for a_{2k} and a_{2k+1} to obtain the general solution in the form

$$(7) \quad y = a_0 \left[1 + \sum_{k=1}^{\infty} (k+1) x^{2k} \right] + a_1 \left[x + \sum_{k=1}^{\infty} \frac{2k+3}{3} x^{2k+1} \right].$$

These series converge at least for $|x| < 1$, as we know from the theory. That they converge there and only there can be verified by applying elementary convergence tests.

It happens in this example that the solution (7) may be written more simply as

$$(8) \qquad y = a_0 \sum_{k=0}^{\infty} (k+1) x^{2k} + a_1 \sum_{k=0}^{\infty} \frac{2k+3}{3} x^{2k+1}.$$

Indeed, the series can be summed in terms of elementary functions,

$$y = \frac{a_0}{(1-x^2)^2} + \frac{a_1(3x - x^3)}{3(1-x^2)^2}.$$

Such simplifications may be important when they can be accomplished in a particular problem, but it must be realized that our goal was to obtain equation (7) and to know where it is a valid solution. Additional steps taken after that goal is reached are frequently irrelevant to the essential desire to find a computable solution of the differential equation.

The length of the work in solving this particular equation is largely due to detailed steps, many of which will be taken mentally as we acquire more experience.

EXAMPLE (b): Solve the equation

$$(9) \qquad y'' + (x - 1)^2 y' - 4(x - 1)y = 0$$

about the ordinary point $x = 1$.

To solve an equation "about the point $x = x_0$" means to obtain solutions valid in a region surrounding the point, solutions expressed in powers of $(x - x_0)$.

We first translate the axes, putting $x - 1 = v$. Then equation (9) becomes

$$(10) \qquad \frac{d^2y}{dv^2} + v^2 \frac{dy}{dv} - 4vy = 0.$$

Always in a pure translation, $x - x_0 = v$, we have $\dfrac{dy}{dx} = \dfrac{dy}{dv}$, etc.

As usual we put

$$(11) \qquad y = \sum_{n=0}^{\infty} a_n v^n$$

and from (10) obtain

$$(12) \qquad \sum_{n=0}^{\infty} n(n-1)a_n v^{n-2} + \sum_{n=0}^{\infty} n a_n v^{n+1} - \sum_{n=0}^{\infty} 4 a_n v^{n+1} = 0.$$

Collecting like terms in (12) yields

$$\sum_{n=0}^{\infty} n(n-1)a_n v^{n-2} + \sum_{n=0}^{\infty} (n-4) a_n v^{n+1} = 0,$$

which, with a shift of index from n to $(n-3)$ in the second series, gives

$$(13) \qquad \sum_{n=0}^{\infty} n(n-1)a_n v^{n-2} + \sum_{n=3}^{\infty} (n-7) a_{n-3} v^{n-2} = 0.$$

Therefore a_0 and a_1 are arbitrary and for the remainder we have

$$n = 2: \quad 2a_2 = 0,$$

$$n \geq 3: \quad n(n-1)a_n + (n-7)a_{n-3} = 0,$$

$$a_n = -\frac{n-7}{n(n-1)} a_{n-3}.$$

This time the a's fall into three groups, those that come from a_0, from a_1, and from a_2. We use three columns:

a_0 arb.	a_1 arb.	$a_2 = 0$
$a_3 = -\dfrac{-4}{3 \cdot 2} a_0$	$a_4 = -\dfrac{-3}{4 \cdot 3} a_1$	$a_5 = -\dfrac{-2}{5 \cdot 4} a_2 = 0$
$a_6 = -\dfrac{-1}{6 \cdot 5} a_3$	$a_7 = -\dfrac{0}{7 \cdot 6} a_4 = 0$	$a_8 = (\ ) a_5 = 0$
$a_9 = -\dfrac{2}{9 \cdot 8} a_6$	$a_{10} = -\dfrac{3}{10 \cdot 9} a_7 = 0$	$a_{11} = 0$
.	.	.
.	.	.
.	.	.

$$a_{3k} = -\frac{3k-7}{3k(3k-1)} a_{3k-3} \qquad a_{3k+1} = 0, \ k \geq 2 \qquad a_{3k+2} = 0, \ k \geq 1.$$

With the usual multiplication scheme, the first column yields

$$k \geq 1: \quad a_{3k} = \frac{(-1)^k[(-4)(-1) \cdot 2 \cdots (3k-7)]a_0}{[3 \cdot 6 \cdot 9 \cdots (3k)][2 \cdot 5 \cdot 8 \cdots (3k-1)]}.$$

For the a's which are determined by a_1, we see that $a_4 = \frac{1}{4} a_1$ but that each of the others is zero. Since $a_2 = 0$, all the a's proportional to it, a_5, a_8, etc., are also zero.

For y we now have

$$y = a_0 \left[1 + \sum_{k=1}^{\infty} \frac{(-1)^k[(-4)(-1) \cdot 2 \cdots (3k-7)]v^{3k}}{[3 \cdot 6 \cdot 9 \cdots (3k)][2 \cdot 5 \cdot 8 \cdots (3k-1)]} \right]$$
$$+ a_1(v + \tfrac{1}{4} v^4).$$

Since $v = x - 1$, the solution appears as

$$(14) \quad y = a_0 \left[1 + \sum_{k=1}^{\infty} \frac{(-1)^k[(-4)(-1) \cdot 2 \cdots (3k-7)](x-1)^{3k}}{[3 \cdot 6 \cdot 9 \cdots (3k)][2 \cdot 5 \cdot 8 \cdots (3k-1)]} \right]$$
$$+ a_1[(x-1) + \tfrac{1}{4}(x-1)^4].$$

The original differential equation has no singular point in the finite plane, so the series in (14) is convergent for all finite x. In computations, of course, it is most useful in the neighborhood of the point $x = 1$.

The coefficient of $(x-1)^{3k}$ is sufficiently complicated to warrant attempts to simplify it. In the product $3 \cdot 6 \cdot 9 \cdots (3k)$ there are k factors, each a multiple of 3. Thus we arrive at

$$3 \cdot 6 \cdot 9 \cdots (3k) = 3^k(1 \cdot 2 \cdot 3 \cdots k) = 3^k k!.$$

Furthermore, all but the first two factors inside the square bracket in the numerator also appear in the denominator. With a little more argument, testing the terms $k = 0, 1, 2$, since the factors to be cancelled do not appear until $k > 2$, it can be shown that

$$(15) \qquad y = a_0 \sum_{k=0}^{\infty} \frac{4(-1)^k(x-1)^{3k}}{3^k(3k-1)(3k-4)k!} + a_1[(x-1) + \tfrac{1}{4}(x-1)^4].$$

In the exercises below, the equations are mostly homogeneous and of second order. Raising the order of the equation introduces nothing except additional labor, as can be seen by doing Ex. 16. A nonhomogeneous equation with right member having a power series expansion is theoretically no worse to handle than a homogeneous one; it is merely a matter of equating coefficients in two power series.

The treatment of equations leading to recurrence relations involving more than two different a's is left for Chapter 23.

Exercises

Unless it is otherwise requested, find the general solution valid near the origin. Always state the region of validity of the solution.

1. $y'' + 3xy' + 3y = 0.$

ANS. $y = a_0 \left[1 + \sum_{k=1}^{\infty} \frac{(-3)^k x^{2k}}{2^k k!} \right]$

$\qquad + a_1 \left[x + \sum_{k=1}^{\infty} \frac{(-3)^k x^{2k+1}}{3 \cdot 5 \cdot 7 \cdots (2k+1)} \right]$;

valid for all finite x.

2. $(1 + 4x^2)y'' - 8y = 0.$

ANS. $y = a_0(1 + 4x^2) + a_1 \sum_{k=0}^{\infty} \frac{(-1)^{k+1} 2^{2k} x^{2k+1}}{4k^2 - 1}$;

valid for $|x| < \tfrac{1}{2}$.

3. $(1 + x^2)y'' - 4xy' + 6y = 0.$

ANS. $y = a_0(1 - 3x^2) + a_1(x - \tfrac{1}{3}x^3)$;

valid for all finite x.

4. $(1 + x^2)y'' + 10xy' + 20y = 0.$

ANS. $y = \frac{a_0}{3} \sum_{k=0}^{\infty} (-1)^k(k+1)(2k+1)(2k+3)x^{2k}$

$\qquad + \frac{a_1}{6} \sum_{k=0}^{\infty} (-1)^k(k+1)(k+2)(2k+3)x^{2k+1}$;

valid for $|x| < 1$.

5. $(x^2 + 4)y'' + 2xy' - 12y = 0.$

ANS. $y = a_0\left[1 + \displaystyle\sum_{k=1}^{\infty} \frac{3(-1)^k(k+1)x^{2k}}{2^{2k}(2k-1)(2k-3)}\right]$

$+ a_1(x + \tfrac{5}{12}x^3);$ valid for $|x| < 2.$

6. $(x^2 - 9)y'' + 3xy' - 3y = 0.$

ANS. $y = a_0\left[1 - \displaystyle\sum_{k=1}^{\infty} \frac{[3 \cdot 5 \cdot 7 \cdots (2k+1)]x^{2k}}{(18)^k(2k-1)k!}\right]$

$+ a_1x;$ valid for $|x| < 3.$

7. $y'' + 2xy' + 5y = 0.$

ANS. $y = a_0\left[1 + \displaystyle\sum_{k=1}^{\infty} \frac{(-1)^k[5 \cdot 9 \cdot 13 \cdots (4k+1)]x^{2k}}{(2k)!}\right]$

$+ a_1\left[x + \displaystyle\sum_{k=1}^{\infty} \frac{(-1)^k[7 \cdot 11 \cdot 15 \cdots (4k+3)]x^{2k+1}}{(2k+1)!}\right];$

valid for all finite $x.$

8. $(x^2 + 4)y'' + 6xy' + 4y = 0.$

ANS. $y = a_0\left[1 + \displaystyle\sum_{k=1}^{\infty} \frac{(-1)^k(k+1)x^{2k}}{2^{2k}}\right]$

$+ a_1\left[x + \displaystyle\sum_{k=1}^{\infty} \frac{(-1)^k(2k+3)x^{2k+1}}{3 \cdot 2^{2k}}\right];$ valid for $|x| < 2.$

9. $2y'' + xy' - 4y = 0.$

ANS. $y = a_0(1 + x^2 + \tfrac{1}{12}x^4)$

$+ a_1 \displaystyle\sum_{k=0}^{\infty} \frac{3(-1)^k x^{2k+1}}{2^{2k}k!(2k-3)(2k-1)(2k+1)};$

valid for all finite $x.$

10. $(1 + 2x^2)y'' - 5xy' + 3y = 0.$

ANS. $y = a_0\left[1 + \displaystyle\sum_{k=1}^{\infty} \frac{3(-1)^k[(-1) \cdot 3 \cdot 7 \cdots (4k-5)]x^{2k}}{2^k k!(2k-3)(2k-1)}\right]$

$+ a_1(x + \tfrac{1}{3}x^3);$ valid for $|x| < 1/\sqrt{2}.$

11. $y'' + x^2y = 0.$

ANS. $y = a_0\left[1 + \displaystyle\sum_{k=1}^{\infty} \frac{(-1)^k x^{4k}}{2^{2k}k! \cdot 3 \cdot 7 \cdot 11 \cdots (4k-1)}\right]$

$+ a_1\left[x + \displaystyle\sum_{k=1}^{\infty} \frac{(-1)^k x^{4k+1}}{2^{2k}k! \cdot 5 \cdot 9 \cdot 13 \cdots (4k+1)}\right];$

valid for all finite $x.$

12. $y'' - 2(x + 3)y' - 3y = 0$. Solve about $x = -3$.

$$\text{ANS.} \quad y = a_0\left[1 + \sum_{k=1}^{\infty} \frac{3 \cdot 7 \cdot 11 \cdots (4k - 1)(x + 3)^{2k}}{(2k)!}\right]$$
$$+ a_1\left[(x + 3) + \sum_{k=1}^{\infty} \frac{5 \cdot 9 \cdot 13 \cdots (4k + 1)(x + 3)^{2k+1}}{(2k + 1)!}\right];$$

valid for all finite x.

13. $y'' + (x - 2)y = 0$. Solve about $x = 2$.

$$\text{ANS.} \quad y = a_0\left[1 + \sum_{k=1}^{\infty} \frac{(-1)^k(x - 2)^{3k}}{3^k k![2 \cdot 5 \cdot 8 \cdots (3k - 1)]}\right]$$
$$+ a_1\left[(x - 2) + \sum_{k=1}^{\infty} \frac{(-1)^k(x - 2)^{3k+1}}{3^k k![4 \cdot 7 \cdot 10 \cdots (3k + 1)]}\right];$$

valid for all finite x.

14. $(1 - 4x^2)y'' + 6xy' - 4y = 0$.

$$\text{ANS.} \quad y = a_0(1 + 2x^2) + a_1\left[x - \sum_{k=1}^{\infty} \frac{1 \cdot 5 \cdot 9 \cdots (4k - 3)x^{2k+1}}{k!(4k^2 - 1)}\right];$$

valid for $|x| < \frac{1}{2}$.

15. $(1 + 2x^2)y'' + 3xy' - 3y = 0$.

$$\text{ANS.} \quad y = a_1x + a_0\left[1 + \sum_{k=1}^{\infty} \frac{(-1)^{k+1} 3 \cdot 7 \cdot 11 \cdots (4k - 1)x^{2k}}{2^k(2k - 1)k!}\right];$$

valid for $|x| < 1/\sqrt{2}$.

16. $y''' + x^2y'' + 5xy' + 3y = 0$.

$$\text{ANS.} \quad y = a_0\left[1 + \sum_{k=1}^{\infty} \frac{(-1)^k x^{3k}}{2 \cdot 5 \cdot 8 \cdots (3k - 1)}\right]$$
$$+ a_1\left[x + \sum_{k=1}^{\infty} \frac{(-1)^k x^{3k+1}}{3^k k!}\right]$$
$$+ a_2\left[x^2 + \sum_{k=1}^{\infty} \frac{(-1)^k x^{3k+2}}{4 \cdot 7 \cdot 10 \cdots (3k + 1)}\right];$$

valid for all finite x.

17. $y'' + xy' + 3y = x^2$.

$$\text{ANS.} \quad y = -\tfrac{2}{15} + \tfrac{1}{5}x^2 + a_0 \sum_{k=0}^{\infty} \frac{(-1)^k(2k + 1)x^{2k}}{2^k k!}$$
$$+ a_1 \sum_{k=0}^{\infty} \frac{(-1)^k(k + 1)x^{2k+1}}{1 \cdot 3 \cdot 5 \cdots (2k + 1)};$$

valid for all finite x.

18. Solve the equation $y'' + y = 0$ both by series and by elementary methods and compare your answers.

19. Solve the equation $y'' - 4y = 0$ by series and by elementary methods.

20. $y'' + 2xy' + 2y = 0$.

21. $y'' + 3xy' + 7y = 0$.

22. $2y'' + 9xy' - 36y = 0$.

23. $(x^2 + 4)y'' + xy' - 9y = 0$.

24. $(x^2 + 4)y'' + 3xy' - 8y = 0$.

25. $(1 + 9x^2)y'' - 18y = 0$.

26. $(x^2 - 2x + 2)y'' - 4(x - 1)y' + 6y = 0$; solve about $x = 1$.

27. $(1 + 3x^2)y'' + 13xy' + 7y = 0$.

28. $(1 + 2x^2)y'' + 11xy' + 9y = 0$.

CHAPTER **21**

Solutions Near Regular
Singular Points

104. Regular singular points

Suppose that the point $x = x_0$ is a singular point of the equation

(1) $$b_0(x)y'' + b_1(x)y' + b_2(x)y = 0$$

with polynomial coefficients. Then $b_0(x_0) = 0$, so $b_0(x)$ has a factor $(x - x_0)$ to some power.

Let us put equation (1) into the form

(2) $$y'' + p(x)y' + q(x)y = 0.$$

Since $x = x_0$ is a singular point, and since $p(x)$ and $q(x)$ are rational functions of x, at least one (maybe both) of $p(x)$ and $q(x)$ has a denominator that contains the factor $(x - x_0)$.

If $x = x_0$ is a singular point of equation (2), and if the denominator of $p(x)$ does not contain the factor $(x - x_0)$ to a power higher than one, and if the denominator of $q(x)$ does not contain the factor $(x - x_0)$ to a power higher than two, then $x = x_0$ is called a *regular singular point* of equation (2).

If $x = x_0$ is a singular point but is not a regular singular point, then it is called an *irregular singular point*.

312

EXAMPLE (a): Classify the singular points, in the finite plane, of the equation

(3) $$x(x - 1)^2(x + 2)y'' + x^2y' - (x^3 + 2x - 1)y = 0.$$

For this equation

$$p(x) = \frac{x}{(x - 1)^2(x + 2)}$$

and

$$q(x) = \frac{-(x^3 + 2x - 1)}{x(x - 1)^2(x + 2)}.$$

The singular points in the finite plane are $x = 0, 1, -2$. Consider $x = 0$. The factor x is absent from the denominator of $p(x)$ and it appears to the first power in the denominator of $q(x)$. Hence $x = 0$ is a regular singular point of equation (3).

Now consider $x = 1$. The factor $(x - 1)$ appears to the second power in the denominator of $p(x)$. That is a higher power than is permitted in the definition of a regular singular point. Hence it does not matter how $(x - 1)$ appears in $q(x)$; the point $x = 1$ is an irregular singular point.

The factor $(x + 2)$ appears to the first power in the denominator of $p(x)$, just as high as is permitted, and to the first power also in the denominator of $q(x)$, so $x = -2$ is a regular singular point.

In summary, equation (3) has in the finite plane the following singular points: regular singular points at $x = 0$, $x = -2$; irregular singular point at $x = 1$. The methods of Section 125 will show that (3) has also an irregular singular point "at infinity."

EXAMPLE (b): Classify the singular points in the finite plane for the equation

$$x^4(x^2 + 1)(x - 1)^2y'' + 4x^3(x - 1)y' + (x + 1)y = 0.$$

Here

$$p(x) = \frac{4}{x(x^2 + 1)(x - 1)} = \frac{4}{x(x - i)(x + i)(x - 1)}$$

and

$$q(x) = \frac{x + 1}{x^4(x + i)(x - i)(x - 1)^2}.$$

Therefore the desired classification is:

R.S.P. at $x = i, -i, 1$; I.S.P. at $x = 0$.

Singular points of a linear equation of higher order are classified in much the same way. For instance, the singular point $x = x_0$ of the equation

$$y''' + p_1(x)y'' + p_2(x)y' + p_3(x)y = 0$$

is called regular if the factor $(x - x_0)$ does not appear in the denominator of $p_1(x)$ to a power higher than one, of $p_2(x)$ to a power higher than two, of $p_3(x)$ to a power higher than three. If it is not regular, a singular point is irregular.

This chapter is devoted to the solution of linear equations near regular singular points. Solutions near irregular singular points present a great deal more difficulty and are touched upon lightly in Chapter 23.

Exercises

For each equation, locate and classify all its singular points in the finite plane. (See Section 125 for the concept of a singular point "at infinity.")

1. $x^3(x - 1)y'' + (x - 1)y' + 4xy = 0$.

          ANS. R.S.P. at $x = 1$; I.S.P. at $x = 0$.

2. $x^2(x^2 - 4)y'' + 2x^3y' + 3y = 0$.

          ANS. R.S.P. at $x = 0, 2, -2$; no I.S.P.

3. $y'' + xy = 0$.   ANS. No S.P. (in the finite plane).

4. $x^2y'' + y = 0$.   ANS. R.S.P. at $x = 0$; no I.S.P.

5. $x^4y'' + y = 0$.   ANS. No R.S.P.; I.S.P. at $x = 0$.

6. $(x^2 + 1)(x - 4)^3y'' + (x - 4)^2y' + y = 0$.

          ANS. R.S.P. at $x = i, -i$; I.S.P. at $x = 4$.

7. $x^2(x - 2)y'' + 3(x - 2)y' + y = 0$.

          ANS. R.S.P. at $x = 2$; I.S.P. at $x = 0$.

8. $x^2(x - 4)^2y'' + 3xy' - (x - 4)y = 0$.

          ANS. R.S.P. at $x = 0$; I.S.P. at $x = 4$.

9. $x^2(x + 2)y'' + (x + 2)y' + 4y = 0$.

10. $x(x + 3)y'' + y' - y = 0$.

11. $x^3y'' + 4y = 0$.

12. $(x - 1)(x + 2)y'' + 5(x + 2)y' + x^2y = 0$.

13. $(1 + 4x^2)y'' + 6xy' - 9y = 0$.

14. $(1 + 4x^2)^2y'' + 6x(1 + 4x^2)y' - 9y = 0$.

15. $(1 + 4x^2)^2y'' + 6xy' - 9y = 0$.

16. $(x - 1)^2(x + 4)^2y'' + (x + 4)y' + 7y = 0$.

17. $(2x + 1)^4y'' + (2x + 1)y' - 8y = 0$.

18. $x^4y'' + 2x^3y' + 4y = 0$.

19. Ex. 1, p. 301.

105. The indicial equation

As in Chapter 20, whenever we wish to obtain solutions about a point other than $x = 0$, we first translate the origin to that point and then proceed with the usual technique. Hence we concentrate our attention on solutions valid about $x = 0$.

Let $x = 0$ be a regular singular point of the equation

$$(1) \qquad y'' + p(x)y' + q(x)y = 0$$

where p and q are rational functions of x. Then $p(x)$ cannot have in its denominator the factor x to a power higher than one. Therefore

$$p(x) = \frac{r(x)}{x}$$

where $r(x)$ is a rational function of x and $r(x)$ exists at $x = 0$. We know that such a rational function, this $r(x)$, has a power series expansion about $x = 0$. Then there exists the expansion

$$(2) \qquad p(x) = \frac{p_0}{x} + p_1 + p_2 x + p_3 x^2 + \cdots,$$

valid in some region surrounding $x = 0$.

By a similar argument we find that there exists an expansion

$$(3) \qquad q(x) = \frac{q_0}{x^2} + \frac{q_1}{x} + q_2 + q_3 x + q_4 x^2 + \cdots$$

about $x = 0$.

We shall see in a formal manner that it is reasonable to expect equation (1) to have a solution of the form

$$(4) \qquad y = \sum_{n=0}^{\infty} a_n x^{n+c} = a_0 x^c + a_1 x^{1+c} + a_2 x^{2+c} + \cdots$$

for properly chosen c and a_n's. The facts will be stated in the next section.

If we put the series for y, $p(x)$, and $q(x)$ into equation (1) and consider only the first few terms, we get

$$c(c-1)a_0 x^{c-2} + (1+c)ca_1 x^{c-1} + (2+c)(1+c)a_2 x^c + \cdots$$

$$+ \left[\frac{p_0}{x} + p_1 + p_2 x + \cdots\right]\left[ca_0 x^{c-1} + (1+c)a_1 x^c + (2+c)a_2 x^{1+c} + \cdots\right]$$

$$+ \left[\frac{q_0}{x^2} + \frac{q_1}{x} + q_2 + \cdots\right]\left[a_0 x^c + a_1 x^{1+c} + a_2 x^{2+c} + \cdots\right] = 0.$$

Performing the indicated multiplications, we find that we have

$$c(c-1)a_0 x^{c-2} + (1+c)ca_1 x^{c-1} + (2+c)(1+c)a_2 x^c + \cdots$$

$$+ p_0 c a_0 x^{c-2} + [p_0(1+c)a_1 + p_1 c a_0]x^{c-1} + \cdots + q_0 a_0 x^{c-2} +$$

$$[q_0 a_1 + q_1 a_0]x^{c-1} + \cdots = 0.$$

From the fact that the coefficient of x^{c-2} must vanish we obtain

$$(5) \qquad [c(c-1) + p_0 c + q_0]a_0 = 0.$$

We may insist that $a_0 \neq 0$ because a_0 is the coefficient of the lowest power of x appearing in the solution (4), no matter what that lowest power is. So from (5) it follows that

$$(6) \qquad c^2 + (p_0 - 1)c + q_0 = 0,$$

which is called the *indicial equation* (at $x = 0$). The p_0 and q_0 are known constants; equation (6) is a quadratic equation giving us two roots, $c = c_1$ and $c = c_2$.

To distinguish between the roots of the indicial equation, we shall denote by c_1 the root whose real part is not smaller than the real part of the other root. Thus, if the roots are real, $c_1 \geqq c_2$; if the roots are imaginary, $\text{Re}(c_1) \geqq \text{Re}(c_2)$. For brevity we call c_1 the "larger" root.

Superficially, it appears that there should be two solutions of the form (4), one from each of these values of c. In each solution the a_0 should be arbitrary and the succeeding a's should be determined by equating to zero the coefficients of the higher powers of $x(x^{c-1}, x^c, x^{1+c}, \text{etc.})$ in the identity just above equation (5).

This superficial conclusion is correct if the difference of the roots c_1 and c_2 is not integral. If that difference is integral, however, a logarithmic term may enter the solution. The reasons for this strange behavior will be made clear when we develop a method for obtaining the solutions.

106. Form and validity of the solutions near a regular singular point

Let $x = 0$ be a regular singular point of the equation

$$(1) \qquad y'' + p(x)y' + q(x)y = 0.$$

It can be proved that equation (1) always has a general solution either of the form

$$(2) \qquad y = A \sum_{n=0}^{\infty} a_n x^{n+c_1} + B \sum_{n=0}^{\infty} b_n x^{n+c_2}$$

or of the form

$$(3) \qquad y = (A + B \ln x) \sum_{n=0}^{\infty} a_n x^{n+c_1} + B \sum_{n=0}^{\infty} b_n x^{n+c_2}$$

in which A and B are arbitrary constants. Furthermore, it is proved that the infinite series which occur in the above forms of solution converge in at least the annular region bounded by two circles centered at $x = 0$, one of arbitrarily small radius, the other extending to the singular point (of the equation) nearest $x = 0$.

107. Indicial equation with difference of roots nonintegral

The equation

$$(1) \qquad 2xy'' + (1 + x)y' - 2y = 0$$

has a regular singular point at $x = 0$ and no other singular points for finite x. Let us assume that there is a solution of the form

$$(2) \qquad y = \sum_{n=0}^{\infty} a_n x^{n+c}.$$

Direct substitution of this y into equation (1) yields

$$\sum_{n=0}^{\infty} 2(n + c)(n + c - 1)a_n x^{n+c-1} + \sum_{n=0}^{\infty} (n + c)a_n x^{n+c-1}$$

$$+ \sum_{n=0}^{\infty} (n + c)a_n x^{n+c} - 2 \sum_{n=0}^{\infty} a_n x^{n+c} = 0,$$

or

$$(3) \quad \sum_{n=0}^{\infty} (n + c)(2n + 2c - 1)a_n x^{n+c-1} + \sum_{n=0}^{\infty} (n + c - 2)a_n x^{n+c} = 0.$$

Having collected like terms, we next shift index to bring all the exponents of x down to the smallest one present. This choice is used to get a recurrence relation for a_n rather than one for a_{n+1} or some other a. In equation (3), we replace the index n in the second summation by $(n - 1)$, thus getting

$$(4) \quad \sum_{n=0}^{\infty} (n + c)(2n + 2c - 1)a_n x^{n+c-1} + \sum_{n=1}^{\infty} (n + c - 3)a_{n-1} x^{n+c-1} = 0.$$

Once more we reason that the total coefficient of each power of x in the left member of (4) must vanish. The second summation does not start its contribution until $n = 1$. Hence the equations for the determination of c and the a's are

$$n = 0: \quad c(2c - 1)a_0 = 0,$$
$$n \geq 1: \quad (n + c)(2n + 2c - 1)a_n + (n + c - 3)a_{n-1} = 0.$$

Since we may without loss of generality assume $a_0 \neq 0$, the indicial equation, that which determines c, is

$$(5) \qquad\qquad c(2c - 1) = 0.$$

The indicial equation always comes from the $n = 0$ term when the technique being presented in this book is employed.

From (5) we see that $c_1 = \frac{1}{2}$ and $c_2 = 0$. The difference of the roots is $s = c_1 - c_2 = \frac{1}{2}$, which is nonintegral. When s is not an integer, the method we are using always gives two linearly independent solutions of the form (2), one with each choice of c.

Let us return to the recurrence relation using the value $c = c_1 = \frac{1}{2}$. We have

$$n \geq 1: \quad (n + \tfrac{1}{2})(2n + 1 - 1)a_n + (n + \tfrac{1}{2} - 3)a_{n-1} = 0,$$

$$n \geq 1: \quad a_n = -\frac{(2n - 5)a_{n-1}}{2n(2n + 1)}.$$

As usual we use a vertical array and then form the product to get a formula for a_n. We have

$$a_0 \ arb.$$

$$a_1 = -\frac{(-3)a_0}{2\cdot 3}$$

$$a_2 = -\frac{(-1)a_1}{4\cdot 5}$$

$$a_3 = -\frac{(1)a_2}{6\cdot 7}$$

$$\cdot$$
$$\cdot$$
$$\cdot$$

$$a_n = -\frac{(2n-5)a_{n-1}}{2n(2n+1)},$$

so the product yields, for $n \geq 1$,

$$(6) \qquad a_n = \frac{(-1)^n[(-3)(-1)(1)\ \cdots\ (2n-5)]a_0}{[2\cdot 4\cdot 6\ \cdots\ (2n)][3\cdot 5\cdot 7\ \cdots\ (2n+1)]}.$$

The formula (6) may be simplified to the form

$$(7) \qquad a_n = \frac{(-1)^n\cdot 3a_0}{2^n n!(2n-3)(2n-1)(2n+1)}.$$

Using $a_0 = 1$, the a_n from (7), and the pertinent value of c, $c_1 = \frac{1}{2}$, we may now write a particular solution. It is

$$(8) \qquad y_1 = x^{\frac{1}{2}} + \sum_{n=1}^{\infty} \frac{(-1)^n 3 x^{n+\frac{1}{2}}}{2^n n!(2n-3)(2n-1)(2n+1)}.$$

The notation y_1 is to emphasize that this particular solution corresponds to the root c_1 of the indicial equation. Our next task will be to get a particular solution y_2 corresponding to the smaller root c_2. Then the general solution, if it is desired, may be written at once as

$$y = Ay_1 + By_2$$

with A and B arbitrary constants.

In returning to the recurrence relation just above the indicial equation (5) with the intention of using $c = c_2 = 0$, it is evident that the a's will be different from those with $c = c_1$. Hence it is wise to change notation. Let us use b's instead of a's. With $c = 0$, the recurrence relation becomes $n \geq 1$: $n(2n-1)b_n + (n-3)b_{n-1} = 0$.

The corresponding vertical array is:

$$\begin{array}{c} b_0 \ arb. \\ \hline \end{array}$$

$$b_1 = -\frac{(-2)b_0}{1\cdot 1}$$

$$b_2 = -\frac{(-1)b_1}{2\cdot 3}$$

$$b_3 = -\frac{(0)b_2}{3\cdot 5}$$

$$\cdot$$
$$\cdot$$
$$\cdot$$

$$b_n = -\frac{(n-3)b_{n-1}}{n(2n-1)}.$$

Then $b_n = 0$ for $n \geq 3$ and, using $b_0 = 1$, b_1 and b_2 may be computed and found to have the values $b_1 = 2$ and $b_2 = \frac{1}{6}b_1 = \frac{1}{3}$. Therefore a second solution is

$$(9) \qquad\qquad y_2 = 1 + 2x + \tfrac{1}{3}x^2.$$

Since the differential equation has no singular point, other than $x = 0$, in the finite plane, we conclude that the linearly independent solutions y_1 of (8) and y_2 of (9) are valid at least for $|x| > 0$. The validity of (9) is evident in this particular example because the series terminates.

The student should associate with each solution the region of validity guaranteed by the general theorem quoted in Section 106, though from now on the printed answers to the exercises will omit statement of the region of validity.

Exercises

For each equation, obtain two linearly independent solutions valid near the origin. Always state the region of validity of each solution that you obtain.

1. $2x(x-1)y'' + 3(x-1)y' - y = 0.$

ANS. $y_1 = 1 - \displaystyle\sum_{n=1}^{\infty} \frac{x^n}{4n^2-1}$; $y_2 = x^{-\frac{1}{2}} - x^{\frac{1}{2}}.$

2. $4xy'' + 3y' - 3y = 0.$

ANS. $y_1 = x^{\frac{1}{4}} + \displaystyle\sum_{n=1}^{\infty} \frac{(-3)^n x^{n+\frac{1}{4}}}{n!5\cdot 9\cdot 13\cdots(4n+1)}$;

$$y_2 = 1 + \sum_{n=1}^{\infty} \frac{(-3)^n x^n}{n!\,3 \cdot 7 \cdot 11 \cdots (4n-1)} \cdot$$

3. $2x^2(x+1)y'' + x(7x-1)y' + y = 0.$

ANS. $\quad y_1 = x + \frac{1}{15} \sum_{n=1}^{\infty} (-1)^n(2n+3)(2n+5)x^{n+1};$

$$y_2 = x^{\frac{1}{2}} + \frac{1}{2} \sum_{n=1}^{\infty} (-1)^n(n+1)(n+2)x^{n+\frac{1}{2}}.$$

4. $2xy'' + 5(1+2x)y' + 5y = 0.$

ANS. $\quad y_1 = 1 + \sum_{n=1}^{\infty} \frac{3(-5)^n x^n}{n!(2n+1)(2n+3)};$

$$y_2 = x^{-\frac{3}{2}} - 10x^{-\frac{1}{2}}.$$

5. $8x^2y'' + 10xy' - (1+x)y = 0.$

ANS. $\quad y_1 = x^{\frac{1}{4}} + \sum_{n=1}^{\infty} \frac{x^{n+\frac{1}{4}}}{2^n n!\,7 \cdot 11 \cdot 15 \cdots (4n+3)};$

$$y_2 = x^{-\frac{1}{2}} + \sum_{n=1}^{\infty} \frac{x^{n-\frac{1}{2}}}{2^n n!\,1 \cdot 5 \cdot 9 \cdots (4n-3)} \cdot$$

6. $3xy'' + (2-x)y' - 2y = 0.$

ANS. $\quad y_1 = \sum_{n=0}^{\infty} \frac{(3n+4)x^{n+\frac{1}{3}}}{4 \cdot 3^n n!};$

$$y_2 = 1 + \sum_{n=1}^{\infty} \frac{(n+1)x^n}{2 \cdot 5 \cdot 8 \cdots (3n-1)} \cdot$$

7. $2x(x+3)y'' - 3(x+1)y' + 2y = 0.$

ANS. $\quad y_1 = x^{\frac{5}{2}} + \sum_{n=1}^{\infty} \frac{(-1)^{n+1}x^{n+\frac{5}{2}}}{3^{n-1}(2n-1)(2n+1)(2n+3)};$

$$y_2 = 1 + \frac{2}{3}x + \frac{1}{9}x^2.$$

8. $2x^2y'' - x(2x+1)y' + (1-5x)y = 0.$

ANS. $\quad y_1 = x + \frac{1}{15} \sum_{n=1}^{\infty} \frac{(2n+3)(2n+5)x^{n+1}}{n!};$

$$y_2 = x^{\frac{1}{2}} + \sum_{n=1}^{\infty} \frac{2^{n-1}(n+1)(n+2)x^{n+\frac{1}{2}}}{1 \cdot 3 \cdot 5 \cdots (2n-1)} \cdot$$

9. $9x^2y'' + 3x(x+3)y' - (1+4x)y = 0.$

ANS. $\quad y_1 = x^{\frac{1}{3}} + \frac{1}{5}x^{\frac{4}{3}};$

$$y_2 = x^{-\frac{1}{3}} + \sum_{n=1}^{\infty} \frac{10(-1)^n x^{n-\frac{1}{3}}}{3^n n!(3n-5)(3n-2)} \cdot$$

10. $2xy'' + (1 - 2x^2)y' - 4xy = 0.$

$$\text{ANS.} \quad y_1 = \sum_{k=0}^{\infty} \frac{x^{2k+\frac{1}{2}}}{2^k k!} = x^{\frac{1}{2}} e^{x^2/2};$$

$$y_2 = 1 + \sum_{k=1}^{\infty} \frac{2^k x^{2k}}{3 \cdot 7 \cdot 11 \cdots (4k - 1)}.$$

11. $x(4 - x)y'' + (2 - x)y' + 4y = 0.$

$$\text{ANS.} \quad y_1 = x^{\frac{1}{2}} + \sum_{n=1}^{\infty} \frac{(2n + 3)[(-3)(-1) \cdot 1 \cdots (2n - 5)]x^{n+\frac{1}{2}}}{3 \cdot 2^{3n} n!};$$

$$y_2 = 1 - 2x + \tfrac{1}{2}x^2.$$

12. $3x^2y'' + xy' - (1 + x)y = 0.$

$$\text{ANS.} \quad y_1 = x + \sum_{n=1}^{\infty} \frac{x^{n+1}}{n!7 \cdot 10 \cdot 13 \cdots (3n + 4)};$$

$$y_2 = x^{-\frac{1}{3}} + \sum_{n=1}^{\infty} \frac{x^{n-\frac{1}{3}}}{n!(-1) \cdot 2 \cdot 5 \cdots (3n - 4)}.$$

13. $2xy'' + (1 + 2x)y' + 4y = 0.$

$$\text{ANS.} \quad y_1 = \sum_{n=0}^{\infty} \frac{(-1)^n(2n + 3)x^{n+\frac{1}{2}}}{3 \cdot n!};$$

$$y_2 = 1 + \sum_{n=1}^{\infty} \frac{(-1)^n 2^n (n + 1)x^n}{1 \cdot 3 \cdot 5 \cdots (2n - 1)}.$$

14. $2xy'' + (1 + 2x)y' - 5y = 0.$

$$\text{ANS.} \quad y_1 = x^{\frac{1}{2}} + \tfrac{4}{3}x^{\frac{3}{2}} + \tfrac{4}{15}x^{\frac{5}{2}};$$

$$y_2 = \sum_{n=0}^{\infty} \frac{15(-1)^{n+1}x^n}{n!(2n - 5)(2n - 3)(2n - 1)}.$$

15. $2x^2y'' - 3x(1 - x)y' + 2y = 0.$

$$\text{ANS.} \quad y_1 = x^2 + \sum_{n=1}^{\infty} \frac{(-1)^n 3^n(n + 1)x^{n+2}}{5 \cdot 7 \cdot 9 \cdots (2n + 3)};$$

$$y_2 = x^{\frac{1}{2}} + \sum_{n=1}^{\infty} \frac{(-1)^{n+1} 3^n(2n - 1)x^{n+\frac{1}{2}}}{2^n n!}.$$

16. $2x^2y'' + x(4x - 1)y' + 2(3x - 1)y = 0.$

$$\text{ANS.} \quad y_1 = \sum_{n=0}^{\infty} \frac{(-1)^n 2^n x^{n+2}}{n!} = x^2 e^{-2x};$$

$$y_2 = x^{-\frac{1}{2}} + \sum_{n=1}^{\infty} \frac{(-1)^n 4^n x^{n-\frac{1}{2}}}{(-3)(-1) \cdot 1 \cdots (2n - 5)}.$$

17. $2xy'' - (1 + 2x^2)y' - xy = 0.$

ANS. $y_1 = x^{\frac{3}{2}} + \displaystyle\sum_{k=1}^{\infty} \frac{2^k x^{2k+\frac{3}{2}}}{7 \cdot 11 \cdot 15 \cdots (4k+3)};$

$$y_2 = 1 + \sum_{k=1}^{\infty} \frac{x^{2k}}{2^k k!} = \exp\left(\tfrac{1}{2}x^2\right).$$

18. The equation of Ex. 17 above has a particular solution $y_2 = \exp\left(\tfrac{1}{2}x^2\right)$ obtained by the series method. Make a change of dependent variable in the differential equation, using $y = v \exp\left(\tfrac{1}{2}x^2\right)$ (the device of Section 84), and thus obtain the general solution in "closed form."

ANS. $y = c_1 \exp\left(\tfrac{1}{2}x^2\right) + c_2 \exp\left(\tfrac{1}{2}x^2\right) \displaystyle\int_0^x \beta^{\frac{1}{2}} \exp\left(-\tfrac{1}{2}\beta^2\right) d\beta.$

In Exs. 19–22, use the power series method. What is causing the recurrence relations to degenerate into one-term relations?

19. $2x^2y'' + xy' - y = 0.$ ANS. $y_1 = x; y_2 = x^{-\frac{1}{2}}.$
20. $2x^2y'' - 3xy' + 2y = 0.$ ANS. $y_1 = x^2; y_2 = x^{\frac{1}{2}}.$
21. $9x^2y'' + 2y = 0.$ ANS. $y_1 = x^{\frac{2}{3}}; y_2 = x^{\frac{1}{3}}.$
22. $2x^2y'' + 5xy' - 2y = 0.$ ANS. $y_1 = x^{\frac{1}{2}}; y_2 = x^{-2}.$

23. Obtain $\dfrac{dy}{dx}$ and $\dfrac{d^2y}{dx^2}$ in terms of derivatives of y with respect to a new independent variable t related to x by $t = \ln x.$

ANS. $\dfrac{dy}{dx} = e^{-t}\dfrac{dy}{dt}, \qquad \dfrac{d^2y}{dx^2} = e^{-2t}\left[\dfrac{d^2y}{dt^2} - \dfrac{dy}{dt}\right].$

24. Use the result of Ex. 23 above to show that the change of independent variable from x to t, where $t = \ln x$, transforms the equation*

$$ax^2 \frac{d^2y}{dx^2} + bx \frac{dy}{dx} + cy = 0,$$

a, b, c constants, into a linear equation with constant coefficients.

Solve Exs. 25–34 by the method implied by Ex. 24 above; that is, by changing independent variable to $t = \ln x.$

25. Ex. 19.   **26.** Ex. 20.
27. Ex. 21.   **28.** Ex. 22.
29. $x^2y'' + 2xy' - 12y = 0.$ ANS. $y_1 = x^3; y_2 = x^{-4}.$
30. $x^2y'' + xy' - 9y = 0.$ ANS. $y_1 = x^3; y_2 = x^{-3}.$

* An equation such as the one of this exercise, which contains only terms of the kind $cx^k D^k y$ with c constant and $k = 0, 1, 2, 3, \cdots$, is called an equation of *Cauchy type*, or of *Euler type*.

31. $x^2y'' - 3xy' + 4y = 0.$ ANS. $y = x^2(c_1 + c_2 \ln x).$

32. $x^2y'' - 5xy' + 9y = 0.$ ANS. $y = x^3(c_1 + c_2 \ln x).$

33. $x^2y'' + 5xy' + 5y = 0.$ ANS. $y = x^{-2}[c_1 \cos(\ln x) + c_2 \sin(\ln x)].$

34. $(x^3D^3 + 4x^2D^2 - 8xD + 8)y = 0.$ You will need to extend the result of Ex. 23 to the third derivative, obtaining

$$x^3 \frac{d^3y}{dx^3} = \frac{d^3y}{dt^3} - 3\frac{d^2y}{dt^2} + 2\frac{dy}{dt}.$$ ANS. $y = c_1x + c_2x^2 + c_3x^{-4}.$

108. Differentiation of a product of functions

It will soon prove necessary for us to differentiate efficiently a product of a number of functions. Suppose that

$$(1) \qquad\qquad u = u_1u_2u_3 \cdots u_n,$$

each of the u's being a function of the parameter c. Let differentiation with respect to c be indicated by primes. Then from

$$\ln u = \ln u_1 + \ln u_2 + \ln u_3 + \cdots + \ln u_n$$

it follows that

$$\frac{u'}{u} = \frac{u_1'}{u_1} + \frac{u_2'}{u_2} + \frac{u_3'}{u_3} + \cdots + \frac{u_n'}{u_n}.$$

Hence

$$(2) \qquad\qquad u' = u\left\{\frac{u_1'}{u_1} + \frac{u_2'}{u_2} + \frac{u_3'}{u_3} + \cdots + \frac{u_n'}{u_n}\right\}.$$

Thus to differentiate a product we may multiply the original product by a conversion factor (which converts the product into its derivative) consisting of the sum of the derivatives of the logarithms of the separate factors.

When the factors involved are themselves powers of polynomials, there is a convenient way of forming mentally the conversion factor. That factor is the sum of the conversion factors for the individual parts.

The way most of us learned to differentiate a power of a quantity is to multiply the exponent, the derivative of the original quantity, and the quantity with its exponent lowered by one. Thus, if

$$y = (ac + b)^k,$$

then

$$\frac{dy}{dc} = y\left\{\frac{ka}{ac + b}\right\},$$

the division by $(ac + b)$ converting $(ac + b)^k$ into $(ac + b)^{k-1}$.

EXAMPLE (a): If

$$u = \frac{c^2(c + 1)}{(4c - 1)^3(7c + 2)^6},$$

then

$$\frac{du}{dc} = u \left\{ \frac{2}{c} + \frac{1}{c + 1} - \frac{12}{4c - 1} - \frac{42}{7c + 2} \right\}.$$

Note that the denominator factors in the function u are thought of as numerator factors with negative exponents.

EXAMPLE (b): If

$$y = \frac{c + n}{c(c + 1)(c + 2) \cdots (c + n - 1)},$$

then

$$\frac{dy}{dc} = y \left\{ \frac{1}{c + n} - \frac{1}{c} - \frac{1}{c + 1} - \frac{1}{c + 2} - \cdots - \frac{1}{c + n - 1} \right\}.$$

EXAMPLE (c): If

$$w = \frac{2^n c^3}{[(c + 2)(c + 3) \cdots (c + n + 1)]^2},$$

then

$$\frac{dw}{dc} = w \left\{ \frac{3}{c} - 2 \left(\frac{1}{c + 2} + \frac{1}{c + 3} + \cdots + \frac{1}{c + n + 1} \right) \right\}.$$

109. Indicial equation with equal roots

When the indicial equation has equal roots, the method of Section 107 cannot yield two linearly independent solutions. The work with one value of c would be a pure repetition of that with the other value of c. A new attack is needed.

Consider the problem of solving the equation

(1) $x^2y'' + 3xy' + (1 - 2x)y = 0$

about the regular singular point $x = 0$. It will turn out that the roots of the indicial equation are equal, a fact which can be determined ahead of time by setting up the indicial equation as developed in the theory, page 316. Here

$$p(x) = \frac{3}{x}, \qquad q(x) = \frac{1 - 2x}{x^2},$$

so $p_0 = 3$ and $q_0 = 1$. The indicial equation is

$$c^2 + 2c + 1 = 0,$$

with roots $c_1 = c_2 = -1$.

Any attempt to obtain solutions by putting

(2)
$$y = \sum_{n=0}^{\infty} a_n x^{n+c}$$

into equation (1) is certain to force us to choose $c = -1$ and thus get only one solution. We know that we must not choose c yet if we are to get two solutions. Hence let us put the y of equation (2) into the left member of equation (1) and try to come as close as we can to making that left member zero without choosing c.

It is convenient to have a notation for the left member of equation (1); let us use

(3)
$$L(y) = x^2 y'' + 3xy' + (1 - 2x)y.$$

For the y of equation (2) we find that

$$L(y) = \sum_{n=0}^{\infty} (n+c)(n+c-1)a_n x^{n+c} + \sum_{n=0}^{\infty} 3(n+c)a_n x^{n+c}$$
$$+ \sum_{n=0}^{\infty} a_n x^{n+c} - \sum_{n=0}^{\infty} 2a_n x^{n+c+1},$$

from which

$$L(y) = \sum_{n=0}^{\infty} [(n+c)^2 + 2(n+c) + 1]a_n x^{n+c} - \sum_{n=0}^{\infty} 2a_n x^{n+c+1}.$$

The usual simplifications lead to

(4)
$$L(y) = \sum_{n=0}^{\infty} (n+c+1)^2 a_n x^{n+c} - \sum_{n=1}^{\infty} 2a_{n-1} x^{n+c}.$$

Recalling that the indicial equation comes from setting the coefficient in the $n = 0$ term equal to zero, we purposely avoid trying to make that term vanish yet. But by choosing the a's and leaving c as a parameter we can make every term but that first one in $L(y)$ vanish. Therefore we set equal to zero each coefficient, except for the $n = 0$ term, of the various powers of x on the right in equation (4); thus

(5)
$$n \geq 1: \quad (n+c+1)^2 a_n - 2a_{n-1} = 0.$$

The successive application of the recurrence relation (5) will determine each a_n, $n \geq 1$, in terms of a_0 and c. Indeed, from the array

$$a_1 = \frac{2a_0}{(c + 2)^2}$$

$$a_2 = \frac{2a_1}{(c + 3)^2}$$

$$\cdot$$
$$\cdot$$
$$\cdot$$

$$a_n = \frac{2a_{n-1}}{(c + n + 1)^2},$$

it follows by the usual multiplication device that

$$n \geq 1: \quad a_n = \frac{2^n a_0}{[(c + 2)(c + 3) \cdots (c + n + 1)]^2}.$$

To arrive at a specific solution, let us choose $a_0 = 1$.

Using the a's determined above, we write a y which is dependent
upon both x and c, namely,

$$(6) \qquad y(x, c) = x^c + \sum_{n=1}^{\infty} a_n(c) x^{n+c},$$

in which

$$(7) \qquad n \geq 1: \quad a_n(c) = \frac{2^n}{[(c + 2)(c + 3) \cdots (c + n + 1)]^2}.$$

The y of equation (6) has been so determined that for that y the right
member of equation (4) must reduce to a single term, the $n = 0$ term.
That is, for the $y(x, c)$ of equation (6), we have

$$(8) \qquad L[y(x, c)] = (c + 1)^2 x^c.$$

A solution of the original differential equation is a function y for
which $L(y) = 0$. Now we see why the choice $c = -1$ yields a solution;
it makes the right member of equation (8) zero.

But the factor $(c + 1)$ occurs squared in equation (8), an automatic
consequence of the equality of the roots of the indicial equation. We
know from elementary calculus that if a function contains a power
of a certain factor, dependent upon c, then the derivative with respect
to c of that function contains the same factor to a power one lower than
in the original.

For equation (8), in particular, differentiation of each member with respect to c yields

(9)　　$\dfrac{\partial}{\partial c} L[y(x, c)] = L\left[\dfrac{\partial y(x, c)}{\partial c}\right] = 2(c + 1)x^c + (c + 1)^2 x^c \ln x,$

the right member containing the factor $(c + 1)$ to the first power, as we knew it must from the theorem quoted.

In (9), the order of differentiations with respect to x and c was interchanged. It is best to avoid the need for justifying such steps by verifying the solutions, (13) and (14) below, directly. The verification in this instance is straightforward but a bit lengthy and is omitted here.

From equations (8) and (9) it can be seen that two solutions of the equation $L(y) = 0$ are

$$y_1 = [y(x, c)]_{c=-1} = y(x, -1)$$

and

$$y_2 = \left[\dfrac{\partial y(x, c)}{\partial c}\right]_{c=-1}$$

because $c = -1$ makes the right member of each of equations (8) and (9) vanish. That y_1 and y_2 are linearly independent will be evident later.

We have

(6)　　　　　　　　$y(x, c) = x^c + \displaystyle\sum_{n=1}^{\infty} a_n(c) x^{n+c}$

and we need $\partial y(x, c)/\partial c$. From (6) it follows that

$$\dfrac{\partial y(x, c)}{\partial c} = x^c \ln x + \sum_{n=1}^{\infty} a_n(c) x^{n+c} \ln x + \sum_{n=1}^{\infty} a_n'(c) x^{n+c},$$

which simplifies at once to the form

(10)　　　　　　$\dfrac{\partial y(x, c)}{\partial c} = y(x, c) \ln x + \displaystyle\sum_{n=1}^{\infty} a_n'(c) x^{n+c}.$

The solutions y_1 and y_2 will be obtained by putting $c = -1$ in equations (6) and (10); that is,

(11)　　　　　　　$y_1 = x^{-1} + \displaystyle\sum_{n=1}^{\infty} a_n(-1) x^{n-1},$

(12)　　　　　　　$y_2 = y_1 \ln x + \displaystyle\sum_{n=1}^{\infty} a_n'(-1) x^{n-1}.$

Therefore we need to evaluate $a_n(c)$ and $a_n'(c)$ at $c = -1$. We know that

$$a_n(c) = \frac{2^n}{[(c + 2)(c + 3) \cdots (c + n + 1)]^2},$$

from which by the method of Section 108 we obtain immediately

$$a_n'(c) = -2a_n(c) \left\{ \frac{1}{c + 2} + \frac{1}{c + 3} + \cdots + \frac{1}{c + n + 1} \right\}.$$

We now use $c = -1$ to obtain

$$a_n(-1) = \frac{2^n}{(n!)^2}$$

and

$$a_n'(-1) = -2 \cdot \frac{2^n}{(n!)^2} \left\{ 1 + \tfrac{1}{2} + \tfrac{1}{3} + \cdots + \tfrac{1}{n} \right\}.$$

A frequently used notation for a partial sum of the harmonic series is useful here. It is

$$H_n = 1 + \frac{1}{2} + \frac{1}{3} + \cdots + \frac{1}{n} = \sum_{k=1}^{n} \frac{1}{k}.$$

We can now write $a_n'(-1)$ more simply as

$$a_n'(-1) = -\frac{2^{n+1}H_n}{(n!)^2}.$$

Finally, the desired solutions can be written in the form

(13)
$$y_1 = x^{-1} + \sum_{n=1}^{\infty} \frac{2^n x^{n-1}}{(n!)^2}$$

and

(14)
$$y_2 = y_1 \ln x - \sum_{n=1}^{\infty} \frac{2^{n+1}H_n x^{n-1}}{(n!)^2}.$$

The general solution, valid for all finite $x \neq 0$, is

$$y = Ay_1 + By_2,$$

with A and B arbitrary constants. The linear independence of y_1 and y_2 should be evident because of the presence of $\ln x$ in y_2. In detail, xy_1 has a power series expansion about $x = 0$, but xy_2 does not, so they cannot be proportional.

Examination of the procedure used in solving this differential equation shows that the method is in no way dependent upon the specific coefficients except that the indicial equation has equal roots. That is, the success of the method is due to the fact that the $n = 0$ term in $L(y)$ contains a square factor.

When the indicial equation has equal roots, $c_2 = c_1$, then two linearly independent solutions will always appear in the form

$$y_1 = x^{c_1} + \sum_{n=1}^{\infty} a_n x^{n+c_1},$$

$$y_2 = y_1 \ln x + \sum_{n=1}^{\infty} b_n x^{n+c_1},$$

where c_1, a_n, b_n are dependent upon the coefficients in the particular equation being solved.

Exercises

Obtain two linearly independent solutions valid about $x = 0$ unless otherwise instructed.

1. $x^2 y'' - x(1 + x)y' + y = 0$.

ANS. $y_1 = \sum_{n=0}^{\infty} \dfrac{x^{n+1}}{n!} = xe^x$; $y_2 = y_1 \ln x - \sum_{n=1}^{\infty} \dfrac{H_n x^{n+1}}{n!}$.

2. $4x^2 y'' + (1 - 2x)y = 0$.

ANS. $y_1 = \sum_{n=0}^{\infty} \dfrac{x^{n+\frac{1}{2}}}{2^n (n!)^2}$; $y_2 = y_1 \ln x - \sum_{n=1}^{\infty} \dfrac{H_n x^{n+\frac{1}{2}}}{2^{n-1}(n!)^2}$.

3. $x^2 y'' + x(x - 3)y' + 4y = 0$.

ANS. $y_1 = \sum_{n=0}^{\infty} \dfrac{(-1)^n (n + 1)x^{n+2}}{n!}$;

$y_2 = y_1 \ln x + \sum_{n=1}^{\infty} \dfrac{(-1)^{n+1}[n + (n + 1)H_n]x^{n+2}}{n!}$.

4. $x^2 y'' + 3xy' + (1 + 4x^2)y = 0$.

ANS. $y_1 = \sum_{k=0}^{\infty} \dfrac{(-1)^k x^{2k-1}}{(k!)^2}$;

$y_2 = y_1 \ln x - \sum_{k=1}^{\infty} \dfrac{(-1)^k H_k x^{2k-1}}{(k!)^2}$.

5. $x(1 + x)y'' + (1 + 5x)y' + 3y = 0.$

ANS. $y_1 = 1 + \frac{1}{2} \sum_{n=1}^{\infty} (-1)^n (n+1)(n+2)x^n;$

$y_2 = y_1 \ln x - \frac{3}{2}(y_1 - 1) + \frac{1}{2} \sum_{n=1}^{\infty} (-1)^n (2n+3)x^n.$

6. $xy'' + y' + xy = 0.$ This is known as Bessel's equation of index zero. It is widely encountered in both pure and applied mathematics. (See also Sections 117 and 118.)

ANS. $y_1 = \sum_{k=0}^{\infty} \frac{(-1)^k x^{2k}}{2^{2k}(k!)^2};$

$y_2 = y_1 \ln x - \sum_{k=1}^{\infty} \frac{(-1)^k H_k x^{2k}}{2^{2k}(k!)^2}.$

7. $x^2 y'' - x(1 + 3x)y' + (1 - 6x)y = 0.$

ANS. $y_1 = \sum_{n=0}^{\infty} \frac{3^n (n+1)(n+2)x^{n+1}}{2 \cdot n!};$

$y_2 = y_1 \ln x + \sum_{n=1}^{\infty} \frac{3^n (n+1)(n+2)(H_{n+2} - 2H_n - \frac{3}{2})x^{n+1}}{2 \cdot n!}.$

8. $x^2 y'' + x(x - 1)y' + (1 - x)y = 0.$

ANS. $y_1 = x; \ y_2 = y_1 \ln x + \sum_{n=1}^{\infty} \frac{(-1)^n x^{n+1}}{n \cdot n!}.$

9. $x(x - 2)y'' + 2(x - 1)y' - 2y = 0.$

ANS. $y_1 = 1 - x; \ y_2 = y_1 \ln x + \frac{5}{2}x - \sum_{n=2}^{\infty} \frac{(n+1)x^n}{2^n n(n-1)}.$

10. Solve the equation of Ex. 9 about the point $x = 2.$

ANS. $y_1 = 1 + (x - 2);$

$y_2 = y_1 \ln (x - 2) - \frac{5}{2}(x - 2) - \sum_{n=2}^{\infty} \frac{(-1)^n (n+1)(x-2)^n}{2^n n(n-1)}.$

11. Solve about $x = 4$: $4(x - 4)^2 y'' + (x - 4)(x - 8)y' + xy = 0.$

ANS. $y_1 = \sum_{n=0}^{\infty} \frac{(-1)^n (n+1)(x-4)^{n+1}}{2^{2n} n!};$

$y_2 = y_1 \ln (x - 4) + \sum_{n=1}^{\infty} \frac{(-1)^n (n+1)(H_{n+1} - 2H_n - 1)(x-4)^{n+1}}{2^{2n} n!}.$

12. $xy'' + (1 - x^2)y' - xy = 0.$

$$\text{ANS.} \quad y_1 = 1 + \sum_{k=1}^{\infty} \frac{1 \cdot 3 \cdot 5 \cdots (2k-1)x^{2k}}{2^{2k}(k!)^2} ;$$

$$y_2 = y_1 \ln x$$

$$+ \sum_{k=1}^{\infty} \frac{1 \cdot 3 \cdot 5 \cdots (2k-1) \left\{ 1 + \frac{1}{3} + \cdots + \frac{1}{2k-1} - H_k \right\} x^{2k}}{2^{2k}(k!)^2} .$$

13. Show that

$$1 + \tfrac{1}{3} + \tfrac{1}{5} + \cdots + \frac{1}{2k-1} = H_{2k} - \tfrac{1}{2}H_k$$

and apply the result to simplification of the formula for y_2 in the answer to Ex. 12.

14. $x^2y'' + x(3 + 2x)y' + (1 + 3x)y = 0$. In simplifying y_2, use the formula given in Ex. 13.

$$\text{ANS.} \quad y_1 = x^{-1} + \sum_{n=1}^{\infty} \frac{(-1)^n 1 \cdot 3 \cdot 5 \cdots (2n-1)x^{n-1}}{(n!)^2} ;$$

$$y_2 = y_1 \ln x + \sum_{n=1}^{\infty} \frac{(-1)^n 1 \cdot 3 \cdot 5 \cdots (2n-1)(2H_{2n} - 3H_n)x^{n-1}}{(n!)^2} .$$

15. $4x^2y'' + 8x(x + 1)y' + y = 0$.

$$\text{ANS.} \quad y_1 = x^{-\frac{1}{2}} + \sum_{n=1}^{\infty} \frac{(-1)^n[(-1) \cdot 1 \cdot 3 \cdot 5 \cdots (2n-3)]x^{n-\frac{1}{2}}}{(n!)^2} ;$$

$$y_2 = y_1 \ln x$$

$$+ \sum_{n=1}^{\infty} \frac{(-1)^n[(-1) \cdot 1 \cdot 3 \cdots (2n-3)](2H_{2n-2} - H_{n-1} - 2H_n - 2)x^{n-\frac{1}{2}}}{(n!)^2} .$$

16. $x^2y'' + 3x(1 + x)y' + (1 - 3x)y = 0$.

$$\text{ANS.} \quad y_1 = x^{-1} + 6 + \tfrac{9}{2}x;$$

$$y_2 = y_1 \ln x - 15 - \tfrac{81}{4}x + \sum_{n=3}^{\infty} \frac{2(-3)^n x^{n-1}}{n!n(n-1)(n-2)} .$$

17. $xy'' + (1 - x)y' - y = 0$.

$$\text{ANS.} \quad y_1 = 1 + \sum_{n=1}^{\infty} \frac{x^n}{n!} = e^x; \qquad y_2 = y_1 \ln x - \sum_{n=1}^{\infty} \frac{H_n x^n}{n!} .$$

18. Refer to Ex. 17 above. There one solution was found to be $y_1 = e^x$. Use the change of dependent variable, $y = ve^x$, to obtain the general solution of the differential equation in the form

$$y = k_1 e^x \int_{k_2}^{x} \beta^{-1} e^{-\beta} d\beta.$$

110. Indicial equation with difference of roots a positive integer, nonlogarithmic case

Consider the equation

(1) $$xy'' - (4 + x)y' + 2y = 0.$$

As usual, let $L(y)$ stand for the left member of (1) and put

(2) $$y = \sum_{n=0}^{\infty} a_n x^{n+c}.$$

At once we find that for the y of equation (2), the left member of equation (1) takes the form

$$L(y) = \sum_{n=0}^{\infty} [(n + c)(n + c - 1) - 4(n + c)]a_n x^{n+c-1}$$

$$- \sum_{n=0}^{\infty} (n + c - 2)a_n x^{n+c}$$

or

$$L(y) = \sum_{n=0}^{\infty} (n + c)(n + c - 5)a_n x^{n+c-1} - \sum_{n=1}^{\infty} (n + c - 3)a_{n-1} x^{n+c-1}.$$

The indicial equation is $c(c - 5) = 0$, so

$$c_1 = 5, \quad c_2 = 0, \quad s = c_1 - c_2 = 5.$$

We reason that we may hope for two power series solutions, one starting with an x^0 term, one with an x^5 term. If we use the large root $c = 5$ and try a series

$$\sum_{n=0}^{\infty} a_n x^{n+5},$$

it is evident that we can get at most one solution; the x^0 term would never enter.

On the other hand, if we use the smaller root $c = 0$, then a trial solution of the form

$$\sum_{n=0}^{\infty} a_n x^{n+0}$$

has a chance of picking up both solutions because the $n = 5$ ($n = s$) term does contain x^5.

If s is a positive integer, we try a series of the form (2) using the smaller root c_2. If a_0 and a_s both turn out to be arbitrary, we obtain the general solution by this method. Otherwise the relation that should determine a_s will be impossible (with our usual assumption that $a_0 \neq 0$) and the general solution will involve a logarithm as it did in the case of equal roots. That logarithmic case will be treated in the next section.

Let us return to the numerical problem. Using the smaller root $c = 0$, we now know that for

$$(3) \qquad\qquad y = \sum_{n=0}^{\infty} a_n x^n$$

we get

$$L(y) = \sum_{n=0}^{\infty} n(n-5)a_n x^{n-1} - \sum_{n=1}^{\infty} (n-3)a_{n-1}x^{n-1}.$$

Therefore, to make $L(y) = 0$, we must have

$$n = 0: \quad 0 \cdot a_0 = 0, \ (a_0 \text{ arbitrary}),$$
$$n \geq 1: \quad n(n-5)a_n - (n-3)a_{n-1} = 0.$$

Since division by $(n-5)$ cannot be accomplished until $n > 5$, it is best to write out the separate relations through the critical one for a_5. We thus obtain

$$n = 1: \quad -4a_1 + 2a_0 = 0,$$
$$n = 2: \quad -6a_2 + a_1 = 0,$$
$$n = 3: \quad -6a_3 + 0 \cdot a_2 = 0,$$
$$n = 4: \quad -4a_4 - a_3 = 0,$$
$$n = 5: \quad 0 \cdot a_5 - 2a_4 = 0,$$
$$n \geq 6: \quad a_n = \frac{(n-3)a_{n-1}}{n(n-5)}.$$

It follows from these relations that

$$a_1 = \tfrac{1}{2}a_0,$$
$$a_2 = \tfrac{1}{6}a_1 = \tfrac{1}{12}a_0,$$
$$a_3 = 0,$$
$$a_4 = 0,$$
$$0 \cdot a_5 = 0,$$

so a_5 is arbitrary. Each a_n, $n > 5$, will be obtained from a_5. In the usual way it is found that

$$a_6 = \frac{3a_5}{6 \cdot 1},$$

$$a_7 = \frac{4a_6}{7 \cdot 2},$$

$$\cdot$$
$$\cdot$$
$$\cdot$$

$$a_n = \frac{(n-3)a_{n-1}}{n(n-5)},$$

from which

$$a_n = \frac{3 \cdot 4 \cdot 5 \cdots (n-3)a_5}{[6 \cdot 7 \cdot 8 \cdots n](n-5)!} = \frac{3 \cdot 4 \cdot 5 a_5}{(n-2)(n-1)n(n-5)!}.$$

Therefore, with a_0 and a_5 arbitrary, the general solution may be written

$$y = a_0(1 + \tfrac{1}{2}x + \tfrac{1}{12}x^2) + a_5\left[x^5 + \sum_{n=6}^{\infty} \frac{60x^n}{(n-5)!n(n-1)(n-2)}\right].$$

The coefficient of a_5 may also be written, with a shift of index, in the form shown below:

$$\sum_{n=0}^{\infty} \frac{60x^{n+5}}{n!(n+5)(n+4)(n+3)}.$$

Before proceeding to the exercises, let us examine an equation for which the fortunate circumstance a_0 and a_s both arbitrary does not occur. For the equation

(4) $$x^2y'' + x(1-x)y' - (1+3x)y = 0$$

the trial

$$y = \sum_{n=0}^{\infty} a_n x^{n+c}$$

leads to

$$L(y) = \sum_{n=0}^{\infty} (n+c+1)(n+c-1)a_n x^{n+c} - \sum_{n=1}^{\infty} (n+c+2)a_{n-1}x^{n+c}.$$

Since $c_1 = 1$ and $c_2 = -1$, we use $c = -1$ and find the relations

$$n \geq 1: \quad n(n-2)a_n - (n+1)a_{n-1} = 0,$$

with a_0 arbitrary. Let us write down the separate relations out to the critical one,

$$n = 1: \quad -a_1 - 2a_0 = 0,$$

$$n = 2: \quad 0 \cdot a_2 - 3a_1 = 0,$$

$$n \geq 3: \quad a_n = \frac{(n+1)a_{n-1}}{n(n-2)}.$$

It follows that

$$a_1 = -2a_0,$$

$$0 \cdot a_2 = 3a_1 = -6a_0.$$

These relations cannot be satisfied except by choosing $a_0 = 0$. But if that is done, a_2 will be the only arbitrary constant and the only solution coming out of the work will be that corresponding to the large value of c, $c = 1$. This is an instance where a logarithmic solution is indicated and the equation will be solved in the next section.

A good way to waste time is to use $a_0 = 0$, $a_1 = 0$, a_2 arbitrary, and to determine a_n, $n \geq 3$, from the above recurrence relation. In that way extra work can be done to get a solution which will be reobtained automatically when solving the equation by the method of the next section.

Exercises

Obtain the general solution near $x = 0$ except when instructed otherwise. State the region of validity of each solution.

1. $x^2y'' + 2x(x-2)y' + 2(2-3x)y = 0.$

ANS. $y = a_0(x - 2x^2 + 2x^3) + a_3\left[x^4 + \sum_{n=4}^{\infty} \frac{6(-2)^{n-3}x^{n+1}}{n!} \right].$

2. $x^2(1+2x)y'' + 2x(1+6x)y' - 2y = 0.$

ANS. $y = a_0(x^{-2} - 6x^{-1} + 24)$

$+ a_3\left[x + \frac{1}{20} \sum_{n=4}^{\infty} (-2)^{n-3}(n+2)(n+1)x^{n-2} \right].$

3. $x^2y'' + x(2+3x)y' - 2y = 0.$

ANS. $y = a_0(x^{-2} - 3x^{-1} + \frac{9}{2}) + a_3\left[x + \sum_{n=4}^{\infty} \frac{2(-1)^{n-3}3^{n-2}x^{n-2}}{n!} \right].$

4. $xy'' - (3 + x)y' + 2y = 0$.

$$\text{ANS.} \quad y = a_0(1 + \tfrac{2}{3}x + \tfrac{1}{6}x^2) + a_4 \sum_{n=4}^{\infty} \frac{24(n-3)x^n}{n!}.$$

5. $x(1 + x)y'' + (x + 5)y' - 4y = 0$.

$$\text{ANS.} \quad y = a_0(x^{-4} + 4x^{-3} + 5x^{-2}) + a_4(1 + \tfrac{4}{5}x + \tfrac{1}{5}x^2).$$

6. Solve the equation of Ex. 5 about the point $x = -1$.

$$\text{ANS.} \quad y = a_0[1 + (x + 1) + \tfrac{1}{2}(x + 1)^2]$$
$$+ \frac{a_5}{12} \sum_{n=5}^{\infty} (n-4)(n-3)(n+1)(x+1)^n.$$

7. $x^2y'' + x^2y' - 2y = 0$.

$$\text{ANS.} \quad y = a_0(x^{-1} - \tfrac{1}{2}) + 6a_3 \sum_{n=3}^{\infty} \frac{(-1)^{n+1}(n-2)x^{n-1}}{n!}.$$

8. $x(1 - x)y'' - 3y' + 2y = 0$.

$$\text{ANS.} \quad y = a_0(1 + \tfrac{2}{3}x + \tfrac{1}{3}x^2) + a_4 \sum_{n=4}^{\infty} (n-3)x^n.$$

9. Solve the equation of Ex. 8 about the point $x = 1$.

$$\text{ANS.} \quad y = a_0[(x-1)^{-2} + 4(x-1)^{-1}] + a_2[1 + \tfrac{2}{3}(x-1) + \tfrac{1}{6}(x-1)^2].$$

10. $xy'' + (4 + 3x)y' + 3y = 0$.

$$\text{ANS.} \quad y = a_0(x^{-3} - 3x^{-2} + \tfrac{9}{2}x^{-1}) + 6a_3 \sum_{n=3}^{\infty} \frac{(-3)^{n-3}x^{n-3}}{n!}.$$

11. $xy'' - 2(x + 2)y' + 4y = 0$.

$$\text{ANS.} \quad y = a_0(1 + x + \tfrac{1}{3}x^2) + a_5 \sum_{n=5}^{\infty} \frac{60 \cdot 2^{n-5}x^n}{(n-5)!n(n-1)(n-2)}.$$

12. $xy'' + (3 + 2x)y' + 4y = 0$.

$$\text{ANS.} \quad y = a_0x^{-2} + a_2 \sum_{n=2}^{\infty} \frac{(-1)^n 2^{n-1}x^{n-2}}{n \cdot (n-2)!}.$$

13. $x(x + 3)y'' - 9y' - 6y = 0$.

$$\text{ANS.} \quad y = a_0(1 - \tfrac{2}{3}x + \tfrac{1}{3}x^2 - \tfrac{4}{27}x^3) + a_4\left[x^4 + \sum_{n=5}^{\infty} \frac{(-1)^n(n+1)x^n}{5 \cdot 3^{n-4}}\right].$$

14. $x(1 - 2x)y'' - 2(2 + x)y' + 8y = 0$.

$$\text{ANS.} \quad y = a_0(1 + 2x + 2x^2) + \tfrac{1}{3}a_5 \sum_{n=5}^{\infty} 2^{n-7}(n-4)(n-3)(n+1)x^n.$$

15. $xy'' + (x^3 - 1)y' + x^2y = 0$.

$$\text{ANS.} \quad y = a_0 \sum_{k=0}^{\infty} \frac{(-1)^k x^{3k}}{3^k k!} + a_2\left[x^2 + \sum_{k=1}^{\infty} \frac{(-1)^k x^{3k+2}}{5 \cdot 8 \cdot 11 \cdots (3k+2)}\right].$$

16. $x^2(4x - 1)y'' + x(5x + 1)y' + 3y = 0.$

ANS. $y = a_0(x^{-1} - 1) + a_4\left[x^3 + 12 \sum_{n=5}^{\infty} \dfrac{13 \cdot 17 \cdot 21 \cdots (4n - 7)x^{n-1}}{(n - 4)! \cdot n(n - 1)} \right].$

111. Indicial equation with difference of roots a positive integer, logarithmic case

In the preceding section we examined the equation

(1) $$x^2 y'' + x(1 - x)y' - (1 + 3x)y = 0$$

and found that its indicial equation has roots $c_1 = 1$, $c_2 = -1$. Since there is no power series solution starting with x^{c_2}, we suspect the presence of a logarithmic term and start to treat the equation in the manner of the previous logarithmic case, that of equal roots.

From the assumed form

$$y = \sum_{n=0}^{\infty} a_n x^{n+c}$$

we easily determine the left member of equation (1) to be

$$L(y) = \sum_{n=0}^{\infty} (n + c + 1)(n + c - 1)a_n x^{n+c} - \sum_{n=0}^{\infty} (n + c + 3)a_n x^{n+c+1}$$

$$= \sum_{n=0}^{\infty} (n + c + 1)(n + c - 1)a_n x^{n+c} - \sum_{n=1}^{\infty} (n + c + 2)a_{n-1} x^{n+c}.$$

As usual, each term after the first one in the series for $L(y)$ can be made zero by choosing the a_n, $n \geq 1$, without choosing c. Let us put

$$n \geq 1: \quad a_n = \frac{(n + c + 2)a_{n-1}}{(n + c + 1)(n + c - 1)},$$

from which it follows at once that

$$n \geq 1: \quad a_n = \frac{(c + 3)(c + 4) \cdots (c + n + 2)a_0}{[(c+2)(c+3) \cdots (c+n+1)][c(c+1) \cdots (c+n-1)]},$$

or

$$n \geq 1: \quad a_n = \frac{(c + n + 2)a_0}{(c + 2)[c(c + 1) \cdots (c + n - 1)]}.$$

For the a_n obtained above, all terms after the first one in the power series for $L(y)$ have been made to vanish, so with

$$(2) \qquad y = a_0 x^c + \sum_{n=1}^{\infty} \frac{(c + n + 2)a_0 x^{n+c}}{(c + 2)[c(c + 1) \cdots (c + n - 1)]}$$

it must follow that

$$(3) \qquad\qquad L(y) = (c + 1)(c - 1)a_0 x^c.$$

From the larger root, $c = 1$, only one solution can be obtained. From the smaller root, $c = -1$, two solutions would be available following the technique of using $y(x, c)$ and $\partial y(x, c)/\partial c$ as in the case of equal roots if the right member of (3) contained the factor $(c + 1)^2$ instead of just $(c + 1)$ to the first power. But a_0 is still arbitrary, so we take

$$a_0 = (c + 1)$$

to get the desired square factor on the right in equation (3).

Another way of seeing that it is desirable to choose $a_0 = (c + 1)$ is as follows. We know that eventually it is going to be necessary to use $c = -1$ in equation (2). But within the series, the denominator contains the factor $(c + 1)$ for all terms after the $n = 1$ term. As equation (2) stands now, the terms $n \geq 2$ would not exist with $c = -1$. Therefore we remove the troublesome factor $(c + 1)$ from the denominator by choosing $a_0 = (c + 1)$.

With $a_0 = (c + 1)$ we have

$$(4) \quad y(x, c) = (c + 1)x^c + \sum_{n=1}^{\infty} \frac{(c + 1)(c + n + 2)x^{n+c}}{(c + 2)[c(c + 1) \cdots (c + n - 1)]}$$

for which

$$(5) \qquad\qquad L[y(x, c)] = (c + 1)^2(c - 1)x^c.$$

The same argument as the one used when the indicial equation had equal roots shows that the two linearly independent solutions being sought may be obtained as

$$(6) \qquad\qquad y_1 = y(x, -1),$$

and

$$(7) \qquad\qquad y_2 = \left(\frac{\partial y(x, c)}{\partial c}\right)_{c=-1}.$$

Naturally, it is wise to cancel the factor $(c + 1)$ from the numerator and denominator in the terms of the series in (4). But the factor $(c + 1)$ does not enter the denominator until the term $n = 2$. Therefore it seems best to write out the terms that far separately. We rewrite equation (4) as

(8) $y(x, c) = (c + 1)x^c + \dfrac{(c + 1)(c + 3)x^{1+c}}{(c + 2)c} + \dfrac{(c + 4)x^{2+c}}{(c + 2)c}$

$$+ \sum_{n=3}^{\infty} \frac{(c + n + 2)x^{n+c}}{(c + 2)c[(c + 2)(c + 3) \cdots (c + n - 1)]}.$$

Differentiation with respect to c of the members of equation (8) yields

(9) $\dfrac{\partial y(x, c)}{\partial c} = y(x, c) \ln x + x^c$

$+ \dfrac{(c + 1)(c + 3)x^{1+c}}{(c + 2)c} \left\{ \dfrac{1}{c + 1} + \dfrac{1}{c + 3} - \dfrac{1}{c + 2} - \dfrac{1}{c} \right\}$

$+ \dfrac{(c + 4)x^{2+c}}{(c + 2)c} \left\{ \dfrac{1}{c + 4} - \dfrac{1}{c + 2} - \dfrac{1}{c} \right\}$

$+ \sum_{n=3}^{\infty} \dfrac{(c+n+2)x^{n+c}\left\{\dfrac{1}{c+n+2} - \dfrac{1}{c+2} - \dfrac{1}{c} - \left(\dfrac{1}{c+2} + \dfrac{1}{c+3} + \cdots + \dfrac{1}{c+n-1}\right)\right\}}{(c + 2)c[(c + 2)(c + 3) \cdots (c + n - 1)]}$.

All that remains to be done is to get y_1 and y_2 by using $c = -1$ in the expressions above for $y(x, c)$ and $\partial y(x, c)/\partial c$. In the third term on the right in equation (9), we first (mentally) insert the factor $(c + 1)$ throughout the quantity in the curly brackets.

The desired solutions are thus found to be

$$y_1 = 0 \cdot x^{-1} + 0 \cdot x^0 - 3x + \sum_{n=3}^{\infty} \frac{(n + 1)x^{n-1}}{(-1)[1 \cdot 2 \cdots (n - 2)]}$$

and

$y_2 = y_1 \ln x + x^{-1} - 2x^0 - 3x\{\tfrac{1}{3} - 1 + 1\}$

$$+ \sum_{n=3}^{\infty} \frac{(n + 1)x^{n-1} \left\{ \dfrac{1}{n + 1} - 1 + 1 - \left(1 + \tfrac{1}{2} + \cdots + \dfrac{1}{n - 2}\right) \right\}}{(-1)[1 \cdot 2 \cdots (n - 2)]}.$$

These results can be written more compactly as

(10) $$y_1 = -3x - \sum_{n=3}^{\infty} \frac{(n + 1)x^{n-1}}{(n - 2)!}$$

and

(11) $y_2 = y_1 \ln x + x^{-1} - 2 - x - \displaystyle\sum_{n=3}^{\infty} \frac{[1 - (n + 1)H_{n-2}]x^{n-1}}{(n - 2)!}.$

It is also possible to absorb one more term into the summation and to improve the appearance of these results. The student can show that

$$y_1 = -\sum_{n=0}^{\infty} \frac{(n+3)x^{n+1}}{n!}$$

and

$$y_2 = y_1 \ln x + x^{-1} - 2 - \sum_{n=0}^{\infty} \frac{[1-(n+3)H_n]x^{n+1}}{n!}$$

as long as the common conventions (definitions) $H_0 = 0$ and $0! = 1$ are used.

The general solution of the original differential equation is

$$y = Ay_1 + By_2,$$

and it is valid for all finite $x \neq 0$, since the differential equation has no other singular points in the finite plane.

The step taken in passing from equation (4) to equation (8) should be used regularly in this type of solution. Without its use indeterminate forms which may cause confusion will be encountered.

An essential point in this method is the choice $a_0 = (c - c_2)$ where c_2 is the smaller root of the indicial equation.

Exercises

Find two linearly independent solutions valid about $x = 0$, unless otherwise instructed.

1. $xy'' + y = 0$.

ANS. $\quad y_1 = \sum_{n=1}^{\infty} \frac{(-1)^n x^n}{n!(n-1)!};$

$$y_2 = y_1 \ln x + 1 + x - \sum_{n=2}^{\infty} \frac{(-1)^n(H_n + H_{n-1})x^n}{n!(n-1)!}.$$

2. $x^2y'' - 3xy' + (3 + 4x)y = 0$.

ANS. $\quad y_1 = \sum_{n=2}^{\infty} \frac{(-1)^{n+1}4^n x^{n+1}}{n!(n-2)!};$

$$y_2 = y_1 \ln x + y_1 + x + 4x^2 + \sum_{n=2}^{\infty} \frac{(-4)^n(H_n + H_{n-2})x^{n+1}}{n!(n-2)!}.$$

3. $2xy'' + 6y' + y = 0.$

$$\text{ANS.} \quad y_1 = \sum_{n=2}^{\infty} \frac{(-1)^{n+1}x^{n-2}}{2^n n!(n-2)!};$$

$$y_2 = y_1 \ln x + y_1 + x^{-2} + \tfrac{1}{2}x^{-1} + \sum_{n=2}^{\infty} \frac{(-1)^n(H_n + H_{n-2})x^{n-2}}{2^n n!(n-2)!}.$$

4. $4x^2y'' + 2x(2-x)y' - (1+3x)y = 0.$

$$\text{ANS.} \quad y_1 = \sum_{n=1}^{\infty} \frac{x^{n-\frac{1}{2}}}{2^{n-1}(n-1)!};$$

$$y_2 = y_1 \ln x + 2x^{-\frac{1}{2}} - \sum_{n=2}^{\infty} \frac{H_{n-1}x^{n-\frac{1}{2}}}{2^{n-1}(n-1)!}.$$

5. $x^2y'' - x(6+x)y' + 10y = 0.$

$$\text{ANS.} \quad y_1 = \sum_{n=3}^{\infty} \frac{(n+1)x^{n+2}}{2(n-3)!};$$

$$y_2 = y_1 \ln x + \tfrac{1}{2}y_1 + x^2 - x^3 + \tfrac{3}{2}x^4 + \sum_{n=3}^{\infty} \frac{[1-(n+1)H_{n-3}]x^{n+2}}{2(n-3)!}.$$

6. $x^2y'' + xy' + (x^2-1)y = 0.$ This is Bessel's equation of index one. See also Sections 117 and 118.

$$\text{ANS.} \quad y_1 = \sum_{k=1}^{\infty} \frac{(-1)^k x^{2k-1}}{2^{2k-1}k!(k-1)!};$$

$$y_2 = y_1 \ln x + x^{-1} - \sum_{k=1}^{\infty} \frac{(-1)^k(H_k + H_{k-1})x^{2k-1}}{2^{2k}k!(k-1)!}.$$

7. $xy'' + (3+2x)y' + 8y = 0.$

$$\text{ANS.} \quad y_1 = \sum_{n=2}^{\infty} \frac{(-1)^{n+1}2^n(n+1)x^{n-2}}{(n-2)!};$$

$$y_2 = y_1 \ln x + x^{-2} + 4x^{-1} + \sum_{n=2}^{\infty} \frac{(-2)^n[(n+1)H_{n-2} - 1]x^{n-2}}{(n-2)!}.$$

8. $x(1-x)y'' + 2(1-x)y' + 2y = 0.$

$$\text{ANS.} \quad y_1 = -2 + 2x;$$

$$y_2 = y_1 \ln x + x^{-1} + 1 - 5x + \sum_{n=3}^{\infty} \frac{2x^{n-1}}{(n-1)(n-2)}.$$

9. Show that the answers to Ex. 8 may be replaced by

$$y_3 = 1 - x; \quad y_4 = y_3 \ln x - \tfrac{1}{2}x^{-1} + 2x - \sum_{n=3}^{\infty} \frac{x^{n-1}}{(n-1)(n-2)}.$$

10. Solve the equation of Ex. 8 near the point $x = 1$.

$$\text{ANS.} \quad y_1 = 2(x - 1);$$

$$y_2 = y_1 \ln (x - 1) + 1 - 3(x - 1) + \sum_{n=2}^{\infty} \frac{(-1)^{n+1}(n + 1)(x - 1)^n}{n - 1}.$$

11. $x^2 y'' - 5xy' + (8 + 5x)y = 0.$

$$\text{ANS.} \quad y_1 = \sum_{n=2}^{\infty} \frac{(-1)^{n+1} 5^n x^{n+2}}{n!(n - 2)!};$$

$$y_2 = y_1 \ln x + y_1 + x^2 + 5x^3 + \sum_{n=2}^{\infty} \frac{(-5)^n (H_n + H_{n-2}) x^{n+2}}{n!(n - 2)!}.$$

12. $xy'' + (3 - x)y' - 5y = 0.$

$$\text{ANS.} \quad y_1 = - \sum_{n=2}^{\infty} \frac{(n + 1)(n + 2) x^{n-2}}{2(n - 2)!};$$

$$y_2 = y_1 \ln x - \tfrac{1}{2} y_1 + x^{-2} - 3x^{-1}$$

$$- \sum_{n=2}^{\infty} \frac{(n + 1)(n + 2)(H_{n+2} - H_n - H_{n-2}) x^{n-2}}{2(n - 2)!}.$$

13. $9x^2 y'' - 15xy' + 7(1 + x)y = 0.$

$$\text{ANS.} \quad y_1 = \sum_{n=2}^{\infty} \frac{(-1)^{n+1} 7^n x^{n+\frac{1}{3}}}{3^{2n-1} n!(n - 2)!};$$

$$y_2 = y_1 \ln x + 3x^{\frac{1}{3}} + \tfrac{7}{3} x^{\frac{4}{3}} + \sum_{n=2}^{\infty} \frac{(-7)^n (H_n + H_{n-2} - 1) x^{n+\frac{1}{3}}}{3^{2n-1} n!(n - 2)!}.$$

14. $x^2 y'' + x(1 - 2x)y' - (x + 1)y = 0.$

$$\text{ANS.} \quad y_1 = \sum_{n=2}^{\infty} \frac{1 \cdot 3 \cdot 5 \cdots (2n - 3) x^{n-1}}{n!(n - 2)!};$$

$$y_2 = y_1 \ln x + x^{-1} + 1 - y_1$$

$$+ \sum_{n=2}^{\infty} \frac{[1 \cdot 3 \cdot 5 \cdots (2n - 3)](2H_{2n-2} - H_n - H_{n-1} - H_{n-2}) x^{n-1}}{n!(n - 2)!}.$$

112. Summary

Confronted by a linear equation

$$(1) \qquad\qquad L(y) = 0,$$

we first determine the location and nature of the singular points of the equation. In practice, the use to which the results will be put will dictate that solutions are desired near a certain point or points. In seeking solutions valid about the point $x = x_0$, always first translate the origin, putting $x - x_0 = v$.

Solutions valid near an ordinary point $x = 0$ of equation (1) take the form

(2) $$y = \sum_{n=0}^{\infty} a_n x^n$$

with a_0 and a_1 arbitrary, if equation (1) is of second order.

If $x = 0$ is a regular singular point of equation (1) and we wish to get solutions valid near $x = 0$, we first put

(3) $$y = \sum_{n=0}^{\infty} a_n x^{n+c}.$$

For the y of (3) we obtain by substitution the series for $L(y)$. From the $n = 0$ term of that series the indicial equation may be written. When the difference of the roots of the indicial equation is not an integer, or if the roots are equal, the technique is straightforward following the method of Section 107 or of Section 109.

When the roots differ by a nonzero integer, then the solution may, or may not, involve $\ln x$. The recurrence relation for $n = s$, where s is the difference of the roots, is the critical one. We must then determine whether the relations for $n = 1, 2, \cdots, s$ leave a_0 and a_s both arbitrary. If they do, two power series of the form (3) will be solutions of the differential equation. If a_0 and a_s are not both arbitrary, the case is a logarithmic one. Then the device of Section 111 may be used.

The technique can be varied, if desired, by always choosing the a_n in terms of c so the series for $L(y)$ reduces to a single term. Thus a series of the form

(4) $$y(x, c) = a_0 \left[x^c + \sum_{n=1}^{\infty} f_n(c) x^{n+c} \right]$$

will be determined for which

(5) $$L[y(x, c)] = a_0(c - c_1)(c - c_2) x^{c-k},$$

where k is zero or one for the equations being treated here and c_1 and c_2 are the roots of the indicial equation. Then it can be determined from the actual coefficients in (4) whether the use of $c = c_1$ and $c = c_2$ will result in two solutions of the differential equation. If $c_1 = c_2$, the results would be identical and the use of $\partial y(x, c)/\partial c$ is indicated. The other logarithmic case will be identified by the fact that some one or more of the coefficients $f_n(c)$ will not exist when $c = c_2$, the smaller root. Then again the differentiation process is needed, after the introduction of $a_0 = c - c_2$.

The method sketched above has a disadvantage in that it seems to tempt the user into automatic application of rules, always a dangerous procedure in mathematics. When a student thoroughly understands what is happening in each of the four possible cases, this method may safely be used and it saves some labor.

Extension of the methods of this and the preceding chapter to linear equations of higher order is direct. As an example, a fourth-order equation whose indicial equation has roots $c = 2, 2, 2, \frac{1}{2}$ would be treated as follows. A series would be determined for $y(x, c)$,

$$y(x, c) = a_0 \left[x^c + \sum_{n=1}^{\infty} f_n(c) x^{n+c} \right]$$

for which the left member of the original equation reduces to one term, such as

$$L[y(x, c)] = (c - 2)^3 (2c - 1) a_0 x^c.$$

Then four linearly independent solutions could be obtained:

$$y_1 = y(x, 2), \quad y_2 = \left[\frac{\partial y(x, c)}{\partial c} \right]_{c=2}, \quad y_3 = \left[\frac{\partial^2 y(x, c)}{\partial c^2} \right]_{c=2}, \quad y_4 = y(x, \tfrac{1}{2}).$$

Miscellaneous Exercises

In each exercise, obtain solutions valid near $x = 0$.

1. $xy'' - (2 + x)y' - y = 0$.
2. $x^2 y'' + 2x^2 y' - 2y = 0$.
3. $x^2(1 + x^2)y'' + 2x(3 + x^2)y' + 6y = 0$.
4. $2xy'' + (1 + 2x)y' - 3y = 0$.
5. $x(1 - x^2)y'' - (7 + x^2)y' + 4xy = 0$.
6. $4x^2 y'' - 2x(2 + x)y' + (3 + x)y = 0$.
7. $2xy'' + y' + y = 0$.
8. $4x^2 y'' - x^2 y' + y = 0$.
9. $2x^2 y'' - x(1 + 2x)y' + (1 + 3x)y = 0$.
10. $4x^2 y'' + 3x^2 y' + (1 + 3x)y = 0$.
11. $4x^2 y'' + 2x^2 y' - (x + 3)y = 0$.
12. $x^2 y'' + x(3 + x)y' + (1 + 2x)y = 0$.

13. $x(1 - 2x)y'' - 2(2 + x)y' + 18y = 0.$

14. $x^2y'' - 3xy' + 4(1 + x)y = 0.$

15. $4x^2y'' + 2x(x - 4)y' + (5 - 3x)y = 0.$

16. $x(1 - x)y'' - (4 + x)y' + 4y = 0.$

$$\text{ANS.} \quad y = a_0(1 + x + \tfrac{1}{2}x^2) + \frac{a_5}{12} \sum_{n=5}^{\infty} (n - 4)(n - 3)(n + 1)x^n.$$

17. Solve the equation of Ex. 16 about the point $x = 1.$

$$\text{ANS.} \quad y = a_0[(x - 1)^{-4} + 4(x - 1)^{-3} + 5(x - 1)^{-2}]$$
$$+ a_4[1 + \tfrac{4}{5}(x - 1) + \tfrac{1}{5}(x - 1)^2].$$

18. $x(1 - x)y'' + (1 - 4x)y' - 2y = 0.$

19. Show that the solutions of Ex. 18 may be written in the form

$$y_1 = (1 - x)^{-2},$$

$$y_2 = (1 - x)^{-2}(\ln x - x).$$

20. $xy'' + (1 - x)y' + 3y = 0.$

$$\text{ANS.} \quad y_1 = 1 - 3x + \tfrac{3}{2}x^2 - \tfrac{1}{6}x^3;$$

$$y_2 = y_1 \ln x + 7x - \tfrac{23}{4}x^2 + \tfrac{11}{12}x^3 - 6 \sum_{n=4}^{\infty} \frac{x^n}{n!n(n - 1)(n - 2)(n - 3)}.$$

21. $xy'' - (2 + x)y' - 2y = 0.$

22. $2x^2y'' - x(2x + 7)y' + 2(x + 5)y = 0.$

23. $(1 - x^2)y'' - 10xy' - 18y = 0.$

24. $y'' + 2xy' - 8y = 0.$

25. $2x(1 - x)y'' + (1 - 2x)y' + 8y = 0.$

26. $2x^2y'' - x(1 + 2x)y' + (1 + 4x)y = 0.$

27. $x^2y'' - x(1 + x^2)y' + (1 - x^2)y = 0.$

28. $x^2y'' + x(x^2 - 3)y' + 4y = 0.$

29. $(1 + x^2)y'' - 2y = 0.$

30. $x^2y'' - 3x(1 + x)y' + 4(1 - x)y = 0.$

31. $y''' + xy = 0.$

32. $xy'' + (1 - x^2)y' + 2xy = 0.$

33. $x(1 - x^2)y'' + 5(1 - x^2)y' - 4xy = 0.$

34. $x^2y'' + xy' - (x^2 + 4)y = 0.$

35. $2xy'' + (3 - x)y' - 3y = 0.$

36. $xy'' + (2 - x)y' - y = 0.$

37. $y'' - 2xy' + 6y = 0.$

38. $x^2y'' - x(3 + 2x)y' + (3 - x)y = 0.$

39. $4x^2y'' + 2x(x + 2)y' + (5x - 1)y = 0.$

40. $xy'' + 3y' - y = 0.$

41. $4x^2y'' + (3x + 1)y = 0.$

42. $x^2y'' + x(3x - 1)y' + (3x + 1)y = 0.$

43. $x^2y'' + x(4x - 3)y' + (8x + 3)y = 0.$

44. $2(1 + x^2)y'' + 7xy' + 2y = 0.$

45. $3xy'' + 2(1 - x)y' - 2y = 0.$

46. $xy'' - (1 + 3x)y' - 4y = 0.$

47. $x^2y'' - x(3 + 2x)y' + (4 - x)y = 0.$

48. $2x(1 - x)y'' + y' + 4y = 0.$

49. $x(1 + 4x)y'' + (1 + 8x)y' + y = 0.$

50. $xy'' + (3 - 2x)y' + 4y = 0.$

51. $x^2y'' + x(2x - 3)y' + (4x + 3)y = 0.$

52. $(1 - x^2)y'' - 2xy' + 12y = 0.$

53. $x^2(1 + x)y'' + x(3 + 5x)y' + (1 + 4x)y = 0.$

54. $x^2y'' + x^2y' + (3x - 2)y = 0.$

55. $2x^2y'' + 3xy' - (1 + x)y = 0.$

CHAPTER 22

Equations of Hypergeometric Type

113. Equations to be treated in this chapter

With the methods studied in Chapters 20 and 21, we are able to solve many equations which appear frequently in modern physics and engineering as well as in pure mathematics. We shall consider briefly the hypergeometric equation, Bessel's equation, and the equations that lead to the study of Laguerre, Legendre, and Hermite polynomials. There are, in mathematical literature, thousands of research papers devoted entirely or in part to the study of the functions that are solutions of the equations to be studied in this chapter. Here we do no more than call to the attention of the student the existence of these special functions which are of such great value to theoretical physicists, engineers, and many mathematicians. An introduction to the properties of these and other special functions can be found in Rainville's Special Functions, New York, the Macmillan Co., 1960.

114. The factorial function

It will be convenient for us to employ a notation which is widely encountered in advanced mathematics. We define the factorial function $(a)_n$ for n equal to zero or a positive integer by

(1) $(a)_n = a(a + 1)(a + 2) \cdots (a + n - 1)$, for $n \geqq 1$;

   $(a)_0 = 1$ for $a \neq 0$.

Thus the symbol $(a)_n$ denotes a product of n factors starting with the factor a, each factor being one larger than the factor before it. For instance,

$$(7)_4 = 7 \cdot 8 \cdot 9 \cdot 10,$$
$$(-5)_3 = (-5)(-4)(-3),$$
$$(-\tfrac{1}{2})_3 = (-\tfrac{1}{2})(\tfrac{1}{2})(\tfrac{3}{2}).$$

The factorial function is a generalization of the ordinary factorial. Indeed,

(2) $$(1)_n = 1 \cdot 2 \cdot 3 \cdots n = n!.$$

In our study of the Gamma function in Section 62, we derived the functional relation

(3) $$\Gamma(x + 1) = x\Gamma(x).$$

By repeated use of the relation (3), we find that if n is an integer,

$$\begin{aligned}
\Gamma(a + n) &= (a + n - 1)\Gamma(a + n - 1) \\
&= (a + n - 1)(a + n - 2)\Gamma(a + n - 2) \\
&= \cdots \\
&= (a + n - 1)(a + n - 2) \cdots (a)\Gamma(a) \\
&= (a)_n\Gamma(a).
\end{aligned}$$

Therefore the factorial function and the Gamma function are related by

(4) $$(a)_n = \frac{\Gamma(a+n)}{\Gamma(a)}, \quad n \text{ integer, } n > 0.$$

Actually (4), but not the proof given here, is valid for any complex a except zero or a negative integer.

115. The hypergeometric equation

It is shown in various places* that any second-order linear differential equation with only three singular points, each of them regular,

* See, for instance, E. D. Rainville, *Intermediate Differential Equations*, 2nd ed. (New York: The Macmillan Co., 1964), Chapter 6.

can be transformed by change of variables into the hypergeometric equation

(1) $$x(1 - x)y'' + [c - (a + b + 1)x] y' - aby = 0,$$

in which a, b, c are fixed parameters.

Let us solve equation (1) about the regular singular point $x = 0$. For the moment let c be not an integer. For (1), the indicial equation has roots zero and $(1 - c)$. We put

$$y = \sum_{n=0}^{\infty} e_n x^n$$

in equation (1) and thus arrive, after the usual simplifications, at

(2) $$\sum_{n=0}^{\infty} n(n + c - 1)e_n x^{n-1} - \sum_{n=0}^{\infty} (n + a)(n + b)e_n x^n = 0.$$

Shift index in (2) to get

(3) $$\sum_{n=0}^{\infty} n(n + c - 1)e_n x^{n-1} - \sum_{n=1}^{\infty} (n + a - 1)(n + b - 1)e_{n-1}x^{n-1} = 0.$$

We thus find that e_0 is arbitrary and, for $n \geqq 1$,

(4) $$e_n = \frac{(n + a - 1)(n + b - 1)}{n(n + c - 1)} e_{n-1}.$$

The recurrence relation (4) may be solved by our customary device. The result is, for $n \geqq 1$,

(5) $$e_n = \frac{a(a+1)(a+2) \cdots (a+n-1) \cdot b(b+1)(b+2) \cdots (b+n-1)e_0}{n!c(c + 1)(c + 2) \cdots (c + n - 1)}.$$

But (5) is greatly simplified by use of the factorial function. We rewrite (5) as

(6) $$e_n = \frac{(a)_n(b)_n}{n!(c)_n} \cdot e_0.$$

Let us choose $e_0 = 1$ and write our first solution of the hypergeometric equation as

(7) $$y_1 = 1 + \sum_{n=1}^{\infty} \frac{(a)_n(b)_n x^n}{(c)_n n!}.$$

The particular solution y_1 in (7) is called the hypergeometric function and for it a common symbol is $F(a, b; c; x)$. That is,

$$F(a, b; c; x) = 1 + \sum_{n=1}^{\infty} \frac{(a)_n(b)_n x^n}{(c)_n n!},$$

and $y_1 = F(a, b; c; x)$ is a solution of equation (1).

The other root of the indicial equation is $(1 - c)$. We may put

$$y = \sum_{n=0}^{\infty} f_n x^{n+1-c}$$

into equation (1), determine f_n in the usual manner, and arrive at a second solution

$$(8) \qquad y_2 = x^{1-c} + \sum_{n=1}^{\infty} \frac{(a + 1 - c)_n (b + 1 - c)_n x^{n+1-c}}{(2 - c)_n n!}.$$

In the hypergeometric notation this second solution (8) may be written

$$y_2 = x^{1-c} F(a + 1 - c, b + 1 - c; 2 - c; x),$$

which means exactly the same as (8). The solutions (7) and (8) are valid in $0 < |x| < 1$, a region extending to the nearest other singular point of the differential equation (1).

If c is an integer, one of the solutions (7) or (8) is correct, but the other involves a zero denominator. For example, if $c = 5$, then in (8), $(2 - c)_n = (-3)_n$ and as soon as $n \geq 4$, $(-3)_n = 0$. For,

$$(-3)_4 = (-3)(-2)(-1)(0) = 0.$$

If c is an integer, but a and b are nonintegral, one of the solutions about $x = 0$ of the hypergeometric equation is of logarithmic type. If c and one or both of a and b are integers, the solution may or may not involve a logarithm. To save space we omit logarithmic solutions of the hypergeometric equation.

116. Laguerre polynomials

The equation

$$(1) \qquad xy'' + (1 - x)y' + ny = 0$$

is called Laguerre's equation. If n is a non-negative integer, one solution of equation (1) is a polynomial.

Consider the solution of (1) about the regular singular point $x = 0$. The indicial equation has equal roots $c = 0, 0$. Hence one solution will involve a logarithm. We seek the nonlogarithmic solution.

Let us put

$$y = \sum_{k=0}^{\infty} a_k x^k$$

into (1) and obtain, in the usual way,

$$(2) \qquad \sum_{k=0}^{\infty} k^2 a_k x^{k-1} - \sum_{k=1}^{\infty} (k - 1 - n) a_{k-1} x^{k-1} = 0.$$

From (2) we find that

$$k \geq 1: \quad a_k = \frac{(k - 1 - n) a_{k-1}}{k^2}$$

$$= \frac{(-n)(-n + 1) \cdots (-n + k - 1) a_0}{(k!)^2} = \frac{(-n)_k}{(k!)^2} a_0.$$

If n is a non-negative integer, $(-n)_k = 0$ for $k > n$. Therefore, with a_0 chosen equal to unity, one solution of equation (1) is

$$(3) \qquad y_1 = \sum_{k=0}^{n} \frac{(-n)_k x^k}{(k!)^2}.$$

The right member of (3) is called the Laguerre polynomial and is usually denoted by $L_n(x)$:

$$(4) \qquad L_n(x) = \sum_{k=0}^{n} \frac{(-n)_k x^k}{(k!)^2} = \sum_{k=0}^{n} \frac{(-1)^k n! x^k}{(k!)^2 (n - k)!}.$$

The student should prove the equivalence of the two summations in (4) by showing that

$$(-n)_k = \frac{(-1)^k n!}{(n - k)!}.$$

One solution of (1) is $y_1 = L_n(x)$. The associated logarithmic solution may, after considerable simplification, be put in the form

$$(5) \quad y_2 = L_n(x) \ln x + \sum_{k=1}^{n} \frac{(-n)_k (H_{n-k} - H_n - 2H_k) x^k}{(k!)^2}$$

$$+ \sum_{k=1}^{\infty} \frac{(-1)^n n! (k - 1)! x^{k+n}}{[(k + n)!]^2}.$$

The solution (3) is valid for all finite x; the solution (5) is valid for $0 < |x| < \infty$.

117. Bessel's equation with index not an integer

The equation

$$(1) \qquad x^2 y'' + x y' + (x^2 - n^2) y = 0$$

is called Bessel's equation of index n. Equation (1) has a regular singular point at $x = 0$, but no other singular points in the finite plane. At $x = 0$ the roots of the indicial equation are $c_1 = n$, $c_2 = -n$. In this section we assume that n is not an integer.

It is a simple exercise in the methods of Chapter 21 to show that if $n \neq$ an integer, then two linearly independent solutions of (1) are

$$(2) \qquad y_1 = \sum_{k=0}^{\infty} \frac{(-1)^k x^{2k+n}}{2^{2k} k! (1+n)_k},$$

$$(3) \qquad y_2 = \sum_{k=0}^{\infty} \frac{(-1)^k x^{2k-n}}{2^{2k} k! (1-n)_k},$$

valid in $0 < |x| < \infty$.
The function

$$y_3 = \frac{1}{2^n \Gamma(1+n)} y_1 = \sum_{k=0}^{\infty} \frac{(-1)^k x^{2k+n}}{2^{2k+n} k! \Gamma(k+n+1)},$$

also a solution of equation (1), is called $J_n(x)$, the Bessel function of the first kind and of index n. Thus

$$(4) \qquad y_3 = J_n(x) = \sum_{k=0}^{\infty} \frac{(-1)^k x^{2k+n}}{2^{2k+n} k! \Gamma(k+n+1)}$$

is a solution of (1) and the general solution of (1) may be written

$$(5) \qquad y = A J_n(x) + B J_{-n}(x), \quad n \neq \text{an integer.}$$

That $J_{-n}(x)$ is a solution of the differential equation (1) should be evident from the fact that the parameter n enters (1) only in the term n^2. It is also true that

$$J_{-n}(x) = \frac{1}{2^{-n} \Gamma(1-n)} y_2.$$

118. Bessel's equation with index an integer

In Bessel's equation

(1) $$x^2y'' + xy' + (x^2 - n^2)y = 0,$$

let n now be zero or a positive integer. Then

(2) $$y_1 = J_n(x) = \sum_{k=0}^{\infty} \frac{(-1)^k x^{2k+n}}{2^{2k+n} k! \Gamma(k + n + 1)}$$

is one solution of equation (1). Any solution linearly independent of (2) must contain $\ln x$. We have already solved (1) for $n = 0$ in Ex. 6, page 331, and for $n = 1$ in Ex. 6, page 342.

For n an integer ≥ 2, put

$$y = \sum_{j=0}^{\infty} a_j x^{j+c},$$

proceed with the technique of Section 111, determine $y(x, c)$ and $\dfrac{\partial}{\partial c} y(x, c)$, and then use $c = -n$ to obtain two solutions:

(3) $$y_2 = \sum_{k=n}^{\infty} \frac{(-1)^k x^{2k-n}}{2^{2k-1}(1 - n)_{n-1}(k - n)! k!}$$

and

(4) $$y_3 = y_2 \ln x + x^{-n} + \sum_{k=1}^{n-1} \frac{(-1)^k x^{2k-n}}{2^{2k}(1 - n)_k k!}$$

$$+ \sum_{k=n}^{\infty} \frac{(-1)^{k+1}(H_{k-n} + H_k - H_{n-1})x^{2k-n}}{2^{2k-1}(1 - n)_{n-1}(k - n)! k!}.$$

A shift of index in (3) from k to $(k + n)$ yields

$$y_2 = \sum_{k=0}^{\infty} \frac{(-1)^{k+n} x^{2k+n}}{2^{2k+2n-1}(1 - n)_{n-1} k! (k + n)!}.$$

But for $n \geq 2$, $(1 - n)_{n-1} = (-1)^{n-1}(n - 1)!$, so

$$y_2 = \frac{-1}{2^{n-1}(n - 1)!} J_n(x).$$

We can therefore replace solution (3) with

(5) $$y_1 = J_n(x).$$

By similar manipulations, we replace solution (4) with

$$(6) \quad y_4 = J_n(x) \ln x + \sum_{k=0}^{n-1} \frac{(-1)^{k+1}(n-1)!x^{2k-n}}{2^{2k+1-n}k!(1-n)_k}$$

$$+ \tfrac{1}{2} \sum_{k=0}^{\infty} \frac{(-1)^{k+1}(H_k + H_{k+n})x^{2k+n}}{2^{2k+n}k!(k+n)!}.$$

For n an integer > 1, equations (5) and (6) can be used as the fundamental pair of linearly independent solutions of Bessel's equation (1).

119. Hermite polynomials

The equation
$$(1) \qquad y'' - 2xy' + 2ny = 0$$
is called Hermite's equation. Since equation (1) has no singular points in the finite plane, $x = 0$ is an ordinary point of the equation. We put

$$y = \sum_{j=0}^{\infty} a_j x^j$$

and employ the methods of Chapter 20 to obtain the general solution

$$(2) \quad y = a_0 \left[1 + \sum_{k=1}^{\infty} \frac{2^k(-n)(-n+2) \cdots (-n+2k-2)x^{2k}}{(2k)!} \right]$$

$$+ a_1 \left[x + \sum_{k=1}^{\infty} \frac{2^k(1-n)(1-n+2) \cdots (1-n+2k-2)x^{2k+1}}{(2k+1)!} \right],$$

valid for all finite x and with a_0 and a_1 arbitrary.

Interest in equation (1) is greatest when n is a positive integer or zero. If n is an even integer, the coefficient of a_0 in (2) terminates, each term for $k \geq \frac{1}{2}(n+2)$ being zero. If n is an odd integer, the coefficient of a_1 in (2) terminates, each term for $k \geq \frac{1}{2}(n+1)$ being zero. Thus Hermite's equation always has a polynomial solution, of degree n, for n zero or a positive integer. It is elementary but tedious to obtain from (2) a single expression for this polynomial solution. The result is

$$(3) \qquad H_n(x) = \sum_{k=0}^{[\frac{1}{2}n]} \frac{(-1)^k n!(2x)^{n-2k}}{k!(n-2k)!},$$

in which $[\frac{1}{2}n]$ stands for the greatest integer $\leq \frac{1}{2}n$.

The polynomial $H_n(x)$ of (3) is the Hermite polynomial; $y = H_n(x)$ is a solution of equation (1).

120. Legendre polynomials

The equation

(1) $$(1 - x^2)y'' - 2xy' + n(n + 1)y = 0$$

is called Legendre's equation. Let us solve (1) about the regular singular point $x = 1$. We put $x - 1 = v$ and obtain the transformed equation

(2) $$v(v + 2)\frac{d^2y}{dv^2} + 2(v + 1)\frac{dy}{dv} - n(n + 1)y = 0.$$

At $v = 0$, equation (2) has, as roots of its indicial equation, $c = 0, 0$. Hence one solution is logarithmic. We are interested here only in the nonlogarithmic solution.

Following the methods of Chapter 21, put

$$y = \sum_{k=0}^{\infty} a_k v^k$$

into equation (2) and thus arrive at the results: a_0 is arbitrary and

(3) $$k \geqq 1: \quad a_k = \frac{-(k - n - 1)(k + n)a_{k-1}}{2k^2}.$$

Solve the recurrence relation (3) and thus obtain

$$a_k = \frac{(-1)^k(-n)_k(1 + n)_k a_0}{2^k(k!)^2},$$

with the factorial notation of Section 114.

We may now write one solution of equation (1) in the form

(4) $$y_1 = 1 + \sum_{k=1}^{\infty} \frac{(-1)^k(-n)_k(n + 1)_k(x - 1)^k}{2^k(k!)^2}.$$

Since $k! = (1)_k$, we may put (4) into the form

(5) $$y_1 = 1 + \sum_{k=1}^{\infty} \frac{(-n)_k(n + 1)_k}{(1)_k k!}\left(\frac{1 - x}{2}\right)^k.$$

The right member of equation (5) is an example of the hypergeometric function which we met in Section 115. In fact,

(6) $$y_1 = F\left(-n, n + 1; 1; \frac{1 - x}{2}\right).$$

If n is a positive integer or zero, the series in (4), (5), or (6) terminates. It is then called the Legendre polynomial and designated $P_n(x)$. We write our nonlogarithmic solution of Legendre's equation as

$$(7) \qquad y_1 = P_n(x) = F\left(-n, n+1; 1; \frac{1-x}{2}\right).$$

121. The confluent* hypergeometric equation

The equation

$$(1) \qquad xy'' + (c - x)y' - ay = 0$$

has a regular singular point at $x = 0$ with zero and $(1 - c)$ as roots of the indicial equation there. Equation (1) is called the confluent hypergeometric equation. If c is not an integer, there is no logarithmic solution of (1) about $x = 0$, so we restrict ourselves here to that simple situation.

In the usual manner we put

$$y = \sum_{n=0}^{\infty} b_n x^n$$

into (1) and thus find that b_0 is arbitrary and

$$n \geq 1: \quad b_n = \frac{(n - 1 + a)b_{n-1}}{n(n - 1 + c)}.$$

The recurrence relation yields

$$n \geq 1: \quad b_n = \frac{(a)_n b_0}{n!(c)_n}$$

in the notation of the factorial function of Section 114.

Therefore equation (1) has a solution

$$(2) \qquad y_1 = 1 + \sum_{n=1}^{\infty} \frac{(a)_n x^n}{(c)_n n!},$$

valid for all finite x. Note how much the right member of (2) resembles the hypergeometric function

---

* The concept of confluence of singularities is treated in Chapter 10 of E. D. Rainville's *Intermediate Differential Equations*, 2nd ed. (New York: The Macmillan Co., 1964).

$$(3) \qquad F(a, b; c; x) = 1 + \sum_{n=1}^{\infty} \frac{(a)_n (b)_n x^n}{(c)_n n!}$$

of Section 115. In (2), the series has only one numerator parameter, a, and one denominator parameter, c. In (3) there are two numerator parameters, a and b, and one denominator parameter, c. It is therefore customary to use for the right member of (2) a notation like that in (3). We write

$$(4) \qquad {}_1F_1(a; c; x) = 1 + \sum_{n=1}^{\infty} \frac{(a)_n x^n}{(c)_n n!},$$

with the subscripts before and after the F denoting the number of numerator and denominator parameters, respectively. When it is thought desirable, the function symbol on the left in (3) is similarly written ${}_2F_1(a, b; c; x)$. Functions of hypergeometric type with any number of numerator and denominator parameters have been studied for many years.

The subscripts on the F play a useful role when the nature of the function, but not its specific parameters, is under discussion. For instance, we say, "Any ${}_0F_1$ is essentially a Bessel function of the first kind," and "The Laguerre polynomial is a terminating ${}_1F_1$." The detailed statements are as follows.

$$(5) \qquad J_n(x) = \frac{(x/2)^n}{\Gamma(n+1)} \, {}_0F_1\left(-; n+1; -\frac{x^2}{4}\right),$$

$$(6) \qquad L_n(x) = {}_1F_1(-n; 1; x).$$

We have seen that the differential equation (1) has one solution, as indicated in (2),

$$(7) \qquad y_1 = {}_1F_1(a; c; x).$$

The student can show that another solution, linearly independent of (7), is

$$(8) \qquad y_2 = x^{1-c} {}_1F_1(a+1-c; 2-c; x),$$

as long as c is not an integer.

Again we omit discussion of the logarithmic solutions which may enter if c is integral.

CHAPTER 23

Additional Topics on

Power Series Solutions

122. Many-term recurrence relations, ordinary points

In Chapters 20 and 21, the equations to be solved were chosen carefully to be certain that each led to a recurrence relation involving only two different coefficients. Nothing in the method dictates such a restriction, but those recurrence relations are the only ones for which we know how to obtain a reasonably useful explicit form of solution. As a matter of fact, recurrence relations that cannot be solved explicitly may still be useful and do, indeed, exhibit in an emphatic way the power of the theory behind our work.

Consider the equation

$$(1) \qquad\qquad y'' - y' + xy = 0,$$

which has no singular points in the finite plane. Let us solve the equation in the vicinity of $x = 0$. We know that there is a solution that assumes the form

$$(2) \qquad\qquad y = \sum_{n=0}^{\infty} a_n x^n,$$

with a_0 and a_1 arbitrary, and for which the power series involved converge for all finite x. To find the a_n, $n > 1$, we put the y of (2) into equation (1). We thus obtain, after appropriate shifting of the indices of summation,

$$\sum_{n=0}^{\infty} n(n-1)a_n x^{n-2} - \sum_{n=1}^{\infty} (n-1)a_{n-1}x^{n-2} + \sum_{n=3}^{\infty} a_{n-3}x^{n-2} = 0,$$

from which the relations for the determination of the a's are seen to be

$$n = 2: \quad 2a_2 - a_1 = 0,$$

$$n \geq 3: \quad n(n-1)a_n - (n-1)a_{n-1} + a_{n-3} = 0.$$

We cannot obtain an explicit formula for a_n, but we can compute as many coefficients as may be desired and we do know, from the theory not proved here, that the series solutions converge for all finite x. Knowledge of the convergence means much to us this time since we cannot fall back on the ratio test because we do not even have a formula for the general term in the series.

It is frequently desirable to tabulate, or to represent graphically, the solutions of a particular equation. With this in mind let us specialize our constants, a_0 and a_1. As long as the choices made lead to linearly independent solutions, it does not matter what values we use for the constants. Define as y_1 that solution with $a_0 = 1$, $a_1 = 0$, and as y_2 that solution in which $a_0 = 0$, $a_1 = 1$; then y_1 and y_2 will be linearly independent.

The complete solution of the differential equation of the present example is $y = Ay_1 + By_2$, where A and B are arbitrary constants; where y_1 is given by

$$(3) \qquad\qquad y_1 = \sum_{n=0}^{\infty} a_n x^n,$$

in which $a_0 = 1$, $a_1 = 0$, $a_2 = 0$; and for

$$n \geq 3: \quad a_n = \frac{(n-1)a_{n-1} - a_{n-3}}{n(n-1)};$$

and where y_2 is given by

$$(4) \qquad\qquad y_2 = \sum_{n=0}^{\infty} b_n x^n,$$

in which $b_0 = 0$, $b_1 = 1$, $b_2 = \frac{1}{2}$, and for

$$n \geq 3: \quad b_n = \frac{(n-1)b_{n-1} - b_{n-3}}{n(n-1)}.$$

It is sometimes interesting and helpful to compute several coefficients in the series solution. For the present example it can be shown that

(5) $y_1 = 1 - \frac{1}{6}x^3 - \frac{1}{24}x^4 - \frac{1}{120}x^5 + \frac{1}{240}x^6 + \frac{1}{630}x^7 + \cdots$,

(6) $y_2 = x + \frac{1}{2}x^2 + \frac{1}{6}x^3 - \frac{1}{24}x^4 - \frac{1}{30}x^5 - \frac{1}{90}x^6 - \frac{1}{1680}x^7 + \cdots$.

Equations (5) and (6) do not by any means define the functions y_1 and y_2; they contain no indication of the coefficients of higher powers of x. For complete descriptions of the series we must fall back on equations (3) and (4) with the relations on the a_n and b_n given with those equations.

Exercises

Solve each equation about $x = 0$ unless otherwise instructed. State where your solutions are valid.

1. $y'' + (1 + x + x^2)y = 0$.

ANS. $y_1 = \sum_{n=0}^{\infty} a_n x^n$, in which $a_0 = 1$, $a_1 = 0$, $a_2 = -\frac{1}{2}$, $a_3 = -\frac{1}{6}$,

$$n \geq 4: \quad a_n = \frac{-1}{n(n-1)}(a_{n-2} + a_{n-3} + a_{n-4});$$

$y_2 = \sum_{n=0}^{\infty} b_n x^n$, in which $b_0 = 0$, $b_1 = 1$, $b_2 = 0$, $b_3 = -\frac{1}{6}$,

$$n \geq 4: \quad b_n = -\frac{1}{n(n-1)}(b_{n-2} + b_{n-3} + b_{n-4}).$$

2. Show that the series in the answers to Ex. 1 start out as follows:

$y_1 = 1 - \frac{1}{2}x^2 - \frac{1}{6}x^3 - \frac{1}{24}x^4 + \frac{1}{30}x^5 + \frac{17}{720}x^6 + \frac{1}{240}x^7 + \cdots$

and

$y_2 = x - \frac{1}{6}x^3 - \frac{1}{12}x^4 - \frac{1}{24}x^5 + \frac{1}{120}x^6 + \frac{1}{144}x^7 + \cdots$.

3. $(1 - x)y'' + (2 + x)y' - 2y = 0$.

ANS. $y_1 = \sum_{n=0}^{\infty} a_n x^n$, in which $a_0 = 1$, $a_1 = 0$,

$$n \geq 2: \quad a_n = \frac{(n-4)}{n(n-1)}[(n-1)a_{n-1} - a_{n-2}];$$

$y_2 = \sum_{n=0}^{\infty} b_n x^n$, in which $b_0 = 0$, $b_1 = 1$,

$$n \geq 2: \quad b_n = \frac{(n-4)}{n(n-1)}[(n-1)b_{n-1} - b_{n-2}].$$

4. Show that the answers to Ex. 3 start out as follows:

$$y_1 = 1 + x^2 - \tfrac{1}{3}x^3 + \tfrac{1}{60}x^5 + \tfrac{1}{180}x^6 + \tfrac{1}{840}x^7 + \cdots$$

and

$$y_2 = x - x^2 + \tfrac{1}{2}x^3 - \tfrac{1}{40}x^5 - \tfrac{1}{120}x^6 - \tfrac{1}{560}x^7 + \cdots .$$

5. In Ex. 3, make the choices $a_0 = 3$, $a_1 = 2$, and determine the corresponding solution of the differential equation.

ANS. $y_3 = 3 + 2x + x^2.$

6. $(1 + x)y'' + 2y' - y = 0.$

ANS. $y_1 = \displaystyle\sum_{n=0}^{\infty} a_n x^n$, in which $a_0 = 1$, $a_1 = 0$,

$$n \geq 2: \quad a_n = -a_{n-1} + a_{n-2}/[n(n-1)];$$

$$y_2 = \sum_{n=0}^{\infty} b_n x^n, \text{ in which } b_0 = 0, \ b_1 = 1,$$

$$n \geq 2: \quad b_n = -b_{n-1} + b_{n-2}/[n(n-1)].$$

7. Show that the series in the answers for Ex. 6 start out as follows:

$$y_1 = 1 + \tfrac{1}{2}x^2 - \tfrac{1}{2}x^3 + \tfrac{13}{24}x^4 - \tfrac{17}{30}x^5 + \tfrac{421}{720}x^6 + \cdots ,$$

$$y_2 = x - x^2 + \tfrac{7}{6}x^3 - \tfrac{5}{4}x^4 + \tfrac{157}{120}x^5 - \tfrac{27}{20}x^6 + \cdots .$$

8. In the answers for Ex. 6, prove that the coefficients alternate in sign for $n \geq 2$. Put $a_n = (-1)^n t_n$ and consider the recurrence relation for t_n.

9. Let $\sigma_n = t_n/t_{n-1}$ where $t_n = |a_n|$ as in Ex. 8. Show that

$$\sigma_n = 1 + \frac{1}{n(n-1)\sigma_{n-1}}$$

and conclude that for $n > 4$, $1 < \sigma_n < 21/20$.

10. For $0 < x < 1$, the ratio of the absolute values of consecutive terms of the series for y_1 in Ex. 6 is given by

$$\frac{|a_n x^n|}{|a_{n-1} x^{n-1}|} = \sigma_n x$$

with the notation of Ex. 9. Show that for $n > 4$ and $0 < x < 0.95$ it follows that $0 < \sigma_n x < 1$. Hence prove that for these values of x the terms in the y_1 series steadily decrease in numerical value.

11. Use the results of Exs. 8 and 10 to prove that if E_n is the error made in replacing y_1 with the sum of its terms out to and including $a_n x^n$, then for $n > 4$ and $0 < x < 0.95$ it is true that

$$|E_n| < |a_{n+1} x^{n+1}|.$$

12. Follow the procedure of Exs. 9, 10, and 11 and arrive at similar conclusions for the series y_2 in Ex. 6.

13. Compute y_1 and y_2 of Ex. 6 correct to three decimal places when $x = 0.1$. ANS. $y_1(0.1) = 1.005, y_2(0.1) = 0.091$.

14. Prove that for any fixed x in the interval $0 < x < 1$ there exists an n_0 such that for $n > n_0$ the terms in the series for y_1 (or for y_2) steadily decrease in numerical value.

15. Prove that for $n > 4$ and $-0.95 < x < 0$,

$$|E_n| < |a_{n+1}x^{n+1}| \cdot \frac{20}{20 + 21x},$$

where the E_n is as defined in Ex. 11.

16. Compute y_1 and y_2 of Ex. 6 to three decimal places for $x = -0.1$. ANS. $y_1(-0.1) = 1.006, y_2(-0.1) = -0.111$.

17. Solve the equation of Ex. 6 near the regular singular point $x = -1$.

$$\text{ANS.} \quad y_3 = \sum_{n=1}^{\infty} \frac{(x+1)^{n-1}}{n!(n-1)!};$$

$$y_4 = y_3 \ln (x+1) + (x+1)^{-1} - \sum_{n=1}^{\infty} \frac{(H_n + H_{n-1})(x+1)^{n-1}}{n!(n-1)!}.$$

18. $y'' - (1 + x^3)y = 0$.

19. $(1 - x)y'' + xy' + y = 0$.

20. Solve the equation of Ex. 19 about its regular singular point.

123. Many-term recurrence relations, regular singular point

In solving an equation near a regular singular point it will sometimes happen that a many-term recurrence relation is encountered. In nonlogarithmic cases, the methods developed in Chapter 21 are easily applied and no complications result except that usually no explicit formula will be obtained for the coefficients.

In logarithmic cases, the methods introduced in Chapter 21, constructing $y(x, c)$ and $\partial y(x, c)/\partial c$, can become awkward when a many-term recurrence relation is present. There is another attack which has its good points.

Consider the problem of solving the equation

(1) $\qquad L(y) = x^2 y'' + x(3 + x)y' + (1 + x + x^2)y = 0$

near the origin. From

(2)
$$y = \sum_{n=0}^{\infty} a_n x^{n+c}$$

it is easily shown that

(3) $\quad L(y) = \sum_{n=0}^{\infty} (n + c + 1)^2 a_n x^{n+c} + \sum_{n=1}^{\infty} (n + c) a_{n-1} x^{n+c}$

$$+ \sum_{n=2}^{\infty} a_{n-2} x^{n+c}.$$

Therefore the indicial equation is $(c + 1)^2 = 0$.

Since the roots of the indicial equation are equal, $c = -1, -1$, it follows that there exist the solutions

(4)
$$y_1 = \sum_{n=0}^{\infty} a_n x^{n-1},$$

(5)
$$y_2 = y_1 \ln x + \sum_{n=1}^{\infty} b_n x^{n-1},$$

valid for all finite $x \neq 0$. The region of validity is obtained from the differential equation; the form of the solutions can be seen by the reasoning in Section 109.

We shall determine the a_n, $n > 0$, by requiring that $L(y_1) = 0$. Then the b_n, $n \geq 1$, will be determined in terms of the a_n by requiring that $L(y_2) = 0$.

From $L(y_1) = 0$ it follows that

$$\sum_{n=0}^{\infty} n^2 a_n x^{n-1} + \sum_{n=1}^{\infty} (n - 1) a_{n-1} x^{n-1} + \sum_{n=2}^{\infty} a_{n-2} x^{n-1} = 0.$$

Let us choose $a_0 = 1$. Then the rest of the a's are determined by

$$n = 1: \quad a_1 + 0 \cdot a_0 = 0,$$

$$n \geq 2: \quad n^2 a_n + (n - 1) a_{n-1} + a_{n-2} = 0.$$

Therefore one solution of the differential equation (1) is

(6)
$$y_1 = \sum_{n=0}^{\infty} a_n x^{n-1},$$

in which $a_0 = 1$, $a_1 = 0$,

$$n \geq 2: \quad a_n = - \frac{(n - 1) a_{n-1} + a_{n-2}}{n^2}.$$

Next we wish to require that $L(y_2) = 0$. From

(5)
$$y_2 = y_1 \ln x + \sum_{n=1}^{\infty} b_n x^{n-1}$$

it follows that

$$y_2' = y_1' \ln x + x^{-1}y_1 + \sum_{n=1}^{\infty} (n-1)b_n x^{n-2}$$

and

$$y_2'' = y_1'' \ln x + 2x^{-1}y_1' - x^{-2}y_1 + \sum_{n=1}^{\infty} (n-1)(n-2)b_n x^{n-3}.$$

Now direct computation of $L(y_2)$ yields

$$L(y_2) = L(y_1) \ln x + 2xy_1' - y_1 + xy_1 + 3y_1 + \sum_{n=1}^{\infty} n^2 b_n x^{n-1}$$
$$+ \sum_{n=2}^{\infty} (n-1)b_{n-1}x^{n-1} + \sum_{n=3}^{\infty} b_{n-2}x^{n-1}.$$

Since $L(y_1) = 0$, the requirement $L(y_2) = 0$ leads to the equation

(7)
$$\sum_{n=1}^{\infty} n^2 b_n x^{n-1} + \sum_{n=2}^{\infty} (n-1)b_{n-1}x^{n-1} + \sum_{n=3}^{\infty} b_{n-2}x^{n-1}$$
$$= -2xy_1' - 2y_1 - xy_1$$
$$= -\sum_{n=1}^{\infty} 2na_n x^{n-1} - \sum_{n=1}^{\infty} a_{n-1}x^{n-1},$$

in which the right member has been simplified by using equation (6). From the identity (7), relations for the determination of the b_n from the a_n follow. They are

$n = 1:$ $\qquad b_1 = -2a_1 - a_0,$

$n = 2:$ $\qquad 4b_2 + b_1 = -4a_2 - a_1,$

$n \geq 3:$ $\quad n^2 b_n + (n-1)b_{n-1} + b_{n-2} = -2na_n - a_{n-1}.$

Therefore the original differential equation has the two linearly independent solutions given by the y_1 of equation (6) and by

(8)
$$y_2 = y_1 \ln x + \sum_{n=1}^{\infty} b_n x^{n-1},$$

in which $b_1 = -1$, $b_2 = \frac{1}{2}$,

$$n \geq 3: \quad b_n = -\frac{(n-1)b_{n-1} + b_{n-2}}{n^2} - \frac{2a_n}{n} - \frac{a_{n-1}}{n^2}.$$

If the indicial equation has roots that differ by a positive integer and if a logarithmic solution exists, then the two solutions will have the form

$$y_1 = \sum_{n=0}^{\infty} a_n x^{n+c_1},$$

$$y_2 = y_1 \ln x + \sum_{n=0}^{\infty} b_n x^{n+c_2},$$

where c_1 is the larger and c_2 the smaller root of the indicial equation. The a_n and b_n can still be determined by the procedure used in this section.

124. Bounding the error in computations

If series solutions of a differential equation are to be used in numerical computations, it is highly desirable to have bounds on the error made by stopping with a specified term of the series. If the terms of the series are known explicitly, as in the answers in Chapters 20 through 22, the problem becomes one usually treated to some extent in calculus. It is the purpose of this section to show that such bounds can be obtained for series whose terms are known only through a many-term recurrence relation such as those encountered so far in this chapter.

Suppose that we wish to compute with the series in the solutions $y_1(x)$ and $y_2(x)$ of the example in the preceding section. We had

$$(1) \qquad\qquad y_1(x) = \sum_{n=0}^{\infty} a_n x^{n-1}$$

in which $a_0 = 1$, $a_1 = 0$,

$$(2) \qquad\qquad n \geq 2: \quad a_n = -\frac{(n-1)a_{n-1} + a_{n-2}}{n^2}.$$

Let $E_n(x)$ be the error made in computing $y_1(x)$ by using the terms on the right in (1) only out to and including the term $a_n x^{n-1}$. Then $E_n(x)$

is equal to the sum of the remaining terms:

$$(3) \qquad E_n(x) = \sum_{s=n+1}^{\infty} a_s x^{s-1},$$

and

$$(4) \qquad |E_n(x)| \le \sum_{s=n+1}^{\infty} |a_s x^{s-1}|.$$

First we need to bound $|a_n|$ where a_n is determined by the recurrence relation (2). We know $a_0 = 1$, $a_1 = 0$. We compute a few more, finding that $a_2 = -\frac{1}{4}$, $a_3 = \frac{1}{18}$, $a_4 = \frac{1}{192}$, etc. Next we search for an inequality on $|a_n|$ that is satisfied by trial for small values of n and that can be proved for all n thereafter by induction based on the recurrence relation (2). This is the only difficult step. Often it takes much experience, some skill, and many trials to obtain an inequality strong enough to be useful and weak enough for us to establish it.

Consider the inequality

$$(5) \qquad |a_k| < \frac{2^k}{k!},$$

which is clearly satisfied for $k = 1, 2, 3, 4$. We assume that (5) is satisfied for all k in the range $1 \le k < n$ and must prove that it follows from (2) that (5) is also satisfied for $k = n$. From (2) we obtain, for $n \ge 3$,

$$(6) \qquad |a_n| \le \frac{1}{n^2} [(n-1)|a_{n-1}| + |a_{n-2}|].$$

Since (5) is assumed true for $k = n-1$ and $k = n-2$, the inequality (6) yields

$$|a_n| < \frac{1}{n^2} \left[\frac{2^{n-1}(n-1)}{(n-1)!} + \frac{2^{n-2}}{(n-2)!} \right]$$

$$< \frac{2^{n-2}}{n^2} \left[\frac{2}{(n-2)!} + \frac{1}{(n-2)!} \right]$$

$$< \frac{3 \cdot 2^{n-2}}{n^2(n-2)!}$$

$$< \frac{3(n-1)}{4n} \cdot \frac{2^n}{n!}$$

$$< \frac{2^n}{n!},$$

since $3(n - 1) < 4n$. It follows by induction that we have proved that

(7)
$$|a_n| < \frac{2^n}{n!}, \quad \text{for } n \geq 1.$$

We now return to (4) and find that, for $n \geq 1$,

(8)
$$|E_n(x)| < \sum_{s=n+1}^{\infty} \frac{2^s |x|^{s-1}}{s!}.$$

To simplify the series in (8), we shift index from s to $(s + n + 1)$ and obtain

(9)
$$|E_n(x)| < \sum_{s=0}^{\infty} \frac{2^{s+n+1} |x|^{s+n}}{(s + n + 1)!}.$$

Since $(s + n + 1)!$ is unwieldy, we replace it by something simpler and smaller, thus making the right member of (9) larger. For positive s and n,

$$(n + 1)! s! < (s + n + 1)!.$$

Hence

$$|E_n(x)| < \sum_{s=0}^{\infty} \frac{2^{s+n+1} |x|^{s+n}}{(n + 1)! s!} = \frac{2^{n+1} |x|^n}{(n + 1)!} \sum_{s=0}^{\infty} \frac{2^s |x|^s}{s!},$$

and, finally,

(10)
$$|E_n(x)| < \frac{2^{n+1} |x|^n e^{2|x|}}{(n + 1)!}.$$

Let us compute $y_1(\tfrac{1}{4})$ to two decimal places. We know that the $y_1(x)$ series starts out

(11)
$$y_1(x) = x^{-1} + 0 - \tfrac{1}{4}x + \tfrac{1}{18}x^2 + \tfrac{1}{192}x^3 + \cdots .$$

If we stop with the x^3 term, $n - 1 = 3$, $n = 4$, and we need to bound $E_4(\tfrac{1}{4})$. From (10),

$$|E_4(\tfrac{1}{4})| < \frac{2^5 (\tfrac{1}{4})^4 e^{\tfrac{1}{2}}}{5!} = \frac{e^{\tfrac{1}{2}}}{960} = 0.0017.$$

Then

$$y_1(\tfrac{1}{4}) = 4 - \tfrac{1}{4}(\tfrac{1}{4}) + \tfrac{1}{18}(\tfrac{1}{4})^2 + \tfrac{1}{192}(\tfrac{1}{4})^3$$
$$= 4 - 0.0625 + 0.0035 + 0.0001$$
$$= 3.9411,$$

with an error less than 0.0017. We conclude that, to two decimal places, $y_1(\tfrac{1}{4}) = 3.94$.

Turn now to $y_2(x)$, which was found in Section 123 to be given by

$$(12) \qquad y_2(x) = y_1(x) \ln x + \sum_{n=1}^{\infty} b_n x^{n-1},$$

in which $b_1 = -1$, $b_2 = \frac{1}{2}$,

$$(13) \qquad n \geq 3: \quad b_n = -\frac{(n-1)b_{n-1} + b_{n-2}}{n^2} - \frac{2a_n}{n} - \frac{a_{n-1}}{n^2}.$$

We show now that $|b_n| < 2^{n+1}/n!$. From (13) it follows that

$$b_3 = -\tfrac{1}{108}, \quad b_4 = -\tfrac{41}{1152}, \text{ etc.}$$

Let us assume

$$(14) \qquad |b_k| < \frac{2^{k+1}}{k!}$$

for $1 \leq k < n$. We know (14) is satisfied for $k = 1, 2, 3, 4$. From (13), (14), and (7), it follows that, for $n \geq 3$,

$$|b_n| < \frac{1}{n^2}\left[\frac{2^n(n-1)}{(n-1)!} + \frac{2^{n-1}}{(n-2)!}\right] + \frac{2^{n+1}}{n \cdot n!} + \frac{2^{n-1}}{n^2(n-1)!}$$

$$< \frac{2^n + 2^{n-1}}{n^2(n-2)!} + \frac{2^{n+1} + 2^{n-1}}{n \cdot n!}$$

$$< \frac{3 \cdot 2^{n-1}}{n^2(n-2)!} + \frac{5 \cdot 2^{n-1}}{n \cdot n!}$$

$$< \frac{2^{n-1}[3(n-1) + 5]}{n \cdot n!}$$

$$< \frac{3n+2}{4n} \cdot \frac{2^{n+1}}{n!}$$

$$< \frac{2^{n+1}}{n!},$$

since $3n + 2 \leq 4n$ for $n \geq 2$. Therefore, by induction,

$$(15) \qquad |b_n| < \frac{2^{n+1}}{n!}, \; n \geq 1.$$

Now let $E_n^*(x)$ be the error made in computing $\sum_{n=1}^{\infty} b_n x^{n-1}$ by using the terms up to and including $b_n x^{n-1}$. Then

$$E_n^*(x) = \sum_{s=n+1}^{\infty} b_s x^{s-1}$$

and by (15), for $n \geq 1$,

$$|E_n^*(x)| < \sum_{s=n+1}^{\infty} \frac{2^{s+1}|x|^{s-1}}{s!}$$

$$< \sum_{s=0}^{\infty} \frac{2^{s+n+2}|x|^{s+n}}{(s+n+1)!}$$

$$< \sum_{s=0}^{\infty} \frac{2^{s+n+2}|x|^{s+n}}{(n+1)!s!},$$

so

(16) $$|E_n^*(x)| < \frac{2^{n+2}|x|^n e^{2|x|}}{(n+1)!}.$$

The solution $y_2(x)$ starts out as

$$y_2(x) = y_1(x) \ln x - 1 + \tfrac{1}{2}x - \tfrac{1}{108}x^2 - \tfrac{41}{1152}x^3 + \cdots.$$

Let us compute $y_2(\tfrac{1}{4})$ to two decimal places. First we see that

$$|E_4^*(\tfrac{1}{4})| < \frac{2^6(\tfrac{1}{4})^4 e^{\tfrac{1}{2}}}{5!} = \frac{e^{\tfrac{1}{2}}}{480} = 0.003.$$

Then

$$y_2(\tfrac{1}{4}) = (3.94)(-1.386) - 1 + \tfrac{1}{8} - \tfrac{1}{108}(\tfrac{1}{4})^2 - \tfrac{41}{1152}(\tfrac{1}{4})^3$$

$$= -6.34.$$

Exercises

Solve each equation about $x = 0$ unless otherwise instructed.

1. $x^2 y'' + 3xy' + (1 + x + x^3)y = 0.$

ANS. $y_1 = \displaystyle\sum_{n=0}^{\infty} a_n x^{n-1}$, in which $a_0 = 1$, $a_1 = -1$, $a_2 = \tfrac{1}{4}$,

$$n \geq 3: \quad a_n = -\frac{a_{n-1} + a_{n-3}}{n^2};$$

$$y_2 = y_1 \ln x + \sum_{n=1}^{\infty} b_n x^{n-1}, \text{ in which } b_1 = 2, \ b_2 = -\tfrac{3}{4}, \ b_3 = \tfrac{19}{108}.$$

$$n \geq 4: \quad b_n = -\frac{b_{n-1} + b_{n-3}}{n^2} - \frac{2a_n}{n}.$$

2. $2x(1-x)y'' + (1-2x)y' + (2+x)y = 0.$

ANS. $y_1 = \displaystyle\sum_{n=0}^{\infty} a_n x^{n+\frac{1}{2}}$, in which $a_0 = 1$, $a_1 = -\frac{1}{2}$,

$$n \geq 2: \quad a_n = \frac{(2n+1)(2n-3)a_{n-1} - 2a_{n-2}}{2n(2n+1)};$$

$$y_2 = \sum_{n=0}^{\infty} b_n x^n, \text{ in which } b_0 = 1, \; b_1 = -2,$$

$$n \geq 2: \quad b_n = \frac{2n(n-2)b_{n-1} - b_{n-2}}{n(2n-1)}.$$

3. $xy'' + y' + x(1+x)y = 0.$

ANS. $y_1 = \displaystyle\sum_{n=0}^{\infty} a_n x^n$, in which $a_0 = 1$, $a_1 = 0$, $a_2 = -\frac{1}{4}$,

$$n \geq 3: \quad a_n = -\frac{a_{n-2} + a_{n-3}}{n^2};$$

$$y_2 = y_1 \ln x + \sum_{n=1}^{\infty} b_n x^n, \text{ in which } b_1 = 0, \; b_2 = \tfrac{1}{4}, \; b_3 = \tfrac{2}{27},$$

$$n \geq 4: \quad b_n = -\frac{b_{n-2} + b_{n-3}}{n^2} - \frac{2a_n}{n}.$$

4. $x^2 y'' + x(1+x)y' - (1 - 3x + 6x^2)y = 0.$

ANS. $y = \displaystyle\sum_{n=0}^{\infty} a_n x^{n-1}$, in which a_0 is arbitrary, $a_1 = 2a_0$, a_2 is arbitrary,

$$n \geq 3: \quad a_n = -\frac{(n+1)a_{n-1} - 6a_{n-2}}{n(n-2)}.$$

5. Show that the series in the answer to Ex. 4 start out as follows:

$$y = a_0(x^{-1} + 2 + 4x^2 - \tfrac{5}{2}x^3 + \tfrac{13}{5}x^4 - \tfrac{83}{60}x^5 + \cdots)$$
$$+ a_2(x - \tfrac{4}{3}x^2 + \tfrac{19}{12}x^3 - \tfrac{7}{6}x^4 + \tfrac{53}{72}x^5 + \cdots).$$

6. $xy'' + xy' + (1 + x^4)y = 0.$ Here the indicial equation has roots $c = 0$, $c = 1$, and an attempt to get a complete solution without $\ln x$ fails. Then we put

$$y_1 = \sum_{n=0}^{\infty} a_n x^{n+1},$$

$$y_2 = y_1 \ln x + \sum_{n=0}^{\infty} b_n x^n.$$

The coefficient $b_1(s = 1)$ turns out to be arbitrary and we choose it to be zero. Show that the indicated y_1 and y_2 are solutions if $a_0 = 1$,

$$a_1 = -1, \ a_2 = \tfrac{1}{2}, \ a_3 = -\tfrac{1}{6}, \ a_4 = \tfrac{1}{24},$$

$$n \geq 5: \quad a_n = -\frac{(n + 1)a_{n-1} + a_{n-5}}{n(n + 1)},$$

and if the b's are given by

$$b_0 = -1, \ b_1 = 0 \ \text{(so chosen)}, \ b_2 = 1, \ b_3 = -\tfrac{3}{4}, \ b_4 = \tfrac{11}{36},$$

$$n \geq 5: \quad b_n = -\frac{nb_{n-1} + b_{n-5}}{n(n - 1)} - \frac{(2n - 1)a_{n-1} + a_{n-2}}{n(n - 1)}.$$

7. For the y_1 in Ex. 6, prove that the a_n alternate in sign. Also compute the terms of y_1 out to the x^7 term.

ANS. $y_1 = x - x^2 + \tfrac{1}{2}x^3 - \tfrac{1}{6}x^4 + \tfrac{1}{24}x^5 - \tfrac{3}{24}x^6 + \tfrac{31}{1008}x^7 + \cdots$.

8. $x(x - 2)^2 y'' - 2(x - 2)y' + 2y = 0$.

ANS. $y_1 = 1 - \tfrac{1}{2}x$;

$$y_2 = y_1 \ln x + \sum_{n=1}^{\infty} b_n x^n, \text{ in which } b_1 = \tfrac{1}{2}, \ b_2 = -\tfrac{1}{8}, \ b_3 = -\tfrac{1}{48},$$

$$n \geq 4: \quad b_n = \frac{n - 2}{4n^2}[2(2n - 1)b_{n-1} - (n - 3)b_{n-2}].$$

9. Solve the equation of Ex. 8 about the point $x = 2$.

ANS. $y_1 = (x - 2)$;

$$y_2 = y_1 \ln (x - 2) + \sum_{n=1}^{\infty} \frac{(-1)^n(x - 2)^{n+1}}{2^n n}.$$

10. $2xy'' + (1 - x)y' - (1 + x)y = 0$.

ANS. $y_1 = \sum_{n=0}^{\infty} a_n x^{n+\frac{1}{2}}$ in which $a_0 = 1, \ a_1 = \tfrac{1}{2}$,

$$n \geq 2: \quad a_n = \frac{(2n + 1)a_{n-1} + 2a_{n-2}}{2n(2n + 1)};$$

$$y_2 = \sum_{n=0}^{\infty} b_n x^n \text{ in which } b_0 = 1, \ b_1 = 1,$$

$$n \geq 2: \quad b_n = \frac{nb_{n-1} + b_{n-2}}{n(2n - 1)}.$$

11. Show that the answers to Ex. 10 are also given by

$$y_2 = e^x, \ y_1 = e^x \int_0^{\sqrt{x}} \exp\left(-\tfrac{3}{2}\beta^2\right) d\beta.$$

125. Solution for large x

The power series solutions that have been studied up to this stage converge in regions surrounding some point $x = x_0$, usually the origin. Such solutions, although they may converge for large values of x, are apt to do so with discouraging slowness. For this reason, and for others of a more theoretical nature, we shall investigate the problem of obtaining solutions particularly useful for large x.

Consider the equation

$$(1) \qquad b_0(x)y'' + b_1(x)y' + b_2(x)y = 0$$

with polynomial coefficients. Let us put

$$(2) \qquad w = \frac{1}{x}$$

Then

$$\frac{dy}{dx} = \frac{dw}{dx}\frac{dy}{dw} = -\frac{1}{x^2}\frac{dy}{dw} = -w^2\frac{dy}{dw}$$

and

$$\frac{d^2y}{dx^2} = \frac{dw}{dx}\frac{d}{dw}\left(-w^2\frac{dy}{dw}\right) = -w^2\left(-w^2\frac{d^2y}{dw^2} - 2w\frac{dy}{dw}\right)$$

$$= w^4\frac{d^2y}{dw^2} + 2w^3\frac{dy}{dw}.$$

Thus equation (1) is transformed into the following equation in y and w:

$$(3) \quad b_0\left(\frac{1}{w}\right)w^4\frac{d^2y}{dw^2} + \left[2w^3b_0\left(\frac{1}{w}\right) - w^2b_1\left(\frac{1}{w}\right)\right]\frac{dy}{dw} + b_2\left(\frac{1}{w}\right)y = 0.$$

Since b_0, b_1, and b_2 are polynomials, equation (3) is readily converted into an equation with polynomial coefficients.

If the point $w = 0$ is an ordinary point or a regular singular point of equation (3), then our previous methods of attack will yield solutions valid for small w. But $w = \frac{1}{x}$, so small w means large x.

As a matter of terminology, whatever is true about equation (3) at $w = 0$ is said to be true about equation (1) "at the point at infinity." For instance, if the transformed equation has $w = 0$ as an ordinary point, then we say that equation (1) has an ordinary point at infinity. (See Exs. 1–6, pages 375–376.)

EXAMPLE: Obtain solutions valid for large x for the equation

(4) $$x^2 y'' + (3x - 1)y' + y = 0.$$

This equation has an irregular singular point at the origin and has no other singular points in the finite plane. To investigate the nature of equation (4) for large x, put $x = 1/w$. We have already found that

(5) $$\frac{dy}{dx} = -w^2 \frac{dy}{dw}$$

and

(6) $$\frac{d^2 y}{dx^2} = w^4 \frac{d^2 y}{dw^2} + 2w^3 \frac{dy}{dw}.$$

With the aid of (5) and (6) we see that equation (4) becomes

$$\frac{1}{w^2}\left(w^4 \frac{d^2 y}{dw^2} + 2w^3 \frac{dy}{dw}\right) + \left(\frac{3}{w} - 1\right)\left(-w^2 \frac{dy}{dw}\right) + y = 0,$$

or

(7) $$w^2 \frac{d^2 y}{dw^2} - w(1 - w)\frac{dy}{dw} + y = 0,$$

an equation which we wish to solve about $w = 0$.

Since $w = 0$ is a regular singular point of equation (7), the point at infinity is a regular singular point of equation (4).

From the assumed form

$$y = \sum_{n=0}^{\infty} a_n w^{n+c},$$

it follows from equation (7) by our usual methods that

$$L(y) = \sum_{n=0}^{\infty} (n + c - 1)^2 a_n w^{n+c} + \sum_{n=1}^{\infty} (n + c - 1)a_{n-1}w^{n+c},$$

in which $L(y)$ now represents the left member of equation (7). The indicial equation has equal roots, $c = 1, 1$. Let us set up $y(w, c)$ as usual. From the recurrence relation

$$n \geqq 1: \quad a_n = -\frac{a_{n-1}}{n + c - 1},$$

it follows that

$$a_n = \frac{(-1)^n a_0}{c(c + 1) \cdots (c + n - 1)}.$$

Hence we choose

$$y(w, c) = w^c + \sum_{n=1}^{\infty} \frac{(-1)^n w^{n+c}}{c(c+1) \cdots (c+n-1)},$$

and then find that

$$\frac{\partial y(w, c)}{\partial c} = y(w, c) \ln w$$

$$- \sum_{n=1}^{\infty} \frac{(-1)^n w^{n+c} \left\{ \dfrac{1}{c} + \dfrac{1}{c+1} + \cdots + \dfrac{1}{c+n-1} \right\}}{c(c+1) \cdots (c+n-1)}.$$

Employing the root $c = 1$, we arrive at the solutions

$$y_1 = w + \sum_{n=1}^{\infty} \frac{(-1)^n w^{n+1}}{n!}$$

and

$$y_2 = y_1 \ln w - \sum_{n=1}^{\infty} \frac{(-1)^n H_n w^{n+1}}{n!}.$$

Therefore the original differential equation has the two linearly independent solutions

$$(8) \qquad y_1 = \sum_{n=0}^{\infty} \frac{(-1)^n x^{-n-1}}{n!} = x^{-1} e^{-1/x}$$

and

$$(9) \qquad y_2 = y_1 \ln (1/x) - \sum_{n=1}^{\infty} \frac{(-1)^n H_n x^{-n-1}}{n!}.$$

These solutions are valid outside a circle centered at the origin and of arbitrarily small radius.

Exercises

In Exs. 1–6, the singular points in the finite plane have already been located and classified. For each equation, determine whether the point at infinity is an ordinary point, a regular singular point, or an irregular singular point. Do not solve the equations.

1. $x^3(x - 1)y'' + (x - 1)y' + 4xy = 0$. (Ex. 1, p. 314.)

ANS.   Reg. Sing. Pt.

2. $x^2(x^2 - 4)y'' + 2x^3y' + 3y = 0$. (Ex. 2, p. 314.)

ANS.   Ord. Pt.

3. $y'' + xy = 0$. (Ex. 3, p. 314.)   ANS.   Irreg. Sing. Pt.

4. $x^2y'' + y = 0$. (Ex. 4, p. 314.)   ANS.   Reg. Sing. Pt.

5. $x^4y'' + y = 0$. (Ex. 5, p. 314.)   ANS.   Reg. Sing. Pt.

6. $x^4y'' + 2x^3y' + 4y = 0$. (Ex. 18, p. 314).   ANS.   Ord. Pt.

In Exs. 7–19, find solutions valid for large x unless otherwise instructed.

7. $x^4y'' + x(1 + 2x^2)y' + 5y = 0$.

$$\text{ANS.}\quad y = a_0 \sum_{k=0}^{\infty} \frac{-15x^{-2k}}{2^k k!(2k-1)(2k-3)(2k-5)}$$
$$+ a_1[x^{-1} - \tfrac{2}{3}x^{-3} + \tfrac{1}{15}x^{-5}].$$

8. $2x^3y'' - x(2 - 5x)y' + y = 0$.

$$\text{ANS.}\quad y_1 = x^{-\frac{1}{2}} + \sum_{n=1}^{\infty} \frac{(-2)^n(n+1)x^{-n-\frac{1}{2}}}{5\cdot 7\cdot 9\cdots(2n+3)};$$
$$y_2 = \sum_{n=0}^{\infty} \frac{(-1)^{n+1}(2n-1)x^{-n}}{n!}.$$

9. $x(1-x)y'' - 3y' + 2y = 0$, the equation of Ex. 8, page 337.

$$\text{ANS.}\quad y = a_0(x^2 + 2x + 3) + \tfrac{1}{4}a_3 \sum_{n=0}^{\infty} (n+4)x^{-n-1}.$$

10. $x^3y'' + x(2 - 3x)y' - (5 - 4x)y = 0$. See Ex. 13, page 332.

$$\text{ANS.}\quad y_1 = x^2 + \sum_{n=1}^{\infty} \frac{1\cdot 3\cdot 5\cdots(2n-1)x^{-n+2}}{(n!)^2};$$
$$y_2 = y_1 \ln(1/x) + \sum_{n=1}^{\infty} \frac{1\cdot 3\cdot 5\cdots(2n-1)(2H_{2n}-3H_n)x^{-n+2}}{(n!)^2}.$$

11. $2x^2(x-1)y'' + x(5x-3)y' + (x+1)y = 0$.

$$\text{ANS.}\quad y_1 = x^{-1}; \; y_2 = -\sum_{n=0}^{\infty} \frac{x^{-n-\frac{1}{2}}}{2n-1}.$$

12. Solve the equation of Ex. 11 about the point $x = 0$.

$$\text{ANS.}\quad y_3 = \sum_{n=0}^{\infty} \frac{3x^{n+\frac{1}{2}}}{2n+3}; \; y_4 = x^{-1}.$$

13. $2x^2(1-x)y'' - 5x(1+x)y' + (5-x)y = 0$.

$$\text{ANS.}\quad y_1 = \tfrac{1}{15} \sum_{n=0}^{\infty} (n+1)(2n+3)(2n+5)x^{-n-1};$$
$$y_2 = \tfrac{1}{2} \sum_{n=0}^{\infty} (n+1)(n+2)(2n+1)x^{-n-\frac{1}{2}}.$$

14. Solve the equation of Ex. 13 about the point $x = 0$.

$$\text{ANS.} \quad y_3 = \tfrac{1}{10} \sum_{n=0}^{\infty} (n+1)(n+2)(2n+5)x^{n+\frac{5}{2}};$$

$$y_4 = -\sum_{n=0}^{\infty} (n+1)(2n-1)(2n+1)x^{n+1}.$$

15. $x(1+x)y'' + (1+5x)y' + 3y = 0$, the equation of Ex. 5, page 331.

$$\text{ANS.} \quad y_1 = \sum_{n=2}^{\infty} (-1)^{n+1} n(n-1)x^{-n-1};$$

$$y_2 = y_1 \ln (1/x) + x^{-1} + x^{-2} + \sum_{n=2}^{\infty} (-1)^{n+1}(n^2+n-1)x^{-n-1}.$$

16. $x^2(4+x^2)y'' + 2x(4+x^2)y' + y = 0.$

$$\text{ANS.} \quad y_1 = 1 + \sum_{k=1}^{\infty} \frac{(-1)^k[(-1)\cdot 3 \cdot 7 \, \cdots \, (4k-5)]^2 x^{-2k}}{(2k)!};$$

$$y_2 = x^{-1} + \sum_{k=1}^{\infty} \frac{(-1)^k[1 \cdot 5 \cdot 9 \, \cdots \, (4k-3)]^2 x^{-2k-1}}{(2k+1)!}.$$

17. $x(1-x)y'' + (1-4x)y' - 2y = 0$, the equation of Ex. 18, page 346.

$$\text{ANS.} \quad y_1 = \sum_{n=1}^{\infty} n x^{-n-1}; \, y_2 = y_1 \ln (1/x) + \sum_{n=0}^{\infty} x^{-n-1}.$$

18. $x(1+4x)y'' + (1+8x)y' + y = 0$, the equation of Ex. 49, page 347.

$$\text{ANS.} \quad y_1 = x^{-\frac{1}{2}} + \sum_{n=1}^{\infty} \frac{(-1)^n[1 \cdot 3 \cdot 5 \, \cdots \, (2n-1)]^2 x^{-n-\frac{1}{2}}}{2^{4n}(n!)^2};$$

$$y_2 = y_1 \ln (1/x) + \sum_{n=1}^{\infty} \frac{(-1)^n[1 \cdot 3 \cdot 5 \, \cdots \, (2n-1)]^2 (H_{2n} - H_n)x^{-n-\frac{1}{2}}}{2^{4n-2}(n!)^2}.$$

19. The equation of Ex. 6 above.

$$\text{ANS.} \quad y_1 = \cos (2x^{-1}); \, y_2 = \sin (2x^{-1}).$$

126. An equation with an irregular singular point

In the preceding section we solved the equation

$$(1) \qquad\qquad x^2 y'' + (3x-1)y' + y = 0$$

for large values of x. Let us now attempt a solution near the irregular singular point $x = 0$.

Proceeding in the manner developed for the treatment of regular singular points, let us put

$$(2) \qquad\qquad y = \sum_{n=0}^{\infty} a_n x^{n+c}.$$

Then the left member of equation (1) may be found to be

$$L(y) = \sum_{n=0}^{\infty} [(n+c)(n+c-1) + 3(n+c) + 1]a_n x^{n+c} - \sum_{n=0}^{\infty} (n+c)a_n x^{n+c-1}$$

$$= \sum_{n=0}^{\infty} (n+c+1)^2 a_n x^{n+c} - \sum_{n=0}^{\infty} (n+c)a_n x^{n+c-1}$$

$$= \sum_{n=1}^{\infty} (n+c)^2 a_{n-1} x^{n+c-1} - \sum_{n=0}^{\infty} (n+c)a_n x^{n+c-1}.$$

Therefore the indicial equation is $c = 0$. Already something has happened which could not occur at a regular singular point: the indicial equation has degenerated from a quadratic to a linear equation.

Let us employ this one root $c = 0$ in the hope of obtaining at least one solution of the differential equation. The a_n will be determined from

$$n \geqq 1: \quad n^2 a_{n-1} - n a_n = 0,$$

or

$$(3) \qquad\qquad a_n = n a_{n-1}.$$

At once it follows that $a_n = n!a_0$, so the root $c = 0$ has led us to the tentative solution

$$(4) \qquad\qquad y_1 = 1 + \sum_{n=1}^{\infty} n!x^n.$$

Since we are dealing with an irregular singular point, the theorems quoted earlier on the convergence of the results do not apply, so we turn to the standard ratio test for information. With the ratio test it is easy to show that the series in (4) diverges for $x \neq 0$. Evidently the series converges at $x = 0$. There is therefore no *region* whatever in which the relation (4) is a solution of the differential equation from our elementary standpoint.

Intuitively, we may reason that equation (4) was determined by the differential equation, even though by an unjustified process, and that therefore there may be some way in which it will lead us to a proper solution of the differential equation.

We then proceed to use a device commonly employed by professional mathematicians. Retiring to some place of ensured privacy, perhaps a study with drawn shades, we manipulate the recalcitrant expression (for us, a divergent series) with whatever procedures, legitimate or not, seem promising. When we finally arrive at a mathematically defensible position [for us, equation (6) below], we come out of seclusion and present to the public eye a formal, rigorous demonstration of the validity of the result [for us, (7) to (16) below] with no need to indicate the methods used to obtain it.

We already know from our study of the Gamma function that, for non-negative integral n,

$$n! = \Gamma(n + 1) = \int_0^\infty e^{-t} t^n \, dt,$$

a relation which is also easily obtained without knowledge of the Gamma function by iterated integration by parts. Let us then rewrite equation (4) as

$$(5) \qquad y_1 = \sum_{n=0}^\infty \int_0^\infty e^{-t} t^n \, dt \, x^n.$$

Without regard to justification, we interchange order of integration and summation to get

$$y_1 = \int_0^\infty e^{-t} \sum_{n=0}^\infty (xt)^n \, dt,$$

or

$$(6) \qquad y_1 = \int_0^\infty \frac{e^{-t}}{1 - xt} \, dt.$$

We shall now prove that the y_1 of (6) is a solution of the differential equation (1) on the semi-infinite range $x \leq 0$. If x is to be complex, the same sort of discussion can be used to show that y_1 is a solution in the region for which the real part of x is nonpositive.

In (6), the variable of integration is never negative, $t \geq 0$. For $x \leq 0$, we therefore have

$$-xt \geq 0$$

so $(1 - xt) \geq 1$, from which we conclude that

$$(7) \qquad 0 < \frac{1}{1 - xt} \leq 1.$$

Because of (7), the integral in (6) converges:

$$(8) \qquad \left| \int_0^\infty \frac{e^{-t} \, dt}{1 - xt} \right| \leq \int_0^\infty e^{-t} = 1.$$

Indeed, the methods of advanced calculus show that because of (8), the integral in (6) is absolutely and uniformly convergent on any closed interval in the range $x \le 0$. The same inequality (7) leads to the conclusion that the formal derivative of y_1,

$$(9) \qquad y_1' = \int_0^\infty \frac{te^{-t}\,dt}{(1-xt)^2},$$

is the actual derivative of y_1 because

$$(10) \qquad \left| \int_0^\infty \frac{te^{-t}\,dt}{(1-xt)^2} \right| \le \int_0^\infty te^{-t}\,dt = 1.$$

A similar result holds for y_1''.

Now that we know that the y_1 of (6) and its derivatives have meaning on the range $x \le 0$, the final task is to show that y_1 satisfies the differential equation

$$(1) \qquad x^2 y'' + (3x - 1)y' + y = 0.$$

From (6)

$$(11) \qquad xy_1 = \int_0^\infty \frac{xe^{-t}\,dt}{1-xt}$$

and the derivatives of both members of (11) make sense because of the inequality (7). Hence on the range $x \le 0$,

$$xy_1' + y_1 = \int_0^\infty e^{-t} \left[\frac{1}{1-xt} + \frac{xt}{(1-xt)^2} \right] dt;$$

that is,

$$(12) \qquad xy_1' + y_1 = \int_0^\infty \frac{e^{-t}\,dt}{(1-xt)^2}.$$

From (12) we obtain

$$(13) \qquad x^2 y_1' + xy_1 = \int_0^\infty \frac{xe^{-t}\,dt}{(1-xt)^2}.$$

Let us integrate by parts on the right in (13) with the choice shown in the table.

$\dfrac{x\,dt}{(1-xt)^2}$	e^{-t}
$\dfrac{1}{1-xt}$	$-e^{-t}\,dt$

We thus get

$$x^2 y_1' + x y_1 = \left[\frac{e^{-t}}{1 - xt} \right]_0^\infty + \int_0^\infty \frac{e^{-t}\, dt}{1 - xt},$$

or

$$x^2 y_1' + x y_1 = -1 + y_1.$$

Therefore the y_1 of (6) satisfies the equation

(14) $x^2 y_1' + (x - 1) y_1 = -1.$

By differentiating each member of (14) we arrive at

(15) $x^2 y_1'' + (3x - 1) y_1' + y_1 = 0.$

Hence the y_1 of (6) is a solution of the differential equation (1) on the range $x \leqq 0$.

We have thus obtained a usable solution

(16) $$y_1 = \int_0^\infty \frac{e^{-t}\, dt}{1 - xt}, \qquad x \leqq 0,$$

from the divergent series

(17) $$1 + \sum_{n=1}^\infty n!\, x^n.$$

It must be realized that the validity of the result is not at all affected by the manner in which we arrive at that result. The validity is demonstrated by showing directly that for the y_1 of equation (6), $L(y_1) = 0$.

The above discussion leaves many questions unanswered. It is intended as a bare introduction to the topic of solutions near an irregular singular point.

127. The role of the divergent series

In the preceding section the divergent series

(1) $$1 + \sum_{n=1}^\infty n!\, x^n$$

led us to the meaningful function (convergent integral)

(2) $$y_1(x) = \int_0^\infty \frac{e^{-t}\, dt}{1 - xt}, \qquad x \leqq 0.$$

We shall now find that the series (1) is an excellent tool with which to compute $y_1(x)$ near $x = 0$.

Let a partial sum of the series (1) be defined by

$$(3) \qquad s_n(x) = 1 + \sum_{k=1}^{n} k!\, x^k.$$

The difference between the function $y_1(x)$ and the partial sum $s_n(x)$ is

$$(4) \qquad y_1(x) - s_n(x) = \int_0^\infty \frac{e^{-t}\, dt}{1 - xt} - \sum_{k=0}^{n} k!\, x^k.$$

We know that

$$k! = \int_0^\infty e^{-t} t^k \, dt.$$

Therefore we may write

$$(5) \qquad y_1(x) - s_n(x) = \int_0^\infty \frac{e^{-t}\, dt}{1 - xt} - \sum_{k=0}^{n} \int_0^\infty e^{-t} t^k x^k \, dt.$$

In the finite series it is legitimate to interchange order of summation and integration. We may write

$$(6) \qquad y_1(x) - s_n(x) = \int_0^\infty \frac{e^{-t}\, dt}{1 - xt} - \int_0^\infty e^{-t} \sum_{k=0}^{n} (xt)^k \, dt.$$

The sum of a finite geometric series is known from elementary algebra:

$$\sum_{k=0}^{n} r^k = \frac{1 - r^{n+1}}{1 - r}.$$

Using $r = xt$, we may rewrite (6) as

$$y_1(x) - s_n(x) = \int_0^\infty \frac{e^{-t}\, dt}{1 - xt} - \int_0^\infty \frac{e^{-t}[1 - (xt)^{n+1}]\, dt}{1 - xt},$$

or

$$(7) \qquad y_1(x) - s_n(x) = \int_0^\infty \frac{x^{n+1} t^{n+1} e^{-t}\, dt}{1 - xt}, \qquad x \leqq 0.$$

We have already shown that $0 < (1 - xt)^{-1} \leqq 1$ for x in the range $x \leqq 0$. Hence, from (7), we may conclude that

$$|y_1(x) - s_n(x)| \leqq |x|^{n+1} \int_0^\infty t^{n+1} e^{-t} \, dt,$$

from which it follows that

(8) $$|y_1(x) - s_n(x)| \leqq (n+1)!|x|^{n+1}, \qquad x \leqq 0.$$

Examination of the inequality (8) and of (1) and (2) shows us that in computing $y_1(x)$ by means of the divergent series (1), the error made is never greater in magnitude than the first term omitted. For any fixed n, the right member of the first inequality in (8) approaches zero as $x \to 0^-$. Any desired accuracy can be obtained by taking x negative and sufficiently near zero in the computation. We are particularly interested in computations of $y_1(x)$ for x near zero or we would not have solved the differential equation around that point.

Since the series (1) does not converge to $y_1(x)$,

(9) $$\operatorname*{Lim}_{n \to \infty} [y_1(x) - s_n(x)] \neq 0.$$

We say that the series (1) is asymptotic* to $y_1(x)$ as $x \to 0^-$, meaning that

(10) $$\operatorname*{Lim}_{x \to 0^-} \frac{y_1(x) - s_n(x)}{x^n} = 0.$$

In a sense, (10) says that the difference between $y_1(x)$ and any partial sum (n fixed) of the series approaches zero more rapidly than x^n does, as $x \to 0^-$. For our problem, the limit (10) follows from the inequality (8).

By comparing (10) and the corresponding condition for convergence, that the limit in (9) be zero, we can grasp the essential difference between a series being convergent to $y_1(x)$ and a series being asymptotic to $y_1(x)$. For the series to be convergent to y_1, x is held fixed and the error $(y_1 - s_n)$ must approach zero as $n \to \infty$. For the series to be asymptotic to y_1, the number of terms n is held fixed and the error $(y_1 - s_n)$ is to approach zero (with a specified amount of rapidity) as x approaches the pertinent x-value. The two properties are independent; either, both, or neither may be true in a specific instance.

128. The solution of certain linear recurrence relations

In the next section we shall encounter some nonhomogeneous linear recurrence relations of the type

(1) $$n \geqq 1: \quad a_n = f_n a_{n-1} + g_n,$$

in which f_n, g_n, and a_0 are known and a_n, $n > 0$, is to be found.

---

* An introduction to the subject of asymptotic series may be found in E. D. Rainville, *Special Functions* (New York: The Macmillan Co., 1960), Chapter 3.

A special case of (1) is easy to solve. Suppose b_0 and t_n are known and

(2) $n \geqq 1: \quad b_n = b_{n-1} + t_n.$

Iteration of the relation yields

$$b_1 = b_0 + t_1,$$
$$b_2 = b_1 + t_2,$$

$$\cdot$$
$$\cdot$$
$$\cdot$$

$$b_n = b_{n-1} + t_n,$$

so, adding the respective members, we obtain

$$b_n = b_0 + \sum_{k=1}^{n} t_k.$$

All that we need to do to solve the relation (1) is to reduce it to the special case (2). We wish to eliminate f_n. Let us tentatively pass from the unknown a_n to a new unknown b_n by putting

(3) $a_n = \varphi_n b_n$

where the φ_n will be chosen to eliminate f_n. Using (3) in the relation (1) we are led to

$$\varphi_n b_n = f_n \varphi_{n-1} b_{n-1} + g_n,$$

or

(4) $b_n = \dfrac{f_n \varphi_{n-1}}{\varphi_n} b_{n-1} + \dfrac{g_n}{\varphi_n}.$

Now we wish to choose φ_n so that $\varphi_n = f_n \varphi_{n-1}$. We can always do this by methods we have been using throughout, as will be exhibited in the examples below. Once φ_n is so chosen, the relation (4) is of the type of (2) and easily solved for b_n. Then a_n is given by equation (3).

EXAMPLE (a): Let a_0 be arbitrary and find a_n, $n > 0$, from the relation

(5) $n \geqq 1: \quad a_n = n^2 a_{n-1} + n + 1.$

Let us put $a_n = \varphi_n b_n$ with $\varphi_0 = 1$ so $a_0 = b_0$. Then (5) leads to

$$n \geqq 1: \quad \varphi_n b_n = n^2 \varphi_{n-1} b_{n-1} + (n + 1),$$

so we wish to choose φ_n to satisfy

(6) $n \geqq 1: \quad \varphi_n = n^2 \varphi_{n-1}.$

Now

$$\varphi_1 = 1^2\varphi_0,$$

$$\varphi_2 = 2^2\varphi_1,$$

.

.

.

$$\varphi_n = n^2\varphi_{n-1},$$

from which $\varphi_n = (n!)^2\varphi_0 = (n!)^2$.

The relation for the b's now becomes

$$n \geq 1: \quad (n!)^2 b_n = n^2[(n-1)!]^2 b_{n-1} + n + 1,$$

(7) $$n \geq 1: \quad b_n = b_{n-1} + \frac{n+1}{(n!)^2},$$

with $b_0 = a_0$. From (7) it follows at once that

$$b_n = b_0 + \sum_{k=1}^{n} \frac{k+1}{(k!)^2}.$$

Therefore, for $n \geq 1$,

$$a_n = (n!)^2 a_0 + \sum_{k=1}^{n} \frac{(k+1)(n!)^2}{(k!)^2}.$$

EXAMPLE (b): Solve the relation

(8) $$n \geq 1: \quad (n+3)(n+2)a_n + a_{n-1} = 1.$$

At once

$$n \geq 1: \quad a_n = \frac{-a_{n-1}}{(n+3)(n+2)} + \frac{1}{(n+3)(n+2)},$$

so we put $a_n = \varphi_n b_n$, with $\varphi_0 = 1$, and require that

(9) $$n \geq 1: \quad \varphi_n = \frac{-\varphi_{n-1}}{(n+3)(n+2)}.$$

Of course

$$\varphi_n = \frac{(-1)^n\varphi_0}{[4 \cdot 5 \cdots (n+3)][3 \cdot 4 \cdots (n+2)]} = \frac{(-1)^n 12}{(n+3)!(n+2)!}.$$

Thus with $a_n = \varphi_n b_n$, the relation for b_n is found to be

$$\frac{(-1)^n 12 b_n}{(n+3)!(n+2)!} = \frac{-(-1)^{n-1} 12 b_{n-1}}{(n+3)!(n+2)!} + \frac{1}{(n+3)(n+2)},$$

(10) $n \geqq 1: \quad b_n = b_{n-1} + \frac{1}{12}(-1)^n(n+2)!(n+1)!.$

Hence

$$b_n = b_0 + \frac{1}{12} \sum_{k=1}^{n} (-1)^k(k+2)!(k+1)!$$

and, finally,

$$n \geqq 1: \quad a_n = \frac{12(-1)^n a_0}{(n+3)!(n+2)!} + \sum_{k=1}^{n} \frac{(-1)^{n+k}(k+2)!(k+1)!}{(n+3)!(n+2)!}.$$

With a little practice, the φ_n can often be obtained by inspection.

Exercises

For each relation, assume that a_0 is arbitrary and solve for a_n, $n > 0$.

1. $n \geqq 1: \quad a_n = -na_{n-1} + 2.$

> ANS. $n \geqq 1: \quad a_n = (-1)^n n! a_0 + 2 \sum_{k=1}^{n} \frac{(-1)^{n+k} n!}{k!}.$

2. $n \geqq 1: \quad a_n + 2a_{n-1} = 1.$

> ANS. $n \geqq 1: \quad a_n = (-2)^n a_0 + (-2)^n \sum_{k=1}^{n} (-\frac{1}{2})^k.$

3. Sum the series in the answer to Ex. 2 and so obtain the solution
$n \geqq 1: \quad a_n = (-2)^n a_0 + \frac{1}{3}[1 - (-2)^n].$

4. $n \geqq 1: \quad (n+1)a_n - a_{n-1} = n.$

> ANS. $n \geqq 1: \quad a_n = \frac{a_0}{(n+1)!} + \sum_{k=1}^{n} \frac{k(k!)}{(n+1)!}.$

5. $n \geqq 1: \quad na_n - a_{n-1} = \frac{1}{n!}.$ ANS. $n \geqq 1: \quad a_n = (a_0 + H_n)/n!.$

6. $n \geqq 1: \quad n(n+1)a_n - a_{n-1} = n+1.$

> ANS. $n \geqq 1: \quad a_n = \frac{a_0}{n!(n+1)!} + \sum_{k=1}^{n} \frac{(k-1)!(k+1)!}{n!(n+1)!}.$

129. Nonhomogeneous equations

In many instances a nonhomogeneous equation

$$L(y) = R(x)$$

can be solved by essentially the same power series methods as we have been using on homogeneous equations. Instead of using the considerable space it would take to develop a thorough treatment of this topic, all that is done here is to illustrate some points in the subject by means of two examples and a few exercises.

EXAMPLE (a): Solve the equation

$$(1) \qquad\qquad xy'' + y = \frac{x^2}{1 - x}$$

near the point $x = 0$.

The corresponding homogeneous equation

$$(2) \qquad\qquad xy'' + y = 0$$

was solved in Ex. 1, page 341. Its solutions were found to be

$$(3) \qquad\qquad y_1 = \sum_{n=1}^{\infty} \frac{(-1)^n x^n}{n!(n-1)!},$$

$$(4) \qquad y_2 = y_1 \ln x + 1 - \sum_{n=1}^{\infty} \frac{(-1)^n (H_n + H_{n-1}) x^n}{n!(n-1)!}.$$

What we need now is to get a particular solution y_p of equation (1) so the general solution of (1) can, near $x = 0$, be written

$$y = A y_1 + B y_2 + y_p.$$

The right member of equation (1) can be expanded in a power series

$$\frac{x^2}{1 - x} = \sum_{n=0}^{\infty} x^{n+2}.$$

Now our differential equation can be rewritten as

$$(5) \qquad\qquad xy'' + y = \sum_{n=0}^{\infty} x^{n+2},$$

and it is natural to seek a particular solution of the form

$$(6) \qquad\qquad y = \sum_{n=0}^{\infty} a_n x^{n+\gamma}$$

where the a_n and the γ are yet to be determined.

If the y of equation (6) is to satisfy (5), then we must have

$$\sum_{n=0}^{\infty} (n+\gamma)(n+\gamma-1) a_n x^{n+\gamma-1} + \sum_{n=1}^{\infty} a_{n-1} x^{n+\gamma-1} = \sum_{n=0}^{\infty} x^{n+2}$$

identically in some region surrounding $x = 0$. The lowest degree term on the left is $\gamma(\gamma - 1)a_0 x^{\gamma-1}$ and the lowest degree term on the right is x^2. Therefore we choose* $\gamma = 3$. Then the identity to be satisfied is

$$\sum_{n=0}^{\infty} (n+3)(n+2)a_n x^{n+2} + \sum_{n=1}^{\infty} a_{n-1} x^{n+2} = \sum_{n=0}^{\infty} x^{n+2}.$$

For two power series to be identical in a region, the corresponding coefficients must be equal. We conclude that the a_n are given by the relations

$$n = 0: \quad 6a_0 = 1,$$

$$n \geq 1: \quad (n+3)(n+2)a_n + a_{n-1} = 1.$$

It is not unreasonable to stop at this stage and to write the general solution of the original differential equation as

$$y = Ay_1 + By_2 + y_p,$$

in which the y_1 and y_2 are given by equations (3) and (4) and

$$(7) \qquad\qquad y_p = \sum_{n=0}^{\infty} a_n x^{n+3},$$

where $a_0 = \frac{1}{6}$ and

$$n \geq 1: \quad a_n = \frac{1 - a_{n-1}}{(n+3)(n+2)}.$$

As many a's as are desired may be computed from the recurrence relation above.

By the method of the preceding section an explicit formula for the a_n can be found. Indeed, according to Example (b) of that section,

$$n \geq 1: \quad a_n = \frac{12(-1)^n a_0}{(n+3)!(n+2)!} + \sum_{k=1}^{n} \frac{(-1)^{n+k}(k+2)!(k+1)!}{(n+3)!(n+2)!}.$$

Therefore, since $a_0 = \frac{1}{6}$, we may write the particular solution indicated in (7) as

$$(8) \quad y_p = \tfrac{1}{6}x^3 + \sum_{n=1}^{\infty} \left[2 + \sum_{k=1}^{n} (-1)^k (k+2)!(k+1)! \right] \frac{(-1)^n x^{n+3}}{(n+3)!(n+2)!}.$$

Further simplification of equation (8) yields

---

* Here complications would enter if the series on the right had started with a term x^k for k either zero or a negative integer.

(9) $y_p = -2y_1 - 2x + x^2 + \displaystyle\sum_{n=1}^{\infty} \sum_{k=1}^{n} \frac{(-1)^{n+k}(k+1)!(k+2)!x^{n+3}}{(n+3)!(n+2)!}$,

and now the term $(-2y_1)$ can be absorbed into the complementary function if so desired.

It is instructive to go through the details of showing directly from (9) that

$$xy_p'' + y_p = \sum_{n=0}^{\infty} x^{n+2}.$$

EXAMPLE (b): Solve the equation

(10) $2x^2y'' + x(4x - 1)y' + 2(3x - 1)y = x^3 + x^4$

near $x = 0$.

The corresponding homogeneous equation has the linearly independent solutions

(11) $y_1 = \displaystyle\sum_{n=0}^{\infty} \frac{(-2)^n x^{n+2}}{n!} = x^2 e^{-2x}$,

(12) $y_2 = x^{-\frac{1}{2}} + \displaystyle\sum_{n=1}^{\infty} \frac{(-4)^n x^{n-\frac{1}{2}}}{(-3)(-1)\cdot 1 \cdots (2n-5)}$,

as indicated in Ex. 16, page 322.

If we use

$$y = \sum_{n=0}^{\infty} a_n x^{n+\gamma},$$

then equation (10) becomes

$$\sum_{n=0}^{\infty} (2n + 2\gamma + 1)(n + \gamma - 2)a_n x^{n+\gamma} + \sum_{n=1}^{\infty} 2(2n + 2\gamma + 1)a_{n-1}x^{n+\gamma}$$
$$= x^3 + x^4.$$

It is natural to choose $\gamma = 3$. Then the a's will be determined by the relations

$$n = 0: \quad 7a_0 = 1,$$
$$n = 1: \quad 9(2)a_1 + 2(9)a_0 = 1,$$
$$n \geqq 2: \quad (2n + 7)(n + 1)a_n + 2(2n + 7)a_{n-1} = 0.$$

Thus we find that $a_0 = \frac{1}{7}$, $a_1 = -\frac{11}{126}$,

$$n \geq 2: \quad a_n = -\frac{2a_{n-1}}{n+1}.$$

This recurrence relation has the solution

$$a_n = \frac{(-2)^{n-1}a_1}{3 \cdot 4 \cdots (n+1)} = -\frac{11}{126} \cdot \frac{(-1)^{n-1} \cdot 2^n}{(n+1)!}.$$

Hence a particular solution of the original equation is

$$y = \tfrac{1}{7}x^3 - \tfrac{11}{126}\left[x^4 + \sum_{n=2}^{\infty} \frac{(-1)^{n-1}2^n x^{n+3}}{(n+1)!} \right],$$

or

$$y = \tfrac{1}{7}x^3 - \tfrac{11}{126} \sum_{n=1}^{\infty} \frac{(-1)^{n-1}2^n x^{n+3}}{(n+1)!}.$$

This resembles the y_1 of (11) so much that we shift index in the summation to find

$$(13) \qquad y = \tfrac{1}{7}x^3 - \tfrac{11}{126} \sum_{n=2}^{\infty} \frac{(-1)^n 2^{n-1} x^{n+2}}{n!}.$$

The summation involved in equation (13) is the same as that in the expression for y_1 in equation (11) except that two terms of (11) are not included in (13) and a factor 2^{-1} has been introduced. We are thus led to rewrite (13) as

$$y = \tfrac{1}{7}x^3 - \tfrac{11}{252}(y_1 - x^2 + 2x^3).$$

But the term proportional to y_1 can be absorbed in the complementary function. Therefore, the differential equation (10) has a particular solution

$$y_p = \tfrac{1}{7}x^3 + \tfrac{11}{252}x^2 - \tfrac{11}{126}x^3,$$

or

$$(14) \qquad y_p = \tfrac{11}{252}x^2 + \tfrac{1}{18}x^3,$$

which is easily verified by direct substitution.

If in this example we had chosen $\gamma = 2$, a less apparent choice perhaps, then the a's would have been determined by the relations

$$n = 0: \quad 0 \cdot a_0 = 0, \ (a_0 \text{ arbitrary}),$$
$$n = 1: \quad 7a_1 + 14a_0 = 1,$$
$$n = 2: \quad 18a_2 + 18a_1 = 1,$$
$$n \geq 3: \quad na_n + 2a_{n-1} = 0.$$

If we can force a_2 to be zero, then $a_n = 0$ for $n > 2$. If $a_2 = 0$,

$$a_1 = \tfrac{1}{18},$$
$$a_0 = \tfrac{1}{14} - \tfrac{1}{2}a_1 = \tfrac{11}{252}.$$

Thus the choices $\gamma = 2$ and $a_0 = \tfrac{11}{252}$ lead to $a_n = 0$ for $n \geq 2$ and so give us again the solution (14).

Exercises

For each equation below, the corresponding homogeneous differential equation occurs earlier in the book. Two linearly independent solutions of the homogeneous equation may be found at the reference given. Obtain a particular solution for each equation.

1. $xy'' + (1 - x)y' - y = x/(1 - x)$. See Ex. 17, page 332.

$$\text{ANS.} \quad y_p = \tfrac{1}{4}x^2 + \sum_{n=1}^{\infty} \left[\tfrac{1}{2} + \sum_{k=1}^{n} \frac{(k+1)!}{k+2} \right] \frac{x^{n+2}}{(n+2)!}.$$

2. Show from the answer to Ex. 1 that another particular solution of the differential equation is

$$y = -\tfrac{1}{2}(1 + x) + \sum_{n=1}^{\infty} \sum_{k=1}^{n} \frac{(k+1)!x^{n+2}}{(k+2)(n+2)!}.$$

3. $xy'' + y = xe^x$. See Ex. 1, page 341.

$$\text{ANS.} \quad y_p = \tfrac{1}{2}x^2 + \sum_{n=1}^{\infty} \left[1 + \sum_{k=1}^{n} (-1)^k(k+1)! \right] \frac{(-1)^n x^{n+2}}{(n+2)!(n+1)!}.$$

4. Show that the answer to Ex. 3 leads also to the particular solution

$$y = x + \sum_{n=1}^{\infty} \sum_{k=1}^{n} \frac{(-1)^{n+k}(k+1)!x^{n+2}}{(n+2)!(n+1)!}.$$

5. $x^2y'' + x(x - 1)y' + (1 - x)y = x^2$. See Ex. 8, page 331.

$$\text{ANS.} \quad y_p = \sum_{n=0}^{\infty} \frac{(-1)^n x^{n+2}}{(n+1)(n+1)!}.$$

6. Show that the equation $xy'' + y = e^x$ has a solution of the form

$$y = \sum_{n=0}^{\infty} a_n x^n$$

with a_1 arbitrary. Put $a_1 = 0$ and determine the resultant particular solution.

$$\text{ANS.} \quad y = 1 + \sum_{n=2}^{\infty} \sum_{k=2}^{n} \frac{(-1)^{n+k}(k-2)!x^n}{n!(n-1)!}.$$

7. Show that the equation

$$L(y) = x^2 y'' + x(x-1)y' + (1-x)y = x$$

has no solution of the form $y = \sum_{n=0}^{\infty} a_n x^{n+\gamma}$.

8. Verify by computing $L(y)$ that the equation of Ex. 7 has the particular solution

$$y = \frac{x}{2} \ln^2 x + \ln x \sum_{n=1}^{\infty} \frac{(-1)^n x^{n+1}}{n \cdot n!} + \sum_{n=1}^{\infty} \frac{(-1)^{n+1}\left(\frac{1}{n} + H_n\right) x^{n+1}}{n \cdot n!}.$$

CHAPTER 24

Numerical Methods

130. General remarks

There is no general method for obtaining an explicit formula for the solution of a differential equation. Specific equations do occur for which no known attack yields a solution or for which the explicit forms of solution are not well adapted to computation. For these reasons, systematic, efficient methods for the numerical approximation to solutions are important. Unfortunately, a clear grasp of good numerical methods requires time-consuming practice and often also the availability of modern computing machines.

This chapter is restricted to a fragmentary discussion of some simple and moderately useful methods. The purpose here is to give the student a concept of the fundamental principles of numerical approximations to solutions. We shall take one problem, which does not yield to the methods developed earlier and apply to it several simple numerical processes.

131. The increment method

We seek to obtain that solution of the differential equation

$$(1) \qquad y' = y^2 - x^2$$

for which $y = 1$ when $x = 0$. We wish to know the solution $y = y(x)$ in the range $0 \leqq x \leqq \frac{1}{2}$.

Equation (1) may be written in differential form as

$$(2) \qquad dy = (y^2 - x^2)\, dx.$$

393

Figure 49 shows the geometrical significance of the differential dy and of Δy, the actual change in y, as induced by an increment dx (or Δx) applied to x. In calculus it is shown that near a point where the derivative exists, dy can be made to approximate Δy as closely as desired by taking Δx sufficiently small.

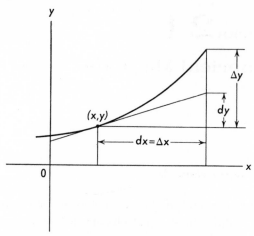

FIGURE 49

We know the value of y at $x = 0$; we wish to compute y for $0 \leq x \leq \frac{1}{2}$. Suppose we choose $\Delta x = 0.1$; then dy can be computed from

$$dy = (y^2 - x^2)\, \Delta x.$$

Indeed, $dy = (1 - 0)(0.1) = 0.1$. Thus for $x = 0 + 0.1$, the approximate value of y is $1 + 0.1$. Now we have $x = 0.1$, $y = 1.1$. Let us choose $\Delta x = 0.1$ again. Then

$$dy = [(1.1)^2 - (0.1)^2]\, \Delta x,$$

so $dy = 0.12$. Hence at $x = 0.2$, the approximate value of y is 1.22. The complete computation using $\Delta x = 0.1$ is shown in Table 1.

Table 1

$\Delta x = 0.1$

x	y	y^2	x^2	$(y^2 - x^2)$	dy
0.0	1.00	1.00	0.00	1.00	0.10
0.1	1.10	1.21	0.01	1.20	0.12
0.2	1.22	1.49	0.04	1.45	0.14
0.3	1.36	1.85	0.09	1.76	0.18
0.4	1.54	2.37	0.16	2.21	0.22
0.5	1.76				

The increment Δx need not be constant throughout the interval. Where the slope is larger it pays to take the increment smaller. For simplicity in computations, equal increments are used here.

It is helpful to repeat the computation with a smaller increment and to note the changes that result in the approximate values of y. Table 2 shows a computation with $\Delta x = 0.05$ throughout.

Table 2

$\Delta x = 0.05$

x	y	y^2	x^2	$(y^2 - x^2)$	dy
0.00	1.000	1.000	0.000	1.000	0.050
0.05	1.050	1.102	0.002	1.100	0.055
0.10	1.105	1.221	0.010	1.211	0.061
0.15	1.166	1.360	0.022	1.338	0.067
0.20	1.233	1.520	0.040	1.480	0.074
0.25	1.307	1.708	0.062	1.646	0.082
0.30	1.389	1.929	0.090	1.839	0.092
0.35	1.481	2.193	0.122	2.071	0.104
0.40	1.585	2.512	0.160	2.352	0.118
0.45	1.703	2.900	0.202	2.698	0.135
0.50	1.838				

In Table 3 the value of y obtained from the computations in Tables 1 and 2 and also the values of y obtained by using $\Delta x = 0.01$ (computation not shown) are exhibited beside the values of y correct to two decimal places. The correct values are obtained by the method of Section 135. Their availability is in a sense accidental. Frequently, we know of no way

Table 3

	$\Delta x = 0.1$	$\Delta x = 0.05$	$\Delta x = 0.01$	correct
x	y	y	y	y
0.0	1.00	1.00	1.00	1.00
0.1	1.10	1.11	1.11	1.11
0.2	1.22	1.23	1.24	1.25
0.3	1.36	1.39	1.41	1.42
0.4	1.54	1.58	1.62	1.64
0.5	1.76	1.84	1.91	1.93

to obtain the y value correct to a specified degree of accuracy. In such instances it is customary to resort to decreasing the size of the increment until the y values show changes no larger than the errors we are willing to permit. Then it is *hoped* that the steadying down of the y values is due to our being close to the correct solution rather than (as is quite possible) to the slowness of convergence of the process used.

Exercises

1. Use the increment method with $\Delta x = 0.1$ to compute, in the range $0 \leq x \leq 1$, that solution of the equation

$$y' = x + y$$

for which $y = 1$ when $x = 0$. Also, solve the boundary value problem exactly by elementary methods and compare the y values at intervals of 0.1 in x.

2. Use $\Delta x = 0.05$ in the problem of Ex. 1.

3. Use the method of increments on the boundary value problem

$$y' = e^{-xy}; \text{ when } x = 0, \ y = 0,$$

first with $\Delta x = 0.2$ and then with $\Delta x = 0.1$, computing y for the interval $0 \leq x \leq 2$.

4. Perform the same computations as in Ex. 3 but for the problem

$$y' = (1 + x^2 + y^2)^{-1}; \text{ when } x = 0, \ y = 0.$$

132. A method of successive approximation

Next let us attack the same problem as before,

(1) $$y' = y^2 - x^2; \quad x = 0, \quad y = 1,$$

with y desired in the interval $0 \leq x \leq \frac{1}{2}$, by the method suggested in the discussion of the existence theorem in Chapter 17. Applying the statements made in that discussion, we conclude that the desired solution is $y = y(x)$ where

$$y(x) = \lim_{n \to \infty} y_n(x)$$

and the sequence of approximations $y_n(x)$ is given by $y_0(x) = 1$ and, for $n \geq 1$,

(2) $$y_n(x) = 1 + \int_0^x [y^2_{n-1}(t) - t^2] \, dt.$$

For the problem at hand

$$y_1(x) = 1 + \int_0^x (1 - t^2) \, dt,$$

$$y_1(x) = 1 + x - \tfrac{1}{3}x^3.$$

Next we obtain a second approximation, finding $y_2(x)$ from $y_1(x)$

by means of (2). Thus we find that

$$y_2(x) = 1 + \int_0^x [(1 + t - \tfrac{1}{3}t^3)^2 - t^2] \, dt,$$

$$y_2(x) = 1 + x + x^2 - \tfrac{1}{6}x^4 - \tfrac{2}{15}x^5 + \tfrac{1}{63}x^7.$$

Then $y_3(x)$, $y_4(x)$, $\cdot\cdot\cdot$, can be obtained in a similar manner, each from the preceding element of the sequence $y_n(x)$.

In Table 4 the values taken on by $y_1(x)$, $y_2(x)$, and $y_3(x)$ at intervals of 0.1 in x are shown beside the corresponding values of $y(x)$, correct to two decimal places, as obtained in Section 135.

Table 4

x	$y_1(x)$	$y_2(x)$	$y_3(x)$	$y(x)$
0.0	1.00	1.00	1.00	1.00
0.1	1.10	1.11	1.11	1.11
0.2	1.20	1.24	1.25	1.25
0.3	1.29	1.39	1.41	1.42
0.4	1.38	1.56	1.62	1.64
0.5	1.46	1.74	1.87	1.93

It must be realized that the usefulness of this method is not dependent upon our being able to carry out the integrations in a formal sense.

It may be best to perform the integrations mechanically with a planimeter, or by some numerical process such as Simpson's rule.

Exercises

1. Apply the method of this section to the problem

$$y' = x + y; \text{ when } x = 0, \ y = 1,$$

of Ex. 1, Section 131. Obtain $y_1(x)$, $y_2(x)$, and $y_3(x)$.

ANS. $y_1(x) = 1 + x + \tfrac{1}{2}x^2$;
$y_2(x) = 1 + x + x^2 + \tfrac{1}{6}x^3$;
$y_3(x) = 1 + x + x^2 + \tfrac{1}{3}x^3 + \tfrac{1}{24}x^4.$

2. Compute a table of values to two decimal places of y_1, y_2, y_3 of Ex. 1 for $x = 0$ to $x = 1$ at intervals of 0.1. Tabulate also the correct values of y obtained from the elementary solution to the problem.

133. An improvement on the preceding method

In the method used in Section 132, each of the $y_n(x)$; $n = 0, 1, 2,$ $\cdot\cdot\cdot$, yields an approximation to the solution $y = y(x)$. It is plausible that usually the more nearly correct a particular approximation $y_k(x)$, the better will be its successor $y_{k+1}(x)$.

The boundary value problem we are treating is

$$y' = y^2 - x^2; \quad x = 0, \quad y = 1$$

and it tells us at once that at $x = 0$, the slope is $y' = 1$. But in Section 132, by blindly following the suggestion in Chapter 17, we started out with $y_0(x) = 1$, a line which does not have the correct slope at $x = 0$.

It is therefore reasonable to alter our initial approximation by choosing $y_0(x)$ to have the correct slope at $x = 0$, still making it also pass through the desired point $x = 0$, $y = 1$. Hence we choose

$$y_0(x) = 1 + x$$

and proceed to compute $y_1(x)$, $y_2(x)$, $\cdots$, as before. The successive stages of approximation to $y(x)$ now become

$$y_1(x) = 1 + \int_0^x [(1 + t)^2 - t^2] \, dt,$$
$$y_1(x) = 1 + x + x^2;$$

and

$$y_2(x) = 1 + \int_0^x [(1 + t + t^2)^2 - t^2] \, dt,$$
$$y_2(x) = 1 + x + x^2 + \tfrac{2}{3}x^3 + \tfrac{1}{2}x^4 + \tfrac{1}{5}x^5;$$

and so on.

In Table 5 the values of y_1, y_2, y_3 obtained by this method are shown beside the correct values of y.

Table 5

x	$y_1(x)$	$y_2(x)$	$y_3(x)$	$y(x)$
0.0	1.00	1.00	1.00	1.00
0.1	1.11	1.11	1.11	1.11
0.2	1.24	1.25	1.25	1.25
0.3	1.39	1.41	1.42	1.42
0.4	1.56	1.62	1.64	1.64
0.5	1.75	1.87	1.92	1.93

Exercises

1. Apply the method of this section to obtain approximations y_1, y_2, y_3 for the problem of Ex. 1 of Section 131.

   ANS. $y_1(x) = 1 + x + x^2$; $y_2(x) = 1 + x + x^2 + \tfrac{1}{3}x^3$;
   $y_3(x) = 1 + x + x^2 + \tfrac{1}{3}x^3 + \tfrac{1}{12}x^4$.

2. Tabulate to two decimal places y_1, y_2, y_3 of Ex. 1 beside the corresponding values of the exact solution $y(x) = 2e^x - 1 - x$.

134. A purely graphical attack

In treating the boundary value problem

(1) $y' = f(x, y); \quad x = a, \quad y = b,$

the steps taken in forming the sequence of approximations $y_0(x)$, $y_1(x)$, $y_2(x)$, $\cdots$, are frequently performed graphically.

In such a procedure, a curve $y = y_0(x)$, a reasonable first guess, is sketched over the desired interval, with care taken to make the curve pass through the point (a, b) and have the proper slope at (a, b) as given by equation (1). Frequently, this starting point, the curve $y = y_0(x)$, can be improved in practical problems by the use of additional information. For instance, it may be known, or strongly suspected, that the desired solution is concave upward in the interval for which it is desired. The use of such a piece of information would permit us to get off to a better start in building our sequence of approximations.

From the initial guess, $y = y_0(x)$, the first approximation would be obtained from

$$y_1(x) = b + \int_a^x f[t, y_0(t)]\, dt,$$

then $y_2(x)$ from $y_1(x)$ in the same manner, etc. The process would be continued until the graph had settled down; that is, until two successive curves, $y = y_k(x)$ and $y = y_{k+1}(x)$, were not appreciably different.

The method is open to many objections. One danger is that the convergence of the process may be so slow that no appreciable change can be observed graphically between two successive approximations even though a considerable error is still present.

135. Power series

The numerical problem on which we are concentrating in this chapter is that of computing for $0 \leqq x \leqq \frac{1}{2}$ that solution of

(1) $y' = y^2 - x^2$

for which $y = 1$ when $x = 0$. Let us assume that a power series solution exists. Put

(2) $y = \sum_{n=0}^{\infty} a_n x^n,$

in which $a_0 = 1$ so $y = 1$ when $x = 0$. Direct substitution into equation (1) yields

$$\sum_{n=1}^{\infty} na_n x^{n-1} = \left(\sum_{n=0}^{\infty} a_n x^n\right)^2 - x^2,$$

or

$$\sum_{n=1}^{\infty} na_n x^{n-1} = -x^2 + \sum_{n=0}^{\infty} \sum_{k=0}^{n} a_k a_{n-k} x^n.$$

A shift of index on the right gives us

$$\sum_{n=1}^{\infty} na_n x^{n-1} = -x^2 + \sum_{n=1}^{\infty} \sum_{k=0}^{n-1} a_k a_{n-1-k} x^{n-1}.$$

We know $a_0 = 1$. The other a's may be computed one at a time from

$$n = 1: \quad a_1 = a_0 a_0,$$
$$n = 2: \quad 2a_2 = a_0 a_1 + a_1 a_0,$$
$$n = 3: \quad 3a_3 = -1 + (a_0 a_2 + a_1 a_1 + a_2 a_0),$$
$$n \geq 4: \quad na_n = a_0 a_{n-1} + a_1 a_{n-2} + \cdots + a_{n-2} a_1 + a_{n-1} a_0.$$

The first few terms of the desired series are found to be as given in

$$y = 1 + x + x^2 + \tfrac{2}{3}x^3 + \tfrac{5}{6}x^4 + \tfrac{4}{5}x^5 + \tfrac{23}{30}x^6 + \tfrac{236}{315}x^7 + \cdots.$$

It is fortunate in this example that convergence of the series solution can be demonstrated by elementary devices.

Direct computation has already yielded $a_0 = 1$, $a_1 = 1$, $a_2 = 1$, $a_3 = \tfrac{2}{3}$, etc. Let us assume that

$$(3) \qquad\qquad 0 < a_k \leq 1$$

for each k less than n; i.e., for $0 \leq k \leq (n-1)$. Now we know that a_n is determined, for $n \geq 4$, by

$$(4) \qquad\qquad na_n = \sum_{k=0}^{n-1} a_k a_{n-1-k}.$$

Each of the a's on the right in (4) is positive and does not exceed unity. Hence, each product $a_k a_{n-1-k}$ is positive and not greater than one,

$$0 < a_k a_{n-1-k} \leq 1.$$

There are n such terms on the right in equation (4). Therefore from (3) and (4) it follows that $0 < na_n \leq n$, or

(5) $$0 < a_n \leqq 1.$$

Since we knew that the property (5) held for $n = 0, 1, 2,$ and 3, we may now conclude by induction that (5) holds for each integral n.

Because of the inequality (5) it can be seen that the series

$$y(x) = \sum_{n=0}^{\infty} a_n x^n$$

converges at least for $|x| < 1$.

For the range in which we are interested, $0 \leq x \leq \frac{1}{2}$, let the error caused by stopping with the term $a_n x^n$ be denoted $E_n(x)$; that is, let

$$E_n(x) = \sum_{k=n+1}^{\infty} a_k x^k.$$

Since $0 < a_n \leqq 1$, it is true for all x in the range $0 \leq x \leq \frac{1}{2}$ that

$$|E_n(x)| \leq \sum_{k=n+1}^{\infty} |a_k x^k| \leq \sum_{k=n+1}^{\infty} (\tfrac{1}{2})^k = \frac{(\tfrac{1}{2})^{n+1}}{1 - \tfrac{1}{2}} = (\tfrac{1}{2})^n.$$

As a matter of fact it is not difficult to improve upon this bound on the error. But the essential point is that for the range of x in which we are interested, we can bound the error made in computing with the power series. Thus we can be certain of two-decimal-point accuracy, something not so readily accomplished with the methods described earlier in this chapter.

CHAPTER **25**

Partial Differential Equations

136. Remarks on partial differential equations

A partial differential equation is an equation that contains one or more partial derivatives. Such equations occur frequently in applications of mathematics. They also enter pure mathematics. The subject of partial differential equations offers sufficient ramifications and difficulties to be of interest for its own sake.

In this book we shall devote the space allotted to partial differential equations almost entirely to a kind of boundary value problem which enters modern applied mathematics at every turn.

Partial differential equations can have solutions involving arbitrary functions and solutions involving an unlimited number of arbitrary constants. In rough language the general solution of a partial differential equation of order n may be defined as a solution involving n arbitrary functions.

The general solution of a partial differential equation is almost never (the wave equation is one of the few exceptions) of any practical use in solving boundary value problems associated with that equation.

137. Some partial differential equations of applied mathematics

Certain partial differential equations enter applied mathematics so frequently and in so many connections that their study is remarkably remunerative. A sufficiently thorough study of these equations would lead the student eventually into every phase of classical mathematics and, in particular, would lead almost at once to contact with special functions that are widely used in modern quantum theory and elsewhere in theoretical physics and engineering.

The derivation of the differential equations to be listed here is beyond the scope of this book. These derivations can be found (not all in each book) in the books listed for reference at the end of this section.

Some of the ways in which these equations are useful will appear in the detailed applications in Chapters 28 and 30.

Let x, y, z be rectangular coordinates in ordinary space. Then, as stated in Chapter 5, the equation

$$(1) \qquad \frac{\partial^2 V}{\partial x^2} + \frac{\partial^2 V}{\partial y^2} + \frac{\partial^2 V}{\partial z^2} = 0$$

is called Laplace's equation. It enters problems in steady-state temperature, electrostatic potential, fluid flow of the steady-state variety, etc.

If a problem involving equation (1) is such that a physical object in the problem is a circular cylinder, then it is possible that cylindrical coordinates will facilitate solution of the problem. We shall encounter such a problem later. It is a matter of advanced calculus to change equation (1) into an equation in which the independent variables are cylindrical coordinates r, θ, z, related to the x, y, z of equation (1) by the equations

$$x = r \cos \theta, \quad y = r \sin \theta, \quad z = z.$$

The resulting equation, Laplace's equation in cylindrical coordinates, is

$$(2) \qquad \frac{\partial^2 V}{\partial r^2} + \frac{1}{r}\frac{\partial V}{\partial r} + \frac{1}{r^2}\frac{\partial^2 V}{\partial \theta^2} + \frac{\partial^2 V}{\partial z^2} = 0.$$

Note that the use of z in both coordinate systems above is safe in making the change of variables only because z is not involved in the equations with other variables. That is, in a change of independent variables such as

$$x = x_1 + y_1 + z_1, \quad y = x_1 - y_1, \quad z = z_1,$$

or its equivalent

$$x_1 = \tfrac{1}{2}(x + y - z), \quad y_1 = \tfrac{1}{2}(x - y - z), \quad z_1 = z,$$

incorrect conclusions would often result from any attempt to drop the subscript on the z_1, even though $z = z_1$. For instance, from the change of variables under discussion, it follows that

$$\frac{\partial V}{\partial z} = -\frac{1}{2}\frac{\partial V}{\partial x_1} - \frac{1}{2}\frac{\partial V}{\partial y_1} + \frac{\partial V}{\partial z_1}.$$

Hence

$$\frac{\partial V}{\partial z} \neq \frac{\partial V}{\partial z_1}$$

even though $z = z_1$.

Let us return to Laplace's equation. In spherical coordinates ρ, θ, φ, related to x, y, z by the equations

$$x = \rho \sin \theta \cos \varphi, \quad y = \rho \sin \theta \sin \varphi, \quad z = \rho \cos \theta,$$

Laplace's equation is

(3) $$\frac{\partial^2 V}{\partial \rho^2} + \frac{2}{\rho}\frac{\partial V}{\partial \rho} + \frac{1}{\rho^2}\frac{\partial^2 V}{\partial \theta^2} + \frac{\cot \theta}{\rho^2}\frac{\partial V}{\partial \theta} + \frac{\csc^2 \theta}{\rho^2}\frac{\partial^2 V}{\partial \varphi^2} = 0.$$

With an additional independent variable t representing time, and with a constant denoted by a, we can write the wave equation in rectangular coordinates,

(4) $$\frac{\partial^2 V}{\partial t^2} = a^2 \left(\frac{\partial^2 V}{\partial x^2} + \frac{\partial^2 V}{\partial y^2} + \frac{\partial^2 V}{\partial z^2} \right).$$

Equation (4) occurs in problems involving wave motions. We shall meet it later in the problem of the vibrating string.

Whenever the physical problem suggests a different choice for a coordinate system, usually by the shape of the objects involved, the pertinent partial differential equation can be transformed into one with the desired new independent variables. The actual change of variables in partial differential equations is left to advanced calculus; here we use the result.

Suppose that for some solid under consideration, u represents the temperature at a point with rectangular coordinates x, y, z and at time t. The origin of coordinates and the initial time $t = 0$ may be assigned at our convenience. If there are no heat sources present, then the temperature u must satisfy the heat equation

(5)
$$\frac{\partial u}{\partial t} = h^2 \left(\frac{\partial^2 u}{\partial x^2} + \frac{\partial^2 u}{\partial y^2} + \frac{\partial^2 u}{\partial z^2} \right),$$

in which h^2 is a physical constant called thermal diffusivity. Equation (5) is derived under the assumption that the density, specific heat, and thermal conductivity are constant for the solid being studied. More comment on the question of the validity of equation (5) will be made in Section 155.

Equation (5) is the equation that pertains in many types of diffusion, not just when heat is being diffused. It is often called the equation of diffusion.

In the subject of elasticity, certain problems in plane stress can be solved with the aid of Airy's stress function φ, which must satisfy the partial differential equation

(6)
$$\frac{\partial^4 \varphi}{\partial x^4} + 2 \frac{\partial^4 \varphi}{\partial x^2 \partial y^2} + \frac{\partial^4 \varphi}{\partial y^4} = 0.$$

Numerous other partial differential equations occur in applications, though not with the dominating insistency of equations (1), (4), and (5).

In this book two methods for solving boundary value problems in partial differential equations will be examined. The Laplace transform, which was studied in Chapters 11 and 12 and applied in Chapters 13 through 15, is a useful tool for certain kinds of boundary value problems. The transform technique will be further developed in Chapter 29 and then used in Chapter 30.

A second method, the classical one of separation of variables, will be discussed in the remainder of this chapter. We shall find that two other topics, orthogonal sets and Fourier series, need to be treated before we can proceed, in Chapter 28, to use separation of variables efficiently to solve problems involving partial differential equations.

References

Churchill, R. V. *Fourier Series and Boundary Value Problems*, 2nd edition. New York: McGraw-Hill Book Co., 1963.

Churchill, R. V. *Operational Mathematics*, 2nd edition. New York: McGraw-Hill Book Co., 1958.

Hopf, L. *Differential Equations of Physics*. New York: Dover Publications, 1948.

Jeffreys, H. and Jeffreys, B. S. *Methods of Mathematical Physics*. Cambridge: Cambridge Univ. Press, 1950.

138. Method of separation of variables

Before attacking an actual boundary value problem in partial differential equations, it is wise to become somewhat proficient in getting solutions of the differential equations. When we have acquired some facility in obtaining solutions, then we can tackle the tougher problem of fitting them together to satisfy stipulated boundary conditions.

The device to be exhibited here is particularly useful in connection with linear equations, although it does not always apply to such equations.

Consider the equation

$$(1) \qquad \frac{\partial u}{\partial t} = h^2 \frac{\partial^2 u}{\partial x^2}$$

with h constant. A solution of equation (1) will in general be a function of the two independent variables t and x and of the parameter h.

Let us seek a solution that is a product of a function of t alone by a function of x alone. We put

$$u = f(t)v(x)$$

in equation (1) and arrive at

$$(2) \qquad f'(t)v(x) = h^2 f(t)v''(x),$$

where primes denote derivatives with respect to the indicated argument.

Dividing each member of (2) by the product $f(t)v(x)$, we get

$$(3) \qquad \frac{f'(t)}{f(t)} = \frac{h^2 v''(x)}{v(x)}.$$

Now equation (3) is said to have its variables (the independent variables) separated; that is, the left member of equation (3) is a function of t alone and the right member of equation (3) is a function of x alone.

Since x and t are independent variables, the only way in which a function of x alone can equal a function of t alone is for each function to be constant. Thus from (3) it follows at once that

$$(4) \qquad \frac{f'(t)}{f(t)} = k,$$

$$(5) \qquad \frac{h^2 v''(x)}{v(x)} = k,$$

in which k is arbitrary.

Another way of obtaining equations (4) and (5) is this. Differentiate each member of equation (3) with respect to t (either independent variable could be used) and thus get

$$\frac{d}{dt} \frac{f'(t)}{f(t)} = 0,$$

since the right member of equation (3) is independent of t. First we obtain equation (4) by integration and then equation (5) follows from (4) and (3).

Equation (4) may be rewritten

$$\frac{df}{dt} = kf,$$

from which its general solution

$$f = c_1 e^{kt}$$

follows immediately.

Before going further into the solution of our problem, we attempt to choose a convenient form for the arbitrary constant introduced in equations (4) and (5). Equation (5) suggests that k be taken as a multiple of h^2.

Let us then return to equations (4) and (5) and put $k = h^2 \beta^2$, so we have

$$(6) \qquad\qquad \frac{f'(t)}{f(t)} = h^2 \beta^2$$

and

$$(7) \qquad\qquad \frac{h^2 v''(x)}{v(x)} = h^2 \beta^2.$$

Using real β and the choice $k = h^2 \beta^2$, we are implying that the constant k is real and positive.* Later we shall obtain solutions corresponding to the choice of a real but negative constant.

From equations (6) and (7) we find at once that

$$(8) \qquad\qquad f(t) = c_1 \exp (h^2 \beta^2 t)$$

and

$$(9) \qquad\qquad v(x) = c_2 \cosh \beta x + c_3 \sinh \beta x.$$

Since $u = f(t)v(x)$, we are led to the result that the partial differential equation

---

* The expression "real and positive" is redundant; if something is positive, it must be real. Such redundant phrases are useful in exposition.

$$(1) \qquad \frac{\partial u}{\partial t} = h^2 \frac{\partial^2 u}{\partial x^2}$$

has solutions

$$(10) \qquad u = \exp{(h^2\beta^2 t)}[a \cosh \beta x + b \sinh \beta x],$$

in which β, a, and b are arbitrary constants. The a and b of equation (10) are respectively given by $a = c_1 c_2$ and $b = c_1 c_3$ in terms of the constants of equations (8) and (9).

If we return to equations (4) and (5) with the choice $k = -h^2\alpha^2$, so k is taken to be a real negative constant, then we find that the partial differential equation (1) has the solutions

$$(11) \qquad u = \exp{(-h^2\alpha^2 t)}[A \cos \alpha x + B \sin \alpha x],$$

in which α, A, and B are arbitrary constants.

Finally, let the constant k be zero. It is straightforward to determine that the corresponding solutions of the differential equation (1) are

$$(12) \qquad u = C_1 + C_2 x,$$

in which C_1 and C_2 are constants.

Direct verification that equations (10), (11), and (12) are actually solutions of equation (1) is simple.

Since the partial differential equation (1) is linear, we may construct solutions by forming linear combinations of solutions. Thus from (10), (11), and (12) with varying choices of α, β, A, B, a, b, C_1, C_2, we can construct as many solutions of (1) as we wish.

The distinction between equations (10) and (11) is dependent upon the parameters and variables remaining real. Our aim is to develop tools for solving physical problems; hence we do intend to keep things real.

Exercises

Except where other instructions are given, use the method of separation of variables to obtain solutions in real form for each differential equation.

1. $\dfrac{\partial^2 u}{\partial t^2} = a^2 \dfrac{\partial^2 u}{\partial x^2}.$

   ANS. $u = [A_1 \cos a\beta t + A_2 \sin a\beta t][B_1 \cos \beta x + B_2 \sin \beta x],$
   $u = (A_3 + A_4 t)(B_3 + B_4 x),$
   and
   $u = [A_5 \cosh a\beta t + A_6 \sinh a\beta t][B_5 \cosh \beta x + B_6 \sinh \beta x],$
   in which β and the A's and B's are arbitrary constants.

2. $\dfrac{\partial^2 v}{\partial x^2} + \dfrac{\partial^2 v}{\partial y^2} = 0.$

> ANS. $v = [A_1 e^{\beta x} + A_2 e^{-\beta x}][B_1 \cos \beta y + B_2 \sin \beta y]$, and
>
> $v = (A_3 + A_4 x)(B_3 + B_4 y),$

in which β and the A's and B's are arbitrary constants; the roles played by x and y in the former solution can be interchanged.

3. $\dfrac{\partial^2 u}{\partial t^2} + 2b \dfrac{\partial u}{\partial t} = a^2 \dfrac{\partial^2 u}{\partial x^2}.$

Show that this equation has the solutions:

$$u = g(t)[B_1 \cos kx + B_2 \sin kx],$$

where $g(t)$ can assume any one of the forms:

$$e^{-bt}[A_1 e^{\gamma t} + A_2 e^{-\gamma t}], \ \gamma^2 = b^2 - a^2 k^2, \text{ if } b^2 - a^2 k^2 > 0,$$

or

$$e^{-bt}[A_3 \cos \delta t + A_4 \sin \delta t], \ \delta^2 = a^2 k^2 - b^2, \text{ if } a^2 k^2 - b^2 > 0,$$

or

$$e^{-bt}[A_5 + A_6 t], \text{ if } a^2 k^2 - b^2 = 0,$$

and the solutions

$$u = (A_7 + A_8 e^{-2bt})(B_3 + B_4 x).$$

Find also solutions containing e^{kx} and e^{-kx}.

4. $\dfrac{\partial w}{\partial y} = y \dfrac{\partial w}{\partial x}.$ ANS. $w = A \exp [k(2x + y^2)]$, k and A arbitrary.

5. $x \dfrac{\partial w}{\partial x} = w + y \dfrac{\partial w}{\partial y}.$ ANS. $w = A x^k y^{k-1}$, k and A arbitrary.

6. Subject the partial differential equation of Ex. 5 to the change of dependent variable $w = v/y$ and show that the resultant equation for v is

$$x \dfrac{\partial v}{\partial x} = y \dfrac{\partial v}{\partial y}.$$

7. Show that the method of separation of variables does not succeed, without modifications, for the equation

$$\dfrac{\partial^2 u}{\partial x^2} + 4 \dfrac{\partial^2 u}{\partial x \, \partial t} + 5 \dfrac{\partial^2 u}{\partial t^2} = 0.$$

8. For the equation of Ex. 7, seek a solution of the form

$$u = e^{kt} f(x)$$

and thus obtain the solutions

$$u = \exp[k(t - 2x)][A_1 \cos kx + A_2 \sin kx],$$

where k, A_1, A_2 are arbitrary. Show also that the equation of Ex. 7 has the solutions $u = Ax + B$ and $u = Ct + D$, with A, B, C, D arbitrary.

9. For the equation

$$\frac{\partial^2 u}{\partial x^2} + 4x \frac{\partial u}{\partial x} + \frac{\partial^2 u}{\partial y^2} = 0,$$

put $u = f(x)g(y)$ and thus obtain solutions

$$u = [A_1 e^{2ky} + A_2 e^{-2ky}][B_1 f_1(x) + B_2 f_2(x)],$$

in which $f_1(x)$ and $f_2(x)$ are any two linearly independent solutions of the equation

$$f'' + 4xf' + 4k^2 f = 0.$$

Obtain also the solutions that correspond to $k = 0$ in the above. For $k \neq 0$, the functions f_1 and f_2 should be obtained by the method of Chapter 20. They may be found in the form

$$f_1(x) = 1 + \sum_{m=1}^{\infty} \frac{(-4)^m (k^2)(k^2 + 2)(k^2 + 4) \cdots (k^2 + 2m - 2)x^{2m}}{(2m)!},$$

$$f_2(x) = x + \sum_{m=1}^{\infty} \frac{(-4)^m (k^2 + 1)(k^2 + 3)(k^2 + 5) \cdots (k^2 + 2m - 1)x^{2m+1}}{(2m + 1)!}.$$

Find similar solutions involving $\cos 2ky$ and $\sin 2ky$.

10. Use the change of variable $u = e^{\beta t}g(x)$ to find solutions of the equation

$$\frac{\partial^2 u}{\partial x^2} + 2\frac{\partial^2 u}{\partial x \partial t} + \frac{\partial^2 u}{\partial t^2} = 0.$$

ANS. $u = \exp[\beta(t - x)][A_1 + A_2 x]$.

11. Show by direct computation that if $f_1(y)$ and $f_2(y)$ are any functions with continuous second derivatives, $f_1''(y)$ and $f_2''(y)$, then

$$u = f_1(x - at) + f_2(x + at)$$

satisfies the simple wave equation (Ex. 1),

$$\frac{\partial^2 u}{\partial t^2} = a^2 \frac{\partial^2 u}{\partial x^2}.$$

12. Show that $v = f(xy)$ is a solution of the equation of Ex. 6.

13. Show that $w = f(2x + y^2)$ is a solution of the equation of Ex. 4.

14. Show that $u = f_1(t - x) + xf_2(t - x)$ is a solution of the equation of Ex. 10.

139. A problem on the conduction of heat in a slab

Among the equations of applied mathematics already stated is the heat equation in rectangular coordinates,

$$(1) \qquad \frac{\partial u}{\partial t} = h^2 \left(\frac{\partial^2 u}{\partial x^2} + \frac{\partial^2 u}{\partial y^2} + \frac{\partial^2 u}{\partial z^2} \right),$$

in which

$$x, y, z = \text{rectangular space coordinates,}$$
$$t = \text{time coordinate,}$$
$$h^2 = \text{thermal diffusivity,}$$
$$u = \text{temperature.}$$

The constant h^2 and the variables x, y, z, t, u may be in any consistent set of units. For instance, we may measure x, y, z in feet, t in hours, u in degrees Fahrenheit, and h^2 in ft.² per hour. The thermal diffusivity (assumed constant in our work) can be defined by

$$h^2 = \frac{K}{\sigma \delta},$$

in terms of quantities of elementary physics,

$$K = \text{thermal conductivity,}$$
$$\sigma = \text{specific heat,}$$
$$\delta = \text{density,}$$

all pertaining to the material composing the solid whose temperature we seek.

For our first boundary value problem in partial differential equations it seems wise to set up as simple a problem as possible. We now construct a temperature problem which is set in such a way that the temperature is independent of two space variables, say y and z. For such a problem, u will be a function of only two independent variables (x and t), which is the smallest number of independent variables possible in a partial differential equation.

Consider a huge flat slab of concrete, or some other material reasonably near homogeneity in texture. Let the thickness of the slab be c units of length. Choose the origin of coordinates on a face of the slab as indicated in Figure 50 and assume that the slab extends very far in the y and z directions.

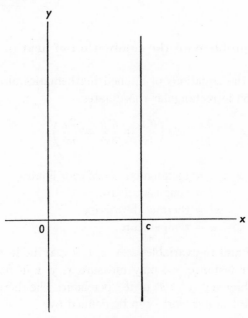

FIGURE 50

Let the initial ($t = 0$) temperature of the slab be $f(x)$, a function of x alone, and let the surfaces $x = 0$, $x = c$ be kept at zero temperature for all $t > 0$. If the slab is considered infinite in the y and z directions, or more specifically, if we treat only cross sections nearby (far from the distant surface of the slab), then the temperature u at any time t and position x is determined by the boundary value problem:

$$\text{(2)} \qquad \frac{\partial u}{\partial t} = h^2 \frac{\partial^2 u}{\partial x^2}, \quad \text{for } 0 < t, \ \ 0 < x < c;$$

(3)   As $t \to 0^+$, $u \to f(x)$,   for $0 < x < c$;

(4)   As $x \to 0^+$, $u \to 0$,   for $0 < t$;

(5)   As $x \to c^-$, $u \to 0$,   for $0 < t$.

In the boundary value problem (2) through (5), the zero on the temperature scale has been chosen as the temperature at which the surfaces of the slab are held. Then the $f(x)$ is really the difference between the actual initial temperature and the subsequent constant boundary temperature.

Such a set of symbols as $t \to 0^+$ means that t approaches zero through values above zero. Similarly, $x \to c^-$ means that x approaches c through values less than c, "c minus something" at each stage during the approach. We may say, for instance, that x approaches c from the left.

It is particularly to be noted that we do not require such a condition as that the function $u(x, t)$ be $f(x)$ when $t = 0$. We require only that as $t \to 0^+$, then $u \to f(x)$ for each x in the range $0 < x < c$.

The question of precisely how many boundary conditions, and of what nature, are to be associated with a given partial differential equation to assure the existence and uniqueness of a solution is a question of considerable difficulty. In this book we shall use the most popular practical guide, physical intuition. Existence is no problem: we seek a solution, and if we find one, we know it exists; if we don't find one, it is hardly balm for our wounds to be told that it exists. To the serious problem of uniqueness we close our eyes entirely.

Let us now attempt to solve the boundary value problem, to find a function $u(x, t)$ that will satisfy the partial differential equation

$$(2) \qquad \frac{\partial u}{\partial t} = h^2 \frac{\partial^2 u}{\partial x^2}, \quad \text{for } 0 < x < c, \quad 0 < t;$$

and that will also satisfy the conditions:

$$(3) \qquad \text{As } t \to 0^+, \quad u \to f(x), \quad \text{for } 0 < x < c;$$
$$(4) \qquad \text{As } x \to 0^+, \quad u \to 0, \qquad \text{for } 0 < t;$$
$$(5) \qquad \text{As } x \to c^-, \quad u \to 0, \qquad \text{for } 0 < t.$$

We already know how to get some solutions of the differential equation (2). Indeed, on pages 406–408 the method of separation of variables was used to arrive at the solutions

$$(6) \qquad u = \exp{(h^2\beta^2 t)}[a \cosh \beta x + b \sinh \beta x],$$

with a, b, β arbitrary constants, and the solutions

$$(7) \qquad u = \exp{(-h^2\alpha^2 t)}[A \cos \alpha x + B \sin \alpha x]$$

with A, B, α arbitrary constants.

It is now necessary to attempt to adjust the solutions (6) or (7) to satisfy the boundary conditions (3), (4), and (5). Trial shows quickly that it is simpler to satisfy conditions (4) and (5) first and then to tackle (3).

Let us try to satisfy (4) and (5) with solutions in the form of equation (6) above. Now condition (4) requires that when we let $x \to 0^+$, then $u \to 0$ for all positive t. Letting $x \to 0^+$ in equation (6) we conclude that

$$0 = \exp (h^2\beta^2t)[a + 0], \text{ for } 0 < t.$$

Thus we are forced to conclude that $a = 0$, so the solution (6) becomes

(8) $$u = b \exp (h^2\beta^2t) \sinh \beta x.$$

By condition (5) we must require that as $x \to c^-$, then again $u \to 0$ for all positive t; that is, from equation (8) and condition (5) we get

$$b \exp (h^2\beta^2t) \sinh \beta c = 0, \text{ for } 0 < t.$$

The exponential $\exp (h^2\beta^2t)$ cannot vanish. For real values of β and c the function $\sinh \beta c$ is zero only when $\beta c = 0$. Hence it follows that $\beta = 0$ or $b = 0$, so $u \equiv 0$ and we have no chance of satisfying the remaining condition, (3). Let us therefore abandon equation (6) and concentrate upon the solutions

(7) $$u = \exp (-h^2\alpha^2t)[A \cos \alpha x + B \sin \alpha x].$$

Let us impose conditions (4) and (5) upon the u of equation (7). First we let $x \to 0^+$ and conclude that

$$0 = \exp (-h^2\alpha^2t)[A + 0], \text{ for } 0 < t,$$

so we must choose $A = 0$. Then (7) reduces to

(9) $$u = B \exp (-h^2\alpha^2t) \sin \alpha x.$$

Next we impose condition (5), that $u \to 0$ when $x \to c^-$, so

$$0 = B \exp (-h^2\alpha^2t) \sin \alpha c, \text{ for } 0 < t.$$

We must not choose $B = 0$, if we are to have any success in satisfying the additional condition (3). The function $\exp (-h^2\alpha^2t)$ does not vanish. Therefore, for the u of (9) to satisfy condition (5), it is necessary that

(10) $$\sin \alpha c = 0.$$

The sine function is zero when, and only when, its argument is an integral multiple of π; that is, $\sin z$ is zero when $z = 0, \pm\pi, \pm 2\pi, \cdots,$ $\pm n\pi, \cdots$. Therefore from (10) it follows that

(11) $$\alpha c = n\pi, n \text{ integral.}$$

Since c is given, equation (11) serves to determine the arbitrary parameter α—rather, to restrict the values of α to those given by (11).

With $\alpha = n\pi/c$, the solutions (9) above become

$$u = B \exp \left[-\left(\frac{n\pi h}{c} \right)^2 t \right] \sin \frac{n\pi x}{c}$$

with n integral and B arbitrary. Since we need not use the same arbitrary constant B for different values of n, it is wiser to write solutions

$$(12) \qquad u_n = B_n \exp\left[-\left(\frac{n\pi h}{c}\right)^2 t\right] \sin\frac{n\pi x}{c}, \, n \text{ integral}.$$

We lose nothing by restricting the n in equation (12) to the positive integers 1, 2, 3, $\cdot\cdot\cdot$, for $n = 0$ leads to the trivial solution $u \equiv 0$ and the negative integral values for n lead to essentially the same solutions as do the positive integral values.

Let us see where we stand at present. Each of the functions u_n defined by equation (12) is a solution of the differential equation

$$(2) \qquad \frac{\partial u}{\partial t} = h^2 \frac{\partial^2 u}{\partial x^2}, \quad \text{for } 0 < x < c, \quad 0 < t,$$

and each of those functions satisfies the two conditions

$$(4) \qquad \text{As } x \to 0^+, \quad u \to 0, \quad \text{for } 0 < t,$$

and

$$(5) \qquad \text{As } x \to c^-, \quad u \to 0, \quad \text{for } 0 < t.$$

It remains to find from the solutions u_n a solution $u(x, t)$ that will also satisfy the boundary (or initial) condition

$$(3) \qquad \text{As } t \to 0^+, \quad u \to f(x), \quad \text{for } 0 < x < c.$$

Since the partial differential equation involved is linear and homogeneous in u and its derivatives, a sum of solutions is also a solution. From the known solutions $u_1, u_2, u_3 \cdot\cdot\cdot, u_n, \cdot\cdot\cdot$, we may thus construct others. With sufficiently strong convergence conditions it is true that even the infinite series

$$u = \sum_{n=1}^{\infty} u_n$$

or

$$(13) \qquad u(x, t) = \sum_{n=1}^{\infty} B_n \exp\left[-\left(\frac{n\pi h}{c}\right)^2 t\right] \sin\frac{n\pi x}{c}$$

is also a solution of the differential equation (2).

The $u(x, t)$ of equation (13) satisfies equation (2) and the boundary conditions (4) and (5). If $u(x, t)$ is to satisfy condition (3), then for each x in the interval $0 < x < c$ the right member of equation (13) should approach $f(x)$ as $t \to 0^+$. We assume that we may interchange the order of limit (as $t \to 0^+$) and summation and conclude that condition (3) formally requires that

$$(14) \qquad f(x) = \sum_{n=1}^{\infty} B_n \sin \frac{n\pi x}{c}, \text{ for } 0 < x < c.$$

Thus we can solve the problem under consideration if we can choose the constants B_n so that the infinite series on the right in (14) has $f(x)$ for its sum for each x in the interval $0 < x < c$. That there exist such coefficients B_n is far from evident. For a large class of functions $f(x)$, an expansion of the type of equation (14) does exist, as will be seen in Chapter 27. Once the B_n are known, they are to be inserted on the right in equation (13), which is then the final solution of the boundary value problem consisting of equation (2) and conditions (3), (4), and (5).

To be able to complete the solution of boundary value problems of the kind under consideration here, we need to acquire a knowledge of methods of expansion of functions into trigonometric series. Chapter 27 is devoted to the development of that type of expansion, providing us with tools for solving numerous boundary value problems in Chapter 28.

CHAPTER 26

Orthogonal Sets

140. Orthogonality

A set of functions $f_0(x)$, $f_1(x)$, $f_2(x)$, $\cdots$, $f_n(x)$, $\cdots$, is said to be *an orthogonal set with respect to the weight function* $w(x)$ *over the interval* $a \leqq x \leqq b$ *if*

$$\int_a^b w(x)f_n(x)f_m(x)\ dx = 0 \text{ for } m \neq n,$$
$$\neq 0 \text{ for } m = n.$$

Orthogonality is a property widely encountered in certain branches of mathematics. Much use is made of the representation of functions in series of the form

$$\sum_{n=0}^{\infty} c_n f_n(x)$$

in which the c_n are numerical coefficients and the $f_n(x)$ is an orthogonal set.

A tremendous literature exists regarding orthogonal sets of functions. A student who wishes to pursue the subject beyond the material in this chapter can get a thorough introduction to it in courses and books on orthogonal polynomials, Fourier series, Fourier analysis, etc. A short list of references is given at the end of Chapter 27.

One simple version of a theorem in the subject of orthogonal functions may be stated as follows:

Given a set of functions

$$\varphi_0(x), \quad \varphi_1(x), \quad \varphi_2(x), \cdots, \quad \varphi_n(x), \cdots,$$

linearly independent (Section 31) and continuous in the interval

$$a \leqq x \leqq b,$$

and given a weight function $w(x)$ positive and continuous in that same interval, then a set of functions

$$f_0(x), \quad f_1(x), \quad f_2(x), \cdots, \quad f_n(x), \cdots,$$

exists with the properties that:

(a) Each $f_n(x)$ is a linear combination of φ's;
(b) The $f_n(x)$ are linearly independent on the interval $a \leqq x \leqq b$;
(c) The $f_n(x)$ is an orthogonal set with respect to the weight function $w(x)$ over the interval $a \leqq x \leqq b$.

We already know that the functions $1, x, x^2, \cdots, x^n, \cdots$, are linearly independent and are continuous over any finite interval. Linear combinations of powers of x are polynomials. Hence, given an interval and a proper weight function, there exists in particular a set of polynomials orthogonal with respect to that weight function over that interval. With added conditions on the weight function the restriction to a finite interval can be removed.

141. Simple sets of polynomials

A set of polynomials $f_n(x)$; $n = 0, 1, 2, 3, \cdots$, is called a simple set if $f_n(x)$ is of degree precisely n. The set then contains one polynomial of each degree, $0, 1, 2, \cdots, n, \cdots$.

An important property of simple sets is that if $g_m(x)$ is any polynomial of degree m and $f_n(x)$ is a simple set of polynomials, then there exist constants c_k such that

$$(1) \qquad g_m(x) = \sum_{k=0}^{m} c_k f_k(x).$$

PROOF. Let the highest degree term in $g_m(x)$ be $a_m x^m$ and the highest degree term in $f_m(x)$ be $b_m x^m$. Define $c_m = a_m/b_m$, noting that $b_m \neq 0$. Then the polynomial

$$g_m(x) - c_m f_m(x)$$

is of degree at most $(m - 1)$. On this polynomial use the same procedure as was used on $g_m(x)$. It follows that c_{m-1} exists so that

$$g_m(x) - c_m f_m(x) - c_{m-1} f_{m-1}(x)$$

is of degree at most $(m - 2)$. Iteration of the process yields equation (1) in $(m + 1)$ steps. Note that any c_k except c_m may be zero.

142. Orthogonal polynomials

We next obtain for polynomials a condition equivalent to our definition (Section 140) of orthogonality.

THEOREM 21: *If $f_n(x)$ is a simple set of polynomials, a necessary and sufficient condition that $f_n(x)$ be orthogonal with respect to $w(x)$ over the interval $a \leq x \leq b$ is that*

(1)
$$\int_a^b w(x) x^k f_n(x)\, dx = 0, \quad k = 0, 1, 2, \cdots, (n - 1),$$
$$\neq 0, \quad k = n.$$

PROOF. Suppose that (1) is satisfied. Since x^k forms a simple set, we can write

(2)
$$f_m(x) = \sum_{k=0}^{m} a_k x^k.$$

If $m < n$, it follows that

$$\int_a^b w(x) f_m(x) f_n(x)\, dx = \sum_{k=0}^{m} a_k \int_a^b w(x) x^k f_n(x)\, dx = 0$$

by (1), since each k involved is less than n. If $m > n$, interchange the roles of m and n, and repeat the argument. If $m = n$ in (2), then $a_n \neq 0$, and we have

$$\int_a^b w(x) f_n{}^2(x)\, dx = \sum_{k=0}^{n} a_k \int_a^b w(x) x^k f_n(x)\, dx$$
$$= a_n \int_a^b w(x) x^n f_n(x)\, dx \neq 0.$$

Thus we see that the condition (1) is sufficient for orthogonality of the $f_n(x)$.

Next suppose the $f_n(x)$ satisfy the condition for orthogonality as laid down in Section 140. Since the $f_n(x)$ form a simple set, we can write

$$(3) \qquad x^k = \sum_{m=0}^{k} b_m f_m(x).$$

If $k < n$, it follows that

$$\int_a^b w(x) x^k f_n(x)\, dx = \sum_{m=0}^{k} b_m \int_a^b w(x) f_m(x) f_n(x)\, dx = 0,$$

since no m can equal n. If $k = n$ in (3), then $b_n \neq 0$, and we have

$$\int_a^b w(x) x^n f_n(x)\, dx = \sum_{m=0}^{n} b_m \int_a^b w(x) f_m(x) f_n(x)\, dx$$

$$= b_n \int_a^b w(x) f_n{}^2(x)\, dx \neq 0.$$

This completes the proof of Theorem 21.

143. Zeros of orthogonal polynomials

We shall show that real orthogonal polynomials have all their zeros real, distinct, and in the interval of orthogonality.

THEOREM 22: *If $f_n(x)$ is a simple set of real polynomials orthogonal with respect to $w(x)$ over the interval $a \leq x \leq b$, and if $w(x) > 0$ over $a < x < b$, then the zeros of $f_n(x)$ are distinct and all lie in the open interval $a < x < b$.*

Proof. For $n \geq 1$, the polynomial $f_n(x)$ does change sign in the interval $a < x < b$ because, by Theorem 21 (with $k = 0$),

$$\int_a^b w(x) f_n(x)\, dx = 0$$

and $w(x)$ cannot change sign in $a < x < b$.

Let $f_n(x)$ change sign in $a < x < b$ at precisely the distinct points $x = \alpha_1, \alpha_2, \cdots, \alpha_s$. The α's are precisely the zeros of odd multiplicity of $f_n(x)$ in the interval. Since $f_n(x)$ is of degree n, it has n zeros, multiplicity counted. Thus we know that $s \leq n$.

Form the function

$$(1) \qquad \psi(x) = (x - \alpha_1)(x - \alpha_2) \cdots (x - \alpha_s).$$

Then, in $a < x < b$, $\psi(x)$ changes sign at $x = \alpha_1, \alpha_2, \cdots, \alpha_s$ and nowhere else.

If $s < n$, $\psi(x)$ is of degree $< n$, so

(2) $$\int_a^b w(x)f_n(x)\psi(x)\, dx = 0$$

by the application of Theorem 21 to each term in the expanded form of $\psi(x)$. But the integrand in (2) does not change sign anywhere in the interval of integration, since $w(x) > 0$ and the functions $f_n(x)$ and $\psi(x)$ change sign at precisely the same points. Therefore the integral in (2) cannot vanish and the assumption $s < n$ has led us to a contradiction.

Thus we have $s = n$. That is, among the n zeros of $f_n(x)$ there are precisely n of odd multiplicity in the open interval $a < x < b$. Therefore each zero is of multiplicity one; the zeros are distinct. The proof of Theorem 22 is complete.

144. Orthogonality of Legendre polynomials

The Legendre polynomials

(1) $$P_n(x) = F\left(-n, n + 1; 1; \frac{1 - x}{2}\right)$$

of Section 120 were obtained by solving the differential equation

(2) $$(1 - x^2)y'' - 2xy' + n(n + 1)y = 0.$$

The $P_n(x)$ form a simple set of polynomials for which we now obtain an orthogonality property.

From (2) we have

$$(1 - x^2)P_n''(x) - 2xP_n'(x) + n(n + 1)P_n(x) = 0,$$

(3) $$D[(1 - x^2)P_n'(x)] + n(n + 1)P_n(x) = 0; \quad D = \frac{d}{dx}.$$

For index m we have

(4) $$D[(1 - x^2)P_m'(x)] + m(m + 1)P_m(x) = 0.$$

We are interested in the product $P_m(x)P_n(x)$. Hence we multiply (3) throughout by $P_m(x)$, (4) throughout by $P_n(x)$, and subtract to obtain

$$P_m(x)D[(1 - x^2)P_n'(x)] - P_n(x)D[(1 - x^2)P_m'(x)]$$
$$+ [n(n + 1) - m(m + 1)]P_m(x)P_n(x) = 0.$$

The equation above may be rewritten as

(5) $(n^2 - m^2 + n - m)P_m(x)P_n(x)$

$$= P_n(x)D[(1 - x^2)P'_m(x)] - P_m(x)D[(1 - x^2)P'_n(x)].$$

Now, by the formula for differentiating a product, we get

$$D[(1 - x^2)P_n(x)P'_m(x)] = P_n(x)D[(1 - x^2)P'_m(x)] + (1 - x^2)P'_n(x)P'_m(x)$$

and

$$D[(1 - x^2)P'_n(x)P_m(x)] = P_m(x)D[(1 - x^2)P'_n(x)] + (1 - x^2)P'_n(x)P'_m(x).$$

Hence

$$D[(1 - x^2)\{P_n(x)P'_m(x) - P'_n(x)P_m(x)\}]$$

$$= P_n(x)D[(1 - x^2)P'_m(x)] - P_m(x)D[(1 - x^2)P'_n(x)].$$

Furthermore, $n^2 - m^2 + n - m = (n - m)(n + m + 1)$. Therefore we can write (5) as

(6) $(n - m)(n + m + 1)P_m(x)P_n(x)$

$$= D[(1 - x^2)\{P_n(x)P'_m(x) - P'_n(x)P_m(x)\}].$$

We have now expressed the product of any two Legendre polynomials as a derivative. Derivatives are easy to integrate. Equation (6) yields

(7) $(n - m)(n + m + 1) \int_a^b P_m(x)P_n(x)\, dx$

$$= \left[(1 - x^2)\{P_n(x)P'_m(x) - P'_n(x)P_m(x)\} \right]_a^b$$

We may choose any a and b that we wish. Since $(1 - x^2)$ is zero at $x = -1$ and $x = 1$, we conclude that

(8) $(n - m)(n + m + 1) \int_{-1}^1 P_m(x)P_n(x)\, dx = 0.$

Since n and m are to be non-negative integers, $n + m + 1 \neq 0$. Hence if $m \neq n$, $n - m \neq 0$ and (8) yields

(9) $\int_{-1}^1 P_m(x)P_n(x)\, dx = 0.$

The Legendre polynomials are real, so $\int_{-1}^1 P_n{}^2(x)\, dx \neq 0.$

We have shown that the Legendre polynomials $P_n(x)$ form an orthogonal set with respect to the weight function $w(x) = 1$ over the interval $-1 < x < 1$. The $P_n(x)$ are a simple set of real polynomials, so the theorems of Section 142 and 143 apply to them.

Further study of $P_n(x)$ would occupy more space than seems appropriate in an elementary differential equations text. We now list a few of the simplest from among the hundreds of known properties of these interesting polynomials:

$$(10) \qquad (1 - 2xt + t^2)^{-\frac{1}{2}} = \sum_{n=0}^{\infty} P_n(x)t^n,$$

$$(11) \qquad \int_{-1}^{1} P_n{}^2(x) \, dx = \frac{2}{2n + 1},$$

$$(12) \qquad P_n(x) = \frac{1}{2^n n!} D^n(x^2 - 1)^n; \; D = \frac{d}{dx},$$

$$(13) \qquad xP_n'(x) = nP_n(x) + P_{n-1}'(x),$$

$$(14) \qquad (x^2 - 1)P_n'(x) = nxP_n(x) - nP_{n-1}(x),$$

$$(15) \qquad nP_n(x) = (2n - 1)xP_{n-1}(x) - (n - 1)P_{n-2}(x).$$

145. Other orthogonal sets

In Chapter 22 we solved several differential equations of hypergeometric type. In Section 116 we encountered the Laguerre polynomial

$$(1) \qquad L_n(x) = \sum_{k=0}^{n} \frac{(-n)_k x^k}{(k!)^2} = \sum_{k=0}^{n} \frac{(-1)^k n! x^k}{(k!)^2(n - k)!}$$

as a solution of the differential equation

$$(2) \qquad xL_n''(x) + (1 - x)L_n'(x) + nL_n(x) = 0.$$

Equation (2) can be put in the form

$$(3) \qquad D[xe^{-x}L_n'(x)] + ne^{-x}L_n(x) = 0,$$

from which the orthogonality of the Laguerre polynomials follows. (See Ex. 1 below.)

The Hermite polynomial of Section 119,

$$(4) \qquad H_n(x) = \sum_{k=0}^{[n/2]} \frac{(-1)^k n! (2x)^{n-2k}}{k!(n - 2k)!},$$

satisfies the differential equation

$$(5) \qquad H_n''(x) - 2xH_n'(x) + 2nH_n(x) = 0.$$

Equation (5) can be put in the form

(6) $D\left[\exp\left(-x^2\right)H'_n(x)\right] + 2n\exp\left(-x^2\right)H_n(x) = 0,$

from which the orthogonality of the Hermite polynomials follows. (See Ex. 3 below.)

The Bessel function $J_n(x)$ of Section 118 can be shown to have orthogonality properties also, but they are beyond the scope of this book. See, for example, R. V. Churchill, *Fourier Series and Boundary Value Problems*, 2nd ed. (New York: McGraw-Hill Book Co., 1963).

Exercises

1. Use equation (3) above and the method of Section 144 to show that the Laguerre polynomials are orthogonal with respect to the weight function e^{-x} over the interval $0 \leqq x < \infty$.

2. Show, with the aid of Ex. 1, that the zeros of the Laguerre polynomial $L_n(x)$ are distinct and positive.

3. Use equation (6) above and the method of Section 144 to show that the Hermite polynomials are orthogonal with respect to the weight function e^{-x^2} over the interval $-\infty < x < \infty$.

4. Show, with the aid of Ex. 3, that the zeros of the Hermite polynomial $H_n(x)$ are real and distinct.

CHAPTER 27

Fourier Series

146. Orthogonality of a set of sines and cosines

The functions $\sin \alpha x$ and $\cos \alpha x$ occur in the formal solution of certain boundary value problems in partial differential equations, as was indicated in Chapter 25. We shall now obtain an orthogonality property for a set of such functions with α specified. An interval must be involved; let the origin be chosen at the center of the interval so the latter appears in the symmetric form: $-c \leqq x \leqq c$.

We shall show that the set of functions,

(A) $\qquad \begin{cases} \sin (n\pi x/c), & n = 1, 2, 3, \cdots, \\ \cos (n\pi x/c), & n = 0, 1, 2, \cdots, \end{cases}$

or

(A) $\quad \begin{cases} \sin (\pi x/c), \sin (2\pi x/c), \sin (3\pi x/c), \cdots, \sin (n\pi x/c), \cdots, \\ 1, \cos (\pi x/c), \cos (2\pi x/c), \cos (3\pi x/c), \cdots, \cos (n\pi x/c), \cdots, \end{cases}$

is orthogonal with respect to the weight function $w(x) = 1$ *over the interval* $-c \leqq x \leqq c$. That is, we shall prove that the integral from $x = -c$ to $x = +c$ of the product of any two different members of the set (A) is zero.

First consider the integral of the product of any of the sine functions in (A) and any of the cosine functions in (A). The result

$$I_1 = \int_{-c}^{c} \sin \frac{n\pi x}{c} \cos \frac{k\pi x}{c}\, dx = 0$$

follows at once from the fact that the integrand is an odd function of x; in this instance the result does not depend upon the fact that k and n are integers.

Next consider the integral of the product of two different sine functions from the set (A),

$$I_2 = \int_{-c}^{c} \sin \frac{n\pi x}{c} \sin \frac{k\pi x}{c}\, dx, \quad k \neq n.$$

Let us introduce a new variable of integration for simplicity in writing; put

$$\frac{\pi x}{c} = \beta,$$

from which

$$dx = \frac{c}{\pi}\, d\beta.$$

Then I_2 can be written

$$I_2 = \frac{c}{\pi} \int_{-\pi}^{\pi} \sin n\beta \sin k\beta\, d\beta.$$

Now from trigonometry we get the formula

$$\sin n\beta \sin k\beta = \tfrac{1}{2}[\cos (n - k)\beta - \cos (n + k)\beta]$$

which is useful in performing the desired integration. Thus it follows that the integral becomes

$$I_2 = \frac{c}{2\pi} \int_{-\pi}^{\pi} [\cos (n - k)\beta - \cos (n + k)\beta]\, d\beta$$

$$= \frac{c}{2\pi} \left[\frac{\sin (n - k)\beta}{n - k} - \frac{\sin (n + k)\beta}{n + k} \right]_{-\pi}^{\pi},$$

since neither $(n - k)$ nor $(n + k)$ can be zero. Because n and k are positive integers, $\sin (n - k)\beta$ and $\sin (n + k)\beta$ each vanish at $\beta = \pi$ and $\beta = -\pi$; then

$$I_2 = 0$$

for $n, k = 1, 2, 3, \cdots$, and $k \neq n$.

Finally, consider the integral of the product of two different cosine functions from the set (A),

$$I_3 = \int_{-c}^{c} \cos \frac{n\pi x}{c} \cos \frac{k\pi x}{c} \, dx,$$

where $n, k = 0, 1, 2, 3, \cdots$; $k \neq n$. The method used on I_2 works equally well here to yield

$$I_3 = \frac{c}{2\pi} \left[\frac{\sin (n-k)\beta}{n-k} + \frac{\sin (n+k)\beta}{n+k} \right]_{-\pi}^{\pi} = 0.$$

It is easy to see that the integral of the square of any function from the set (A) will not vanish—its integrand is positive except at an occasional point. The values of those integrals are readily obtained. The integral

$$I_4 = \int_{-c}^{c} \sin^2 \frac{n\pi x}{c} \, dx$$

has an even integrand. Hence it can be written as

$$I_4 = 2 \int_{0}^{c} \sin^2 \frac{n\pi x}{c} \, dx.$$

Elementary methods of integration yield

$$I_4 = \int_{0}^{c} \left(1 - \cos \frac{2n\pi x}{c} \right) dx$$

$$= \left[x - \frac{c}{2n\pi} \sin \frac{2n\pi x}{c} \right]_{0}^{c} = c.$$

Therefore

$$\int_{-c}^{c} \sin^2 \frac{n\pi x}{c} \, dx = c \text{ for } n = 1, 2, 3, \cdots .$$

In the same way it follows that, for $n > 0$, n integral,

$$I_5 = \int_{-c}^{c} \cos^2 \frac{n\pi x}{c} \, dx$$

$$= \left[x + \frac{c}{2n\pi} \sin \frac{2n\pi x}{c} \right]_{0}^{c} = c.$$

For $n = 0$ the integral I_5 becomes

$$I_6 = \int_{-c}^{c} 1 \cdot dx = 2c.$$

Thus

$$\int_{-c}^{c} \cos^2 \frac{n\pi x}{c}\, dx = c \text{ for } n = 1, 2, 3, \cdots,$$

$$= 2c \text{ for } n = 0.$$

We have shown that the set

(A) $\qquad \begin{cases} \sin{(n\pi x/c)}, & n = 1, 2, 3, \cdots, \\ \cos{(m\pi x/c)}, & m = 0, 1, 2, \cdots, \end{cases}$

is orthogonal with respect to the weight function $w(x) = 1$ over the interval $-c \leqq x \leqq c$. We have also evaluated the integrals of the squares of the functions of the set (A).

147. Fourier series: an expansion theorem

With the assumption that there exists a series expansion of the type

(1)* $\qquad f(x) = \tfrac{1}{2}a_0 + \sum_{n=1}^{\infty} \left(a_n \cos \frac{n\pi x}{c} + b_n \sin \frac{n\pi x}{c} \right),$

valid in the interval $-c \leqq x \leqq c$, it is a simple matter to determine the coefficients, a_n and b_n. Indeed, disregarding the question of validity of interchange of order of summation and integration, we proceed as follows.

Multiply each term of equation (1) by $\sin{(k\pi x/c)}\, dx$, where k is a positive integer, and then integrate each term from $-c$ to $+c$, thus arriving at

(2) $\qquad \displaystyle\int_{-c}^{c} f(x) \sin \frac{k\pi x}{c}\, dx = \tfrac{1}{2}a_0 \int_{-c}^{c} \sin \frac{k\pi x}{c}\, dx$

$$+ \sum_{n=1}^{\infty} \left[a_n \int_{-c}^{c} \cos \frac{n\pi x}{c} \sin \frac{k\pi x}{c}\, dx \right.$$

$$\left. + b_n \int_{-c}^{c} \sin \frac{n\pi x}{c} \sin \frac{k\pi x}{c}\, dx \right].$$

As seen earlier,

(3) $\qquad \displaystyle\int_{-c}^{c} \cos \frac{n\pi x}{c} \sin \frac{k\pi x}{c}\, dx = 0 \text{ for all } k \text{ and } n,$

---

* A reason for the apparently peculiar notation, $\tfrac{1}{2}a_0$, for the constant term will be seen quite soon, page 430.

and

(4) $\displaystyle\int_{-c}^{c} \sin\frac{n\pi x}{c} \sin\frac{k\pi x}{c}\, dx = 0$ for $k \neq n$; $k, n = 1, 2, 3, \cdots$.

Therefore each term on the right-hand side of equation (2) is zero except for the term $n = k$. Thus equation (2) reduces to

(5) $\displaystyle\int_{-c}^{c} f(x) \sin\frac{k\pi x}{c}\, dx = b_k \int_{-c}^{c} \sin^2\frac{k\pi x}{c}\, dx.$

Since

$$\int_{-c}^{c} \sin^2\frac{k\pi x}{c}\, dx = c,$$

we have

$$b_k = \frac{1}{c}\int_{-c}^{c} f(x) \sin\frac{k\pi x}{c}\, dx, \; k = 1, 2, 3, \cdots,$$

from which the coefficients b_n in equation (1) follow by mere replacement of k with n; that is,

(6) $\displaystyle b_n = \frac{1}{c}\int_{-c}^{c} f(x) \sin\frac{n\pi x}{c}\, dx, \; n = 1, 2, 3, \cdots .$

Let us obtain the a_n in a like manner. Using the multiplier $\cos{(k\pi x/c)}\, dx$ throughout equation (1) and then integrating term by term from $x = -c$ to $x = +c$, we get

(7) $\displaystyle\int_{-c}^{c} f(x) \cos\frac{k\pi x}{c}\, dx = \tfrac{1}{2}a_0 \int_{-c}^{c} \cos\frac{k\pi x}{c}\, dx$

$$+ \sum_{n=1}^{\infty}\left[a_n \int_{-c}^{c} \cos\frac{n\pi x}{c} \cos\frac{k\pi x}{c}\, dx \right.$$

$$\left. + b_n \int_{-c}^{c} \sin\frac{n\pi x}{c} \cos\frac{k\pi x}{c}\, dx \right].$$

The coefficient of b_n in (7) is zero for all n and k. If $k \neq 0$, we know that

$$\int_{-c}^{c} \cos\frac{n\pi x}{c} \cos\frac{k\pi x}{c}\, dx = 0 \text{ for } n \neq k,$$

$$= c \text{ for } n = k,$$

and also the coefficient of $\tfrac{1}{2}a_0$ is zero. Thus, for $k \neq 0$, equation (7) reduces to

$$\int_{-c}^{c} f(x) \cos\frac{k\pi x}{c}\, dx = a_k \int_{-c}^{c} \cos^2\frac{k\pi x}{c}\, dx,$$

from which a_k, and therefore a_n, can be found in the way b_k was determined. Thus we get

(8) $$a_n = \frac{1}{c} \int_{-c}^{c} f(x) \cos \frac{n\pi x}{c} \, dx, \; n = 1, 2, 3, \cdots.$$

Next let us determine a_0. Suppose $k = 0$ in equation (7) so we have the equation

$$\int_{-c}^{c} f(x) \, dx = \tfrac{1}{2}a_0 \int_{-c}^{c} dx$$
$$+ \sum_{n=1}^{\infty} \left[a_n \int_{-c}^{c} \cos \frac{n\pi x}{c} \, dx + b_n \int_{-c}^{c} \sin \frac{n\pi x}{c} \, dx \right].$$

The terms involving $n \geq 1$ are each zero. Hence

$$\int_{-c}^{c} f(x) \, dx = \tfrac{1}{2}a_0(2c),$$

from which we obtain

(9) $$a_0 = \frac{1}{c} \int_{-c}^{c} f(x) \, dx.$$

Equation (9) fits in with equation (8) as the special case $n = 0$. Had the factor $\tfrac{1}{2}$ not been inserted as in equation (1), a separate formula would have been needed. As it is, we may write the formal expansion as follows:

(10) $$f(x) = \tfrac{1}{2}a_0 + \sum_{n=1}^{\infty} \left(a_n \cos \frac{n\pi x}{c} + b_n \sin \frac{n\pi x}{c} \right)$$

with

(11) $$a_n = \frac{1}{c} \int_{-c}^{c} f(x) \cos \frac{n\pi x}{c} \, dx, \; n = 0, 1, 2, \cdots,$$

(12) $$b_n = \frac{1}{c} \int_{-c}^{c} f(x) \sin \frac{n\pi x}{c} \, dx, \; n = 1, 2, 3, \cdots.$$

Before proceeding to specific examples and applications it behooves us to state conditions under which the equality in (10) makes sense.

When a_n and b_n are given by (11) and (12) above, then the right-hand member of equation (10) is called the *Fourier series, over the interval* $-c \leq x \leq c$, *for the function* $f(x)$. A statement of conditions sufficient to insure that the Fourier series in (10) represents the function $f(x)$ in a reasonably meaningful manner follows.

Let $f(x)$ be continuous and differentiable at every point in the interval $-c \le x \le c$ except for at most a finite number of points and at those points let $f(x)$ and $f'(x)$ have right- and left-hand limits. Such a function is exhibited in Figure 51.

THEOREM 23: *Under the stipulations of the preceding paragraph, the Fourier series for $f(x)$, namely the series on the right in equation (10) with coefficients given by equations (11) and (12), converges to the value $f(x)$ at*

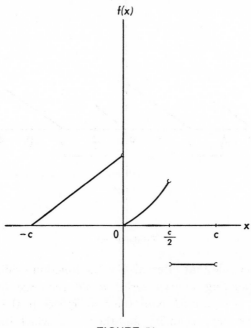

FIGURE 51

each point of continuity of $f(x)$; at each point of discontinuity of $f(x)$ the Fourier series converges to the arithmetic mean of the values approached by $f(x)$ from the right and the left.

Since the Fourier series for $f(x)$ may not converge to the value $f(x)$ everywhere (for instance, at discontinuities of the function), it is customary to replace the equals sign in equation (10) by the symbol $\sim$, which may be read "has for its Fourier series." We write

$$(13) \qquad f(x) \sim \tfrac{1}{2}a_0 + \sum_{n=1}^{\infty}\left(a_n \cos \frac{n\pi x}{c} + b_n \sin \frac{n\pi x}{c}\right),$$

with a_n and b_n given by equations (11) and (12).

An interesting fact and one often useful as a check in numerical problems is that $\frac{1}{2}a_0$ is the average value of $f(x)$ over the interval $-c < x < c$.

The sine and cosine functions are periodic with period 2π, so the terms in the Fourier series (13) for $f(x)$ are periodic with period $2c$. Therefore the series represents (converges to) a function that is as described above for the interval $-c < x < c$ and repeats that structure

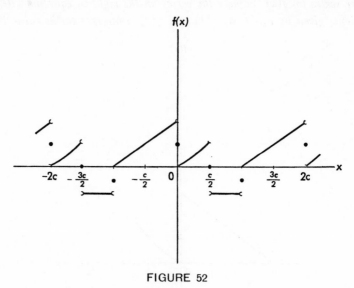

FIGURE 52

over and over outside that interval. For the function exhibited in Figure 51, the corresponding Fourier series would converge to the periodic function shown in Figure 52. Note the convergence to the average value at discontinuities, the periodicity, and the way in which the two together determine the value to which the series converges at $x = c$ and $x = -c$.

These statements will be amply illustrated in the numerical examples and exercises of the next section.

148. Numerical examples of Fourier series

We shall now construct the Fourier series for specific functions.

EXAMPLE (a): Construct the Fourier series, over the interval

$$-2 \leqq x \leqq 2$$

for the function defined by

(1) $f(x) = 2,\quad -2 < x \leqq 0,$

                              $= x,\qquad 0 < x < 2,$

and sketch the function to which the series converges.

First we sketch $f(x)$ itself, the result being exhibited in Figure 53.
Note that $f(x)$ is undefined except for x between $x = -2$ and $x = +2$.

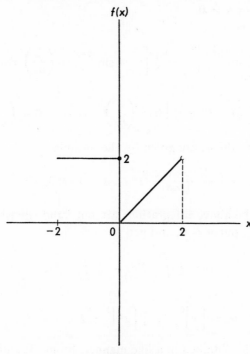

FIGURE 53

For the function described in (1),

$$f(x) \sim \tfrac{1}{2}a_0 + \sum_{n=1}^{\infty}\left(a_n \cos \frac{n\pi x}{2} + b_n \sin \frac{n\pi x}{2}\right),$$

in which

(2) $a_n = \tfrac{1}{2}\displaystyle\int_{-2}^{2} f(x) \cos \frac{n\pi x}{2}\, dx;\ n = 0, 1, 2, \cdots,$

and

(3) $b_n = \tfrac{1}{2}\displaystyle\int_{-2}^{2} f(x) \sin \frac{n\pi x}{2}\, dx;\ n = 1, 2, 3, \cdots.$

Since in the description of $f(x)$, different formulas were used in the
two intervals $-2 < x < 0$ and $0 < x < 2$, it is convenient to separate

the integrals in (2) and (3) into corresponding parts. Thus inserting the $f(x)$ of (1) into the integral (2) leads us to the form

$$(4) \qquad a_n = \tfrac{1}{2} \int_{-2}^{0} 2 \cos \frac{n\pi x}{2} \, dx + \tfrac{1}{2} \int_{0}^{2} x \cos \frac{n\pi x}{2} \, dx.$$

For these integrals, the method of integration will differ according to whether $n = 0$ or $n \neq 0$.

If $n \neq 0$, then

$$a_n = \frac{2}{n\pi} \left[\sin \frac{n\pi x}{2} \right]_{-2}^{0} + \tfrac{1}{2} \left[\frac{2}{n\pi} x \sin \frac{n\pi x}{2} + \left(\frac{2}{n\pi}\right)^2 \cos \frac{n\pi x}{2} \right]_{0}^{2},$$

or

$$a_n = \frac{2}{n\pi} [0 - 0] + \tfrac{1}{2} \left[0 + \left(\frac{2}{n\pi}\right)^2 \cos n\pi - 0 - \left(\frac{2}{n\pi}\right)^2 \right].$$

Hence for $n \neq 0$, the a_n are given by the formula

$$(5) \qquad a_n = \frac{-2(1 - \cos n\pi)}{n^2\pi^2}, \quad n = 1, 2, 3, \cdots.$$

For $n = 0$ the above integrations are not valid (division by n), but we return to (4), put $n = 0$, and get

$$a_0 = \tfrac{1}{2} \int_{-2}^{0} 2 \, dx + \tfrac{1}{2} \int_{0}^{2} x \, dx,$$

from which

$$a_0 = \left[x \right]_{-2}^{0} + \tfrac{1}{4} \left[x^2 \right]_{0}^{2} = 2 + 1 = 3.$$

The b_n may be obtained in a like manner. From (3) and (1) it follows that

$$b_n = \tfrac{1}{2} \int_{-2}^{0} 2 \sin \frac{n\pi x}{2} \, dx + \tfrac{1}{2} \int_{0}^{2} x \sin \frac{n\pi x}{2} \, dx.$$

Thus

$$b_n = \frac{2}{n\pi} \left[- \cos \frac{n\pi x}{2} \right]_{-2}^{0} + \tfrac{1}{2} \left[- \left(\frac{2}{n\pi}\right) x \cos \frac{n\pi x}{2} + \left(\frac{2}{n\pi}\right)^2 \sin \frac{n\pi x}{2} \right]_{0}^{2},$$

from which, since $\cos(-n\pi) = \cos n\pi$,

$$b_n = \frac{2}{n\pi} [-1 + \cos n\pi] + \tfrac{1}{2} \left[-\frac{2}{n\pi} \cdot 2 \cos n\pi + 0 + 0 - 0 \right],$$

or

$$(6) \qquad b_n = -\frac{2}{n\pi}, \quad n = 1, 2, 3, \cdots.$$

For integral n, $\cos n\pi = (-1)^n$, as is seen by examining both sides for even and odd n. Therefore the formula (5) above can also be written

$$(7) \qquad a_n = \frac{-2[1 - (-1)^n]}{n^2\pi^2}, \quad n = 1, 2, 3, \cdots .$$

We can now write the Fourier series, over the interval $-2 < x < 2$ for the $f(x)$ of this example,

$$(8) \qquad f(x) \sim \tfrac{3}{2} - 2 \sum_{n=1}^{\infty} \left[\frac{1 - (-1)^n}{n^2\pi^2} \cos \frac{n\pi x}{2} + \frac{1}{n\pi} \sin \frac{n\pi x}{2} \right].$$

Several pertinent remarks can be made about (8). The right-hand member of (8) converges to the function shown in the sketch in Figure 54.

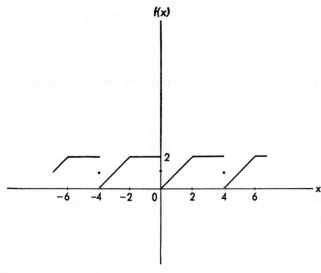

FIGURE 54

It converges to $f(x)$ at each point where $f(x)$ is defined except at the discontinuity at $x = 0$. Though $f(0) = 2$, the series converges to unity at $x = 0$.

We may therefore write

$$(9) \qquad f(x) = \tfrac{3}{2} - 2 \sum_{n=1}^{\infty} \left[\frac{1 - (-1)^n}{n^2\pi^2} \cos \frac{n\pi x}{2} + \frac{1}{n\pi} \sin \frac{n\pi x}{2} \right]$$

for $-2 < x < 0$ and for $0 < x < 2$.

It is sometimes desirable to define a new function $\varphi(x)$ as follows:

$$\varphi(x) = f(x), \quad -2 < x < 0,$$
$$= 1, \qquad\quad x = 0,$$
$$= f(x), \qquad 0 < x < 2,$$

and

$$\varphi(x + 4) = \varphi(x).$$

This $\varphi(x)$ is the function exhibited in Figure 54. If $\varphi(x)$ is put in the place of $f(x)$ in (8) above, then the symbol $\sim$ may be replaced by the symbol $=$ for all x.

Because $[1 - (-1)^n]$ is zero for even n, the Fourier series on the right in (8) may be written in the somewhat more compact form

$$(10) \quad f(x) \sim \tfrac{3}{2} - \frac{4}{\pi^2} \sum_{k=0}^{\infty} \frac{\cos\left[(2k+1)\pi x/2\right]}{(2k+1)^2} - \frac{2}{\pi} \sum_{n=1}^{\infty} \frac{\sin\left(n\pi x/2\right)}{n}.$$

This is one instance in which an infinite rearrangement in the order of terms, passing from (8) to (10), is easily justified. Consider (10) again after studying the sections on Fourier sine series and Fourier cosine series.

Let us next use the expansion in (8) or (10) to sum two numerical series. For instance, if we put $x = 0$ in (10), then the series has the sum unity as indicated above. Hence

$$1 = \tfrac{3}{2} - \frac{4}{\pi^2} \sum_{k=0}^{\infty} \frac{1}{(2k+1)^2} - \frac{2}{\pi} \sum_{n=1}^{\infty} \frac{0}{n},$$

or

$$(11) \qquad\qquad \sum_{k=0}^{\infty} \frac{1}{(2k+1)^2} = \frac{\pi^2}{8}.$$

For $x = 1$, the series in (10) has the sum unity again. Using $x = 1$ in (10) we are led to

$$1 = \tfrac{3}{2} - \frac{4}{\pi^2} \sum_{k=0}^{\infty} \frac{\cos\left[(2k+1)\pi/2\right]}{(2k+1)^2} - \frac{2}{\pi} \sum_{n=1}^{\infty} \frac{\sin\left(n\pi/2\right)}{n}.$$

Now $\cos\left[(2k+1)\pi/2\right] = 0$ and $\sin\left(n\pi/2\right)$ may be obtained as follows. For even n, $n = 2k$, we get

$$\sin \frac{2k\pi}{2} = \sin k\pi = 0.$$

For odd n, $n = 2k + 1$,

$$\sin \frac{(2k+1)\pi}{2} = \sin\left(k\pi + \tfrac{1}{2}\pi\right) = \cos k\pi = (-1)^k.$$

Thus we arrive at the equation

$$1 = \tfrac{3}{2} - \frac{2}{\pi} \sum_{k=0}^{\infty} \frac{(-1)^k}{2k+1},$$

or

(12)
$$\sum_{k=0}^{\infty} \frac{(-1)^k}{2k+1} = \frac{\pi}{4},$$

which can be verified also by the fact that the left-hand member represents Arctan 1.

EXAMPLE (b): Obtain the Fourier series over the interval $-\pi$ to π for the function x^2. We know that

(13)
$$x^2 \sim \tfrac{1}{2}a_0 + \sum_{n=1}^{\infty} [a_n \cos nx + b_n \sin nx]$$

for $-\pi < x < \pi$, where

(14)
$$a_n = \frac{1}{\pi} \int_{-\pi}^{\pi} x^2 \cos nx\, dx; \quad n = 0, 1, 2, \cdots,$$

(15)
$$b_n = \frac{1}{\pi} \int_{-\pi}^{\pi} x^2 \sin nx\, dx; \quad n = 1, 2, 3, \cdots.$$

Now x^2 is an even function* of x and $\sin nx$ is an odd function of x, so the product $x^2 \sin nx$ is an odd function of x. Therefore $b_n = 0$ for every n. Since $x^2 \cos nx$ is an even function of x,

(16)
$$a_n = \frac{2}{\pi} \int_{0}^{\pi} x^2 \cos nx\, dx; \quad n = 0, 1, 2, \cdots.$$

For $n \neq 0$,

$$a_n = \frac{2}{\pi} \left[\frac{x^2 \sin nx}{n} + \frac{2x \cos nx}{n^2} - \frac{2 \sin nx}{n^3} \right]_0^{\pi},$$

from which

$$a_n = \frac{2}{\pi} \left[\frac{2\pi \cos n\pi}{n^2} \right] = \frac{4(-1)^n}{n^2}, \quad n = 1, 2, 3, \cdots.$$

A separate integration is needed for a_0. We get

---

* A review of some properties of even and odd functions of x may be wise at this point. See, for example, C. E. Love and E. D. Rainville, *Differential and Integral Calculus*, 6th ed. (The Macmillan Co., 1962), pp. 101–104; or E. D. Rainville, *Unified Calculus and Analytic Geometry* (New York: The Macmillan Co., 1961), pp. 144–147.

$$a_0 = \frac{2}{\pi} \int_0^\pi x^2 \, dx = \frac{2}{\pi} \cdot \frac{\pi^3}{3} = \frac{2\pi^2}{3}.$$

Therefore, in the interval $-\pi < x < \pi$,

$$x^2 \sim \frac{\pi^2}{3} + 4 \sum_{n=1}^\infty \frac{(-1)^n \cos nx}{n^2}.$$

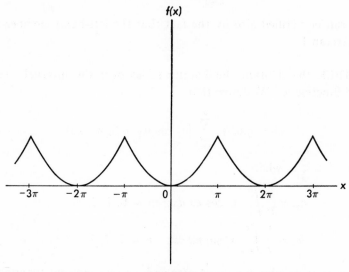

FIGURE 55

Indeed, because of continuity of the function involved, we may write

$$(17) \qquad x^2 = \frac{\pi^2}{3} + 4 \sum_{n=1}^\infty \frac{(-1)^n \cos nx}{n^2}, \quad \text{for } -\pi \le x \le \pi.$$

Beyond the indicated interval, the series on the right in equation (17) represents the periodic extension of the original function. The sum of the series is sketched in Figure 55.

Exercises

In Exs. 1–22, obtain the Fourier series, over the indicated interval, for the given function. Always sketch the function that is the sum of the series obtained.

1. Interval, $-c < x < c$; function, $f(x) = 0, \qquad -c < x < 0,$
$$= c - x, \qquad 0 < x < c.$$

ANS. $f(x) \sim \dfrac{c}{4} + \dfrac{c}{\pi^2} \displaystyle\sum_{n=1}^{\infty} \dfrac{1}{n^2} \left[\{1 - (-1)^n\} \cos \dfrac{n\pi x}{c} + n\pi \sin \dfrac{n\pi x}{c} \right].$

2. Interval, $-c < x < c$; function, $f(x) = x$.

ANS. $f(x) \sim \dfrac{2c}{\pi} \displaystyle\sum_{n=1}^{\infty} \dfrac{(-1)^{n+1} \sin (n\pi x/c)}{n}.$

3. Interval, $-c < x < c$; function, $f(x) = x^2$. Check your answer with that in Example (b) in the text.

ANS. $f(x) \sim \dfrac{c^2}{3} + \dfrac{4c^2}{\pi^2} \displaystyle\sum_{n=1}^{\infty} \dfrac{(-1)^n \cos (n\pi x/c)}{n^2}.$

4. Interval, $-c < x < c$; function, $f(x) = 0,$ $\quad -c < x < 0,$
$$= (c - x)^2, \quad 0 < x < c.$$

ANS. $f(x) \sim \dfrac{c^2}{6}$

$$+ \dfrac{c^2}{\pi^3} \sum_{n=1}^{\infty} \dfrac{1}{n^3} \left[2n\pi \cos \dfrac{n\pi x}{c} + \{n^2\pi^2 - 2 + 2(-1)^n\} \sin \dfrac{n\pi x}{c} \right].$$

5. Interval, $-c < x < c$; function, $f(x) = 0,$ $\quad -c < x < 0,$
$$= 1, \quad 0 < x < c.$$

ANS. $f(x) \sim \tfrac{1}{2} + \displaystyle\sum_{n=1}^{\infty} \dfrac{1 - (-1)^n}{n\pi} \sin \dfrac{n\pi x}{c},$

or

$$f(x) \sim \tfrac{1}{2} + \dfrac{2}{\pi} \sum_{k=0}^{\infty} \dfrac{\sin [(2k + 1)\pi x/c]}{2k + 1}.$$

6. Interval, $-c < x < c$; function, $f(x) = x^3$.

ANS. $f(x) \sim \dfrac{2c^3}{\pi^3} \displaystyle\sum_{n=1}^{\infty} (-1)^{n+1} \dfrac{(n^2\pi^2 - 6) \sin (n\pi x/c)}{n^3}.$

7. Interval, $-\pi < x < \pi$; function,
$$f(x) = 3\pi + 2x, \quad -\pi < x < 0,$$
$$= \pi + 2x, \quad 0 < x < \pi.$$

ANS. $f(x) \sim 2\pi - 2 \displaystyle\sum_{k=1}^{\infty} \dfrac{\sin 2kx}{k}.$

8. Interval, $-c < x < c$; function, $f(x) = x(c + x),$ $\quad -c < x < 0,$
$$= (c - x)^2, \quad 0 < x < c.$$

ANS. $f(x) \sim \dfrac{c^2}{12} + \dfrac{c^2}{\pi^2} \displaystyle\sum_{n=1}^{\infty} \dfrac{1}{n^2} \left[\{3 + (-1)^n\} \cos \dfrac{n\pi x}{c} + n\pi \sin \dfrac{n\pi x}{c} \right].$

9. Interval, $-2 < x < 2$; function, $f(x) = x + 1$, $-2 < x < 0$,
                                $= 1$, $0 \leq x < 2$.

ANS. $f(x) \sim \frac{1}{2}$

$$+ \frac{2}{\pi^2} \sum_{n=1}^{\infty} \frac{1}{n^2} [\{1 - (-1)^n\} \cos \frac{1}{2} n\pi x + n\pi(-1)^{n+1} \sin \frac{1}{2} n\pi x].$$

10. Interval, $-1 < x < 1$; function, $f(x) = 0$, $-1 < x < 0$,
                                $= 1$, $0 < x < \frac{1}{2}$,
                                $= 0$, $\frac{1}{2} < x < 1$.

ANS. $f(x) \sim \frac{1}{4} + \frac{1}{\pi} \sum_{n=1}^{\infty} \frac{1}{n} \left[\sin \frac{n\pi}{2} \cos n\pi x + \left(1 - \cos \frac{n\pi}{2}\right) \sin n\pi x \right]$.

11. Interval, $-\pi < x < \pi$; function, $f(x) = 0$, $-\pi < x < 0$,
                                $= x^2$, $0 < x < \pi$.

ANS. $f(x) \sim \frac{\pi^2}{6} + 2 \sum_{n=1}^{\infty} \frac{(-1)^n \cos nx}{n^2}$

$$+ \frac{1}{\pi} \sum_{n=1}^{\infty} \frac{1}{n^3} [(-1)^{n+1} n^2 \pi^2 - 2 + 2(-1)^n] \sin nx.$$

12. Interval, $-\pi < x < \pi$; function, $f(x) = \cos 2x$.   ANS. $f(x) \sim \cos 2x$.

13. Interval, $-\pi < x < \pi$; function, $f(x) = \cos (x/2)$.

ANS. $f(x) \sim \frac{2}{\pi} + \frac{4}{\pi} \sum_{n=1}^{\infty} \frac{(-1)^{n+1} \cos nx}{(2n - 1)(2n + 1)}$.

14. Interval, $-\pi < x < \pi$; function, $f(x) = \sin^2 x$.

ANS. $\sin^2 x \sim \frac{1}{2} - \frac{1}{2} \cos 2x$.

15. Interval, $-c < x < c$; function, $f(x) = e^x$.

ANS. $f(x) \sim \frac{\sinh c}{c}$

$$+ \sum_{n=1}^{\infty} \frac{2(-1)^n \sinh c[c \cos (n\pi x/c) - n\pi \sin (n\pi x/c)]}{c^2 + n^2 \pi^2}.$$

16. Interval, $-c < x < c$; function, $f(x) = 0$, $-c < x < 0$,
                                $= e^{-x}$, $0 < x < c$.

ANS. $f(x) \sim \frac{1 - e^{-c}}{2c}$

$$+ \sum_{n=1}^{\infty} \frac{1 - (-1)^n e^{-c}}{c^2 + n^2 \pi^2} \left(c \cos \frac{n\pi x}{c} + n\pi \sin \frac{n\pi x}{c} \right).$$

17. Interval, $-c < x < c$; function, $f(x) = 0$, $-c < x < \frac{1}{2}c$,
                                $= 1$, $\frac{1}{2}c < x < c$.

ANS. $f(x) \sim \frac{1}{4}$

$$-\frac{1}{\pi} \sum_{n=1}^{\infty} \frac{1}{n} \left[\sin \tfrac{1}{2}n\pi \cos \frac{n\pi x}{c} + (\cos n\pi - \cos \tfrac{1}{2}n\pi) \sin \frac{n\pi x}{c} \right].$$

18. Interval, $-c < x < c$; function, $f(x) = 0$, $-c < x < 0$,
                         $= x$, $0 < x < c$.

ANS. $f(x) \sim \frac{1}{4}c$

$$-\frac{c}{\pi^2} \sum_{n=1}^{\infty} \frac{1}{n^2} \left[\{1 - (-1)^n\} \cos \frac{n\pi x}{c} + n\pi(-1)^n \sin \frac{n\pi x}{c} \right].$$

19. Interval, $-4 < x < 4$; function, $f(x) = 1$, $-4 < x < 2$,
                         $= 0$, $2 < x < 4$.

20. Interval, $-c < x < c$; function, $f(x) = 0$, $-c < x < 0$,
                         $= x(c - x)$, $0 < x < c$.

21. Interval, $-c < x < c$; function, $f(x) = c + x$, $-c < x < 0$,
                         $= 0$, $0 < x < c$.

22. Interval, $-c < x < c$; function, $f(x) = x^4$.

ANS. $f(x) \sim \dfrac{c^4}{5} + 8c^4 \displaystyle\sum_{n=1}^{\infty} (-1)^n \dfrac{n^2\pi^2 - 6}{n^4\pi^4} \cos \dfrac{n\pi x}{c}.$

23. Use the answer to Ex. 3 to show that $\displaystyle\sum_{n=1}^{\infty} \frac{(-1)^{n+1}}{n^2} = \frac{\pi^2}{12}.$

24. Use the answer to Ex. 8 to show that $\displaystyle\sum_{n=1}^{\infty} \frac{1}{n^2} = \frac{\pi^2}{6}.$

25. Use the answer to Ex. 22 to show that

$$\sum_{n=1}^{\infty} \frac{1}{n^4} = \frac{\pi^4}{90}.$$

26. Use $x = 0$ in the answer to Ex. 15 to sum the series $\displaystyle\sum_{n=1}^{\infty} \frac{(-1)^n}{c^2 + n^2\pi^2}.$

ANS. $\dfrac{c - \sinh c}{2c^2 \sinh c}.$

27. Let $c \to 0$ in the result of Ex. 26 and check with Ex. 23.

149. Fourier sine series

On page 416 we found it desirable to have an expansion of a function $f(x)$ in a series involving only sine functions, the expansion to represent the original $f(x)$ in an interval $0 < x < c$. With the notation we have been using, the Fourier series

$$\tfrac{1}{2}a_0 + \sum_{n=1}^{\infty} \left(a_n \cos\frac{n\pi x}{c} + b_n \sin\frac{n\pi x}{c} \right)$$

will reduce to a series with each term containing a sine function if somehow the a_n; $n = 0, 1, 2, \cdots$, can be made to be zero. Examining the formula for a_n, page 430, reveals that the a_n will vanish if the function being expanded is an odd function over the interval $-c < x < c$.

Therefore, to get a sine series for $f(x)$ we introduce a new function $g(x)$ defined to equal $f(x)$ in the interval $0 < x < c$ and to be the odd extension of that function in the remaining interval, $-c < x < 0$. That is, we define $g(x)$ by

$$\begin{aligned} g(x) &= f(x), & 0 < x < c, \\ &= -f(-x), & -c < x < 0. \end{aligned}$$

Then $g(x)$ is an odd function over the interval $-c < x < c$. Hence from

$$g(x) \sim \tfrac{1}{2}a_0 + \sum_{n=1}^{\infty} \left(a_n \cos\frac{n\pi x}{c} + b_n \sin\frac{n\pi x}{c} \right)$$

it follows that

$$a_n = \frac{1}{c} \int_{-c}^{c} g(x) \cos\frac{n\pi x}{c}\, dx = 0, \quad n = 0, 1, 2, \cdots .$$

and that

$$b_n = \frac{1}{c} \int_{-c}^{c} g(x) \sin\frac{n\pi x}{c}\, dx = \frac{2}{c} \int_{0}^{c} f(x) \sin\frac{n\pi x}{c}\, dx.$$

The resultant series represents $f(x)$ in the interval $0 < x < c$, since $g(x)$ and $f(x)$ are identical over that portion of the whole interval.

Thus we have

(1) $$f(x) \sim \sum_{n=1}^{\infty} b_n \sin\frac{n\pi x}{c}, \quad 0 < x < c,$$

in which

(2) $$b_n = \frac{2}{c} \int_{0}^{c} f(x) \sin\frac{n\pi x}{c}\, dx, \quad n = 1, 2, 3, \cdots .$$

The representation (1) is called the *Fourier sine series* for $f(x)$ over the interval $0 < x < c$.

It should be realized that the device of introducing the function $g(x)$ was a tool for arriving at (1) and (2); there is no need to repeat it in specific problems. Those we handle by direct use of (1) and (2) above.

EXAMPLE: Expand $f(x) = x^2$ in a Fourier sine series over the interval $0 < x < 1$.

At once we may write, for $0 < x < 1$,

$$(3) \qquad x^2 \sim \sum_{n=1}^{\infty} b_n \sin n\pi x,$$

in which

$$(4) \qquad b_n = 2 \int_0^1 x^2 \sin n\pi x \, dx$$

$$= 2 \left[-\frac{x^2 \cos n\pi x}{n\pi} + \frac{2x \sin n\pi x}{(n\pi)^2} + \frac{2 \cos n\pi x}{(n\pi)^3} \right]_0^1$$

$$= 2 \left[-\frac{\cos n\pi}{n\pi} + \frac{2 \cos n\pi}{n^3\pi^3} - \frac{2}{n^3\pi^3} \right].$$

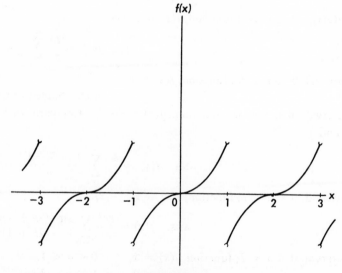

FIGURE 56

Hence the Fourier sine series, over $0 < x < 1$, for x^2 is

$$(5) \qquad x^2 \sim 2 \sum_{n=1}^{\infty} \left[\frac{(-1)^{n+1}}{n\pi} - \frac{2\{1 - (-1)^n\}}{n^3\pi^3} \right] \sin n\pi x.$$

The series on the right in (5) converges to the function exhibited in Figure 56, that function being called the odd periodic extension, with period 2, of the function

$$f(x) = x^2, \quad 0 < x < 1.$$

Exercises

In each exercise, obtain the Fourier sine series over the stipulated interval for the function given. Sketch the function that is the sum of the series obtained.

1. Interval, $0 < x < c$; function, $f(x) = 1$.

$$\text{ANS.} \quad f(x) \sim \frac{4}{\pi} \sum_{k=0}^{\infty} \frac{\sin [(2k + 1)\pi x/c]}{2k + 1}.$$

2. Interval, $0 < x < c$; function, $f(x) = x$. Compare your result with that in Ex. 2, page 439.

3. Interval, $0 < x < c$; function, $f(x) = x^2$. Check your answer with that for the example in the text above.

$$\text{ANS.} \quad f(x) \sim 2c^2 \sum_{n=1}^{\infty} \left[\frac{(-1)^{n+1}}{n\pi} - \frac{2\{1 - (-1)^n\}}{n^3\pi^3} \right] \sin \frac{n\pi x}{c}.$$

4. Interval, $0 < x < c$; function, $f(x) = c - x$.

$$\text{ANS.} \quad f(x) \sim \frac{2c}{\pi} \sum_{n=1}^{\infty} \frac{1}{n} \sin \frac{n\pi x}{c}.$$

5. Interval, $0 < x < 2c$; function, $f(x) = c - x$.

$$\text{ANS.} \quad \text{Same as in Ex. 4.}$$

6. Interval, $0 < x < 4c$; function, $f(x) = c - x$. Compare with Exs. 4 and 5.

$$\text{ANS.} \quad f(x) \sim \frac{2c}{\pi} \sum_{n=1}^{\infty} \frac{1 + 3(-1)^n}{n} \sin \frac{n\pi x}{4c}.$$

7. Interval, $0 < x < c$; function, $f(x) = x(c - x)$.

$$\text{ANS.} \quad f(x) \sim \frac{8c^2}{\pi^3} \sum_{k=0}^{\infty} \frac{\sin [(2k + 1)\pi x/c]}{(2k + 1)^3}.$$

8. Interval, $0 < x < 2$; function, $f(x) = x, \qquad 0 < x < 1,$
$$= 2 - x, \ 1 < x < 2.$$

$$\text{ANS.} \quad f(x) \sim \frac{8}{\pi^2} \sum_{k=0}^{\infty} \frac{(-1)^k}{(2k + 1)^2} \sin [(2k + 1)\pi x/2].$$

9. Interval, $0 < t < t_1$; function, $f(t) = 1, \quad 0 < t < t_0,$
$$= 0, \quad t_0 < t < t_1.$$

$$\text{ANS.} \quad f(t) \sim \frac{2}{\pi} \sum_{n=1}^{\infty} \frac{1}{n} \left(1 - \cos \frac{n\pi t_0}{t_1} \right) \sin \frac{n\pi t}{t_1}.$$

10. Interval, $0 < x < 1$; function, $f(x) = 0, \quad 0 < x < \frac{1}{2},$
$$= 1, \quad \frac{1}{2} < x < 1.$$

ANS. $f(x) \sim \dfrac{2}{\pi} \displaystyle\sum_{n=1}^{\infty} \dfrac{1}{n} \left(\cos \dfrac{n\pi}{2} - \cos n\pi \right) \sin n\pi x.$

11. Interval, $0 < x < 1$; function, $f(x) = 0, \qquad 0 < x < \frac{1}{2},$
$$= x - \tfrac{1}{2}, \ \tfrac{1}{2} < x < 1.$$

ANS. $f(x) \sim \displaystyle\sum_{n=1}^{\infty} \left[\dfrac{(-1)^{n+1}}{n\pi} - \dfrac{2 \sin (n\pi/2)}{n^2\pi^2} \right] \sin n\pi x.$

12. Interval, $0 < x < \pi$; function, $f(x) = \sin 3x.$ ANS. $f(x) \sim \sin 3x.$

13. Interval, $0 < x < \pi$; function, $f(x) = \cos 2x.$ Note the special treatment necessary for the evaluation of b_2.

ANS. $f(x) \sim \dfrac{4}{\pi} \displaystyle\sum_{k=0}^{\infty} \dfrac{(2k+1) \sin [(2k+1)x]}{(2k-1)(2k+3)} .$

14. Interval, $0 < x < \pi$; function, $f(x) = \cos x.$

ANS. $f(x) \sim \dfrac{8}{\pi} \displaystyle\sum_{k=1}^{\infty} \dfrac{k \sin 2kx}{4k^2 - 1} .$

15. Interval, $0 < x < c$; function, $f(x) = e^{-x}.$

ANS. $f(x) \sim \displaystyle\sum_{n=1}^{\infty} \dfrac{2n\pi[1 - (-1)^n e^{-c}] \sin (n\pi x/c)}{c^2 + n^2\pi^2} .$

16. Interval, $0 < x < c$; function, $f(x) = \sinh kx.$

ANS. $f(x) \sim \sinh kc \displaystyle\sum_{n=1}^{\infty} \dfrac{(-1)^{n+1}2n\pi}{(kc)^2 + (n\pi)^2} \sin \dfrac{n\pi x}{c} .$

17. Interval, $0 < x < c$; function, $f(x) = \cosh kx.$

ANS. $f(x) \sim \displaystyle\sum_{n=1}^{\infty} \dfrac{2n\pi[1 + (-1)^{n+1} \cosh kc]}{(kc)^2 + (n\pi)^2} \sin \dfrac{n\pi x}{c} .$

18. Interval, $0 < x < c$; function, $f(x) = x^3.$ ANS.   See Ex. 6, p. 439.

19. Interval, $0 < x < c$; function, $f(x) = x^4.$

ANS. $f(x) \sim \dfrac{2c^4}{\pi} \displaystyle\sum_{n=1}^{\infty} \left[(-1)^{n+1} \left\{ \dfrac{1}{n} - \dfrac{12}{\pi^2 n^3} + \dfrac{24}{\pi^4 n^5} \right\} + \dfrac{24}{\pi^4 n^5} \right] \sin \dfrac{n\pi x}{c} .$

20. Interval, $0 < x < c$; function, $f(x) = x, \quad 0 < x < \frac{1}{2}c,$
$$= 0, \ \tfrac{1}{2}c < x < c.$$

ANS. $f(x) \sim \dfrac{c}{\pi^2} \displaystyle\sum_{n=1}^{\infty} \left(\dfrac{2}{n^2} \sin \dfrac{n\pi}{2} - \dfrac{\pi}{n} \cos \dfrac{n\pi}{2} \right) \sin \dfrac{n\pi x}{c} .$

21. Interval, $0 < x < 1$; function, $f(x) = (x - 1)^2.$

ANS. $f(x) \sim \dfrac{2}{\pi^3} \displaystyle\sum_{n=1}^{\infty} \dfrac{1}{n^3} [n^2\pi^2 - 2 + 2(-1)^n] \sin n\pi x.$

150. Fourier cosine series

In a manner entirely similar to that used to obtain the Fourier sine series, it is possible to obtain for a function defined over the interval $0 < x < c$ a series of cosine terms including a constant term. Indeed, given $f(x)$ defined over the interval $0 < x < c$ and satisfying there the conditions stipulated in Section 147, we may define an auxiliary function $h(x)$ by

$$h(x) = f(x), \qquad 0 < x < c,$$
$$= f(-x), \quad -c < x < 0.$$

Then $h(x)$ is an even function of x and, of course, it is equal to $f(x)$ over the interval where $f(x)$ was defined. Since $h(x)$ is even, it follows that in its ordinary Fourier expansion over the interval $-c < x < c$, the b_n are all zero,

$$b_n = \frac{1}{c} \int_{-c}^{c} h(x) \sin \frac{n\pi x}{c} \, dx = 0,$$

because of the oddness of the integrand. Furthermore, since $h(x)$ is even, $h(x) \cos (n\pi x/c)$ is also even and

$$a_n = \frac{2}{c} \int_0^c h(x) \cos \frac{n\pi x}{c} \, dx = \frac{2}{c} \int_0^c f(x) \cos \frac{n\pi x}{c} \, dx.$$

Since $h(x)$ and $f(x)$ are identical over the interval $0 < x < c$, we may write what is customarily called the *Fourier cosine series* for $f(x)$ over that interval, namely,

$$(1) \qquad f(x) \sim \tfrac{1}{2}a_0 + \sum_{n=1}^{\infty} a_n \cos \frac{n\pi x}{c}, \quad 0 < x < c,$$

in which

$$(2) \qquad a_n = \frac{2}{c} \int_0^c f(x) \cos \frac{n\pi x}{c} \, dx.$$

EXAMPLE: Find the Fourier cosine series over the interval $0 < x < c$ for the function $f(x) = x$.

At once we have

$$f(x) \sim \tfrac{1}{2}a_0 + \sum_{n=1}^{\infty} a_n \cos \frac{n\pi x}{c},$$

in which

$$a_n = \frac{2}{c} \int_0^c x \cos \frac{n\pi x}{c} \, dx.$$

For $n \neq 0$, the a_n may be evaluated as follows:

$$a_n = \frac{2}{c}\left[\frac{c}{n\pi}x\sin\frac{n\pi x}{c} + \left(\frac{c}{n\pi}\right)^2\cos\frac{n\pi x}{c}\right]_0^c$$

$$= \frac{2}{c}\left[\left(\frac{c}{n\pi}\right)^2\cos n\pi - \left(\frac{c}{n\pi}\right)^2\right]$$

$$= -\frac{2c}{n^2\pi^2}(1 - \cos n\pi), \quad n \neq 0.$$

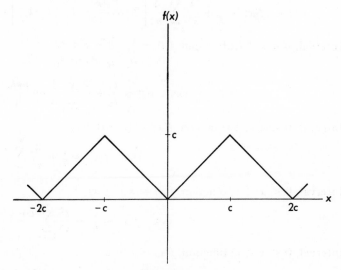

FIGURE 57

The remaining coefficient a_0 is readily obtained;

$$a_0 = \frac{2}{c}\int_0^c x\,dx = \frac{2}{c}\cdot\frac{c^2}{2} = c.$$

Thus the Fourier cosine series over the internal $0 < x < c$ for the function $f(x) = x$ is

$$f(x) \sim \tfrac{1}{2}c - \frac{2c}{\pi^2}\sum_{n=1}^{\infty}\frac{1-(-1)^n}{n^2}\cos\frac{n\pi x}{c},$$

which may also be written in the form

(3) $$f(x) \sim \tfrac{1}{2}c - \frac{4c}{\pi^2}\sum_{k=0}^{\infty}\frac{\cos[(2k+1)\pi x/c]}{(2k+1)^2}.$$

In Figure 57 there is exhibited the sum of the series on the right in (3), often called the even periodic extension of the function x. The sum of the series is, of course, periodic with period $2c$.

Exercises

In each exercise, obtain the Fourier cosine series for the given function over the stipulated interval and sketch the function to which the series converges.

1. Interval, $0 < x < 2$; function, $f(x) = x, \qquad 0 < x < 1,$
$$= 2 - x, \quad 1 < x < 2.$$

ANS. $f(x) \sim \frac{1}{2} + \frac{4}{\pi^2} \sum_{n=1}^{\infty} \frac{1}{n^2} \left[2 \cos \frac{n\pi}{2} - 1 - (-1)^n \right] \cos \frac{n\pi x}{2}.$

2. Interval, $0 < t < t_1$; function, $f(t) = 1, \quad 0 < t < t_0,$
$$= 0, \quad t_0 < t < t_1.$$

ANS. $f(t) \sim \frac{t_0}{t_1} + \frac{2}{\pi} \sum_{n=1}^{\infty} \frac{1}{n} \sin \frac{n\pi t_0}{t_1} \cos \frac{n\pi t}{t_1}.$

3. Interval, $0 < x < 1$; function, $f(x) = (x - 1)^2.$

ANS. $f(x) \sim \frac{1}{3} + \frac{4}{\pi^2} \sum_{n=1}^{\infty} \frac{\cos n\pi x}{n^2}.$

4. Interval, $0 < x < c$; function, $f(x) = x(c - x).$

ANS. $f(x) \sim \frac{c^2}{6} - \frac{c^2}{\pi^2} \sum_{k=1}^{\infty} \frac{\cos (2k\pi x/c)}{k^2}.$

5. Interval, $0 < x < c$; function, $f(x) = c - x.$

ANS. $f(x) \sim \frac{1}{2}c + \frac{4c}{\pi^2} \sum_{k=0}^{\infty} \frac{\cos [(2k + 1)\pi x/c]}{(2k + 1)^2}.$

6. Interval, $0 < x < 1$; function, $f(x) = 0, \quad 0 < x < \frac{1}{2},$
$$= 1, \quad \frac{1}{2} < x < 1.$$

ANS. $f(x) \sim \frac{1}{2} - \frac{2}{\pi} \sum_{k=0}^{\infty} \frac{(-1)^k \cos [(2k + 1)\pi x]}{2k + 1}.$

7. Interval, $0 < x < 1$; function, $f(x) = 0, \qquad 0 < x < \frac{1}{2},$
$$= x - \frac{1}{2}, \quad \frac{1}{2} < x < 1.$$

ANS. $f(x) \sim \frac{1}{8} + \frac{2}{\pi^2} \sum_{n=1}^{\infty} \frac{1}{n^2} \left(\cos n\pi - \cos \frac{n\pi}{2} \right) \cos n\pi x.$

8. Interval, $0 < x < 1$; function, $f(x) = \frac{1}{2} - x, \quad 0 < x < \frac{1}{2},$
$$= 0, \qquad \frac{1}{2} < x < 1.$$

ANS. $f(x) \sim \frac{1}{8} + \frac{2}{\pi^2} \sum_{n=1}^{\infty} \frac{1}{n^2} \left(1 - \cos \frac{n\pi}{2} \right) \cos n\pi x.$

9. Interval, $0 < x < \pi$; function, $f(x) = \cos 2x$.   ANS. $f(x) \sim \cos 2x$.

10. Interval, $0 < x < \pi$; function, $f(x) = \sin 2x$.

$$\text{ANS.}\quad f(x) \sim -\frac{8}{\pi} \sum_{k=0}^{\infty} \frac{\cos\left[(2k+1)x\right]}{(2k-1)(2k+3)}.$$

11. Interval, $0 < x < c$; function, $f(x) = x$, $\quad 0 < x < \tfrac{1}{2}c$,
$$= 0, \quad \tfrac{1}{2}c < x < c.$$

$$\text{ANS.}\quad f(x) \sim \frac{c}{8} + \frac{c}{\pi^2} \sum_{n=1}^{\infty} \frac{1}{n^2}\left[n\pi \sin \tfrac{1}{2}n\pi - 2(1 - \cos \tfrac{1}{2}n\pi)\right] \cos \frac{n\pi x}{c}.$$

12. Interval, $0 < x < c$; function, $f(x) = e^{-x}$. Notice how the a_0 term fits in with the others this time, making separate integration unnecessary.

$$\text{ANS.}\quad f(x) \sim \frac{1 - e^{-c}}{c} + 2c \sum_{n=1}^{\infty} \frac{1 - (-1)^n e^{-c}}{c^2 + n^2\pi^2} \cos \frac{n\pi x}{c}.$$

13. Interval, $0 < x < c$; function, $f(x) = \cosh kx$.

$$\text{ANS.}\quad f(x) \sim \frac{\sinh kc}{kc} + \sinh kc \sum_{n=1}^{\infty} \frac{2kc(-1)^n}{(kc)^2 + (n\pi)^2} \cos \frac{n\pi x}{c}.$$

14. Interval, $0 < x < c$; function, $f(x) = \sinh kx$.

$$\text{ANS.}\quad f(x) \sim \frac{\cosh kc - 1}{kc} + \sum_{n=1}^{\infty} \frac{2kc[(-1)^n \cosh kc - 1]}{(kc)^2 + (n\pi)^2} \cos \frac{n\pi x}{c}.$$

15. Interval, $0 < x < c$; function, $f(x) = x^3$.

$$\text{ANS.}\quad f(x) \sim \frac{c^3}{4} + \frac{6c^3}{\pi^2} \sum_{n=1}^{\infty} \left[\frac{(-1)^n}{n^2} + \frac{2}{\pi^2} \cdot \frac{1 - (-1)^n}{n^4}\right] \cos \frac{n\pi x}{c}.$$

16. Interval, $0 < x < c$; function, $f(x) = x^4$.

ANS. See Ex. 22, p. 441.

151. Numerical Fourier analysis

In the preceding sections and in the applications in the next chapter, the functions for which Fourier series are required are expressed by means of formulas, as for example

$$f(x) = x, \qquad 0 < x < 1,$$
$$= 2 - x, \quad 1 < x < 2.$$

Then the Fourier coefficients, a_n, b_n, are obtained by formal integrations.

In practice it often happens that a function will in the first place be described only by a graph or by a table of numerical values. Then the

Fourier coefficients should be determined by performing the appropriate integrations by some numerical, mechanical, or graphical method. For instance, in the heat-conduction problem studied in Section 139, page 411, the initial temperature distribution $f(x)$ might well consist of a table of initial temperature readings for points at various distances from one surface of the slab. At the end of Section 139, on page 415, it is seen that the solution

$$(13) \qquad u(x, t) = \sum_{n=1}^{\infty} B_n \exp\left[-\left(\frac{n\pi h}{c}\right)^2 t\right] \sin \frac{n\pi x}{c}$$

of the temperature problem involves the coefficients B_n, which are to be chosen so that

$$(14) \qquad f(x) = \sum_{n=1}^{\infty} B_n \sin \frac{n\pi x}{c}, \quad \text{for } 0 < x < c.$$

We can see now that (14) is to be the Fourier sine series expansion of $f(x)$. Hence the B_n are given by

$$B_n = \frac{2}{c} \int_0^c f(x) \sin \frac{n\pi x}{c} \, dx$$

from which B_n is to be found numerically and then inserted in (13).

It is natural that in this book there is a marked tendency to consider each topic encountered only in the light of its bearing on differential equations, or even on a particular phase of the subject of differential equations. In all fairness it must be mentioned that Fourier series are involved in many other ways in mathematics and in other sciences. For contact with the subject of curve-fitting and the method of least squares, see Churchill's *Fourier Series and Boundary Value Problems*, cited at the end of Section 137. The next section is a brief excursion into an application of Fourier series not dependent upon differential equations.

152. Electrocardiography

Since Fourier series yield a periodic representation for a wide class of functions, it seems reasonable to think of Fourier series in connection with a function that is actually periodic in its natural state. One kind of such naturally periodic function is widely used in medical science, particularly as an aid in the diagnosis of diseases of the heart.

It was found long ago that there is an electric current caused by activity of the heart and that it is possible to record graphically a picture of the voltage involved, the finished product being called an electrocardiogram. Figures 58–61 show representative portions of electrocardiograms.*

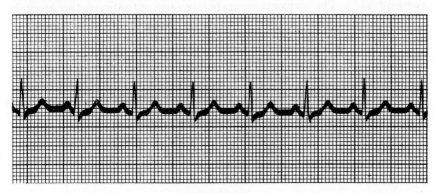

FIGURE 58

A galvanometer (see any elementary physics text) is an instrument which measures the difference in the electric potential between two specific points, an electric current, or an electromotive force (voltage)

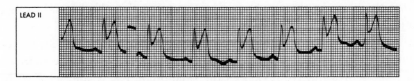

FIGURE 59

associated with the current, depending upon the kind of galvanometer involved. An electrocardiograph is a particular type of galvanometer, one that records voltage.

When physicians desire to obtain electrocardiograms for a patient, the technicians who are to obtain the desired data follow certain fairly

* We are indebted to Ernest W. Reynolds, Jr., M.D., of the University of Michigan Medical Center, for permission to reproduce the normal electrocardiogram in Figure 58. The inclusion of the electrocardiograms in Figures 59 and 60 is made possible by the generous cooperation of the Collis P. and Howard Huntington Memorial Hospital of Pasadena, California, and in particular the cooperation of Mr. Alden B. Mills, administrator of that institution at the time they were made and released. We wish to thank Arthur W. Allen, M.D., of Ann Arbor, Michigan, for permission to use the electrocardiogram in Figure 61.

standard procedures which are here outlined without the many finer points of technique. The machine (electrocardiograph) is connected with the patient at two points—say, at the right arm above the wrist and at the left leg just above the ankle. (This arrangement is known technically as "lead II.") The current generated by the activity of the heart is allowed to pass from the patient's left leg through the galvanometer to the patient's right arm and proceeds to complete the circuit. The electrocardiograph measures a voltage associated with that current and records it on a graph to a desired scale. The result is an electrocardiogram, lead II, one unit in the numerous collection of pieces of information weighed by physicians before reaching a diagnosis.

A damaged or diseased portion of the heart will resist, totally or partially, the flow of electric current and will thus alter the appearance of the electrocardiogram. The shape, size, and location of the portion causing the deviations from the norm will affect those deviations as will the character of the disease or injury present. Several leads, or combinations of places where the galvanometer and the body are connected, are used.

By means of physical theory, laboratory experiment, and observations on patients, physicians and electrocardiographers have built up a considerable knowledge of the correlation between specific sets of variations from the norm in the electrocardiograms (of various leads) and cardiac injuries and diseases.*

Suppose we let t represent time measured in seconds, let $2t_2$ be the duration of a complete period in Figure 58 (a lead II), choose the midpoint of some representative period as the time origin $t = 0$, and let $F_2(t)$ be the ordinate as exhibited in the lead II electrocardiogram. Then $F_2(t)$ has $2t_2$ as its period,

$$(1) \qquad\qquad F_2(t + 2t_2) = F_2(t).$$

There will be a Fourier series for $F_2(t)$,

$$(2) \qquad F_2(t) = \tfrac{1}{2}a_0 + \sum_{n=1}^{\infty} \left(a_n \cos \frac{n\pi t}{t_2} + b_n \sin \frac{n\pi t}{t_2} \right),$$

for which the coefficients a_n and b_n can be determined directly from the graphical data by mechanical means, using a harmonic analyzer.

---

* For details, see the excellent exposition by G. E. Burch and Travis Winsor, *A Primer of Electrocardiography*, 2nd ed. (Philadelphia: Lea and Febiger, 1949, 245 pages).

Assume that the above expansion in Fourier series of the function in the electrocardiogram for lead II has been obtained for normal persons of each sex, weight, and age, at sufficiently close intervals of the latter two to pick up significant changes. Then the $F_2(t)$ for the patient could be expanded in its Fourier series and the coefficients compared with the appropriate normal ones. The same could be done with cardiograms from other leads.

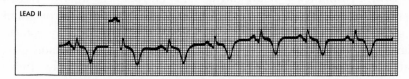

FIGURE 60

That the coefficients in the Fourier series for $F_2(t)$ will show marked changes as we pass from one to another of Figures 58 through 61 seems apparent. Figure 58 is an example of a normal EKG (short term for electrocardiogram). Figures 59 and 60 were taken during diagnosis and treatment of a patient suffering a coronary thrombosis. Figure 61 was taken of the same patient many years later.

The identification of Fourier series coefficient changes associated with each cardiac injury, disease, or other phenomenon could be interesting and conceivably useful. Studies along these lines are being made at various medical centers.

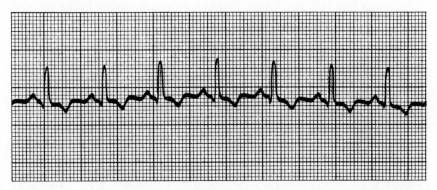

FIGURE 61

An important step toward understanding the mathematical situation can be made by obtaining explicit expansions for various idealized EKG's. We can, for example, fit the curve by straight line segments or by straight lines and segments of simple polynomial curves. Because the principle of superposition is applicable, we can even break up the work into the obtaining of Fourier series expansions of functions, each corresponding to only one medically significant portion of the EKG and remaining zero throughout the remainder of each period. The author has found such simple idealizations helpful in understanding what is going on in the changes of Fourier series coefficients. In the *Journal of the British Institution of Radio Engineers*, 1949, pages 170–183. W. E. Benham published a Fourier analysis of certain idealized electrocardiograms.

The import of high-frequency peculiarities not revealed by conventional electrocardiograms but noticeably present in those made using cathode-ray oscillographs with expanded time scales are being studied by Paul H. Langner, Jr., M. D., Medical Director of the Provident Mutual Life Insurance Company of Philadelphia. Dr. Langner is currently involved in studies of the curves representing time derivatives of the functions in EKG's. The derivative naturally exhibits in a violent manner any high-frequency fluctuations of the original function.

153. Improvement in rapidity of convergence

In practical problems, trigonometric series occur sometimes without the sum function being known in any other form. Computations with such series can be irksome unless the series converge with reasonable rapidity.

Suppose that it is desired to compute, at several points in the interval $0 < x < \pi$, the sum of the series

$$(1) \qquad \sum_{n=1}^{\infty} \frac{(-1)^n n \cos nx}{n^3 + 7}.$$

The series in (1) converges absolutely since its general term is less in absolute value than $1/n^2$ and $\sum_{n=1}^{\infty} 1/n^2$ converges. Let the sum of the series in (1) be denoted by $\varphi(x)$.

For large n the coefficients in the series (1) are well approximated by $(-1)^n/n^2$. But we know the sum of the corresponding series with those coefficients; on pages 437–438 we showed that

$$(2) \qquad x^2 = \frac{\pi^2}{3} + 4 \sum_{n=1}^{\infty} \frac{(-1)^n \cos nx}{n^2}, \quad \text{for } -\pi \leqq x \leqq \pi.$$

Therefore,

(3) $$\tfrac{1}{4}\left(x^2 - \frac{\pi^2}{3}\right) = \sum_{n=1}^{\infty} \frac{(-1)^n \cos nx}{n^2}, \quad -\pi \leqq x \leqq \pi.$$

Since the coefficients in the series in (3) and those in the series for $\varphi(x)$,

(4) $$\varphi(x) = \sum_{n=1}^{\infty} \frac{(-1)^n n \cos nx}{n^3 + 7}, \quad 0 < x < \pi,$$

are nearly equal for large n, it follows that the difference of those coefficients should be small. So we subtract the members of equation (3) from the corresponding ones of equation (4) and get

$$\varphi(x) - \tfrac{1}{4}\left(x^2 - \frac{\pi^2}{3}\right) = \sum_{n=1}^{\infty} (-1)^n \left[\frac{n}{n^3 + 7} - \frac{1}{n^2}\right] \cos nx$$

$$= \sum_{n=1}^{\infty} \frac{7(-1)^{n+1} \cos nx}{n^2(n^3 + 7)}.$$

Thus we obtain for $\varphi(x)$ the formula

(5) $$\varphi(x) = \tfrac{1}{4}\left(x^2 - \frac{\pi^2}{3}\right) + 7 \sum_{n=1}^{\infty} \frac{(-1)^{n+1} \cos nx}{n^2(n^3 + 7)}, \quad 0 < x < \pi,$$

with which computation of $\varphi(x)$ is simplified, since the coefficients of $\cos nx$ in (5) get small more rapidly than those in (4) as n increases.

The device illustrated above is worth keeping in mind when computing with infinite series—whether trigonometric or not. The method is largely dependent upon the presence of a collection of series for which the sum is known.

References on Fourier Series

Churchill, R. V. *Fourier Series and Boundary Value Problems*, 2nd edition. New York: McGraw-Hill Book Co., 1963.

Jackson, Dunham. *Fourier Series and Orthogonal Polynomials*. Carus Mathematical Monograph No. 6. Menasha, Wis.: Mathematical Association of America, 1941.

Langer, R. E. *Fourier Series, The Genesis and Evolution of a Theory*. The first Slaught memorial paper, published as a supplement to the *Amer. Math. Monthly*, **54**, 1947.

CHAPTER **28**

Boundary Value Problems

154. The one-dimensional heat equation

The equation that governs the conduction of heat,

$$(1) \qquad \frac{\partial u}{\partial t} = h^2 \left(\frac{\partial^2 u}{\partial x^2} + \frac{\partial^2 u}{\partial y^2} + \frac{\partial^2 u}{\partial z^2} \right),$$

was introduced on page 405. The symbols in it, and a set of consistent units often employed in engineering practice, are described below:

$$x, y, z = \text{rectangular space coordinates (ft.),}$$
$$t = \text{time (hours),}$$
$$u = \text{temperature (°F),}$$
$$h^2 = \text{thermal diffusivity (ft.}^2/\text{hr.).}$$

Another frequently used set of units for the above quantities replaces feet by centimeters, hours by seconds, and degrees Fahrenheit by degrees centigrade.

It has already been indicated in Section 139 that under proper physical conditions it is reasonable to study a certain special case of equation (1), the one-dimensional heat equation

$$\frac{\partial u}{\partial t} = h^2 \frac{\partial^2 u}{\partial x^2}.$$

456

In Section 139 we obtained from the boundary value problem

(2) $$\frac{\partial u}{\partial t} = h^2 \frac{\partial^2 u}{\partial x^2}, \quad \text{for } 0 < t, \quad 0 < x < c;$$

(3)   As $t \to 0^+$, $\quad u \to f(x)$, $\quad$ for $0 < x < c$;

(4)   As $x \to 0^+$, $\quad u \to 0$ $\quad\quad$ for $0 < t$;

(5)   As $x \to c^-$, $\quad u \to 0$, $\quad\quad$ for $0 < t$,

the relation

(6) $$u(x, t) = \sum_{n=1}^{\infty} B_n \exp\left[-\left(\frac{n\pi h}{c}\right)^2 t \right] \sin \frac{n\pi x}{c},$$

where the B_n were to be determined so that

(7) $$f(x) = \sum_{n=1}^{\infty} B_n \sin \frac{n\pi x}{c}, \quad \text{for } 0 < x < c.$$

Then in Chapter 27 we found that equation (7) suggests that the series on the right be the Fourier sine series for $f(x)$ over the interval $0 < x < c$, and therefore that

(8) $$B_n = \frac{2}{c} \int_0^c f(x) \sin \frac{n\pi x}{c} \, dx.$$

It is not difficult, but requires material beyond this course, to verify that (6) with coefficients B_n given by (8) is actually a solution; that is, that (6) possesses, for properly chosen $f(x)$, the required convergence properties in addition to its formal satisfaction of the differential equation (2) and the boundary conditions (3), (4), and (5).

The amount of heat that flows across an element of surface in a specified time is proportional to the rate of change of temperature in the direction normal (perpendicular) to that surface. Thus the flux of heat in the x direction (across a surface normal to the x direction) is taken to be

$$-K \frac{\partial x}{\partial u},$$

the constant of proportionality being K, the thermal conductivity of the material involved. The significance of the negative sign can be seen by considering an example in which the temperature increases with increasing x. Then $\partial u / \partial x$ is positive, but heat flows toward negative x, from the warmer portion to the colder portion; hence the flux is taken to be negative.

For us the expression for flux of heat will be used most often in forming boundary conditions involving insulation. If there is total insulation at a surface normal to the x direction, then there is no flux of heat across that surface, so

$$\frac{\partial u}{\partial x} = 0$$

at that surface.

EXAMPLE: Find the temperature in a flat slab of unit width such that:

(a) Its initial temperature varies uniformly from zero at one face to u_0 at the other;

(b) The temperature of the face initially at zero remains at zero for $t > 0$; and

(c) The face initially at temperature u_0 is insulated for $t > 0$.

If x is measured from the face at zero temperature, the problem may be written

(9) $$\frac{\partial u}{\partial t} = h^2 \frac{\partial^2 u}{\partial x^2}, \quad \text{for } 0 < x < 1, \quad 0 < t;$$

(10) As $t \to 0^+$, $u \to u_0 x$,   for $0 < x < 1$;

(11) As $x \to 0^+$, $u \to 0$,   for $0 < t$;

(12) As $x \to 1^-$, $\dfrac{\partial u}{\partial x} \to 0$,   for $0 < t$.

First we seek functions that satisfy the differential equation (9), using the technique of separating the independent variables. As before we get

(13) $$u = \exp(-h^2\alpha^2 t)[A \cos \alpha x + B \sin \alpha x]$$

with α, A, and B arbitrary. Condition (11) demands that

$$0 = A \exp(-h^2\alpha^2 t), \quad \text{for } 0 < t,$$

so we must take $A = 0$. We now have

(14) $$u = B \exp(-h^2\alpha^2 t) \sin \alpha x,$$

which satisfies (9) and (11). From (14) it follows that

$$\frac{\partial u}{\partial x} = \alpha B \exp(-h^2\alpha^2 t) \cos \alpha x,$$

so condition (12) requires that

$$0 = \alpha B \exp\left(-h^2\alpha^2 t\right)\cos\alpha, \quad \text{for } 0 < t.$$

We must not choose $\alpha = 0$ or $B = 0$ because then (14) would yield $u = 0$, which cannot satisfy the remaining condition (10). The factor $\exp\left(-h^2\alpha^2 t\right)$ cannot vanish for any t, much less for all positive t. Thus we conclude that

$$(15) \qquad\qquad\qquad \cos\alpha = 0.$$

From (15) it follows that

$$\alpha = (2k + 1)\pi/2; \quad k = 0, 1, 2, \cdots.$$

We now have the functions

$$u = B_k \exp\left[-\tfrac{1}{4}h^2(2k + 1)^2\pi^2 t\right]\sin\left[(2k + 1)\pi x/2\right]; \quad k = 0, 1, 2, \cdots,$$

each of which satisfies (9), (11), and (12). To attack the condition (10), we form the series

$$(16) \quad u(x, t) = \sum_{k=0}^{\infty} B_k \exp\left[-\tfrac{1}{4}h^2(2k + 1)^2\pi^2 t\right]\sin\left[(2k + 1)\pi x/2\right]$$

and require, because of (10), that

$$(17) \qquad u_0 x = \sum_{k=0}^{\infty} B_k \sin\left[(2k + 1)\pi x/2\right], \quad \text{for } 0 < x < 1.$$

Comparison of the right member of (17) with the general Fourier sine series expansion for the interval $0 < x < c$ shows that the series in (17) is an expansion over the interval

$$0 < x < 2$$

and that its even-numbered terms are missing. That is, we seek a Fourier sine series expansion

$$(18) \qquad\qquad f(x) \sim \sum_{n=1}^{\infty} b_n \sin\frac{n\pi x}{2}, \quad \text{for } 0 < x < 2$$

where

$$f(x) = u_0 x, \quad \text{for } 0 < x < 1,$$

and $f(x)$ is so chosen for $1 < x < 2$ that in (18) the terms with even n will drop out.

Physically, it is not difficult to see that we wish to extend the slab its own width beyond $x = 1$ in some way to prevent the heat from flowing across the insulated face $x = 1$. Once that fact is realized it soon follows that we need all temperature conditions to be symmetric with respect to that insulated face $x = 1$.

The initial temperature $f(x)$ of our original slab is shown in Figure 62. Let us prescribe $f(x)$ over $1 < x < 2$ to be the reflection through $x = 1$ of the initial temperature, so in $0 < x < 2$ the initial temperature of the extended slab is as shown in Figure 63.

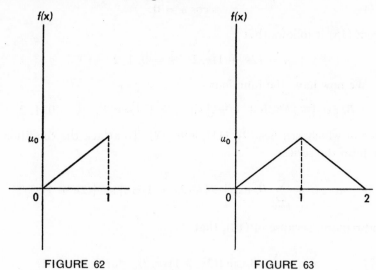

FIGURE 62   FIGURE 63

The boundary value problem (9) through (12) can now be replaced by a new one with slab width 2, initial temperature as exhibited in Figure 63, and with faces $x = 0$ and $x = 2$ held at zero temperature for $t > 0$. The solution to the old problem is the same as that to the new problem except that it is to be used only for $0 < x < 1$.

An alternative procedure is to revert to equation (18) with

$$f(x) = u_0 x, \qquad \text{for } 0 < x < 1,$$
$$ = u_0(2 - x), \quad \text{for } 1 < x < 2,$$

and thus to obtain b_n from which the B_k of (16) and (17) follows.

One more method deserves mention. After justification, such as in Ex. 10 below, it is permissible to obtain the B_k directly from equation (17) without open recourse to any devices such as the ones above.

The student can show in one or more of these ways that the problem (9) through (12) has for a solution

$$(19) \quad u(x, t) = \frac{8u_0}{\pi^2} \sum_{k=0}^{\infty} \frac{(-1)^k}{(2k + 1)^2} \exp\left[-\tfrac{1}{4}h^2(2k + 1)^2\pi^2 t\right] \sin \frac{(2k + 1)\pi x}{2}.$$

Exercises

1. Use the method, not the formulas, of this section to solve the problem of a flat slab initially at a constant temperature u_0 throughout and having its faces $x = 0$ and $x = c$ held at zero temperature for $t > 0$.

   ANS. $\quad u = \dfrac{4u_0}{\pi} \displaystyle\sum_{k=0}^{\infty} \dfrac{1}{2k+1} \exp\left[-\dfrac{h^2\pi^2(2k+1)^2t}{c^2}\right] \sin \dfrac{(2k+1)\pi x}{c}.$

2. Obtain the average temperature across the slab of Ex. 1 for $t > 0$.

   ANS. $\quad u_m(t) = \dfrac{8u_0}{\pi^2} \displaystyle\sum_{k=0}^{\infty} \dfrac{1}{(2k+1)^2} \exp\left[-\dfrac{h^2\pi^2(2k+1)^2t}{c^2}\right].$

3. For the one-dimensional heat equation, (2) above, find a solution u such that u is independent of t, $u = A$ for $x = 0$, and $u = 0$ for $x = c$; A is constant.   ANS. $\quad u = A(c - x)/c.$

4. With the aid of the result of Ex. 3, solve the problem of a slab of width c, with initial temperature zero throughout, and with faces $x = 0$ and $x = c$ held at temperatures A and zero respectively for $t > 0$.

   ANS. $\quad u = A(c - x)/c - \dfrac{2A}{\pi} \displaystyle\sum_{n=1}^{\infty} \dfrac{1}{n} \exp\left[-\left(\dfrac{hn\pi}{c}\right)^2 t\right] \sin \dfrac{n\pi x}{c}.$

5. Combine the result of Ex. 4 with the material of this section to solve the problem of the slab such that

$$\text{As } t \to 0^+, \quad u \to f(x), \quad \text{for } 0 < x < c;$$
$$\text{As } x \to 0^+, \quad u \to A, \quad\quad \text{for } 0 < t;$$
$$\text{As } x \to c^-, \quad u \to 0, \quad\quad \text{for } 0 < t.$$

6. For a particular concrete, the thermal diffusivity h^2 is about 0.04 (ft.^{2}/hr.), so we may reasonably choose $h^2\pi^2 = 0.4$. A slab 20 feet thick is initially at temperature 130 °F and has its surfaces held at 60 °F for $t > 0$. Show that the temperature in degrees Fahrenheit at the center of the slab is given by the formula

$$u = 60 + \frac{280}{\pi} \sum_{k=0}^{\infty} \frac{(-1)^k}{2k+1} \exp\left[-\frac{(2k+1)^2t}{1000}\right].$$

7. Two slabs of the concrete of Ex. 6 (with $h^2\pi^2 = 0.4$ ft.^{2}/hr.), one slab 15 feet thick and the other 5 feet thick, are placed side by side. The thicker slab is initially at temperature 120 °F, the thinner one at 30 °F. The outside faces are to be held at 30 °F for $t > 0$. Find the temperature throughout the slab for $t > 0$. Measure x from the outer face of the thicker slab.

ANS. $u = 30 + \dfrac{180}{\pi} \displaystyle\sum_{n=1}^{\infty} \dfrac{1 - \cos(3n\pi/4)}{n} \exp\left(-\dfrac{n^2 t}{1000}\right) \sin\dfrac{n\pi x}{20}.$

8. Two slabs of the same material, one 2 feet thick and the other 1 foot thick, are to be placed side by side. The thicker slab is initially at temperature A, the thinner one initially at zero. The outside faces are to be held at zero temperature for $t > 0$. Find the temperature at the center of the 2-foot slab.

ANS. $\dfrac{4A}{\pi} \displaystyle\sum_{n=1}^{\infty} \dfrac{1}{n} \sin^3\dfrac{n\pi}{3} \exp\left[-\left(\dfrac{hn\pi}{3}\right)^2 t\right].$

9. Knowing that the temperature function that is the answer to Ex. 8 has the value A at $t = 0$, show that

$$\sum_{k=0}^{\infty} \frac{(-1)^k(2k+1)}{(3k+1)(3k+2)} = \frac{2\pi}{9\sqrt{3}}.$$

10. By extending $f(x)$ in a proper way (see the example of this section), prove that with an $f(x)$ defined in $0 < x < c$ and satisfying the conditions of the convergence theorem stated in Section 147, the right member in the expansion

$$f(x) \sim \sum_{k=0}^{\infty} B_k \sin\frac{(2k+1)\pi x}{2c}, \text{ for } 0 < x < c,$$

in which

$$B_k = \frac{2}{c}\int_0^c f(x) \sin\frac{(2k+1)\pi x}{2c}\, dx,$$

represents the extended function in the sense of Section 147.

11. Interpret as a heat conduction problem and solve equation (2) of this section with the conditions that

$$\begin{aligned} &\text{As } x \to 0^+, \quad \partial u/\partial x \to 0, &&\text{for } 0 < t; \\ &\text{As } x \to c^-, &&u \to 0, &&\text{for } 0 < t; \\ &\text{As } t \to 0^+, &&u \to f(x), &&\text{for } 0 < x < c. \end{aligned}$$

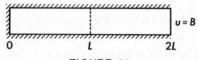

0   L $2L$ $u = B$

FIGURE 64

12. Two metal rods of the same material, each of length L, have their sides insulated so that heat can flow only longitudinally. One rod is at tem-

perature A, the other at temperature zero. At time $t = 0$ the rods are placed end to end as in Figure 64. The exposed end of the first rod is then insulated; the exposed end of the second rod is thereafter held at temperature B. Determine the temperature at the juncture of the rods for $t > 0$.

155. Experimental verification of the validity of the heat equation

It is reassuring to have our mathematical formulas supported in comparison with observed phenomena and pleasant to see those same formulas being of practical* value. Both experiences are encountered in the study of the conduction of heat in concrete dams.

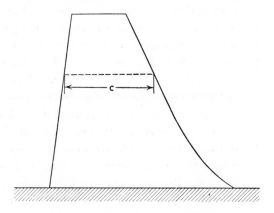

FIGURE 65

When concrete is poured a chemical reaction causes heat to be generated in the material. Exposure to air temperatures cools the concrete, the inner portions cooling more slowly than those near the surface. The temperature differences create stresses and cause expansions and contractions. Because of these facts it is customary when building a large dam to leave contraction joints, openings to facilitate the safe expansion and contraction of the concrete. After the concrete has lost most of its heat of setting, the dam is grouted (the contraction joints

---

* There is a story, perhaps a legend, that H. J. S. Smith, a mathematician of no mean standing, once proposed the toast: "To pure mathematics, may it never be of use to anyone!" Many mathematicians, including the author, regard as pure any part of mathematics that seems to us worthy of study primarily because of its inherent beauty, regardless of applicability to mundane affairs.

filled) and the dam is ready for use so far as the temperature problem is concerned.

The question of when the dam will be ready for grouting is a serious one for the designer. If it is known that the waiting period would be extremely long without special procedures, the concrete may be cooled as it is poured. This was done with Boulder Dam (Hoover Dam), which was designed by the United States Bureau of Reclamation. For Boulder Dam the waiting period would have been one-and-a-half centuries; it is a large dam.

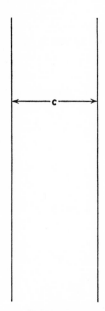

FIGURE 66

The temperature problem needs extensive idealization to bring it down to the level for which decently computable solutions are known. Figure 65 shows a typical dam cross section; on it is indicated the thickness c at a random elevation. The designing engineers sometimes proceed to determine the temperatures to be expected at various elevations by replacing the temperature problem for Figure 65 by that for the flat slab in Figure 66. The width c may be varied to approximate the thickness at various elevations.

The designer knows what the initial temperature of the concrete will be (laboratory tests) and he knows what air temperatures to expect (United States Weather Bureau). The solution of the heat problem for Figure 66, with known initial temperature and variable surface temperatures, may be handled by superposition of solutions (see the next section), using, for instance, the successive mean monthly anticipated air temperatures. The designer can then predict concrete temperatures across the dam at various elevations and from them conclude when it would be safe to grout the dam.

Replacing Figure 66 by a wedge-shaped cross section to get closer to the appearance of Figure 65 seems to make a negligible difference in the end result, the predicted time for grouting.

During the construction of some large dams, thermocouples are installed to permit future readings of temperature at various points in the dam. Years later computations are made by the method described above and the computed temperature curves are compared to the observed ones. The results are pleasant to behold. Frequently, the observed temperature history and the predicted temperature agree within two or three degrees Fahrenheit for years at a time, through the gradual dissipation of the heat of setting and the nearly periodic fluctuations due to seasonal changes in air temperatures.

156. Surface temperature varying with time

As indicated in the preceding section, a practical problem may force us to consider variable surface temperatures. A commonly encountered example is that of a slab initially at constant temperature A_0 and with surfaces maintained thereafter at the variable air temperature $A(t)$. We are thus led to consider the simple heat equation

(1) $$\frac{\partial u}{\partial t} = h^2 \frac{\partial^2 u}{\partial x^2}, \quad \text{for } 0 < t, 0 < x < c,$$

with conditions

(2)   As $t \to 0^+$, $u \to A_0$,   for $0 < x < c$;
(3)   As $x \to 0^+$, $u \to A(t)$,   for $0 < t$;
(4)   As $x \to c^-$, $u \to A(t)$,   for $0 < t$.

Here $A(t)$ represents surface (air) temperature as a function of time. We are concerned only with $A(t)$ of the form exhibited in Figure 67. It may help to think of $A(t)$ as giving mean monthly predicted air temperature, A_1 over the first month

$$0 < t < t_1,$$

A_2 over the second month

$$t_1 < t < t_2,$$

etc.

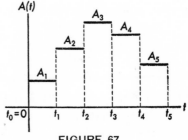

FIGURE 67

The function $A(t)$ may be expressed, using $t_0 = 0$, by

(5) $A(t) = A_n$,   for $t_{n-1} < t < t_n$; $n = 1, 2, 3, \cdots$.

For our purpose there is no need for the time intervals to be equal, but it is necessary that $A(t)$ be constant within each time interval. This problem is also amenable to treatment by Laplace transform methods, but will be solved by only one method in this book.

Since equation (1) is linear and homogeneous in u, any linear combination of solutions of (1) is also a solution. Since t enters (1) only in $\partial u/\partial t$, any solution remains a solution under a translation of the time origin; that is, if $u(x, t)$ satisfies equation (1), then $u(x, t - t_n)$ satisfies (1) for any constant t_n.

The fundamental solution on which we base our treatment of the problem (1) through (4) is

$$(6) \qquad F(x, t) = 1$$

$$- \frac{4}{\pi} \sum_{k=0}^{\infty} \frac{1}{2k+1} \exp\left[- \frac{(2k+1)^2 h^2 \pi^2 t}{c^2} \right] \sin \frac{(2k+1)\pi x}{c},$$

for $0 < t, 0 < x < c$. Directly, or by comparison with Ex. 1, page 444, the function $F(x, t)$ of (6) can be seen to be a solution of the heat equation (1) and to have the properties:

$$(7) \qquad \text{As } t \to 0^+, \quad F(x, t) \to 0, \quad \text{for } 0 < x < c;$$
$$(8) \qquad \text{As } x \to 0^+, \quad F(x, t) \to 1, \quad \text{for } 0 < t;$$
$$(9) \qquad \text{As } x \to c^-, \quad F(x, t) \to 1, \quad \text{for } 0 < t.$$

Since $F(x, t)$ in (6) was undefined for $t \leq 0$, let us take the liberty of defining it as identically zero whenever its second argument t is nonpositive.

$$(10) \qquad\qquad F(x, t) \equiv 0, \quad \text{for } t \leq 0.$$

Then the desired solution of the problem (1) through (4) can be written at once as

$$(11) \quad u(x, t) = A_0 + \sum_{n=1}^{\infty} (A_n - A_{n-1}) F(x, t - t_{n-1}),$$

$$\text{for } 0 < t, \quad 0 < x < c.$$

Note that the series on the right in (11) terminates for any specific t, since sooner or later (as n increases) the argument $(t - t_{n-1})$ becomes and remains negative.

The u of (11) is a linear combination of solutions of (1); it satisfies (2) because of (7). As $x \to 0^+$ or $x \to c^-$, in any range $t_{k-1} < t \leq t_k$,

$$u \to A_0 + \sum_{n=1}^{k} (A_n - A_{n-1}) = A_k,$$

because of (8) and (9) and the fact that $F(x, t - t_{n-1}) \equiv 0$ for $t \leq t_{n-1}$.

In actual practice, computations with the solution (11) are greatly simplified because the $F(x, t)$ of (6) is essentially the same for all diffusivities and all slab widths. In equation (6), put $h^2 \pi^2 t / c^2 = \tau$ and $\pi x / c = \zeta$. The manner in which the new arguments τ and ζ are chosen will be discussed in Section 167.

We may now write

$$F(x, t) = 1 - \frac{4}{\pi} \sum_{k=0}^{\infty} \frac{\exp\left[-(2k+1)^2\tau\right]\sin(2k+1)\zeta}{2k+1} = \varphi(\zeta, \tau),$$

for $0 < \tau$, $0 < \zeta < \pi$. The function φ can be tabulated at intervals of ζ and τ. For a particular slab problem, values of h^2, c, t, and x are used to compute the pertinent ζ and τ and the values of φ are read from the table.

157. Heat conduction in a sphere

Consider a solid sphere initially at a known temperature that depends only upon distance from the center of the sphere. Let the surface of the sphere be held at zero temperature for $t > 0$. We shall determine the temperature in the sphere for positive t under the assumption that the heat equation

$$(1) \qquad \frac{\partial u}{\partial t} = h^2 \left(\frac{\partial^2 u}{\partial x^2} + \frac{\partial^2 u}{\partial y^2} + \frac{\partial^2 u}{\partial z^2} \right)$$

is valid.

Since the object under study is a sphere, we choose the origin at the center of the sphere and introduce spherical coordinates, related to x, y, z, by

$$x = \rho \sin \theta \cos \varphi, \quad y = \rho \sin \theta \sin \varphi, \quad z = \rho \cos \theta.$$

Then the heat equation (1) becomes

$$(2) \qquad \frac{\partial u}{\partial t} = h^2 \left(\frac{\partial^2 u}{\partial \rho^2} + \frac{2}{\rho} \frac{\partial u}{\partial \rho} + \frac{1}{\rho^2} \frac{\partial^2 u}{\partial \theta^2} + \frac{\cot \theta}{\rho^2} \frac{\partial u}{\partial \theta} + \frac{\csc^2 \theta}{\rho^2} \frac{\partial^2 u}{\partial \varphi^2} \right).$$

For the problem we wish to solve, the temperature is independent of the coordinates θ and φ, so equation (2) reduces to

$$(3) \qquad \frac{\partial u}{\partial t} = h^2 \left(\frac{\partial^2 u}{\partial \rho^2} + \frac{2}{\rho} \frac{\partial u}{\partial \rho} \right).$$

Let R be the radius of the sphere and $f(\rho)$ be the initial temperature. Then the problem confronting us is

$$(4) \qquad \frac{\partial u}{\partial t} = h^2 \left(\frac{\partial^2 u}{\partial \rho^2} + \frac{2}{\rho} \frac{\partial u}{\partial \rho} \right), \quad \text{for } 0 < t, \quad 0 < \rho < R;$$

$$(5) \qquad \text{As } \rho \to R^-, \quad u \to 0, \qquad \text{for } 0 < t;$$

$$(6) \qquad \text{As } t \to 0^+, \quad u \to f(\rho), \quad \text{for } 0 \leqq \rho < R.$$

The student can easily show that the change of dependent variable,

(7)
$$u = \frac{v}{\rho},$$

transforms the problem (4) through (6) into the problem

(8)
$$\frac{\partial v}{\partial t} = h^2 \frac{\partial^2 v}{\partial \rho^2}, \quad \text{for } 0 < t, \ 0 < \rho < R;$$

(9) $$\text{As } \rho \to R^-, \quad v \to 0, \qquad \text{for } 0 < t;$$

(10) $$\text{As } \rho \to 0^+, \quad \frac{v}{\rho} \to \text{a limit}, \quad \text{for } 0 < t;$$

(11) $$\text{As } t \to 0^+, \quad v \to \rho f(\rho), \qquad \text{for } 0 < \rho < R.$$

The added condition (10) is a reflection of the fact that the temperature u is to exist at $\rho = 0$ in spite of relation (7). The new problem (8) through (11) is much like those treated at the beginning of this chapter. Its solution is left as an exercise.

The corresponding problem of finding the temperatures in a solid cylinder is less elementary and involves series of Bessel functions. It may be found worked out in many books.*

Exercises

1. Solve the problem (4) through (6) by the method outlined above.

ANS. $\quad u = \dfrac{1}{\rho} \displaystyle\sum_{n=1}^{\infty} b_n \exp\left[-\left(\dfrac{hn\pi}{R}\right)^2 t\right] \sin \dfrac{n\pi\rho}{R}$, in which

$$b_n = \frac{2}{R} \int_0^R \rho f(\rho) \sin \frac{n\pi\rho}{R} \, d\rho.$$

2. A sphere of radius R is initially at a constant temperature u_0 throughout, then has its surface held at temperature u_1 for $t > 0$. Find the temperature throughout the sphere for $t > 0$ and in particular the temperature u_c at the center of the sphere.

ANS. $\quad u = u_1 + \dfrac{2R(u_0 - u_1)}{\rho\pi} \displaystyle\sum_{n=1}^{\infty} \dfrac{(-1)^{n+1}}{n} \exp\left[-\left(\dfrac{hn\pi}{R}\right)^2 t\right] \sin \dfrac{n\pi\rho}{R};$

$$u_c = u_1 + 2(u_0 - u_1) \sum_{n=1}^{\infty} (-1)^{n+1} \exp\left[-\left(\frac{hn\pi}{R}\right)^2 t\right], \text{ for } t > 0.$$

---

* See, for example, E. D. Rainville, *Intermediate Differential Equations*, 2nd ed. (New York: The Macmillan Co., 1964), p. 279; or R. V. Churchill, *Fourier Series and Boundary Value Problems*, 2nd ed. (New York: McGraw-Hill Book Co., 1963).

158. The simple wave equation

If an elastic string held fixed at two points is taut, and then is displaced from its equilibrium position and released, the subsequent displacements from the position of equilibrium may be determined by solving a boundary value problem. Figure 68 shows a representative displacement of the string, which is to be held fixed at $x = 0$ and $x = c$. The displacement y for $0 < x < c$ and $0 < t$ is to be found from the known initial displacement $f(x)$, the initial velocity $\varphi(x)$, and the fact that y must satisfy the one-dimensional wave equation

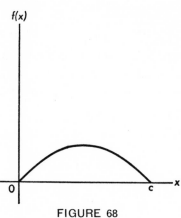

FIGURE 68

$$(1) \qquad \frac{\partial^2 y}{\partial t^2} = a^2 \frac{\partial^2 y}{\partial x^2},$$

in which the parameter a is a constant which depends upon the physical properties of the string.

The boundary value problem to be solved is

$$(2) \qquad \frac{\partial^2 y}{\partial t^2} = a^2 \frac{\partial^2 y}{\partial x^2}, \quad \text{for} \ \ 0 < x < c, \ \ 0 < t;$$

$(3) \qquad$ As $x \to 0^+$, $\quad y \to 0$, $\qquad$ for $0 < t$;

$(4) \qquad$ As $x \to c^-$, $\quad y \to 0$, $\qquad$ for $0 < t$;

$(5) \qquad$ As $t \to 0^+$, $\quad y \to f(x)$, $\qquad$ for $0 < x < c$;

$(6) \qquad$ As $t \to 0^+$, $\quad \dfrac{\partial y}{\partial t} \to \varphi(x)$, $\quad$ for $0 < x < c$.

It is inherent in the string problem that $f(x)$ be continuous and that $f(0) = f(c) = 0$. Either $f(x)$ or $\varphi(x)$ may be zero throughout the interval. Indeed, the boundary value problem (2) through (6) can always be replaced by two problems, one with $f(x)$ replaced by zero, the other with $\varphi(x)$ replaced by zero. The sum of the solutions of those two problems is the solution of the problem with both an initial velocity and an initial displacement.

The solution of problems such as (2) through (6) with various $f(x)$ and $\varphi(x)$ can be accomplished by the method of separation of variables and use of Fourier series as was done with the heat conduction problems earlier. That work is left for exercises for the student, since it involves no new technique. Note the usefulness of the solutions determined in Ex. 1, page 408.

Exercises

In Exs. 1–5, find the displacement for $t > 0$ of the vibrating string problem of this section under the condition that the initial velocity is to be zero and that the initial displacement is given by the $f(x)$ described.

1. $f(x) = x$, for $0 \leq x \leq c/2$,
   $= c - x$, for $c/2 \leq x \leq c$.

ANS. $y = \dfrac{4c}{\pi^2} \displaystyle\sum_{k=0}^{\infty} \dfrac{(-1)^k \cos\,[(2k+1)a\pi t/c] \sin\,[(2k+1)\pi x/c]}{(2k+1)^2}$.

2. $f(x) = x(c - x)/c$.

ANS. $y = \dfrac{8c}{\pi^3} \displaystyle\sum_{k=0}^{\infty} \dfrac{\cos\,[(2k+1)a\pi t/c] \sin\,[(2k+1)\pi x/c]}{(2k+1)^3}$.

3. $f(x) = x$, for $0 \leq x \leq c/4$,
   $= c/4$, for $c/4 \leq x \leq 3c/4$,
   $= c - x$, for $3c/4 \leq x \leq c$.   See Figure 69.

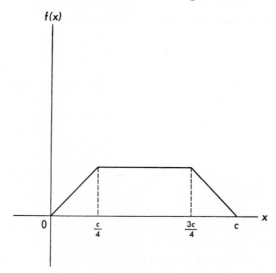

FIGURE 69

ANS. $y = \dfrac{2c}{\pi^2} \displaystyle\sum_{n=1}^{\infty} \dfrac{1}{n^2}\left(\sin\dfrac{n\pi}{4} + \sin\dfrac{3n\pi}{4}\right) \cos\dfrac{na\pi t}{c} \sin\dfrac{n\pi x}{c}$.

4. $f(x) = x$, for $0 \leq x \leq \frac{1}{4}c$,

$\qquad = \frac{1}{2}c - x$, for $\frac{1}{4}c \leq x \leq 3c/4$,

$\qquad = x - c$, for $3c/4 \leq x \leq c$. See Figure 70.

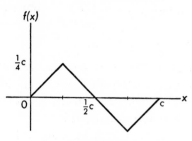

FIGURE 70

ANS. $y = \dfrac{2c}{\pi^2} \displaystyle\sum_{k=0}^{\infty} \dfrac{(-1)^k \cos\left[(4k+2)\pi at/c\right] \sin\left[(4k+2)\pi x/c\right]}{(2k+1)^2}$.

5. $f(x) = x$, for $0 \leq x \leq \frac{1}{4}c$,

$\qquad = \frac{1}{2}c - x$, for $\frac{1}{4}c \leq x \leq \frac{1}{2}c$,

$\qquad = 0$, for $\frac{1}{2}c \leq x \leq c$.

ANS. $y = \dfrac{2c}{\pi^2} \displaystyle\sum_{n=1}^{\infty} \dfrac{1}{n^2} (2 \sin \tfrac{1}{4}n\pi - \sin \tfrac{1}{2}n\pi) \cos \dfrac{n\pi at}{c} \sin \dfrac{n\pi x}{c}$.

6. Find the displacement of the string of this section if the initial displacement is zero and the initial velocity is given by $\varphi(x) = ax(c - x)/(4c^2)$.

ANS. $y = \dfrac{2c}{\pi^4} \displaystyle\sum_{k=0}^{\infty} \dfrac{\sin\left[(2k+1)a\pi t/c\right] \sin\left[(2k+1)\pi x/c\right]}{(2k+1)^4}$.

7. Find the displacement of the string of this section if the initial displacement is zero and the initial velocity is given by

$$\varphi(x) = 0, \text{ for } 0 \leq x \leq c/3,$$
$$= v_0, \text{ for } c/3 \leq x \leq 2c/3,$$
$$= 0, \text{ for } 2c/3 \leq x \leq c.$$

ANS. $y = \dfrac{2v_0 c}{\pi^2 a} \displaystyle\sum_{n=1}^{\infty} \dfrac{[\cos(n\pi/3) - \cos(2n\pi/3)] \sin(n\pi at/c) \sin(n\pi x/c)}{n^2}$.

8. Solve the problem (2) through (6) of this section with $\varphi(x) = 0$.

9. Solve the problem (2) through (6) of this section with $f(x) = 0$.

ANS. $y = \displaystyle\sum_{n=1}^{\infty} B_n \sin \dfrac{n\pi at}{c} \sin \dfrac{n\pi x}{c}$,

in which $B_n = \dfrac{2}{n\pi a} \displaystyle\int_0^c \varphi(x) \sin \dfrac{n\pi x}{c} \, dx$.

159. Laplace's equation in two dimensions

On pages 85–91 of Chapter 5 there was some discussion of Laplace's equation, in particular of the two-dimensional case

(1)
$$\frac{\partial^2 u}{\partial x^2} + \frac{\partial^2 u}{\partial y^2} = 0.$$

The dependent variable u may represent any one of various quantities, steady-state temperature, electrostatic potential, etc., although in this section we shall use the language of steady-state temperature problems for simplicity in wording and visualization.

The Fourier series method as it is being utilized in this chapter is particularly well adapted to solving steady-state temperature problems for a flat rectangular plate. Let the two faces of the plate be insulated; let no heat flow in the direction normal to them. Then the problem is two-dimensional. Each edge of the plate may be either insulated or held at a known temperature.

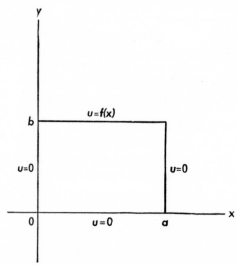

FIGURE 71

Consider a flat rectangular plate with edges of length a and b. Let three edges be kept at zero temperature and the remaining one, one of those of length a, be kept at a specified temperature, a function of distance along that edge. Let us choose a coordinate system and accompanying notation as shown in Figure 71.

The steady-state temperature problem associated with Figure 71 may be written

$$(2) \qquad \frac{\partial^2 u}{\partial x^2} + \frac{\partial^2 u}{\partial y^2} = 0, \quad \text{for } 0 < x < a, \quad 0 < y < b;$$

$(3) \qquad\qquad$ As $x \to 0^+, \quad u \to 0, \qquad$ for $0 < y < b$;

$(4) \qquad\qquad$ As $x \to a^-, \quad u \to 0, \qquad$ for $0 < y < b$;

$(5) \qquad\qquad$ As $y \to 0^+, \quad u \to 0, \qquad$ for $0 < x < a$;

$(6) \qquad\qquad$ As $y \to b^-, \quad u \to f(x), \quad$ for $0 < x < a$.

The solution of the problem (2) through (6) is found by the same method as was used on boundary value problems for the one-dimensional heat equation. Results appear in the exercises below.

When a rectangular plate has nonzero temperatures at more than one edge, the problem can be separated into two or more problems of the type of (2) through (6). Insulation of an edge can be treated by doubling the size of the plate with the insulated edge becoming the new center line and then creating temperature conditions symmetric about that center line so no heat can flow across it. See the methods used in Section 154 at the start of this chapter.

Next let us consider a flat circular plate of radius R subjected to assigned fixed temperatures at its edge and left until it reaches the steady-state condition. Using cylindrical coordinates r, θ, z and conditions that permit no heat flow normal to the faces of the plate, we arrive at a two-dimensional problem,

$$(7) \qquad \frac{\partial^2 u}{\partial r^2} + \frac{1}{r} \frac{\partial u}{\partial r} + \frac{1}{r^2} \frac{\partial^2 u}{\partial \theta^2} = 0, \quad \text{for } 0 < r < R, \quad 0 < \theta < 2\pi;$$

$(8) \qquad\qquad$ As $r \to R^-, \quad u \to f(\theta), \quad$ for $0 \leq \theta < 2\pi$;

$(9) \qquad\qquad \underset{r \to 0^+}{\text{Lim}} u$ exists, $\quad$ for $0 \leq \theta < 2\pi$;

$(10) \qquad\qquad \underset{\theta \to 0^+}{\text{Lim}} u = \underset{\theta \to 2\pi^-}{\text{Lim}} u, \quad$ for $0 \leq r < R$.

If we are willing to define the edge temperature $f(\theta)$ for all θ and make it have the period 2π, then the condition (10) can be replaced by the requirement that u be a periodic function of θ with period 2π.

The corresponding problems of a wedge, or of a portion of a wedge with concentric circular edges, do not involve any requirement of periodicity in their physical nature.

Separation of variables in equation (7) leads to a need for solving an ordinary equation of Euler-Cauchy type,

$$(11) \qquad\qquad r^2 \psi''(r) + r\psi'(r) - \alpha^2 \psi(r) = 0,$$

where α is constant. See Exs. 19–34, page 323.

Exercises

Each of Exs. 1–7 below refers to the steady-state temperature problem for the rectangular plate of Figure 71, but with edge conditions as described in the individual exercise.

1. Edges $x = 0$, $x = a$, $y = 0$ held at zero temperature; the edge $y = b$ held at temperature $f(x)$.

$$\text{ANS.} \quad u = \sum_{n=1}^{\infty} c_n \sinh \frac{n\pi y}{a} \sin \frac{n\pi x}{a},$$

in which

$$c_n \sinh \frac{n\pi b}{a} = \frac{2}{a} \int_0^a f(x) \sin \frac{n\pi x}{a} \, dx.$$

2. Edges $x = 0$, $x = a$, $y = 0$ held at zero; the edge $y = b$ held at temperature unity. Solve the problem directly or by using the result of Ex. 1.

$$\text{ANS.} \quad u = \frac{4}{\pi} \sum_{k=0}^{\infty} \frac{\sinh [(2k+1)\pi y/a] \sin [(2k+1)\pi x/a]}{(2k+1) \sinh [(2k+1)\pi b/a]}.$$

3. Ex. 2 with the change that the edge $y = b$ is to be held at unity for $0 < x < a/2$ and at zero for $a/2 < x < a$.

$$\text{ANS.} \quad u = \frac{2}{\pi} \sum_{n=1}^{\infty} \frac{[1 - \cos (n\pi/2)] \sinh (n\pi y/a) \sin (n\pi x/a)}{n \sinh (n\pi b/a)}.$$

4. Edges $x = 0$ and $x = a$ held at zero; edge $y = 0$ insulated; edge $y = b$ held at temperature $f(x)$.

5. Edge $x = 0$ insulated; edges $x = a$ and $y = 0$ held at zero; edge $y = b$ held at temperature unity.

$$\text{ANS.} \quad u = \frac{4}{\pi} \sum_{k=0}^{\infty} \frac{(-1)^k \sinh [(2k+1)\pi y/(2a)] \cos [(2k+1)\pi x/(2a)]}{(2k+1) \sinh [(2k+1)\pi b/(2a)]}.$$

6. Edges $x = 0$ and $y = 0$ held at zero; edge $x = a$ insulated; edge $y = b$ held at temperature unity.

$$\text{ANS.} \quad u = \frac{4}{\pi} \sum_{k=0}^{\infty} \frac{\sinh [(2k+1)\pi y/(2a)] \sin [(2k+1)\pi x/(2a)]}{(2k+1) \sinh [(2k+1)\pi b/(2a)]}.$$

7. Edges $x = 0$ and $y = 0$ insulated; edge $x = a$ held at zero; edge $y = b$ held at temperature unity.

$$\text{ANS.} \quad u = \frac{4}{\pi} \sum_{k=0}^{\infty} \frac{(-1)^k \cosh [(2k+1)\pi y/(2a)] \cos [(2k+1)\pi x/(2a)]}{(2k+1) \cosh [(2k+1)\pi b/(2a)]}.$$

8. Show that the temperature at the center of the plate of Ex. 2 above is

$$\frac{2}{\pi} \sum_{k=0}^{\infty} \frac{(-1)^k \operatorname{sech} [(2k+1)\pi b/(2a)]}{2k+1}.$$

9. For a square plate, show by superposition of solutions, without obtaining any solution explicitly, that when one face is held at temperature unity and the others are held at zero, then the temperature at the center is $\frac{1}{4}$. Then, by comparing your result with Ex. 8, using $b = a$, conclude that

$$\sum_{k=0}^{\infty} \frac{(-1)^k \operatorname{sech}\,[(2k+1)\pi/2]}{2k+1} = \frac{\pi}{8}.$$

10. A circular plate has radius R. The edge $r = R$ of the plate is held at temperature unity for $0 < \theta < \pi$, at zero temperature for $\pi < \theta < 2\pi$. Find the temperature throughout the plate.

ANS. $u = \frac{1}{2} + \dfrac{2}{\pi} \displaystyle\sum_{k=0}^{\infty} \left(\dfrac{r}{R}\right)^{2k+1} \dfrac{\sin\,(2k+1)\theta}{2k+1}.$

11. A plate with concentric circular boundaries $r = a$ and $r = b, 0 < a < b$, has its inner boundary held at temperature A, its outer one at temperature B. Find the temperature throughout.

ANS. $u = \dfrac{B \ln\,(r/a) - A \ln\,(r/b)}{\ln\,(b/a)}.$

12. The plate of Ex. 11 has its inner edge $r = a$ insulated, its outer edge held at temperature unity for $0 < \theta < \pi$ and held at temperature zero for $\pi < \theta < 2\pi$. Find the temperature throughout.

ANS. $u = \dfrac{1}{2} + \dfrac{2}{\pi} \displaystyle\sum_{k=0}^{\infty} \dfrac{(r/b)^{2k+1} + (a/r)^{2k+1}(a/b)^{2k+1}}{1 + (a/b)^{4k+2}} \cdot \dfrac{\sin\,(2k+1)\theta}{2k+1}.$

13. A flat wedge is defined in polar coordinates by the region $0 < r < R$, $0 < \theta < \beta$. Find the temperature throughout if the edges $\theta = 0$ and $\theta = \beta$ are held at temperature zero and the curved edge $r = R$ is held at temperature unity.

ANS. $u = \dfrac{4}{\pi} \displaystyle\sum_{k=0}^{\infty} \left(\dfrac{r}{R}\right)^{(2k+1)\pi/\beta} \dfrac{\sin\,[(2k+1)\pi\theta/\beta]}{2k+1}.$

14. For the flat wedges of Ex. 13, find the temperature if the edge $\theta = 0$ is held at zero, the edge $\theta = \beta$ is held at temperature unity, and the curved edge $r = R$ is held at temperature $f(\theta)$ for $0 < \theta < \beta$.

ANS. $u = \theta/\beta + \displaystyle\sum_{n=1}^{\infty} A_n \left(\dfrac{r}{R}\right)^{n\pi/\beta} \sin\dfrac{n\pi\theta}{\beta},$

in which

$$A_n = \frac{2}{\beta} \int_0^\beta [f(\theta) - \theta/\beta] \sin\frac{n\pi\theta}{\beta}\,d\theta.$$

CHAPTER 29

Additional Properties of the

Laplace Transform

160. Power series and inverse transforms

To use the Laplace transform on boundary value problems involving partial differential equations, we need certain transforms and inverse transforms that we did not obtain in Chapters 11 and 12.

Before proceeding to illustrative examples, we list certain elementary power series expansions for easy reference.

$$(1) \qquad \frac{1}{1-x} = \sum_{n=0}^{\infty} x^n, \qquad\qquad |x| < 1;$$

$$(2) \qquad e^x = \sum_{n=0}^{\infty} \frac{x^n}{n!}, \qquad\qquad \text{all } x;$$

$$(3) \qquad \cos x = \sum_{n=0}^{\infty} \frac{(-1)^n x^{2n}}{(2n)!}, \qquad\qquad \text{all } x;$$

$$(4) \qquad \sin x = \sum_{n=0}^{\infty} \frac{(-1)^n x^{2n+1}}{(2n+1)!}, \qquad\qquad \text{all } x;$$

$$(5) \qquad \cosh x = \sum_{n=0}^{\infty} \frac{x^{2n}}{(2n)!}, \qquad\qquad \text{all } x;$$

$$(6) \qquad \sinh x = \sum_{n=0}^{\infty} \frac{x^{2n+1}}{(2n+1)!}, \qquad \text{all } x;$$

$$(7) \qquad \text{Arctan } x = \sum_{n=0}^{\infty} \frac{(-1)^n x^{2n+1}}{2n+1}, \qquad |x| < 1;$$

$$(8) \qquad \frac{1}{(1-x)^m} = 1 + \sum_{n=1}^{\infty} \frac{m(m+1) \cdots (m+n-1)x^n}{n!}, \qquad |x| < 1;$$

$$(9) \qquad \ln(1+x) = \sum_{n=0}^{\infty} \frac{(-1)^n x^{n+1}}{n+1}, \qquad |x| < 1;$$

$$(10) \qquad \ln \frac{1+x}{1-x} = 2 \sum_{n=0}^{\infty} \frac{x^{2n+1}}{2n+1}, \qquad |x| < 1.$$

In seeking the Laplace transform, or the inverse transform, of a given function, we may find it inconvenient, difficult, or even beyond us to obtain the desired result by direct use of the theorems of Chapters 11 and 12 in a finite number of steps. Then we frequently turn to infinite series. If we can expand our function into a series such that we know how to obtain the desired transform or inverse transform of each term, we can thus solve our original problem.

EXAMPLE (a): Given that $L^{-1}\{f(s)\} = F(t)$, evaluate

$$L^{-1} \left\{ \frac{f(s)}{\sinh(cs)} \right\}.$$

We know that $\sinh z = \frac{1}{2}(e^z - e^{-z})$. Then

$$(11) \qquad \frac{f(s)}{\sinh(cs)} = \frac{2f(s)}{e^{cs} - e^{-cs}}.$$

For $h > 0, s > 0$, we know how to evaluate $L^{-1}\{e^{-hs}f(s)\}$ by Theorem 19, page 188. Indeed,

$$(12) \qquad L^{-1}\{e^{-hs}f(s)\} = F(t-h)\alpha(t-h), \qquad h > 0, \quad s > 0.$$

We therefore rewrite (11) as

$$(13) \qquad \frac{f(s)}{\sinh(cs)} = \frac{2f(s)e^{-cs}}{1 - e^{-2cs}}$$

because we can use the power series (1) to expand $(1 - e^{-2cs})^{-1}$ in a series of exponentials with negative arguments. From (1) we get

$$\frac{1}{1 - e^{-2cs}} = \sum_{n=0}^{\infty} \exp(-2ncs),$$

so, by (13),

(14) $$\frac{f(s)}{\sinh(cs)} = 2 \sum_{n=0}^{\infty} f(s) \exp(-2ncs - cs).$$

We now use (12) to obtain, for $c > 0$, $s > 0$,

(15) $$L^{-1} \frac{f(s)}{\sinh(cs)} = 2 \sum_{n=0}^{\infty} F(t - 2nc - c)\alpha(t - 2nc - c).$$

It is important to realize that the series on the right in (15) is a finite series. No matter how large the value of t nor how small the (positive) c, the argument of the α function will become negative for sufficiently large n and for all succeeding n-values. Thus each term of the series will be zero for all n such that $(2n + 1)c > t$.

The procedure used in this example is of value to us in applications involving boundary value problems in partial differential equations, to be discussed in Chapter 30.

EXAMPLE (b): Evaluate $L \left\{ \dfrac{1 - e^{-t}}{t} \right\}$.

By (2) we obtain

$$e^{-t} = \sum_{n=0}^{\infty} \frac{(-1)^n t^n}{n!} = 1 + \sum_{n=1}^{\infty} \frac{(-1)^n t^n}{n!}.$$

Therefore we may write

$$\frac{1 - e^{-t}}{t} = \sum_{n=1}^{\infty} \frac{(-1)^{n+1} t^{n-1}}{n!}.$$

A shift in index from n to $(n + 1)$ yields

$$\frac{1 - e^{-t}}{t} = \sum_{n=0}^{\infty} \frac{(-1)^n t^n}{(n + 1)!}.$$

We know that $L \left\{ \dfrac{t^n}{n!} \right\} = \dfrac{1}{s^{n+1}}.$ Hence

$$L \left\{ \frac{1 - e^{-t}}{t} \right\} = \sum_{n=0}^{\infty} \frac{(-1)^n}{(n + 1)s^{n+1}},$$

so comparison with (9) above yields

$$(16) \qquad L\left\{\frac{1 - e^{-t}}{t}\right\} = \ln\left(1 + \frac{1}{s}\right), \qquad s > 0.$$

The restriction $s > 0$ may be obtained by examining the integral definition of the left member of (16). Note also the connection with Ex. 15, page 182.

EXAMPLE (c): Evaluate $L^{-1}\left\{\ln\frac{s+1}{s-1}\right\}$.

From (10) we have

$$\ln\frac{s+1}{s-1} = \ln\frac{1 + \frac{1}{s}}{1 - \frac{1}{s}} = 2\sum_{n=0}^{\infty}\frac{1}{(2n+1)s^{2n+1}}.$$

Now $L^{-1}\left\{\frac{1}{s^{2n+1}}\right\} = \frac{t^{2n}}{(2n)!}$. Hence

$$L^{-1}\left\{\ln\frac{s+1}{s-1}\right\} = 2\sum_{n=0}^{\infty}\frac{t^{2n}}{(2n+1)!},$$

which, with the aid of (6), yields

$$(17) \qquad L^{-1}\left\{\ln\frac{s+1}{s-1}\right\} = \frac{2}{t}\sinh t.$$

Exercises

1. Evaluate $L\left\{\frac{\sin kt}{t}\right\}$.   ANS. $\operatorname{Arctan}\frac{k}{s}, s > 0.$

2. Evaluate $L\left\{\frac{1 - \cos kt}{t}\right\}$.   ANS. $\frac{1}{2}\ln\left(1 + \frac{k^2}{s^2}\right), s > k > 0.$

3. Evaluate $L\left\{\frac{\sinh(kt)}{t}\right\}$.   ANS. $\frac{1}{2}\ln\frac{s+k}{s-k}, s > k > 0.$

4. Evaluate $L\left\{\frac{1 - \cosh(kt)}{t}\right\}$.   ANS. $\frac{1}{2}\ln\left(1 - \frac{k^2}{s^2}\right), s > k > 0.$

5. Evaluate $F(t) = L^{-1}\left\{\frac{1}{s^3(1 - e^{-2s})}\right\}$ and compute $F(5)$.

ANS. $F(t) = \frac{1}{2}\sum_{n=0}^{\infty}(t - 2n)^2\alpha(t - 2n); F(5) = 17.5.$

6. Evaluate $F(t) = L^{-1}\left\{\dfrac{1}{s^3 \cosh (2s)}\right\}$ and compute $F(12)$.

ANS. $F(t) = \displaystyle\sum_{n=0}^{\infty} (-1)^n(t - 4n - 2)^2\alpha(t - 4n - 2);\ F(12) = 68.$

7. Let $\varphi(t) = L^{-1}\left\{\dfrac{3}{s^4 \sinh (3s)}\right\} \cdot$ Compute $\varphi(10)$.   ANS.   344.

8. Let $c > 0,\ s > 0,$ and let $L^{-1}\{f(s)\} = F(t)$. Prove that

$$L^{-1}\left\{\frac{f(s)}{\cosh (cs)}\right\} = 2 \sum_{n=0}^{\infty} (-1)^n F(t - 2nc - c)\alpha(t - 2nc - c).$$

9. Let $c > 0,\ s > 0,$ and let $L^{-1}\{f(s)\} = F(t)$. Prove that

$$L^{-1}\{f(s) \tanh (cs)\} = F(t) + 2 \sum_{n=1}^{\infty} (-1)^n F(t - 2nc)\alpha(t - 2nc).$$

10. Let $0 < x < 1$, where x does not depend on s.
   Find the inverse transform $y(x, t)$ of

$$\frac{4e^{xs}}{s^3(e^s + e^{-s})}$$

and then compute $y(\tfrac{1}{2},5)$, assuming continuity of y.

ANS. $y(\tfrac{1}{2},5) = 28.5.$

11. In Ex. 4, page 247, replace the alternating current element $E \sin \omega t$ by $E\,Q(t,c)$ in which Q is the square-wave function of Figure 20, page 180.

ANS. $I(t) = \dfrac{E}{R} \exp\left(-\dfrac{t}{RC}\right) + \dfrac{2E}{R} \displaystyle\sum_{n=1}^{\infty} (-1)^n \exp\left(-\dfrac{t - nc}{RC}\right)\alpha(t - nc).$

12. In Ex. 4, page 247, replace $E \sin \omega t$ by $EF(t)$ in which $F(t)$ is the half-wave rectification of $\sin \omega t$ as described in Ex. 13, page 182.

ANS. $I(t) =$

$$\frac{E}{\omega C Z^2} \sum_{n=0}^{\infty} \left[(-1)^n(\cos \omega t + \omega RC \sin \omega t) - \exp\left(-\frac{\omega t - n\pi}{\omega RC}\right)\right] \alpha\left(t - \frac{n\pi}{\omega}\right).$$

161. The error function

The error function, abbreviated "erf," which was mentioned briefly in Section 22, page 75, is defined by

(1) $\text{erf } x = \dfrac{2}{\sqrt{\pi}} \displaystyle\int_0^x \exp (-\beta^2)\, d\beta.$

This function arises in many ways. It is sometimes* studied in elementary courses. We also encounter erf x in evaluating inverse transforms of certain simple functions of s.

We know that $L^{-1}\{s^{-\frac{1}{2}}\} = (\pi t)^{-\frac{1}{2}}$ and therefore that

$$L^{-1}\left\{\frac{1}{\sqrt{s+1}}\right\} = \frac{e^{-t}}{\sqrt{\pi t}}.$$

Then the convolution theorem yields

(2) $$L^{-1}\left\{\frac{1}{s\sqrt{s+1}}\right\} = \int_0^t 1 \cdot \frac{e^{-\beta}}{\sqrt{\pi\beta}}\,d\beta.$$

On the right in (2) put $\sqrt{\beta} = \gamma$. Then $\beta^{-\frac{1}{2}}\,d\beta = 2d\gamma$ and we obtain

$$L^{-1}\left\{\frac{1}{s\sqrt{s+1}}\right\} = \frac{2}{\sqrt{\pi}}\int_0^{\sqrt{t}} \exp\left(-\gamma^2\right)d\gamma.$$

That is,

(3) $$L^{-1}\left\{\frac{1}{s\sqrt{s+1}}\right\} = \operatorname{erf}\left(\sqrt{t}\right).$$

A few basic properties of erf x are useful in our work and will now be obtained. Directly from the definition (1) it follows that the derivative of erf x is given by

(4) $$\frac{d}{dx}\operatorname{erf} x = \frac{2}{\sqrt{\pi}}\exp\left(-x^2\right).$$

From (1) and the power series for $\exp\left(-\beta^2\right)$ we get

(5) $$\operatorname{erf} x = \frac{2}{\sqrt{\pi}}\sum_{n=0}^{\infty} \frac{(-1)^n x^{2n+1}}{(2n+1)n!}.$$

In elementary calculus we found that

(6) $$\int_0^{\infty} \exp\left(-\beta^2\right)d\beta = \frac{\sqrt{\pi}}{2}.$$

From (6) we get

(7) $$\lim_{x\to\infty}\operatorname{erf} x = 1.$$

The values of erf x are easily computed for small x from (5) above and for

* See E. D. Rainville, *Unified Calculus and Analytic Geometry* (New York: The Macmillan Co., 1961), pp. 605–607; or C. E. Love and E. D. Rainville, *Differential and Integral Calculus*, 6th ed. (New York: The Macmillan Co., 1962), pp. 467–470.

larger x from the asymptotic expansion*

$$(8) \qquad \text{erf } x \sim 1 - \frac{\exp(-x^2)}{\sqrt{\pi}} \sum_{n=0}^{\infty} \frac{(-1)^n [1 \cdot 3 \cdot 5 \cdots (2n-1)]}{2^n x^{2n+1}}.$$

It is convenient in our work to use what is called the complementary error function, denoted by erfc x and defined by

$$(9) \qquad \text{erfc } x = 1 - \text{erf } x,$$

which means also that

$$(10) \qquad \text{erfc } x = \frac{2}{\sqrt{\pi}} \int_x^{\infty} \exp(-\beta^2) \, d\beta.$$

The properties of erf x are readily converted to properties of erfc x. It is important that for any fixed m,

$$(11) \qquad \lim_{x \to \infty} x^m \text{ erfc } x = 0,$$

which the student can demonstrate by considering the indeterminate form

$$\frac{\text{erfc } x}{x^{-m}}$$

and using the derivative of erfc x as obtained from (4) above. See the exercises at the end of this section for other properties of erf x and erfc x.

A transform which is important in certain applications (Section 166–169) is

$$L \left\{ \text{erfc} \left(\frac{k}{\sqrt{t}} \right) \right\}$$

in which k is to be independent of t and $k > 0$.

By the definition of erfc x we have

$$(12) \qquad \text{erfc} \left(\frac{k}{\sqrt{t}} \right) = \frac{2}{\sqrt{\pi}} \int_{\frac{k}{\sqrt{t}}}^{\infty} \exp(-\beta^2) \, d\beta.$$

In (12) put $\beta = \dfrac{k}{\sqrt{v}}$ so that the limits of integration become $v = t$ to

* See, for example, E. D. Rainville, *Special Functions* (New York: The Macmillan Co., 1960), pp. 36–38. The function erf x is tabulated under the name "The Probability Integral," in B. O. Peirce and R. M. Foster, *A Short Table of Integrals*, 4th ed. (New York: Ginn and Co., 1956), pp. 128–132.

$v = 0$. Since $d\beta = -\frac{1}{2}kv^{-\frac{3}{2}}\,dv$, we obtain (using the minus sign to reverse the order of integration)

$$(13) \qquad \operatorname{erfc}\left(\frac{k}{\sqrt{t}}\right) = \frac{k}{\sqrt{\pi}} \int_0^t v^{-\frac{3}{2}} \exp\left(-\frac{k^2}{v}\right) dv.$$

The integral on the right in (13) is a convolution integral. Hence

$$L\left\{\operatorname{erfc}\left(\frac{k}{\sqrt{t}}\right)\right\} = \frac{k}{\sqrt{\pi}} L\{1\} \cdot L\left\{t^{-\frac{3}{2}} \exp\left(-\frac{k^2}{t}\right)\right\},$$

or

$$(14) \qquad L\left\{\operatorname{erfc}\left(\frac{k}{\sqrt{t}}\right)\right\} = \frac{k}{s\sqrt{\pi}} L\left\{t^{-\frac{3}{2}} \exp\left(-\frac{k^2}{t}\right)\right\}.$$

Now let

$$(15) \qquad A(s) = L\left\{t^{-\frac{3}{2}} \exp\left(-\frac{k^2}{t}\right)\right\}.$$

Note that the functions $t^m \exp\left(-\dfrac{k^2}{t}\right)$ are of class A, page 171, for each m.

From (15) it follows, by Theorem 13, page 176, that

$$(16) \qquad \frac{dA}{ds} = L\left\{-t^{-\frac{1}{2}} \exp\left(-\frac{k^2}{t}\right)\right\}$$

and

$$(17) \qquad \frac{d^2A}{ds^2} = L\left\{t^{\frac{1}{2}} \exp\left(-\frac{k^2}{t}\right)\right\}.$$

But also, by Theorem 9, page 174,

$$L\left\{\frac{d}{dt} t^{\frac{1}{2}} \exp\left(-\frac{k^2}{t}\right)\right\} = sL\left\{t^{\frac{1}{2}} \exp\left(-\frac{k^2}{t}\right)\right\} - \operatorname*{Lim}_{t \to 0^+}\left[t^{\frac{1}{2}} \exp\left(-\frac{k^2}{t}\right)\right],$$

or

$$(18)$$

$$L\left\{\tfrac{1}{2}t^{-\frac{1}{2}} \exp\left(-\frac{k^2}{t}\right) + k^2 t^{-\frac{3}{2}} \exp\left(-\frac{k^2}{t}\right)\right\} = sL\left\{t^{\frac{1}{2}} \exp\left(-\frac{k^2}{t}\right)\right\} - 0.$$

Because of (15), (16), and (17), equation (18) may be written

$$-\tfrac{1}{2}\frac{dA}{ds} + k^2 A = s\frac{d^2A}{ds^2}.$$

Therefore the desired function $A(s)$ is a solution of the differential equation

$$(19) \qquad s \frac{d^2 A}{ds^2} + \tfrac{1}{2} \frac{dA}{ds} - k^2 A = 0.$$

We need two boundary conditions to go with equation (19). We know that as $s \to \infty$, $A \to 0$. Now consider what happens as $s \to 0^+$.

By (15),

$$\operatorname*{Lim}_{s \to 0^+} A(s) = \operatorname*{Lim}_{s \to 0^+} \int_0^\infty e^{-st} t^{-\frac{3}{2}} \exp\left(-\frac{k^2}{t}\right) dt$$

$$= \int_0^\infty t^{-\frac{3}{2}} \exp\left(-\frac{k^2}{t}\right) dt.$$

Equation (13) yields (with y replacing t)

$$(20) \qquad \int_0^y v^{-\frac{3}{2}} \exp\left(-\frac{k^2}{v}\right) dv = \frac{\sqrt{\pi}}{k} \operatorname{erfc}\left(\frac{k}{\sqrt{y}}\right).$$

Therefore

$$\operatorname*{Lim}_{s \to 0^+} A(s) = \frac{\sqrt{\pi}}{k} \operatorname*{Lim}_{y \to \infty} \operatorname{erfc}\left(\frac{k}{\sqrt{y}}\right) = \frac{\sqrt{\pi}}{k} \operatorname{erfc} 0 = \frac{\sqrt{\pi}}{k}.$$

To get the general solution of the differential equation (19), we change independent variable* from s to $z = \sqrt{s}$. Now by the chain rule of elementary calculus,

$$\frac{dA}{ds} = \frac{dz}{ds} \frac{dA}{dz} = \frac{1}{2\sqrt{s}} \frac{dA}{dz} = \frac{1}{2z} \frac{dA}{dz},$$

and

$$\frac{d^2 A}{ds^2} = \frac{1}{4s} \frac{d^2 A}{dz^2} - \frac{1}{4s\sqrt{s}} \frac{dA}{dz}.$$

Thus

$$s \frac{d^2 A}{ds^2} = \frac{1}{4} \frac{d^2 A}{dz^2} - \frac{1}{4z} \frac{dA}{dz}$$

and equation (19) becomes.

$$(21) \qquad \frac{d^2 A}{dz^2} - 4k^2 A = 0.$$

The general solution of (21) is

$$A = b_1 \exp\left(-2kz\right) + b_2 \exp\left(2kz\right),$$

---

* Such a change of variable is dictated by the test on page 16 of E. D. Rainville, *Intermediate Differential Equations*, 2nd ed. (New York: The Macmillan Co., 1964).

so the general solution of (19) is

$$(22) \qquad A = b_1 \exp(-2k\sqrt{s}) + b_2 \exp(2k\sqrt{s}).$$

We must determine the constants b_1 and b_2 from the conditions that $A \to 0$ as $s \to \infty$ and $A \to \sqrt{\pi}/k$ as $s \to 0^+$. As $s \to \infty$, A will not approach a limit unless $b_2 = 0$. Then, letting $s \to 0^+$, we get

$$\frac{\sqrt{\pi}}{k} = b_1.$$

Therefore

$$A(s) = L\left\{ t^{-\frac{3}{2}} \exp\left(-\frac{k^2}{t}\right)\right\} = \frac{\sqrt{\pi}}{k} \exp(-2k\sqrt{s}).$$

We return to (14) to write the desired transform

$$(23) \qquad L\left\{ \operatorname{erfc}\left(\frac{k}{\sqrt{t}}\right)\right\} = \frac{1}{s} \exp(-2k\sqrt{s}), \qquad k > 0, \quad s > 0.$$

We shall use (23) in the form

$$(24) \qquad L^{-1}\left\{ \frac{1}{s} \exp(-2k\sqrt{s})\right\} = \operatorname{erfc}\left(\frac{k}{\sqrt{t}}\right), \qquad k > 0, \quad s > 0.$$

In Chapter 30 it will be important to combine the use of equation (24) and the series methods of Section 160.

Consider the problem of obtaining

$$(25) \qquad L^{-1}\left\{ \frac{\sinh(x\sqrt{s})}{s \sinh \sqrt{s}}\right\}, \qquad 0 < x < 1, \quad s > 0.$$

If x were greater than unity, the inverse in (25) would not exist because of the behavior of $\sinh(x\sqrt{s})/\sinh\sqrt{s}$ as $s \to \infty$.

Because we know (24), it is wise to turn to exponentials. We write

$$(26) \qquad \frac{\sinh(x\sqrt{s})}{\sinh\sqrt{s}} = \frac{\exp(x\sqrt{s}) - \exp(-x\sqrt{s})}{\exp(\sqrt{s}) - \exp(-\sqrt{s})}.$$

As in Section 160 we seek a series involving exponentials of negative argument. We therefore multiply numerator and denominator on the right in (26) by $\exp(-\sqrt{s})$ and find that

$$(27) \qquad \frac{\sinh(x\sqrt{s})}{\sinh\sqrt{s}} = \frac{\exp[-(1-x)\sqrt{s}] - \exp[-(1+x)\sqrt{s}]}{1 - \exp(-2\sqrt{s})}.$$

Now

(28)
$$\frac{1}{1 - \exp\left(-2\sqrt{s}\right)} = \sum_{n=0}^{\infty} \exp\left(-2n\sqrt{s}\right).$$

Therefore,

$$\frac{\sinh\left(x\sqrt{s}\right)}{s \sinh \sqrt{s}}$$

$$= \sum_{n=0}^{\infty} \frac{1}{s} \left\{\exp\left[-(1 - x + 2n)\sqrt{s}\right] - \exp\left[-(1 + x + 2n)\sqrt{s}\right]\right\} \cdot$$

For $0 < x < 1$ the exponentials have negative arguments and we may use (24) to conclude that

(29) $L^{-1} \left\{ \dfrac{\sinh\left(x\sqrt{s}\right)}{s \sinh \sqrt{s}} \right\}$

$$= \sum_{n=0}^{\infty} \left[\operatorname{erfc}\left(\frac{1 - x + 2n}{2\sqrt{t}}\right) - \operatorname{erfc}\left(\frac{1 + x + 2n}{2\sqrt{t}}\right)\right].$$

Exercises

1. Show that for all real x, $|\operatorname{erf} x| < 1$.
2. Show that $\operatorname{erf} x$ is an odd function of x.
3. Show that $\displaystyle\lim_{x \to 0} \frac{\operatorname{erf} x}{x} = \frac{2}{\sqrt{\pi}} \cdot$
4. Use integration by parts to show that

$$\int_0^x \operatorname{erf} y\, dy = x \operatorname{erf} x - \frac{1}{\sqrt{\pi}}\left[1 - \exp\left(-x^2\right)\right].$$

5. Obtain equation (11), page 482.
6. Start with the power series for $\operatorname{erf} x$, equation (5), page 481, and show that

$$L\{t^{-\frac{1}{2}} \operatorname{erf}\left(\sqrt{t}\right)\} = \frac{2}{\sqrt{\pi s}} \operatorname{Arctan} \frac{1}{\sqrt{s}}, \quad s > 0.$$

7. Use the fact that

$$\frac{1}{1 + \sqrt{1+s}} = \frac{1 - \sqrt{1+s}}{1 - (1+s)} = -\frac{1}{s} + \frac{\sqrt{1+s}}{s} = -\frac{1}{s} + \frac{1+s}{s\sqrt{1+s}}$$

and equation (3), page 481, to show that

$$L^{-1}\left\{\frac{1}{1+\sqrt{1+s}}\right\} = -1 + \text{erf}\,(\sqrt{t}) + \frac{e^{-t}}{\sqrt{\pi t}}$$

$$= \frac{e^{-t}}{\sqrt{\pi t}} - \text{erfc}\,(\sqrt{t}).$$

8. Use equation (3), page 481, to conclude that

$$L^{-1}\left\{\frac{1}{(s-1)\sqrt{s}}\right\} = e^{t}\,\text{erf}\,(\sqrt{t})$$

and therefore that

$$L^{-1}\left\{\frac{1}{\sqrt{s}\,(\sqrt{s}+1)}\right\} = e^{t}\,\text{erfc}\,(\sqrt{t}).$$

9. Evaluate $L^{-1}\left\{\dfrac{1}{\sqrt{s}+1}\right\}$.   ANS. $\dfrac{1}{\sqrt{\pi t}} - e^{t}\,\text{erfc}\,(\sqrt{t}).$

10. Evaluate $L^{-1}\left\{\dfrac{1}{\sqrt{s}-1}\right\}$.   ANS. $\dfrac{1}{\sqrt{\pi t}} + e^{t} + e^{t}\,\text{erf}\,(\sqrt{t}).$

11. Define the function $\varphi(t)$ by

$$\varphi(t) = L^{-1}\left\{\text{erf}\,\frac{1}{s}\right\}.$$

Prove that

$$L\{\varphi(\sqrt{t})\} = \frac{2}{\sqrt{\pi s}}\sin\frac{1}{\sqrt{s}}.$$

12. Show that for $x > 0$,

$$L^{-1}\left\{\frac{\text{sech}\,x\sqrt{s}}{s}\right\} = 2\sum_{n=0}^{\infty}(-1)^{n}\,\text{erfc}\left[\frac{(2n+1)x}{2\sqrt{t}}\right].$$

13. Show that for $x > 0$,

$$L^{-1}\left\{\frac{\text{csch}\,x\sqrt{s}}{s}\right\} = 2\sum_{n=0}^{\infty}\text{erfc}\left[\frac{(2n+1)x}{2\sqrt{t}}\right].$$

14. Derive the result

$$A(s) = L\left\{t^{-\frac{3}{2}}\exp\left(-\frac{k^{2}}{t}\right)\right\} = \frac{\sqrt{\pi}}{k}\exp\,(-2k\sqrt{s}), \qquad k > 0,\ \ s > 0$$

directly from the definition of a transform. In the integral

$$A(s) = \int_0^\infty \exp\left(-st - k^2 t^{-1}\right) t^{-\frac{3}{2}} \, dt$$

put $\beta = \sqrt{t}$ to get

$$A(s) = 2 \int_0^\infty \beta^{-2} \exp\left(-s\beta^2 - k^2\beta^{-2}\right) \, d\beta$$

or

$$A(s) = 2 \exp\left(-2k \sqrt{s}\right) \int_0^\infty \beta^{-2} \exp\left[-(\beta \sqrt{s} - k\beta^{-1})^2\right] \, d\beta.$$

Show that

$$\frac{dA}{ds} = -2 \int_0^\infty \exp\left(-s\beta^2 - k^2\beta^{-2}\right) \, d\beta$$

$$= -2 \exp\left(-2k \sqrt{s}\right) \int_0^\infty \exp\left[-(\beta \sqrt{s} - k\beta^{-1})^2\right] \, d\beta.$$

Thus arrive at the differential equation

$$\sqrt{s}\, \frac{dA}{ds} - kA = -2 \sqrt{\pi} \exp\left(-2k \sqrt{s}\right)$$

and from it obtain the desired function $A(s)$.

162. Bessel functions

The Bessel function

(1)
$$J_n(z) = \sum_{k=0}^\infty \frac{(-1)^k \left(\frac{1}{2}z\right)^{2k+n}}{k!\,\Gamma(k + n + 1)},$$

of the first kind and of index n, appeared in Sections 117 and 118. We meet $J_n(z)$ in a simple application of the series technique of Section 160. If we can expand a given function of s in negative powers of s, surely we can get the inverse transform term by term. A simple example is the following:

$$\frac{1}{s} \exp\left(-\frac{x}{s}\right) = \sum_{k=0}^\infty \frac{(-1)^k x^k}{k!\,s^{k+1}},$$

which leads immediately to

(2)
$$L^{-1}\left\{\frac{1}{s} \exp\left(-\frac{x}{s}\right)\right\} = \sum_{k=0}^\infty \frac{(-1)^k x^k t^k}{k!\,k!}.$$

When $n = 0$ in (1) we get, since $\Gamma(k + 1) = k!$,

$$(3) \qquad J_0(z) = \sum_{k=0}^{\infty} \frac{(-1)^k(\tfrac{1}{2}z)^{2k}}{k!k!}.$$

By comparing (2) with (3) we get

$$(4) \qquad L^{-1}\left\{\frac{1}{s}\exp\left(-\frac{x}{s}\right)\right\} = J_0(2\sqrt{xt}); \qquad x > 0, \quad s > 0.$$

From

$$\frac{1}{s^{n+1}}\exp\left(-\frac{x}{s}\right) = \sum_{k=0}^{\infty}\frac{(-1)^k x^k}{k!s^{k+n+1}}$$

we get

$$L^{-1}\left\{\frac{1}{s^{n+1}}\exp\left(-\frac{x}{s}\right)\right\} = \sum_{k=0}^{\infty}\frac{(-1)^k x^k t^{k+n}}{k!\Gamma(k+n+1)}$$

$$= x^{-\frac{1}{2}n}t^{\frac{1}{2}n}\sum_{k=0}^{\infty}\frac{(-1)^k(\sqrt{xt})^{2k+n}}{k!\Gamma(k+n+1)}.$$

Therefore, at least for $n \geqq 0$,

$$(5) \quad L^{-1}\left\{\frac{1}{s^{n+1}}\exp\left(-\frac{x}{s}\right)\right\} = \left(\frac{t}{x}\right)^{\frac{1}{2}n}J_n(2\sqrt{xt}), \qquad s > 0, \quad x > 0.$$

With more knowledge of the Gamma function, we could use series methods to obtain the transform of $J_n(xt)$ for general n. Here we restrict ourselves to $n = 0$ for simplicity.

From (1) we obtain

$$J_0(xt) = \sum_{k=0}^{\infty}\frac{(-1)^k(\tfrac{1}{2}x)^{2k}t^{2k}}{k!k!}.$$

Then

$$L\{J_0(xt)\} = \sum_{k=0}^{\infty}\frac{(-1)^k(\tfrac{1}{2}x)^{2k}(2k)!}{k!k!s^{2k+1}}.$$

But $(2k)! = 2^k k![1 \cdot 3 \cdot 5 \cdots (2k - 1)]$. Hence

$$L\{J_0(xt)\} = \frac{1}{s}\left[1 + \sum_{k=1}^{\infty}\frac{(-1)^k[1 \cdot 3 \cdot 5 \cdots (2k - 1)]x^{2k}}{2^k \cdot k!s^{2k}}\right],$$

or

$$L\{J_0(xt)\} = \frac{1}{s}\left(1 + \frac{x^2}{s^2}\right)^{-\frac{1}{2}}.$$

Therefore

(6)
$$L\{J_0(xt)\} = \frac{1}{\sqrt{s^2 + x^2}}.$$

From (1) it is easy to conclude that

$$\frac{d}{dz} J_0(z) = -J_1(z).$$

Then

$$\frac{d}{dt} J_0(xt) = -xJ_1(xt)$$

and we obtain

$$L\{-xJ_1(xt)\} = L\left\{\frac{d}{dt} J_0(xt)\right\}$$
$$= s L\{J_0(xt)\} - J_0(0).$$

But $J_0(0) = 1$, so

$$L\{-xJ_1(xt)\} = \frac{s}{\sqrt{s^2 + x^2}} - 1,$$

or

(7)
$$L\{J_1(xt)\} = \frac{\sqrt{s^2 + x^2} - s}{x\sqrt{s^2 + x^2}}.$$

Exercise

1. The modified Bessel function of the first kind and of index n is

$$I_n(z) = \sum_{k=0}^{\infty} \frac{(\frac{1}{2}z)^{2k+n}}{k!\Gamma(k+n+1)}.$$

Show that

$$L^{-1}\left\{\frac{1}{s^{n+1}} \exp\left(\frac{x}{s}\right)\right\} = \left(\frac{t}{x}\right)^{\frac{1}{2}n} I_n(2\sqrt{xt}).$$

163. Differential equations with variable coefficients

Any reader who has become overly optimistic about the efficacy of the Laplace transform as a tool in treating linear differential equations should keep in mind that we have restricted our work so far to equations with constant coefficients.

Suppose that we are confronted with a boundary value problem involving the equation

(1) $F''(t) + t^2 F(t) = 0.$

Let $L\{F(t)\} = f(s)$ and put $F(0) = A, F'(0) = B$. Then application of the operator L transforms equation (1) into

$$s^2 f(s) - sA - B + \frac{d^2}{ds^2} f(s) = 0,$$

or

(2) $f''(s) + s^2 f(s) = As + B.$

The problem of getting the complementary function for equation (2) is the same as it is for equation (1); no progress has been made. The left member of (1) remained essentially unchanged under the Laplace transformation.

The behavior of (1) under L is not unique. Indeed, the differential equations with polynomial coefficients that remain invariant under the Laplace transformation have been classified.*

Since $L\{t^n F(t)\} = (-1)^n \dfrac{d^n}{ds^n} f(s)$, it follows that the operator L can be used to transform a differential equation with polynomial coefficients into a differential equation with polynomial coefficients and that the order of the new equation will equal the maximum degree of the polynomial coefficients in the original equation. The Laplace transform is simply not the proper tool for attacking differential equations with variable coefficients. For such a purpose, the classical method of solution by power series is a good tool to use.

* E. D. Rainville, "Linear Differential Invariance Under an Operator Related to the Laplace Transformation," *Amer. Journal of Math.*, **62** (1940), 391–405.

CHAPTER 30

Partial Differential Equations;

Transform Methods

164. Boundary value problems

For some boundary value problems involving partial differential equations, the Laplace transform provides an effective method of attack; for other problems the transform method contributes additional information even when the older techniques, such as separation of variables and Fourier series, may be easier to use. There remain problems for which the Laplace transform method contributes nothing but complications.

In this chapter we present a few applications and a detailed study of the solution of some simple problems. Our goal is to give the student sufficient background to enable him to use the Laplace transform on problems he encounters in practice and to give him some criteria to use in deciding whether the transform method is an appropriate tool for a given problem.

We first solve some artificial problems which have been constructed to exhibit the technique and underlying ideas without introducing the complexities common to many physical applications. The student who fully understands and can execute the solutions of such simple problems will find no difficulty, other than an increase in amount of labor, in solving corresponding problems arising in physical situations.

EXAMPLE: Solve the problem consisting of the equation

(1) $$\frac{\partial^2 y}{\partial x^2} = 16\frac{\partial^2 y}{\partial t^2}, \qquad \text{for } t > 0, \quad x > 0;$$

with the conditions

(2) $\qquad\qquad t \to 0^+, \qquad y \to 0, \quad \text{for } x > 0;$

(3) $\qquad\qquad t \to 0^+, \qquad \dfrac{\partial y}{\partial t} \to -1, \quad \text{for } x > 0;$

(4) $\qquad\qquad x \to 0^+, \qquad y \to t^2, \quad \text{for } t > 0;$

(5) $\qquad\qquad \underset{x \to \infty}{\text{Lim }} y(x, t) \text{ exists, for fixed } t > 0.$

The characteristics of the problem that suggest that it is worthwhile to try the Laplace transform technique are:

(a) The differential equation is linear (necessary),
(b) The equation has constant coefficients (highly desirable),
(c) At least one independent variable has the range 0 to ∞ (highly desirable),
(d) There are appropriate initial ($t = 0$) conditions involving the independent variable in (c) above (desirable).

In this problem the independent variable x also has the range 0 to ∞, but there is only one condition at $x = 0$; two conditions are needed in transforming a second derivative. We shall therefore attack this problem with Laplace transforms with respect to the variable t.

Let

(6) $$L\{y(x, t)\} = w(x, s),$$

in which x is treated as a constant (parameter) as far as the Laplace transformation is concerned. Since we shall verify our solution, there is no risk in assuming that the operations of differentiations with respect to x and Laplace transforms with respect to t are commutative.

Because (1) has constant coefficients, derivatives with respect to the transform variable s will not appear. The partial differential equation (1) will be transformed into an ordinary differential equation with independent variable x and with s involved as a parameter. In view of (6), application of the operator L transforms (1), (2), and (3) into

(7) $$\frac{d^2 w}{dx^2} = 16(s^2 w + 1), \qquad x > 0.$$

The conditions (4) and (5) become

(8)
$$x \to 0^+, \qquad w \to \frac{2}{s^3},$$

(9)
$$\operatorname*{Lim}_{x \to \infty} w(x, s) \text{ exists.}$$

We now solve the new problem, (7), (8), and (9), for $w(x, s)$ and then obtain $y(x, t)$ as the inverse transform of w. Let us rewrite (7) in the form

(10)
$$\frac{d^2w}{dx^2} - 16s^2w = 16$$

and keep in mind that x is the independent variable and s is a parameter. When we get the general solution of (10) the arbitrary constants in it may well be functions of s; they must not involve x.

The general solution of (10) should be found by inspection. It is

(11) $\quad w = -\dfrac{1}{s^2} + c_1(s) \exp(-4sx) + c_2(s) \exp(4sx), \qquad x > 0, \quad s > 0.$

Because of (9), the w of (11) is to approach a limit as $x \to \infty$. The first two terms on the right in (11) approach limits as $x \to \infty$, but the term with the positive exponent, $\exp(4sx)$, will not do so unless

(12)
$$c_2(s) \equiv 0.$$

That is, (9) forces (12) upon us. The w of (11) then becomes

(13)
$$w = -\frac{1}{s^2} + c_1(s) \exp(-4sx), \qquad x > 0, \quad s > 0.$$

Application of condition (8) to the w of (13) yields

$$\frac{2}{s^3} = c_1(s) - \frac{1}{s^2}; \qquad c_1(s) = \frac{2}{s^3} + \frac{1}{s^2}.$$

Thus we find that

(14) $\quad w(x, s) = -\dfrac{1}{s^2} + \left(\dfrac{2}{s^3} + \dfrac{1}{s^2}\right) \exp(-4sx), \qquad x > 0, \quad s > 0.$

We already know that if

$$L^{-1}\{f(s)\} = F(t),$$

(15)
$$L^{-1}\{e^{-cs}f(s)\} = F(t - c)\alpha(t - c).$$

Therefore the application of the operator L^{-1} throughout (14) gives us

(16) $\quad y(x, t) = -t + [(t - 4x)^2 + (t - 4x)]\alpha(t - 4x), \qquad x > 0, \quad t > 0.$

It is our contention that the y of (16) satisfies the boundary value problem (1) through (5). Let us now verify the solution in detail.

From (16) it follows that

(17) $\dfrac{\partial y}{\partial t} = -1 + [2(t - 4x) + 1]\alpha(t - 4x), \qquad x > 0, \quad t > 0, \quad t \neq 4x.$

Note the discontinuity in the derivative for $t = 4x$. This is forcing us into the admission that we obtain a solution of the problem only on each side of the line $t = 4x$ in the first quadrant of the xt-plane. Our y will not satisfy the differential equation along that line because the second derivative cannot exist there. This is a reflection of the fact that (1) is a "hyperbolic differential equation." Whether the "solution" does or does not satisfy the differential equation along what are called the characteristic lines of the equation depends upon the specific boundary conditions. We shall treat each problem individually with no attempt to examine the general situation.

From (17) we obtain

(18) $\dfrac{\partial^2 y}{\partial t^2} = 2\alpha(t - 4x), \qquad x > 0, \quad t > 0, \quad t \neq 4x.$

Equation (16) also yields

(19) $\dfrac{\partial y}{\partial x} = [-8(t - 4x) - 4]\alpha(t - 4x), \qquad x > 0, \quad t > 0, \quad t \neq 4x,$

and

(20) $\dfrac{\partial^2 y}{\partial x^2} = 32\alpha(t - 4x), \qquad x > 0, \quad t > 0, \quad t \neq 4x.$

Equations (18) and (20) combine to show that the y of (16) is a solution of the differential equation (1) in the xt region desired except along the line $t = 4x$ where the second derivatives do not exist.

Next we verify that our y satisfies the boundary conditions. To see whether y satisfies condition (2), we must hold x fixed, but positive, and then let t approach zero through positive values. As

$t \to 0^+,\ y \to 0 + [(-4x)^2 + (-4x)]\alpha(-4x) = 0, \quad \text{for } x > 0.$

Thus (2) is satisfied. Note that $\alpha(-4x)$ would not have been zero for negative x.

From (17), with x fixed and positive, it follows that as

$t \to 0^+,\ \dfrac{\partial y}{\partial t} \to -1 + [2(-4x) + 1]\alpha(-4x) = -1, \text{ for } x > 0.$

Thus (3) is satisfied. Once more the fact that x is positive plays an important role in the verification.

Consider condition (4). In it we must hold t fixed and positive. Then, by (16), as

$$x \to 0^+, \ y \to -t + (t^2 + t)\alpha(t) = -t + t^2 + t = t^2, \quad \text{for } t > 0.$$

Then (4) is satisfied.

Finally, the y of (16) satisfies condition (5), since

$$\text{Lim } y(x, t) = -t + 0 = -t, \text{ for } t > 0,$$
$$x \to \infty$$

because for sufficiently large x and fixed t, $(t - 4x)$ is negative and therefore $\alpha(t - 4x) = 0$. This completes the verification of the solution (16).

Exercises

In each exercise, solve the problem and verify your solution completely.

1. $\dfrac{\partial y}{\partial x} + 4\dfrac{\partial y}{\partial t} = -8t, \qquad$ for $t > 0, \ x > 0$;

   $t \to 0^+, \ y \to 0, \qquad$ for $x > 0$;

   $x \to 0^+, \ y \to 2t^2, \qquad$ for $t > 0$.

   ANS. $\ y(x, t) = -t^2 + 3(t - 4x)^2\alpha(t - 4x).$

2. $\dfrac{\partial y}{\partial x} + 2\dfrac{\partial y}{\partial t} = 4t, \qquad$ for $t > 0, \ x > 0$;

   $t \to 0^+, \ y \to 0, \qquad$ for $x > 0$;

   $x \to 0^+, \ y \to 2t^3, \qquad$ for $t > 0$.

   ANS. $\ y(x, t) = t^2 + [2(t - 2x)^3 - (t - 2x)^2]\alpha(t - 2x).$

3. Solve Ex. 1 with the condition as $t \to 0^+$ replaced by $t \to 0^+, \ y \to x$.

   ANS. $\ y(x, t) = x - \frac{1}{4}t - t^2 + [3(t - 4x)^2 + \frac{1}{4}(t - 4x)]\alpha(t - 4x).$

4. Solve Ex. 2 with the condition as $t \to 0^+$ replaced by $t \to 0^+, \ y \to 2x$.

   ANS. $\ y(x, t) = 2x - t + t^2 + [2(t - 2x)^3 - (t - 2x)^2 + (t - 2x)]\alpha(t - 2x).$

5. $\dfrac{\partial^2 y}{\partial x^2} = 16\dfrac{\partial^2 y}{\partial t^2}, \qquad$ for $t > 0, \ x > 0$;

   $t \to 0^+, \ y \to 0, \qquad$ for $x > 0$;

   $t \to 0^+, \dfrac{\partial y}{\partial t} \to -2, \qquad$ for $x > 0$;

   $x \to 0^+, \ y \to t, \qquad$ for $t > 0$;

   $\text{Lim } y(x, t)$ exists for $t > 0$.
   $x \to \infty$

   ANS. $\ y = 3(t - 4x)\alpha(t - 4x) - 2t.$

6. $\dfrac{\partial^2 y}{\partial t^2} = 4\dfrac{\partial^2 y}{\partial x^2}, \qquad$ for $t > 0, \ x > 0$;

$t \to 0^+, y \to 0, \qquad$ for $x > 0$;

$t \to 0^+, \dfrac{\partial y}{\partial t} \to 2, \qquad$ for $x > 0$;

$x \to 0^+, y \to \sin t, \qquad$ for $t > 0$;

$\underset{x \to \infty}{\text{Lim}}\ y(x, t)$ exists for $t > 0$.

ANS. $y = 2t + [\sin (t - \tfrac{1}{2}x) - 2(t - \tfrac{1}{2}x)]\alpha(t - \tfrac{1}{2}x).$

165. The wave equation

The transverse displacement y of an elastic string must satisfy the one-dimensional wave equation

$$\frac{\partial^2 y}{\partial t^2} = a^2 \frac{\partial^2 y}{\partial x^2}$$

of Section 158, in which the positive constant a has the dimensions of a velocity, cm. per sec., etc.

Suppose a long elastic string is initially taut and at rest so that we may take, at $t = 0$,

$$y = 0 \quad \text{and} \quad \frac{\partial y}{\partial t} = 0, \qquad \text{for } x \geq 0.$$

We assume the string long enough that the assumption that it extends from $x = 0$ to ∞ introduces no appreciable error over the time interval in which we are interested.

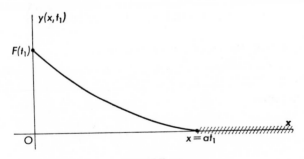

FIGURE 72

Suppose also that that end of the string far distant from the y-axis is held fixed, $y \to 0$, as $x \to \infty$, but that at the y-axis end the string is moved up and down according to some prescribed law, $y \to F(t)$ as $x \to 0^+$, with $F(t)$ known. Figure 72 shows the position of the string at some $t > 0$.

The problem of determining the transverse displacement y in terms of x and t is that of solving the boundary value problem:

(1) $$\frac{\partial^2 y}{\partial t^2} = a^2 \frac{\partial^2 y}{\partial x^2}, \qquad \text{for } t > 0, \quad x > 0;$$

(2) $$t \to 0^+, \qquad y \to 0, \quad \text{for } x \geqq 0;$$

(3) $$t \to 0^+, \qquad \frac{\partial y}{\partial t} \to 0, \quad \text{for } x > 0;$$

(4) $$x \to 0^+, \qquad y \to F(t), \quad \text{for } t \geqq 0;$$

(5) $$\operatorname*{Lim}_{x \to \infty} y(x, t) = 0, \qquad \text{for all } t \geqq 0.$$

The prescribed function $F(t)$ must vanish at $t = 0$ to retain continuity of the string.

This problem satisfies the criteria, page 493, that suggest the use of the Laplace transform. Let

(6) $$L\{y(x, t)\} = u(x, s), \qquad L\{F(t)\} = f(s).$$

Note that $F(t)$ must be continuous because of its physical meaning here. The operator L converts the problem (1) through (5) into the new problem

(7) $$s^2 u = a^2 \frac{d^2 u}{dx^2}, \qquad \text{for } x > 0;$$

(8) $$x \to 0^+, \qquad u \to f(s);$$

(9) $$\operatorname*{Lim}_{x \to \infty} u(x, s) = 0.$$

From (7) we write at once the general solution

(10) $$u(x, s) = c_1(s) \exp\left(-\frac{sx}{a}\right) + c_2(s) \exp\left(\frac{sx}{a}\right).$$

With $s > 0$, $x > 0$, the condition (9) requires

(11) $$c_2(s) \equiv 0.$$

Thus (10) becomes

(12) $$u(x, s) = c_1(s) \exp\left(-\frac{sx}{a}\right),$$

and (8) requires that

$$f(s) = c_1(s).$$

We therefore have

(13) $$u(x, s) = f(s) \exp\left(-\frac{sx}{a}\right), \qquad x > 0, \quad s > 0.$$

Equation (13) yields the desired solution

(14) $y(x, t) = F\left(t - \dfrac{x}{a}\right)\alpha\left(t - \dfrac{x}{a}\right), \qquad x > 0, \quad t > 0,$

in which we assume that $F(t)$ is defined in some manner for negative argument so that Theorem 19, page 188, can be used.

Verification of the solution (14) is a simple matter. Note that

$$\frac{\partial y}{\partial t} = F'\left(t - \frac{x}{a}\right)\alpha\left(t - \frac{x}{a}\right), \quad \frac{\partial y}{\partial x} = -\frac{1}{a}F'\left(t - \frac{x}{a}\right)\alpha\left(t - \frac{x}{a}\right)$$

and

$$\frac{\partial^2 y}{\partial t^2} = F''\left(t - \frac{x}{a}\right)\alpha\left(t - \frac{x}{a}\right), \quad \frac{\partial^2 y}{\partial x^2} = \frac{1}{a^2}F''\left(t - \frac{x}{a}\right)\alpha\left(t - \frac{x}{a}\right).$$

We are forced to assume existence of two derivatives of the prescribed function $F(t)$. It is particularly convenient to choose $F(t)$ so that $F'(0)$ and $F''(0)$ vanish along with $F(0)$, so that the continuity of y and its derivatives is not interrupted along the line $x = at$. Completion of the verification of the solution is left to the student.

In Section 158 we studied the transverse displacement of a string of finite length held fixed at both ends. Fourier series methods seem superior to Laplace transform techniques for such problems. Try, for instance, transform methods on Ex. 1, p. 470.

Exercise

1. Interpret and solve the problem:

$$\frac{\partial^2 y}{\partial t^2} = \frac{\partial^2 y}{\partial x^2}, \qquad \text{for } t > 0, 0 < x < 1;$$

$$t \to 0^+, \ y \to x - x^2, \qquad \text{for } 0 < x < 1;$$

$$t \to 0^+, \ \frac{\partial y}{\partial t} \to 0, \qquad \text{for } 0 < x < 1;$$

$$x \to 0^+, \ y \to 0, \qquad \text{for } t > 0;$$

$$x \to 1^-, \ y \to 0, \qquad \text{for } t > 0.$$

Verify your solution directly.

ANS. $y = x - x^2 - t^2 + \displaystyle\sum_{n=0}^{\infty} (-1)^n[(t - n - x)^2\alpha(t - n - x)$
$$+ (t - n - 1 + x)^2\alpha(t - n - 1 - x)].$$

166. Diffusion in a semi-infinite solid

Consider the solid defined by $x \geq 0$, occupying one half of three dimensional space. If the initial temperature within the solid and the conditions at the surface $x = 0$ are independent of the coordinates y and z, the temperature u will be independent of y and z for all $t > 0$. We may visualize, for example, a huge flat slab of concrete with an initial temperature distribution dependent upon only the distance from the plane surface of the slab. If the temperature at that surface is thereafter $(t > 0)$ maintained at some specified function of t, or if the surface is insulated, the problem of finding the temperature for all positive x and t is one involving the simple heat equation (2) of Section 154.

EXAMPLE: Consider a semi-infinite slab $x \geq 0$, initially at a fixed temperature $u = A$ and thereafter subjected to a surface temperature $(x \to 0^+)$ which is $u = B$ for $0 < t < t_0$ and then $u = 0$ for $t \geq t_0$. Find the temperature within the solid for $x > 0, t > 0$.

The boundary value problem to be solved is:

(1) $$\frac{\partial u}{\partial t} = h^2 \frac{\partial^2 u}{\partial x^2}, \qquad \text{for } x > 0, \quad t > 0;$$

(2) $$t \to 0^+, \quad u \to A, \qquad \text{for } x > 0;$$

(3) $$x \to 0^+, \quad u \to B, \qquad \text{for } 0 < t < t_0,$$
$$u \to 0, \qquad \text{for } t > t_0;$$

(4) $$\lim_{x \to \infty} u(x, t) \text{ exists, for each fixed } t > 0.$$

In this problem A, B, and h^2 are constants. We use the α function to reword the boundary condition (3) in the form

(5) $$x \to 0^+, u \to B[1 - \alpha(t - t_0)], \qquad \text{for } t > 0.$$

Note also that the physical problem dictates that the value of the limit in (4) is to be A. This furnishes us with an additional check on our work.

The problem satisfies the criteria, page 493, that suggest the use of the Laplace transform. Let

(6) $$L\{u(x, t)\} = w(x, s), \qquad x > 0, \quad s > 0.$$

The equation (1) with condition (2) is transformed into

$$sw - A = h^2 \frac{d^2 w}{dx^2}, \qquad x > 0,$$

or

$$(7) \qquad \frac{d^2w}{dx^2} - \frac{s}{h^2} w = -\frac{A}{h^2}, \qquad x > 0.$$

Conditions (4) and (5) become

$$(8) \qquad \operatorname*{Lim}_{x \to \infty} w(x, s) \text{ exists, for fixed } s > 0,$$

and

$$(9) \qquad x \to 0^+, \; w \to \frac{B}{s} [1 - \exp(-t_0 s)].$$

The differential equation (7) has the general solution

$$(10) \quad w = c_1 \exp\left(-\frac{x\sqrt{s}}{h}\right) + c_2 \exp\left(\frac{x\sqrt{s}}{h}\right) + \frac{A}{s}, \qquad x > 0, \; s > 0,$$

in which c_1 and c_2 may be functions of s, but not of x. As $x \to \infty$, the w of (10) will approach a limit if and only if $c_2 = 0$. Hence condition (8) yields the result

$$(11) \qquad c_2 = 0$$

and the w of (10) becomes

$$(12) \qquad w = c_1 \exp\left(-\frac{x\sqrt{s}}{h}\right) + \frac{A}{s}.$$

Using (9) we obtain, by letting $x \to 0^+$,

$$(13) \qquad \frac{B}{s}[1 - \exp(-t_0 s)] = c_1 + \frac{A}{s}.$$

Therefore the solution of the problem (7) through (9) is

$$(14) \quad w(x, s) = \frac{A}{s}\left[1 - \exp\left(-\frac{x\sqrt{s}}{h}\right)\right]$$

$$+ \frac{B}{s} \exp\left(-\frac{x\sqrt{s}}{h}\right)[1 - \exp(-t_0 s)].$$

We know that

$$(15) \qquad L^{-1}\left\{\frac{1}{s}\exp\left(-\frac{x\sqrt{s}}{h}\right)\right\} = \operatorname{erfc}\left(\frac{x}{2h\sqrt{t}}\right), \qquad x > 0.$$

Hence we may write

$$(16) \quad L^{-1}\left\{\frac{1}{s}\exp\left(-\frac{x\sqrt{s}}{h}\right)\exp(-t_0 s)\right\} = \operatorname{erfc}\left(\frac{x}{2h|t - t_0|^{\frac{1}{2}}}\right)\alpha\,(t - t_0),$$

where absolute value signs have been inserted to permit t to be used in the range 0 to t_0 in which range the α function will force the right member of (16) to be zero.

We are now in a position to write the inverse transform of the w of equation (14). For $x > 0$ and $t > 0$,

$$(17) \quad u(x, t) = A\left[1 - \operatorname{erfc}\left(\frac{x}{2h\sqrt{t}}\right)\right]$$
$$+ B\left[\operatorname{erfc}\left(\frac{x}{2h\sqrt{t}}\right) - \operatorname{erfc}\left(\frac{x}{2h|t - t_0|^{\frac{1}{2}}}\right)\alpha(t - t_0)\right],$$

or

$$(18) \quad u(x, t) = A\operatorname{erf}\left(\frac{x}{2h\sqrt{t}}\right)$$
$$+ B\left[\operatorname{erfc}\left(\frac{x}{2h\sqrt{t}}\right) - \operatorname{erfc}\left(\frac{x}{2h|t - t_0|^{\frac{1}{2}}}\right)\alpha(t - t_0)\right].$$

The u of (17), or of (18), is the desired solution.

It is a matter of direct substitution to show that each term of (18) is a solution of the one-dimensional heat equation. That the conditions (2), (3), and (4) are also satisfied follows rapidly from the properties

$$\operatorname*{Lim}_{z \to 0} \operatorname{erf} z = 0, \qquad \operatorname*{Lim}_{z \to \infty} \operatorname{erf} z = 1$$

and the corresponding properties of the erfc function. Indeed, for the u of (18),

As $x \to 0^+$, $u \to A \cdot 0 + B[1 - \alpha(t - t_0)] = B[1 - \alpha(t - t_0)]$, for $t > 0$;

As $t \to 0^+$, $u \to A \cdot 1 + B(0 - 0) = A$, for $x > 0$;

As $x \to \infty$, $u \to A \cdot 1 + B \cdot 0 = A$, for $0 < t < t_0$;

As $x \to \infty$, $u \to A \cdot 1 + B(0 - 0) = A$, for $t > t_0$.

167. Canonical variables

As we attack problems of increasing complexity, it becomes important that we simplify our work by the introduction of what are called *canonical variables*. These variables are dimensionless combinations of the physical variables and parameters of the original problem. We now illustrate a method for selecting such variables.

In Section 168 we shall solve a diffusion problem which can be expressed in the following way:

(1) $$\frac{\partial u}{\partial t} = h^2 \frac{\partial^2 u}{\partial x^2}, \qquad \text{for } t > 0, \quad 0 < x < c;$$

(2) $$t \to 0^+, u \to A, \qquad \text{for } 0 < x < c;$$

(3) $$x \to 0^+, u \to 0, \qquad \text{for } t > 0;$$

(4) $$x \to c^-, u \to 0, \qquad \text{for } t > 0.$$

A consistent set of units for the measure of the various constants (parameters) and variables in this problem is:

$$u = \text{temperature (°F)},$$
$$t = \text{time (hr.)},$$
$$x = \text{space coordinate (ft.)}$$
$$h^2 = \text{thermal diffusivity (ft.}^2 \text{ per hr.)},$$
$$c = \text{length (ft.)},$$
$$A = \text{initial temperature (°F)}.$$

We seek dimensionless new variables ζ, τ, ψ, proportional to the physical variables x, t, u. For the moment let

(5) $$x = \beta\zeta, \qquad t = \gamma\tau, \qquad u = \delta\psi,$$

in which β, γ, δ are positive constants to be so determined that the new variables will each be of dimension zero. The changes of variable (5) transform (1) through (4) into

(6) $$\frac{\delta}{\gamma} \frac{\partial \psi}{\partial \tau} = \frac{h^2 \delta}{\beta^2} \frac{\partial^2 \psi}{\partial \zeta^2}, \qquad \text{for } \tau > 0, \quad 0 < \beta\zeta < c;$$

(7) $$\tau \to 0^+, \delta\psi \to A, \qquad \text{for } 0 < \beta\zeta < c;$$

(8) $$\zeta \to 0^+, \psi \to 0, \qquad \text{for } \tau > 0;$$

(9) $$\beta\zeta \to c^-, \psi \to 0, \qquad \text{for } \tau > 0.$$

Because of (7), we choose $\delta = A$ and $\beta = c$. Because of (6), we choose

$$\frac{1}{\gamma} = \frac{h^2}{\beta^2},$$

from which

$$\gamma = \frac{c^2}{h^2}.$$

We thus find that the introduction of the new variables

(10) $$\zeta = \frac{x}{c}, \qquad \tau = \frac{h^2 t}{c^2}, \qquad \psi = \frac{u}{A},$$

transforms the problem (1) through (4) into the canonical form

$$(11) \qquad \frac{\partial \psi}{\partial \tau} = \frac{\partial^2 \psi}{\partial \zeta^2}, \qquad \text{for } \tau > 0, \quad 0 < \zeta < 1;$$

$$(12) \qquad \tau \to 0^+, \; \psi \to 1, \qquad \text{for } 0 < \zeta < 1;$$

$$(13) \qquad \zeta \to 0^+, \; \psi \to 0, \qquad \text{for } \tau > 0;$$

$$(14) \qquad \zeta \to 1^-, \; \psi \to 0, \qquad \text{for } \tau > 0.$$

Note that the canonical variables in (10) are of dimension zero; ζ has dimension ft. over ft., etc.

The solution of (11) through (14) is independent of the parameters $h^2, c,$ and A of the original problem, a fact of great importance in applications. The solution of the original problem (1) through (4) is a function of two variables and three parameters,

$$(15) \qquad u = f(x, t, c, h, A).$$

The solution of (11) through (14), for which see Section 168, is a function of two variables

$$(16) \qquad \psi = F(\zeta, \tau),$$

so (15) actually takes the form

$$(17) \qquad u = AF\left(\frac{x}{c}, \frac{h^2 t}{c^2}\right).$$

The function F, of two variables, can be tabulated and it thus yields the solution of the original problem no matter what the values of c, A and h^2.

There are problems, such as in the study of temperatures in a concrete dam, in which it is important to know the mean value with respect to x of the temperature u of (15) over the range $0 < x < c$. That mean value may be computed by using (16) and the result is a function of the one variable τ. Thus a single curve can be drawn in the $\psi\tau$-plane to give the pertinent mean temperature for all problems (1) through (4).

168. Diffusion in a slab of finite width

We shall now solve by transform methods the slab problem of Section 139 for the special case $f(x) = A$. Let the thickness of the slab be c units of length. Let the coordinate x denote distance from one face of the slab and assume that the slab extends very far in the y and z directions. Assume that the initial temperature of the slab is a constant A and that the surfaces $x = 0$, $x = c$ are maintained at zero temperature for all $t > 0$. If the slab is considered infinite in the y and z directions, or more specifically, if we treat only cross-sections nearby (far from the distant surfaces of the slab), then the temperature u at any time t and position x is determined by the boundary value problem:

$$(1) \qquad \frac{\partial u}{\partial t} = h^2 \frac{\partial^2 u}{\partial x^2}, \qquad \text{for } t > 0, \quad 0 < x < c;$$

$$(2) \qquad t \to 0^+, \ u \to A, \qquad \text{for } 0 < x < c;$$

$$(3) \qquad x \to 0^+, \ u \to 0, \qquad \text{for } t > 0;$$

$$(4) \qquad x \to c^-, \ u \to 0, \qquad \text{for } t > 0.$$

We shall solve the corresponding problem in canonical variables. That is, in (1) through (4) we put

$$(5) \qquad \zeta = \frac{x}{c}, \qquad \tau = \frac{h^2 t}{c^2}, \qquad \psi = \frac{u}{A}.$$

In the new variables ζ, τ, ψ, the problem to be solved is

$$(6) \qquad \frac{\partial \psi}{\partial \tau} = \frac{\partial^2 \psi}{\partial \zeta^2}, \qquad \text{for } \tau > 0, \quad 0 < \zeta < 1;$$

$$(7) \qquad \tau \to 0^+, \ \psi \to 1, \qquad \text{for } 0 < \zeta < 1;$$

$$(8) \qquad \zeta \to 0^+, \ \psi \to 0, \qquad \text{for } \tau > 0;$$

$$(9) \qquad \zeta \to 1^-, \ \psi \to 0, \qquad \text{for } \tau > 0.$$

Let

$$(10) \qquad L\{\psi(\zeta, \tau)\} = w(\zeta, s) = \int_0^\infty e^{-s\tau} \psi(\zeta, \tau) \, d\tau.$$

Application of the Laplace operator transforms the problem (6) through (9) into

$$(11) \qquad sw - 1 = \frac{d^2 w}{d\zeta^2}, \qquad \text{for } 0 < \zeta < 1;$$

$$(12) \qquad \zeta \to 0^+, \ w \to 0;$$

$$(13) \qquad \zeta \to 1^-, \ w \to 0.$$

The general solution of (11) may be written

$$(14) \qquad w = c_1 \sinh (\zeta \sqrt{s}) + c_2 \cosh (\zeta \sqrt{s}) + \frac{1}{s}.$$

From (12) it follows that

$$(15) \qquad 0 = c_2 + \frac{1}{s}$$

and (13) yields

(16) $$0 = c_1 \sinh \sqrt{s} + c_2 \cosh \sqrt{s} + \frac{1}{s}.$$

By solving (15) and (16) we obtain

(17) $$c_2 = -\frac{1}{s}, \; c_1 = \frac{\cosh \sqrt{s} - 1}{s \sinh \sqrt{s}},$$

from which we see that

(18) $$w = \frac{1}{s} + \frac{(\cosh \sqrt{s} - 1) \sinh (\zeta \sqrt{s}) - \sinh \sqrt{s} \cosh (\zeta \sqrt{s})}{s \sinh \sqrt{s}}.$$

Since

$$\sinh B_1 \cosh B_2 - \cosh B_1 \sinh B_2 = \sinh (B_1 - B_2),$$

the w of (18) may be written in the form

(19) $$w(\zeta, s) = \frac{1}{s} \left[1 - \frac{\sinh (\zeta \sqrt{s})}{\sinh \sqrt{s}} - \frac{\sinh \{(1 - \zeta) \sqrt{s}\}}{\sinh \sqrt{s}} \right].$$

The desired solution $\psi(\zeta, \tau)$ is the inverse of the $w(\zeta, s)$ of (19), with ζ on the range $0 < \zeta < 1$.

We already know from equation (29), page 486, that for $0 < x < 1$,

(20) $$L^{-1} \left\{ \frac{\sinh (x \sqrt{s})}{s \sinh \sqrt{s}} \right\}$$
$$= \sum_{n=0}^{\infty} \left[\operatorname{erfc} \left(\frac{1 - x + 2n}{2 \sqrt{t}} \right) - \operatorname{erfc} \left(\frac{1 + x + 2n}{2 \sqrt{t}} \right) \right].$$

Applying (20) twice, once with ζ and once with $(1 - \zeta)$ replacing x, we obtain from (19) the desired solution

(21) $$\psi(\zeta, \tau) = 1 - \sum_{n=0}^{\infty} \left[\operatorname{erfc} \left(\frac{1 - \zeta + 2n}{2 \sqrt{\tau}} \right) - \operatorname{erfc} \left(\frac{1 + \zeta + 2n}{2 \sqrt{\tau}} \right) \right]$$
$$- \sum_{n=0}^{\infty} \left[\operatorname{erfc} \left(\frac{\zeta + 2n}{2 \sqrt{\tau}} \right) - \operatorname{erfc} \left(\frac{2 - \zeta + 2n}{2 \sqrt{\tau}} \right) \right].$$

The complementary error functions in (21) may be replaced by error functions, since

(22) $$\operatorname{erfc} z = 1 - \operatorname{erf} z.$$

With the aid of the properties

(23) $$\operatorname{erfc} 0 = 1, \quad \operatorname*{Lim}_{z \to \infty} \operatorname{erfc} z = 0,$$

the solution (21) is easily verified, assuming that the summation sign and the pertinent limits may be interchanged. With the theorems of advanced calculus the assumption can be shown to be valid.

From (21) we get, as $\zeta \to 0^+$,

$$\psi \to 1 - \sum_{n=0}^{\infty} \left[\operatorname{erfc} \left(\frac{2n+1}{2\sqrt{\tau}} \right) - \operatorname{erfc} \left(\frac{2n+1}{2\sqrt{\tau}} \right) \right]$$
$$- \sum_{n=0}^{\infty} \left[\operatorname{erfc} \left(\frac{n}{\sqrt{\tau}} \right) - \operatorname{erfc} \left(\frac{n+1}{\sqrt{\tau}} \right) \right].$$

In the first series each term is zero. The second series telescopes; in it we replace the series by the limit of the partial sums to get

$$\psi \to 1 - \operatorname*{Lim}_{n \to \infty} \sum_{k=0}^{n} \left[\operatorname{erfc} \left(\frac{k}{\sqrt{\tau}} \right) - \operatorname{erfc} \left(\frac{k+1}{\sqrt{\tau}} \right) \right],$$

or

$$\psi \to 1 - \operatorname*{Lim}_{n \to \infty} \left[\operatorname{erfc} 0 - \operatorname{erfc} \left(\frac{n+1}{\sqrt{\tau}} \right) \right].$$

For fixed $\tau > 0$, $(n+1)/\sqrt{\tau} \to \infty$ as $n \to \infty$. Hence, by (23),

(24) $$\psi \to 1 - 1 + 0 = 0, \quad \text{as } \zeta \to 0^+.$$

The solution (21) is unchanged when ζ is replaced by $(1 - \zeta)$, because the two series merely change places. Therefore, because of (24),

(25) $$\psi \to 0, \quad \text{as } \zeta \to 1^-.$$

For any ζ in the range $0 < \zeta < 1$, the argument of each erfc in (21) is positive and approaches infinity as $\tau \to 0^+$. Hence each erfc $\to 0$ and each term of the two series $\to 0$. Thus, because the order of limit and summation can be interchanged,

(26) $$\psi \to 1, \quad \text{as } \tau \to 0^+, \quad \text{for } 0 < \zeta < 1.$$

Perhaps the most valuable single fact about the solution (21) is the fact that the series converge very rapidly for small τ because the arguments of the various erfc functions are then very large. By the methods of separation of variables and Fourier series, the problem (6) through (9) at the start of this section can be shown to have the solution

$$(27) \qquad \psi(\zeta, \tau) = \frac{4}{\pi} \sum_{k=0}^{\infty} \frac{\exp\left[-\pi^2(2k+1)^2\tau\right] \sin\left[(2k+1)\pi\zeta\right]}{2k+1}.$$

The solutions given by (21) and (27) are identical, though the unique-ness of such solutions is not proved here.

The series in (27) converges rapidly for large τ and slowly for small τ. The series in (21) converge rapidly for small τ and slowly for large τ. The two forms of solution complement each other neatly.

The solution of the original problem (1) through (4) may be obtained from (21) or (27) by making the substitutions in (5).

Exercise

1. Interpret and solve the following problem.

$$\frac{\partial u}{\partial t} = \frac{\partial^2 u}{\partial x^2}, \qquad \text{for } t > 0, \, 0 < x < 1;$$

$$t \to 0^+, \, u \to 1, \qquad \text{for } 0 < x < 1;$$

$$x \to 0^+, \, u \to 0, \qquad \text{for } t > 0;$$

$$x \to 1^-, \, \frac{\partial u}{\partial x} \to 0, \qquad \text{for } t > 0.$$

ANS. $u = 1 - \displaystyle\sum_{n=0}^{\infty} (-1)^n \left[\operatorname{erfc}\left(\frac{2n+x}{2\sqrt{t}}\right) + \operatorname{erfc}\left(\frac{2n+2-x}{2\sqrt{t}}\right) \right].$

169. Diffusion in a quarter-infinite solid

As a final application let us study the temperatures near a square corner of a huge slab initially at a constant temperature and having its surfaces thereafter held at a constant temperature different from the initial interior temperature. We assume that all temperatures are inde-pendent of one rectangular space coordinate. By introducing canonical variables, we may express the mathematical problem as follows:

$$(1) \qquad \frac{\partial u}{\partial t} = \frac{\partial^2 u}{\partial x^2} + \frac{\partial^2 u}{\partial y^2}, \qquad \text{for } t > 0, \quad x > 0, \quad y > 0;$$

$$(2) \qquad t \to 0^+, \, u \to 1, \qquad \text{for } x > 0, \quad y > 0;$$

$$(3) \qquad x \to 0^+, \, u \to 0, \qquad \text{for } t > 0, \quad y > 0;$$

$$(4) \qquad y \to 0^+, \, u \to 0, \qquad \text{for } t > 0, \quad x > 0;$$

$$(5) \qquad \operatorname*{Lim}_{x \to \infty} u(x, y, t) \text{ exists, for fixed positive } t \text{ and } y;$$

$$(6) \qquad \operatorname*{Lim}_{y \to \infty} u(x, y, t) \text{ exists, for fixed positive } t \text{ and } x.$$

The solution of the problem (1) through (6) will be accomplished by combining separation of variables with the Laplace transform technique. First we separate the function u of the three variables x, y, t into the product of a function of x and t alone by a function of y and t alone. This separation is possible only because of the peculiar simplicity of the boundary value problem. Let

(7) $$u(x, y, t) = v(x, t)w(y, t).$$

From (7) it follows that

$$\frac{\partial u}{\partial t} = v\frac{\partial w}{\partial t} + w\frac{\partial v}{\partial t},$$

$$\frac{\partial^2 u}{\partial x^2} = w\frac{\partial^2 v}{\partial x^2},$$

$$\frac{\partial^2 u}{\partial y^2} = v\frac{\partial^2 w}{\partial y^2}.$$

Hence equation (1) yields

(8) $$v\frac{\partial w}{\partial t} + w\frac{\partial v}{\partial t} = w\frac{\partial^2 v}{\partial x^2} + v\frac{\partial^2 w}{\partial y^2},$$

which will be satisfied if both

(9) $$\frac{\partial v}{\partial t} = \frac{\partial^2 v}{\partial x^2}, \qquad \text{for } t > 0, \quad x > 0,$$

and

(10) $$\frac{\partial w}{\partial t} = \frac{\partial^2 w}{\partial y^2}, \qquad \text{for } t > 0, \quad y > 0,$$

are satisfied.

If we impose the conditions

(11) $t \to 0^+,\ v \to 1,$ for $x > 0,$

(12) $t \to 0^+,\ w \to 1,$ for $y > 0,$

condition (2) will be satisfied.

From condition (3) we get

(13) $x \to 0^+,\ v \to 0,$ for $t > 0,$

and from (4),

(14) $y \to 0^+,\ w \to 0,$ for $t > 0.$

Conditions (5) and (6) will be satisfied if

(15) $\qquad$ Lim $v(x, t)$ exists, for fixed positive t,
$\qquad\qquad$ $x \to \infty$

and

(16) $\qquad$ Lim $w(y, t)$ exists, for fixed positive t.
$\qquad\qquad$ $y \to \infty$

We must now find v from

(9) $\qquad \dfrac{\partial v}{\partial t} = \dfrac{\partial^2 v}{\partial x^2}, \qquad$ for $t > 0, \quad x > 0$;

(11) $\qquad t \to 0^+, v \to 1, \qquad$ for $x > 0$;

(13) $\qquad x \to 0^+, v \to 0, \qquad$ for $t > 0$;

(15) $\qquad$ Lim $v(x, t)$ exists, for fixed positive t.
$\qquad\qquad$ $x \to \infty$

The function w must satisfy (10), (12), (14), and (16); it is therefore the same function as v except that y replaces x.

To obtain v we use the Laplace transform. Let

(17) $\qquad L\{v(x, t)\} = g(x, s) = \displaystyle\int_0^\infty e^{-st} v(x, t)\, dt.$

Then (9) and (11) yield

(18) $\qquad sg - 1 = \dfrac{d^2 g}{dx^2},$

for which the general solution is easily written by inspection because of our experience in handling equations with constant coefficients. We thus get

(19) $\qquad g = \dfrac{1}{s} + c_1(s) \exp(-x\sqrt{s}) + c_2(s) \exp(x\sqrt{s}).$

The function g must, because of (13) and (15), satisfy the conditions

(20) $\qquad x \to 0^+, g \to 0,$
(21) $\qquad$ Lim $g(x, s)$ exists.
$\qquad\qquad$ $x \to \infty$

Because of (21), $c_2(s) = 0$. Because of (20),

$$0 = \frac{1}{s} + c_1(s).$$

Therefore

(22) $\qquad g(x, s) = \dfrac{1}{s} - \dfrac{1}{s} \exp(-x\sqrt{s}).$

The function $v(x, t)$ is an inverse transform of $g(x, s)$:

(23) $$v(x, t) = 1 - \text{erfc}\left(\frac{x}{2\sqrt{t}}\right).$$

But $1 - \text{erfc } z = \text{erf } z$. Hence

(24) $$v(x, t) = \text{erf}\left(\frac{x}{2\sqrt{t}}\right).$$

Therefore the solution of our original problem (1) through (6) is

(25) $$u = \text{erf}\left(\frac{x}{2\sqrt{t}}\right)\text{erf}\left(\frac{y}{2\sqrt{t}}\right).$$

The student should verify that the u of (25) satisfies all the conditions of the boundary value problem (1) through (6) introduced at the beginning of this section.

Exercises

1. Show that for the u of (25), $0 < u < 1$, for all $x, y, t > 0$.
2. Let the point with coordinates (x, y, t) be in the first octant of the rectangular x, y, t space. Let that point approach the origin along a curve
$$x^2 = 4a^2t,$$
$$y^2 = 4a^2t,$$

   in which a is positive but otherwise arbitrary. Show that as $x, y, t \to 0^+$ in the manner described above, u may be made to approach any desired number between zero and unity.

Index

Index